STUDENT SOLUTIONS MANUAL

MARK McCOMBS
UNIVERSITY OF NORTH CAROLINA, CHAPEL HILL

TRIGONOMETRY
A UNIT CIRCLE APPROACH
SEVENTH EDITION

SULLIVAN

PEARSON
Prentice
Hall

Upper Saddle River, NJ 07458

Editor-in-Chief: Sally Yagan
Senior Acquisitions Editor: Eric Frank
Project Manager: Dawn Murrin
Executive Managing Editor: Vince O'Brien
Production Editor: Jeffrey Rydell
Supplement Cover Manager: Paul Gourhan
Supplement Cover Designer: Joanne Alexandris
Manufacturing Buyer: Ilene Kahn

© 2005 Pearson Education, Inc.
Pearson Prentice Hall
Pearson Education, Inc.
Upper Saddle River, NJ 07458

Printed in the United States of America

10 9 8 7 6 5 4 3 2 1

ISBN 0-13-143112-9

Pearson Education Ltd., *London*
Pearson Education Australia Pty. Ltd., *Sydney*
Pearson Education Singapore, Pte. Ltd.
Pearson Education North Asia Ltd., *Hong Kong*
Pearson Education Canada, Inc., *Toronto*
Pearson Educación de Mexico, S.A. de C.V.
Pearson Education—Japan, *Tokyo*
Pearson Education Malaysia, Pte. Ltd.

Contents

Chapter 5   Polar Coordinates; Vectors

Chapter 6   The Conics

Chapter 7   Exponential and Logarithmic Functions

Appendix A   Review

Appendix B   Graphing Utilities

v

Preface

The <u>Student</u> <u>Solutions</u> <u>Manual</u> to accompany <u>Trigonometry</u>, <u>7th</u> <u>Edition</u> by Michael Sullivan contains detailed solutions to all of the odd-numbered problems in the textbook. TI-83 graphing calculator screens have been included to demonstrate the use of the graphics calculator in solving and in checking solutions to the problems where requested. Every attempt has been made to make this manual as error free as possible. If you have suggestions, error corrections, or comments please feel free to write to me about them.

A number of people need to be recognized for their contributions in the preparation of this manual. Thanks go to Sally Yagan and Dawn Murrin at Prentice Hall. Thanks also to Cindy Trimble for her meticulous error-checking of the solutions.

I especially wish to thank my mother, Sarah, and my brothers, Kirk and Doug, for their unwavering support and encouragement.

Finally, I want to thank my wife for helping me endure the long hours of editing the manuscript. Thank you, Tate, I love you that much.

Mark A. McCombs
Department of Mathematics
Campus Box 3250
University of North Carolina at Chapel Hill
Chapel Hill, NC 27599
mccombs@math.unc.edu

Graphs and Functions

1.1 Rectangular Coordinates

1. 0

3. $d = |5 - (-3)| = |5 + 3| = |8| = 8$

5. quadrants

7. x-

9. False

11. (a) Quadrant II
    (b) Positive x-axis
    (c) Quadrant III
    (d) Quadrant I
    (e) Negative y-axis
    (f) Quadrant IV

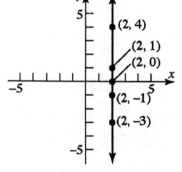

13. The points will be on a vertical line that is two units to the right of the y-axis.

15. $d(P_1, P_2) = \sqrt{(2-0)^2 + (1-0)^2} = \sqrt{2^2 + 1^2} = \sqrt{4+1} = \sqrt{5}$

17. $d(P_1, P_2) = \sqrt{(-2-1)^2 + (2-1)^2} = \sqrt{(-3)^2 + 1^2} = \sqrt{9+1} = \sqrt{10}$

19. $d(P_1, P_2) = \sqrt{(5-3)^2 + (4-(-4))^2} = \sqrt{2^2 + 8^2} = \sqrt{4+64} = \sqrt{68} = 2\sqrt{17}$

21. $d(P_1, P_2) = \sqrt{(6-(-3))^2 + (0-2)^2} = \sqrt{9^2 + (-2)^2} = \sqrt{81+4} = \sqrt{85}$

23. $d(P_1, P_2) = \sqrt{(6-4)^2 + (4-(-3))^2} = \sqrt{2^2 + 7^2} = \sqrt{4+49} = \sqrt{53}$

25. $d(P_1, P_2) = \sqrt{(2.3-(-0.2))^2 + (1.1-0.3)^2} = \sqrt{(2.5)^2 + (0.8)^2}$
$= \sqrt{6.25 + 0.64} = \sqrt{6.89}$

27. $d(P_1, P_2) = \sqrt{(0-a)^2 + (0-b)^2} = \sqrt{a^2 + b^2}$

29. $A = (-2,5)$, $B = (1,3)$, $C = (-1,0)$
$d(A,B) = \sqrt{(1-(-2))^2 + (3-5)^2} = \sqrt{3^2 + (-2)^2}$
$= \sqrt{9+4} = \sqrt{13}$
$d(B,C) = \sqrt{(-1-1)^2 + (0-3)^2} = \sqrt{(-2)^2 + (-3)^2}$
$= \sqrt{4+9} = \sqrt{13}$
$d(A,C) = \sqrt{(-1-(-2))^2 + (0-5)^2} = \sqrt{1^2 + (-5)^2}$
$= \sqrt{1+25} = \sqrt{26}$

Verifying that $\triangle ABC$ is a right triangle by the Pythagorean Theorem:
$$[d(A,B)]^2 + [d(B,C)]^2 = [d(A,C)]^2$$
$$\left(\sqrt{13}\right)^2 + \left(\sqrt{13}\right)^2 = \left(\sqrt{26}\right)^2$$
$$13 + 13 = 26 \Rightarrow 26 = 26$$
The area of a triangle is $A = \frac{1}{2} \cdot bh$. Here,
$$A = \frac{1}{2} \cdot [d(A,B)] \cdot [d(B,C)] = \frac{1}{2} \cdot \sqrt{13} \cdot \sqrt{13} = \frac{1}{2} \cdot 13 = \frac{13}{2} \text{ square units}$$

31. $A = (-5,3)$, $B = (6,0)$, $C = (5,5)$
$d(A,B) = \sqrt{(6-(-5))^2 + (0-3)^2} = \sqrt{11^2 + (-3)^2}$
$= \sqrt{121+9} = \sqrt{130}$
$d(B,C) = \sqrt{(5-6)^2 + (5-0)^2} = \sqrt{(-1)^2 + 5^2}$
$= \sqrt{1+25} = \sqrt{26}$
$d(A,C) = \sqrt{(5-(-5))^2 + (5-3)^2} = \sqrt{10^2 + 2^2}$
$= \sqrt{100+4} = \sqrt{104}$

Verifying that $\triangle ABC$ is a right triangle by the Pythagorean Theorem:

$$[d(A,C)]^2 + [d(B,C)]^2 = [d(A,B)]^2$$

$$\left(\sqrt{104}\right)^2 + \left(\sqrt{26}\right)^2 = \left(\sqrt{130}\right)^2$$

$$104 + 26 = 130 \Rightarrow 130 = 130$$

The area of a triangle is $A = \dfrac{1}{2} \cdot bh$. Here,

$$A = \frac{1}{2} \cdot [d(A,C)] \cdot [d(B,C)] = \frac{1}{2} \cdot \sqrt{104} \cdot \sqrt{26} = \frac{1}{2} \cdot \sqrt{2704} = \frac{1}{2} \cdot 52 = 26 \text{ square units}$$

33. $A = (4,-3), \ B = (0,-3), \ C = (4,2)$

$d(A,B) = \sqrt{(0-4)^2 + (-3-(-3))^2} = \sqrt{(-4)^2 + 0^2}$

$\qquad = \sqrt{16+0} = \sqrt{16} = 4$

$d(B,C) = \sqrt{(4-0)^2 + (2-(-3))^2} = \sqrt{4^2 + 5^2}$

$\qquad = \sqrt{16+25} = \sqrt{41}$

$d(A,C) = \sqrt{(4-4)^2 + (2-(-3))^2} = \sqrt{0^2 + 5^2}$

$\qquad = \sqrt{0+25} = \sqrt{25} = 5$

Verifying that $\triangle ABC$ is a right triangle by the Pythagorean Theorem:

$$[d(A,B)]^2 + [d(A,C)]^2 = [d(B,C)]^2$$

$$4^2 + 5^2 = \left(\sqrt{41}\right)^2 \Rightarrow 16 + 25 = 41 \Rightarrow 41 = 41$$

The area of a triangle is $A = \dfrac{1}{2} \cdot bh$. Here,

$$A = \frac{1}{2} \cdot [d(A,B)] \cdot [d(A,C)] = \frac{1}{2} \cdot 4 \cdot 5 = 10 \text{ square units}$$

35. All points having an x-coordinate of 2 are of the form $(2, y)$. Those which are 5 units from $(-2, -1)$ are:

$$\sqrt{(2-(-2))^2 + (y-(-1))^2} = 5 \Rightarrow \sqrt{4^2 + (y+1)^2} = 5$$

Squaring both sides: $4^2 + (y+1)^2 = 25$

$$16 + y^2 + 2y + 1 = 25$$

$$y^2 + 2y - 8 = 0$$

$$(y+4)(y-2) = 0 \Rightarrow y = -4 \ \text{ or } \ y = 2$$

Therefore, the points are $(2, -4)$ and $(2, 2)$.

37. All points on the x-axis are of the form $(x, 0)$. Those which are 5 units from $(4, -3)$ are:

$$\sqrt{(x-4)^2 + (0-(-3))^2} = 5 \Rightarrow \sqrt{(x-4)^2 + 3^2} = 5$$

Squaring both sides: $(x-4)^2 + 9 = 25$

$$x^2 - 8x + 16 + 9 = 25$$

$$x^2 - 8x = 0$$

$$x(x - 8) = 0 \Rightarrow x = 0 \ \text{ or } \ x = 8$$

Therefore, the points are $(0, 0)$ and $(8, 0)$.

39. The coordinates of the midpoint are:

$$(x,y) = \left(\frac{x_1 + x_2}{2}, \frac{y_1 + y_2}{2}\right) = \left(\frac{5+3}{2}, \frac{-4+2}{2}\right) = \left(\frac{8}{2}, \frac{-2}{2}\right) = (4,-1)$$

41. The coordinates of the midpoint are:

$$(x,y) = \left(\frac{x_1 + x_2}{2}, \frac{y_1 + y_2}{2}\right) = \left(\frac{-3+6}{2}, \frac{2+0}{2}\right) = \left(\frac{3}{2}, \frac{2}{2}\right) = \left(\frac{3}{2},1\right)$$

43. The coordinates of the midpoint are:

$$(x,y) = \left(\frac{x_1 + x_2}{2}, \frac{y_1 + y_2}{2}\right) = \left(\frac{4+6}{2}, \frac{-3+1}{2}\right) = \left(\frac{10}{2}, \frac{-2}{2}\right) = (5,-1)$$

45. The coordinates of the midpoint are:

$$(x,y) = \left(\frac{x_1 + x_2}{2}, \frac{y_1 + y_2}{2}\right) = \left(\frac{-0.2+2.3}{2}, \frac{0.3+1.1}{2}\right) = \left(\frac{2.1}{2}, \frac{1.4}{2}\right) = (1.05, 0.7)$$

47. The coordinates of the midpoint are:

$$(x,y) = \left(\frac{x_1 + x_2}{2}, \frac{y_1 + y_2}{2}\right) = \left(\frac{a+0}{2}, \frac{b+0}{2}\right) = \left(\frac{a}{2}, \frac{b}{2}\right)$$

49. The midpoint of AB is: $D = \left(\frac{0+0}{2}, \frac{0+6}{2}\right) = (0, 3)$

The midpoint of AC is: $E = \left(\frac{0+4}{2}, \frac{0+4}{2}\right) = (2, 2)$

The midpoint of BC is: $F = \left(\frac{0+4}{2}, \frac{6+4}{2}\right) = (2, 5)$

$$d(C,D) = \sqrt{(0-4)^2 + (3-4)^2} = \sqrt{(-4)^2 + (-1)^2} = \sqrt{16+1} = \sqrt{17}$$

$$d(B,E) = \sqrt{(2-0)^2 + (2-6)^2} = \sqrt{2^2 + (-4)^2} = \sqrt{4+16} = \sqrt{20} = 2\sqrt{5}$$

$$d(A,F) = \sqrt{(2-0)^2 + (5-0)^2} = \sqrt{2^2 + 5^2} = \sqrt{4+25} = \sqrt{29}$$

51. $d(P_1,P_2) = \sqrt{(-4-2)^2 + (1-1)^2} = \sqrt{(-6)^2 + 0^2} = \sqrt{36} = 6$

$d(P_2,P_3) = \sqrt{(-4-(-4))^2 + (-3-1)^2} = \sqrt{0^2 + (-4)^2} = \sqrt{16} = 4$

$d(P_1,P_3) = \sqrt{(-4-2)^2 + (-3-1)^2} = \sqrt{(-6)^2 + (-4)^2} = \sqrt{36+16} = \sqrt{52} = 2\sqrt{13}$

Since $\left[d(P_1,P_2)\right]^2 + \left[d(P_2,P_3)\right]^2 = \left[d(P_1,P_3)\right]^2$, the triangle is a right triangle.

53. $d(P_1,P_2) = \sqrt{(0-(-2))^2 + (7-(-1))^2} = \sqrt{2^2 + 8^2} = \sqrt{4+64} = \sqrt{68} = 2\sqrt{17}$

$d(P_2,P_3) = \sqrt{(3-0)^2 + (2-7)^2} = \sqrt{3^2 + (-5)^2} = \sqrt{9+25} = \sqrt{34}$

$d(P_1,P_3) = \sqrt{(3-(-2))^2 + (2-(-1))^2} = \sqrt{5^2 + 3^2} = \sqrt{25+9} = \sqrt{34}$

Since $d(P_2,P_3) = d(P_1,P_3)$, the triangle is isosceles.

Since $[d(P_1,P_3)]^2 + [d(P_2,P_3)]^2 = [d(P_1,P_2)]^2$, the triangle is also a right triangle.

Therefore, the triangle is an isosceles right triangle.

55. $P_1 = (1,3); \ P_2 = (5,15)$

$\begin{aligned} d(P_1,P_2) &= \sqrt{(5-1)^2 + (15-3)^2} \\ &= \sqrt{(4)^2 + (12)^2} \\ &= \sqrt{16+144} \\ &= \sqrt{160} = 4\sqrt{10} \end{aligned}$

57. $P_1 = (-4,6); \ P_2 = (4,-8)$

$\begin{aligned} d(P_1,P_2) &= \sqrt{(4-(-4))^2 + (-8-6)^2} \\ &= \sqrt{(8)^2 + (-14)^2} \\ &= \sqrt{64+196} \\ &= \sqrt{260} = 2\sqrt{65} \end{aligned}$

59. Plot the vertices of the square at $(0, 0)$, $(0, s)$, (s, s), and $(s, 0)$.

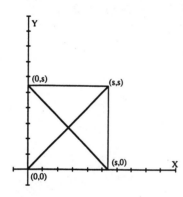

Find the midpoints of the diagonals.

$M_1 = \left(\dfrac{0+s}{2}, \dfrac{0+s}{2}\right) = \left(\dfrac{s}{2}, \dfrac{s}{2}\right)$

$M_2 = \left(\dfrac{0+s}{2}, \dfrac{s+0}{2}\right) = \left(\dfrac{s}{2}, \dfrac{s}{2}\right)$

Since the coordinates of the midpoints are the same, the diagonals of a square intersect at their midpoints.

61. Using the Pythagorean Theorem:

$90^2 + 90^2 = d^2$

$8100 + 8100 = d^2$

$16{,}200 = d^2$

$d = \sqrt{16{,}200} = 90\sqrt{2} \approx 127.28$ feet

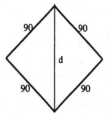

63. (a)   First: (90, 0), Second: (90, 90)
           Third: (0, 90)

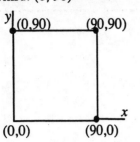

(b) Using the distance formula:
$$d = \sqrt{(310 - 90)^2 + (15 - 90)^2}$$
$$= \sqrt{220^2 + (-75)^2}$$
$$= \sqrt{54{,}025} \approx 232.4 \text{ feet}$$

(c) Using the distance formula:
$$d = \sqrt{(300 - 0)^2 + (300 - 90)^2}$$
$$= \sqrt{300^2 + 210^2}$$
$$= \sqrt{134{,}100} \approx 366.2 \text{ feet}$$

65. The Intrepid heading east moves a distance $30t$ after t
     hours. The truck heading south moves a distance $40t$
     after t hours. Their distance apart after t hours is:

$$d = \sqrt{(30t)^2 + (40t)^2}$$
$$= \sqrt{900t^2 + 1600t^2}$$
$$= \sqrt{2500t^2}$$
$$= 50t$$

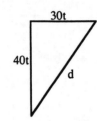

Graphs and Functions

1.2   Graphs of Equations; Circles

1.   add, 4

3.   intercepts

5.   (3,–4)

7.   True

9.
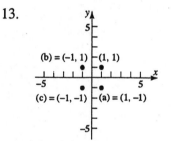

11.
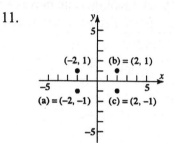

13.
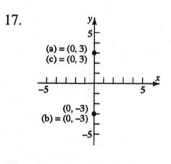

15.
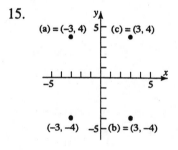

17.

![graph with points (a) = (0, 3), (c) = (0, 3), (0, –3), (b) = (0, –3)]

19.   (a) $(-1, 0), (1, 0)$

(b)   symmetric with respect to the x-axis, y-axis, and origin

21.   (a) $\left(-\dfrac{\pi}{2}, 0\right), \left(\dfrac{\pi}{2}, 0\right), (0, 1)$

(b)   symmetric with respect to the y-axis

23. (a) $(0, 0)$ (b) symmetric with respect to the x-axis

25. (a) $(1, 0)$ (b) not symmetric with respect to x-axis, y-axis, or origin

27. (a) $(-1, 0), (1, 0), (0, -1)$ (b) symmetric with respect to the y-axis

29. (a) none   (b) symmetric with respect to the origin

31. $y = x^4 - \sqrt{x}$

$0 = 0^4 - \sqrt{0}$ $1 = 1^4 - \sqrt{1}$ $0 = (-1)^4 - \sqrt{-1}$

$0 = 0$ $1 \neq 0$ $0 \neq 1 - \sqrt{-1}$

$(0, 0)$ is on the graph of the equation.

33. $y^2 = x^2 + 9$

$3^2 = 0^2 + 9$ $0^2 = 3^2 + 9$ $0^2 = (-3)^2 + 9$

$9 = 9$ $0 \neq 18$ $0 \neq 18$

$(0, 3)$ is on the graph of the equation.

35. $x^2 + y^2 = 4$

$0^2 + 2^2 = 4$ $(-2)^2 + 2^2 = 4$ $\left(\sqrt{2}\right)^2 + \left(\sqrt{2}\right)^2 = 4$

$4 = 4$ $8 \neq 4$ $4 = 4$

$(0, 2)$ and $\left(\sqrt{2}, \sqrt{2}\right)$ are on the graph of the equation.

37. $x^2 = y$

y-intercept: Let $x = 0$, then $0^2 = y \Rightarrow y = 0$ $(0,0)$

x-intercept: Let $y = 0$, then $x^2 = 0 \Rightarrow x = 0$ $(0,0)$

Test for symmetry:

x-axis: Replace y by $-y$: $x^2 = -y$, which is not equivalent to $x^2 = y$.

y-axis: Replace x by $-x$: $(-x)^2 = y$ or $x^2 = y$, which is equivalent to $x^2 = y$.

Origin: Replace x by $-x$ and y by $-y$: $(-x)^2 = -y$ or $x^2 = -y$,

which is not equivalent to $x^2 = y$.

Therefore, the graph is symmetric with respect to the y-axis.

39. $y = 3x$

y-intercept: Let $x = 0$, then $y = 3 \cdot 0 = 0$ $(0,0)$

x-intercept: Let $y = 0$, then $3x = 0 \Rightarrow x = 0$ $(0,0)$

Test for symmetry:

x-axis: Replace y by $-y$: $-y = 3x$, which is not equivalent to $y = 3x$.

y-axis: Replace x by $-x$: $y = 3(-x)$ or $y = -3x$,

which is not equivalent to $y = 3x$.

Origin :   Replace x by $-x$ and y by $-y$: $-y = 3(-x)$ or $y = 3x$,

which is equivalent to $y = 3x$.

Therefore, the graph is symmetric with respect to the origin.

41. $x^2 + y - 9 = 0$

y-intercept :   Let $x = 0$, then $0 + y - 9 = 0 \Rightarrow y = 9$ $(0,9)$

x-intercept :   Let $y = 0$, then $x^2 - 9 = 0 \Rightarrow x = \pm 3$ $(-3,0),(3,0)$

Test for symmetry:

x-axis :   Replace y by $-y$: $x^2 + (-y) - 9 = 0$ or $x^2 - y - 9 = 0$,

which is not equivalent to $x^2 + y - 9 = 0$.

y-axis :   Replace x by $-x$: $(-x)^2 + y - 9 = 0$ or $x^2 + y - 9 = 0$,

which is equivalent to $x^2 + y - 9 = 0$.

Origin :   Replace x by $-x$ and y by $-y$: $(-x)^2 + (-y) - 9 = 0$ or $x^2 - y - 9 = 0$,

which is not equivalent to $x^2 + y - 9 = 0$.

Therefore, the graph is symmetric with respect to the y-axis.

43. $9x^2 + 4y^2 = 36$

y-intercept :   Let $x = 0$, then $4y^2 = 36 \Rightarrow y^2 = 9 \Rightarrow y = \pm 3$ $(0,-3),(0,3)$

x-intercept :   Let $y = 0$, then $9x^2 = 36 \Rightarrow x^2 = 4 \Rightarrow x = \pm 2$ $(-2,0),(2,0)$

Test for symmetry:

x-axis :   Replace y by $-y$: $9x^2 + 4(-y)^2 = 36$ or $9x^2 + 4y^2 = 36$,

which is equivalent to $9x^2 + 4y^2 = 36$.

y-axis :   Replace x by $-x$: $9(-x)^2 + 4y^2 = 36$ or $9x^2 + 4y^2 = 36$,

which is equivalent to $9x^2 + 4y^2 = 36$.

Origin :   Replace x by $-x$ and y by $-y$: $9(-x)^2 + 4(-y)^2 = 36$ or $9x^2 + 4y^2 = 36$,

which is equivalent to $9x^2 + 4y^2 = 36$.

Therefore, the graph is symmetric with respect to the x-axis, the y-axis, and the origin.

45. $y = x^3 - 27$

y-intercept :   Let $x = 0$, then $y = 0^3 - 27 \Rightarrow y = -27$ $(0,-27)$

x-intercept :   Let $y = 0$, then $0 = x^3 - 27 \Rightarrow x^3 = 27 \Rightarrow x = 3$ $(3,0)$

Test for symmetry:

x-axis :   Replace y by $-y$: $-y = x^3 - 27$, which is not

equivalent to $y = x^3 - 27$.

y-axis :   Replace x by $-x$: $y = (-x)^3 - 27$ or $y = -x^3 - 27$,

which is not equivalent to $y = x^3 - 27$.

Origin: Replace x by $-x$ and y by $-y$: $-y = (-x)^3 - 27$ or

$y = x^3 + 27$, which is not equivalent to $y = x^3 - 27$.

Therefore, the graph is not symmetric with respect to the x-axis, the y-axis, or the origin.

47. $y = x^2 - 3x - 4$

y-intercept: Let $x = 0$, then $y = 0^2 - 3(0) - 4 \Rightarrow y = -4$ $(0, -4)$

x-intercept: Let $y = 0$, then $0 = x^2 - 3x - 4 \Rightarrow (x - 4)(x + 1) = 0 \Rightarrow x = 4, x = -1$ $(4, 0), (-1, 0)$

Test for symmetry:

x-axis: Replace y by $-y$: $-y = x^2 - 3x - 4$, which is not

equivalent to $y = x^2 - 3x - 4$.

y-axis: Replace x by $-x$: $y = (-x)^2 - 3(-x) - 4$ or $y = x^2 + 3x - 4$,

which is not equivalent to $y = x^2 - 3x - 4$.

Origin: Replace x by $-x$ and y by $-y$: $-y = (-x)^2 - 3(-x) - 4$ or

$y = -x^2 - 3x + 4$, which is not equivalent to $y = x^2 - 3x - 4$.

Therefore, the graph is not symmetric with respect to the x-axis, the y-axis, or the origin.

49. $y = \dfrac{3x}{x^2 + 9}$

y-intercept: Let $x = 0$, then $y = \dfrac{0}{0 + 9} = 0$ $(0, 0)$

x-intercept: Let $y = 0$, then $0 = \dfrac{3x}{x^2 + 9} \Rightarrow 3x = 0 \Rightarrow x = 0$ $(0, 0)$

Test for symmetry:

x-axis: Replace y by $-y$: $-y = \dfrac{3x}{x^2 + 9}$, which is not

equivalent to $y = \dfrac{3x}{x^2 + 9}$.

y-axis: Replace x by $-x$: $y = \dfrac{3(-x)}{(-x)^2 + 9}$ or $y = \dfrac{-3x}{x^2 + 9}$,

which is not equivalent to $y = \dfrac{3x}{x^2 + 9}$.

Origin: Replace x by $-x$ and y by $-y$: $-y = \dfrac{-3x}{(-x)^2 + 9}$ or

$y = \dfrac{3x}{x^2 + 9}$, which is equivalent to $y = \dfrac{3x}{x^2 + 9}$.

Therefore, the graph is symmetric with respect to the origin.

51. $y = \dfrac{-x^3}{x^2 - 9}$

 y - intercept : Let $x = 0$, then $y = \dfrac{0}{-9} = 0$ $(0,0)$

 x - intercept : Let $y = 0$, then $0 = \dfrac{-x^3}{x^2 - 9} \Rightarrow -x^3 = 0 \Rightarrow x = 0$ $(0,0)$

Test for symmetry:

 x - axis :   Replace y by $-y$: $-y = \dfrac{-x^3}{x^2 - 9}$, which is not equivalent to $y = \dfrac{-x^3}{x^2 - 9}$.

 y - axis :   Replace x by $-x$: $y = \dfrac{-(-x)^3}{(-x)^2 - 9}$ or $y = \dfrac{x^3}{x^2 - 9}$,

 which is not equivalent to $y = \dfrac{-x^3}{x^2 - 9}$.

Origin :   Replace x by $-x$ and y by $-y$: $-y = \dfrac{-(-x)^3}{(-x)^2 - 9}$ or

 $-y = \dfrac{x^3}{x^2 - 9}$, which is equivalent to $y = \dfrac{-x^3}{x^2 - 9}$.

Therefore, the graph is symmetric with respect to the origin.

53. $y = x^3$

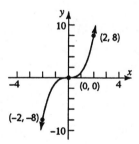

55. $y = \sqrt{x}$

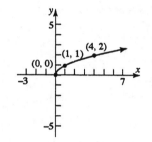

57. $y = 3x + 5$
    $2 = 3a + 5$

    $3a = -3$

    $a = -1$

59. $2x + 3y = 6$
    $2a + 3b = 6$

    $b = 2 - \dfrac{2}{3}a$

61. Center = (2, 1)
Radius = distance from (0,1) to (2,1)
$$= \sqrt{(2-0)^2 + (1-1)^2}$$
$$= \sqrt{4} = 2$$

$$(x-2)^2 + (y-1)^2 = 4$$

63. Center = midpoint of (1,2) and (4,2)
$$= \left(\frac{1+4}{2}, \frac{2+2}{2}\right) = \left(\frac{5}{2}, 2\right)$$
Radius = distance from $\left(\frac{5}{2}, 2\right)$ to (4,2)
$$= \sqrt{\left(4 - \frac{5}{2}\right)^2 + (2-2)^2}$$
$$= \sqrt{\frac{9}{4}} = \frac{3}{2}$$

$$\left(x - \frac{5}{2}\right)^2 + (y-2)^2 = \frac{9}{4}$$

65. $(x-h)^2 + (y-k)^2 = r^2$
$(x-0)^2 + (y-0)^2 = 2^2$
$x^2 + y^2 = 4$
General form: $x^2 + y^2 - 4 = 0$

67. $(x-h)^2 + (y-k)^2 = r^2$
$(x-1)^2 + (y-(-1))^2 = 1^2$
$(x-1)^2 + (y+1)^2 = 1$
General form:
$x^2 - 2x + 1 + y^2 + 2y + 1 = 1$
$x^2 + y^2 - 2x + 2y + 1 = 0$

69. $(x-h)^2 + (y-k)^2 = r^2$
$(x-0)^2 + (y-2)^2 = 2^2$
$x^2 + (y-2)^2 = 4$
General form:
$x^2 + y^2 - 4y + 4 = 4$
$x^2 + y^2 - 4y = 0$

71. $(x-h)^2 + (y-k)^2 = r^2$
$(x-4)^2 + (y-(-3))^2 = 5^2$
$(x-4)^2 + (y+3)^2 = 25$
General form:
$x^2 - 8x + 16 + y^2 + 6y + 9 = 25$
$x^2 + y^2 - 8x + 6y = 0$

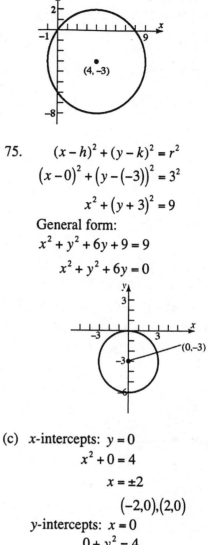

73. $(x-h)^2 + (y-k)^2 = r^2$
$\left(x-(-3)\right)^2 + \left(y-(-6)\right)^2 = 6^2$
$(x+3)^2 + (y+6)^2 = 36$
General form:
$x^2 + 6x + 9 + y^2 + 12y + 36 = 36$
$x^2 + y^2 + 6x + 12y + 9 = 0$

75. $(x-h)^2 + (y-k)^2 = r^2$
$\left(x-0\right)^2 + \left(y-(-3)\right)^2 = 3^2$
$x^2 + (y+3)^2 = 9$
General form:
$x^2 + y^2 + 6y + 9 = 9$
$x^2 + y^2 + 6y = 0$

77. $x^2 + y^2 = 4$
$x^2 + y^2 = 2^2$
(a) Center : (0,0); Radius = 2
(b)

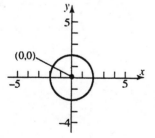

(c) x-intercepts: $y = 0$
$x^2 + 0 = 4$
$x = \pm 2$
$(-2,0),(2,0)$
y-intercepts: $x = 0$
$0 + y^2 = 4$
$y = \pm 2$
$(0,-2),(0,2)$

13

79. $2(x-3)^2 + 2y^2 = 8$

$(x-3)^2 + y^2 = 4$

$(x-3)^2 + y^2 = 2^2$

(a) Center: $(3,0)$; Radius $= 2$

(b)

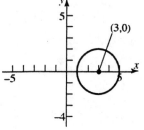

(c) x-intercepts: $y = 0$

$(x-3)^2 + 0 = 4$

$(x-3)^2 = 4$

$x - 3 = \pm 2$

$x = 5, x = 1$

$(1,0), (5,0)$

y-intercepts: $x = 0$

$9 + y^2 = 4$

$y^2 = -5$

no solution $\Rightarrow$ no y - intercepts

81. $x^2 + y^2 + 4x - 4y - 1 = 0$

$x^2 + 4x + y^2 - 4y = 1$

$(x^2 + 4x + 4) + (y^2 - 4y + 4) = 1 + 4 + 4$

$(x+2)^2 + (y-2)^2 = 3^2$

(a) Center: $(-2,2)$; Radius $= 3$

(b)

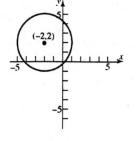

(c) x-intercepts: $y = 0$

$(x+2)^2 + 4 = 9$

$(x+2)^2 = 5$

$x + 2 = \pm\sqrt{5}$

$x = \sqrt{5} - 2, x = -\sqrt{5} - 2$

$\left(-\sqrt{5} - 2, 0\right), \left(\sqrt{5} - 2, 0\right)$

y-intercepts: $x = 0$

$4 + (y-2)^2 = 9$

$(y-2)^2 = 5$

$y - 2 = \pm\sqrt{5}$

$y = \sqrt{5} + 2, y = -\sqrt{5} + 2$

$\left(0, -\sqrt{5} + 2\right), \left(0, \sqrt{5} + 2\right)$

83.
$$x^2 + y^2 - 2x + 4y - 4 = 0$$
$$x^2 - 2x + y^2 + 4y = 4$$
$$(x^2 - 2x + 1) + (y^2 + 4y + 4) = 4 + 1 + 4$$
$$(x-1)^2 + (y+2)^2 = 3^2$$
(a) Center: $(1,-2)$; Radius $= 3$
(b)

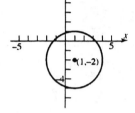

(c) x-intercepts: $y = 0$
$$(x-1)^2 + 4 = 9$$
$$(x-1)^2 = 5$$
$$x + 1 = \pm\sqrt{5}$$
$$x = \sqrt{5} - 1, x = -\sqrt{5} - 1$$
$$\left(-\sqrt{5} - 1, 0\right), \left(\sqrt{5} - 1, 0\right)$$
y-intercepts: $x = 0$
$$1 + (y+2)^2 = 9$$
$$(y+2)^2 = 8$$
$$y + 2 = \pm\sqrt{8}$$
$$y = \sqrt{8} - 2, y = -\sqrt{8} - 2$$
$$\left(0, -\sqrt{8} - 2\right), \left(0, \sqrt{8} - 2\right)$$

85.
$$x^2 + y^2 - x + 2y + 1 = 0$$
$$x^2 - x + y^2 + 2y = -1$$
$$\left(x^2 - x + \frac{1}{4}\right) + (y^2 + 2y + 1) = -1 + \frac{1}{4} + 1$$
$$\left(x - \frac{1}{2}\right)^2 + (y+1)^2 = \left(\frac{1}{2}\right)^2$$
(a) Center: $\left(\frac{1}{2}, -1\right)$; Radius $= \frac{1}{2}$
(b)

(c) x-intercepts: $y = 0$
$$\left(x - \frac{1}{2}\right)^2 + 1 = \frac{1}{4}$$
$$\left(x - \frac{1}{2}\right)^2 = -\frac{3}{4}$$
no solution $\Rightarrow$ no x-intercepts
y-intercepts: $x = 0$
$$\frac{1}{4} + (y+1)^2 = \frac{1}{4}$$
$$(y+1)^2 = 0$$
$$y + 1 = 0$$
$$y = -1$$
$$(0, -1)$$

87. $2x^2 + 2y^2 - 12x + 8y - 24 = 0$
$$x^2 + y^2 - 6x + 4y = 12$$
$$x^2 - 6x + y^2 + 4y = 12$$
$$(x^2 - 6x + 9) + (y^2 + 4y + 4) = 12 + 9 + 4$$
$$(x-3)^2 + (y+2)^2 = 5^2$$
(a) Center: (3,–2); Radius = 5
(b)

(3,–2)

(c) x-intercepts: $y = 0$
$$(x-3)^2 + 4 = 25$$
$$(x-3)^2 = 21$$
$$x - 3 = \pm\sqrt{21}$$
$$x = \sqrt{21} + 3, x = -\sqrt{21} + 3$$
$$\left(-\sqrt{21} + 3,0\right),\left(\sqrt{21} + 3,0\right)$$
y-intercepts: $x = 0$
$$9 + (y+2)^2 = 25$$
$$(y+2)^2 = 16$$
$$y + 2 = \pm 4$$
$$y = 2, y = -6$$
$$(0,-6),(0,2)$$

89. Center at (0,0); containing point (–3, 2).
$$r = \sqrt{(-3-0)^2 + (2-0)^2} = \sqrt{9+4} = \sqrt{13}$$
Equation:
$$(x-0)^2 + (y-0)^2 = \left(\sqrt{13}\right)^2$$
$$x^2 + y^2 = 13$$

91. Center at (2,3); tangent to the x-axis.
$r = 3$
Equation:
$$(x-2)^2 + (y-3)^2 = 3^2$$
$$x^2 - 4x + 4 + y^2 - 6y + 9 = 9$$
$$x^2 + y^2 - 4x - 6y + 4 = 0$$

93. Endpoints of a diameter are (1,4) and (–3,2).
The center is at the midpoint of that diameter:
Center: $\left(\dfrac{1+(-3)}{2}, \dfrac{4+2}{2}\right) = (-1,3)$
Radius: $r = \sqrt{(1-(-1))^2 + (4-3)^2} = \sqrt{4+1} = \sqrt{5}$
Equation: $\left(x-(-1)\right)^2 + (y-3)^2 = \left(\sqrt{5}\right)^2$
$$x^2 + 2x + 1 + y^2 - 6y + 9 = 5$$
$$x^2 + y^2 + 2x - 6y + 5 = 0$$

95. (c)

97. (b)

99. (b), (c), (e) and (g)

101. $x^2 + y^2 + 2x + 4y - 4091 = 0$
$$x^2 + 2x + y^2 + 4y - 4091 = 0$$
$$x^2 + 2x + 1 + y^2 + 4y + 4 = 4091 + 5$$
$$(x+1)^2 + (y+2)^2 = 4096$$
The circle representing Earth has center $(-1,-2)$ and radius $= \sqrt{4096} = 64$
So the radius of the satellite's orbit is $64 + 0.6 = 64.6$ units.

The equation of the orbit is

$$(x+1)^2 + (y+2)^2 = (64.6)^2$$

$$x^2 + y^2 + 2x + 4y - 4168.16 = 0$$

103–105.   Answers will vary

Graphs and Functions

1.3   Functions and Their Graphs

1. $(-1, 3)$

3.   We must not allow the denominator to be 0.
$x + 4 \neq 0 \Rightarrow x \neq -4$; Domain: $\{x | x \neq -4\}$.

5.   independent, dependent

7.   False

9.   False

11.   vertical

13. $f(x) = ax^2 + 4$
$a(-1)^2 + 4 = 2 \Rightarrow a = -2$

15.   False

17.   Function
Domain: {Dad, Colleen, Kaleigh, Marissa}
Range: {Jan. 8, Mar. 15, Sept. 17}

19.   Not a function

21.   Not a function

23.   Function
Domain: {1, 2, 3, 4}
Range: {3}

25.   Not a function

27.   Function
Domain: {-2, -1, 0, 1}
Range: {4, 1, 0}

29. $f(x) = 3x^2 + 2x - 4$
   (a) $f(0) = 3(0)^2 + 2(0) - 4 = -4$
   (b) $f(1) = 3(1)^2 + 2(1) - 4 = 3 + 2 - 4 = 1$
   (c) $f(-1) = 3(-1)^2 + 2(-1) - 4 = 3 - 2 - 4 = -3$
   (d) $f(-x) = 3(-x)^2 + 2(-x) - 4 = 3x^2 - 2x - 4$
   (e) $-f(x) = -(3x^2 + 2x - 4) = -3x^2 - 2x + 4$

(f) $f(x+1) = 3(x+1)^2 + 2(x+1) - 4 = 3(x^2 + 2x + 1) + 2x + 2 - 4$
$$= 3x^2 + 6x + 3 + 2x + 2 - 4$$
$$= 3x^2 + 8x + 1$$

(g) $f(2x) = 3(2x)^2 + 2(2x) - 4 = 12x^2 + 4x - 4$

(h) $f(x+h) = 3(x+h)^2 + 2(x+h) - 4 = 3(x^2 + 2xh + h^2) + 2x + 2h - 4$
$$= 3x^2 + 6xh + 3h^2 + 2x + 2h - 4$$

31. $f(x) = \dfrac{x}{x^2 + 1}$

(a) $f(0) = \dfrac{0}{0^2 + 1} = \dfrac{0}{1} = 0$

(b) $f(1) = \dfrac{1}{1^2 + 1} = \dfrac{1}{2}$

(c) $f(-1) = \dfrac{-1}{(-1)^2 + 1} = \dfrac{-1}{1+1} = -\dfrac{1}{2}$

(d) $f(-x) = \dfrac{-x}{(-x)^2 + 1} = \dfrac{-x}{x^2 + 1}$

(e) $-f(x) = -\left(\dfrac{x}{x^2 + 1}\right) = \dfrac{-x}{x^2 + 1}$

(f) $f(x+1) = \dfrac{x+1}{(x+1)^2 + 1} = \dfrac{x+1}{x^2 + 2x + 1 + 1} = \dfrac{x+1}{x^2 + 2x + 2}$

(g) $f(2x) = \dfrac{2x}{(2x)^2 + 1} = \dfrac{2x}{4x^2 + 1}$

(h) $f(x+h) = \dfrac{x+h}{(x+h)^2 + 1} = \dfrac{x+h}{x^2 + 2xh + h^2 + 1}$

33. $f(x) = |x| + 4$

(a) $f(0) = |0| + 4 = 0 + 4 = 4$

(b) $f(1) = |1| + 4 = 1 + 4 = 5$

(c) $f(-1) = |-1| + 4 = 1 + 4 = 5$

(d) $f(-x) = |-x| + 4 = |x| + 4$

(e) $-f(x) = -(|x| + 4) = -|x| - 4$

(f) $f(x+1) = |x+1| + 4$

(g) $f(2x) = |2x| + 4 = 2|x| + 4$

(h) $f(x+h) = |x+h| + 4$

35. $f(x) = \dfrac{2x+1}{3x-5}$

(a) $f(0) = \dfrac{2(0)+1}{3(0)-5} = \dfrac{0+1}{0-5} = -\dfrac{1}{5}$

(b) $f(1) = \dfrac{2(1)+1}{3(1)-5} = \dfrac{2+1}{3-5} = \dfrac{3}{-2} = -\dfrac{3}{2}$

(c) $f(-1) = \dfrac{2(-1)+1}{3(-1)-5} = \dfrac{-2+1}{-3-5} = \dfrac{-1}{-8} = \dfrac{1}{8}$

(d) $f(-x) = \dfrac{2(-x)+1}{3(-x)-5} = \dfrac{-2x+1}{-3x-5} = \dfrac{2x-1}{3x+5}$

(e) $-f(x) = -\left(\dfrac{2x+1}{3x-5}\right) = \dfrac{-2x-1}{3x-5}$

(f) $f(x+1) = \dfrac{2(x+1)+1}{3(x+1)-5} = \dfrac{2x+2+1}{3x+3-5} = \dfrac{2x+3}{3x-2}$

(g) $f(2x) = \dfrac{2(2x)+1}{3(2x)-5} = \dfrac{4x+1}{6x-5}$

(h) $f(x+h) = \dfrac{2(x+h)+1}{3(x+h)-5} = \dfrac{2x+2h+1}{3x+3h-5}$

37. Graph $y = x^2$. The graph passes the vertical line test. Thus, the equation represents a function.

39. Graph $y = \dfrac{1}{x}$. The graph passes the vertical line test. Thus, the equation represents a function.

41. $y^2 = 4 - x^2$
Solve for y: $y = \pm\sqrt{4 - x^2}$
For $x = 0, y = \pm 2$. Thus, (0, 2) and (0, –2) are on the graph. This is not a function, since a distinct x corresponds to two different y's.

43. $x = y^2$
Solve for y: $y = \pm\sqrt{x}$
For $x = 1, y = \pm 1$. Thus, (1, 1) and (1, –1) are on the graph. This is not a function, since a distinct x corresponds to two different y's.

45. Graph $y = 2x^2 - 3x + 4$. The graph passes the vertical line test. Thus, the equation represents a function.

47. $2x^2 + 3y^2 = 1$
Solve for y:

$$2x^2 + 3y^2 = 1 \Rightarrow 3y^2 = 1 - 2x^2 \Rightarrow y^2 = \dfrac{1-2x^2}{3} \Rightarrow y = \pm\sqrt{\dfrac{1-2x^2}{3}}$$

For $x = 0, y = \pm\sqrt{\dfrac{1}{3}}$. Thus, $\left(0, \sqrt{\dfrac{1}{3}}\right)$ and $\left(0, -\sqrt{\dfrac{1}{3}}\right)$ are on the graph. This is not a function, since a distinct x corresponds to two different y's.

49. $f(x) = -5x + 4$

Domain: $\{x \mid x \text{ is any real number}\}$

51. $f(x) = \dfrac{x}{x^2 + 1}$

Domain: $\{x \mid x \text{ is any real number}\}$

53. $g(x) = \dfrac{x}{x^2 - 16}$

$x^2 - 16 \neq 0$

$x^2 \neq 16 \Rightarrow x \neq \pm 4$

Domain: $\{x \mid x \neq -4, \; x \neq 4\}$

55. $F(x) = \dfrac{x - 2}{x^3 + x}$

$x^3 + x \neq 0$

$x(x^2 + 1) \neq 0$

$x \neq 0, \quad x^2 \neq -1$

Domain: $\{x \mid x \neq 0\}$

57. $h(x) = \sqrt{3x - 12}$

$3x - 12 \geq 0$

$3x \geq 12$

$x \geq 4$

Domain: $\{x \mid x \geq 4\}$

59. $f(x) = \dfrac{4}{\sqrt{x - 9}}$

$x - 9 > 0$

$x > 9$

Domain: $\{x \mid x > 9\}$

61. $f(x) = 4x + 3$

$\dfrac{f(x+h) - f(x)}{h} = \dfrac{4(x+h) + 3 - 4x - 3}{h}$

$= \dfrac{4x + 4h + 3 - 4x - 3}{h} = \dfrac{4h}{h} = 4$

63. $f(x) = x^2 - x + 4$

$\dfrac{f(x+h) - f(x)}{h} = \dfrac{(x+h)^2 - (x+h) + 4 - (x^2 - x + 4)}{h}$

$= \dfrac{x^2 + 2xh + h^2 - x - h + 4 - x^2 + x - 4}{h}$

$= \dfrac{2xh + h^2 - h}{h}$

$= 2x + h - 1$

65. $f(x) = x^3 - 2$

$\dfrac{f(x+h) - f(x)}{h} = \dfrac{(x+h)^3 - 2 - (x^3 - 2)}{h}$

$= \dfrac{x^3 + 3x^2h + 3xh^2 + h^3 - 2 - x^3 + 2}{h}$

$= \dfrac{3x^2h + 3xh^2 + h^3}{h}$

$= 3x^2 + 3xh + h^2$

67. (a) $f(0) = 3$ since $(0,3)$ is on the graph.
           $f(-6) = -3$ since $(-6,-3)$ is on the graph.
     (b) $f(6) = 0$ since $(6,0)$ is on the graph.
           $f(11) = 1$ since $(11,1)$ is on the graph.
     (c) $f(3)$ is positive since $f(3) \approx 3.7$.
     (d) $f(-4)$ is negative since $f(-4) \approx -1$.
     (e) $f(x) = 0$ when $x = -3$, $x = 6$, and $x = 10$.
     (f) $f(x) > 0$ when $-3 < x < 6$, and $10 < x \leq 11$.
     (g)   The domain of f is $\{x | -6 \leq x \leq 11\}$ or $[-6, 11]$
     (h)   The range of f is $\{y | -3 \leq y \leq 4\}$ or $[-3, 4]$
     (i)   The x-intercepts are $(-3, 0)$, $(6, 0)$, and $(11, 0)$.
     (j)   The y-intercept is $(0, 3)$
     (k)   The line $y = \dfrac{1}{2}$ intersects the graph 3 times.
     (l)   The line $x = 5$ intersects the graph 1 time
     (m) $f(x) = 3$ when $x = 0$ and $x = 4$.
     (n) $f(x) = -2$ when $x = -5$ and $x = 8$.

69. Not a function since vertical lines will intersect the graph in more than one point.

71. Function   (a)   Domain: $\{x | -\pi \leq x \leq \pi\}$;   Range: $\{y | -1 \leq y \leq 1\}$
                 (b)   intercepts: $\left(-\dfrac{\pi}{2}, 0\right)$, $\left(\dfrac{\pi}{2}, 0\right)$, $(0,1)$

73. Not a function since vertical lines will intersect the graph in more than one point.

75. Function   (a)   Domain: $\{x | x > 0\}$;   Range: $\{y | y \text{ is any real number}\}$
                 (b)   intercepts: $(1, 0)$

77. Function   (a)   Domain: $\{x | x \text{ is any real number}\}$;   Range: $\{y | y \leq 2\}$
                 (b)   intercepts: $(-3,0)$, $(3,0)$, $(0,2)$

79. Function   (a)   Domain: $\{x | x \text{ is any real number}\}$;   Range: $\{y | y \geq -3\}$
                 (b)   intercepts: $(1,0)$, $(3,0)$, $(0,9)$

81. $f(x) = 2x^3 + Ax^2 + 4x - 5$ and $f(2) = 5$
     $f(2) = 2(2)^3 + A(2)^2 + 4(2) - 5$
     $5 = 16 + 4A + 8 - 5 \Rightarrow 5 = 4A + 19$
     $-14 = 4A \Rightarrow A = -\dfrac{7}{2}$

83. $f(x) = \dfrac{3x + 8}{2x - A}$ and $f(0) = 2$
     $f(0) = \dfrac{3(0) + 8}{2(0) - A}$
     $2 = \dfrac{8}{-A} \Rightarrow -2A = 8 \Rightarrow A = -4$

85. $f(x) = \dfrac{2x - A}{x - 3}$ and $f(4) = 0$

$$f(4) = \dfrac{2(4) - A}{4 - 3}$$

$$0 = \dfrac{8 - A}{1}$$

$$0 = 8 - A$$

$$A = 8$$

f is undefined when $x = 3$.

87. $f(x) = 2x^2 - x - 1$

(a) $f(-1) = 2(-1)^2 - (-1) - 1 = 2$ $(-1,2)$ is on the graph of f.

(b) $f(-2) = 2(-2)^2 - (-2) - 1 = 9$ $(-2,9)$ is on the graph of f.

(c) Solve for x:

$$-1 = 2x^2 - x - 1 \Rightarrow 0 = 2x^2 - x$$

$$0 = x(2x - 1) \Rightarrow x = 0, x = \dfrac{1}{2}$$

$(0, -1)$ and $\left(\dfrac{1}{2}, -1\right)$ are on the graph of f.

(d) The domain of f is: $\{x \mid x \text{ is any real number}\}$.

(e) x-intercepts:

$$f(x) = 0 \Rightarrow 2x^2 - x - 1 = 0$$

$$(2x + 1)(x - 1) = 0 \Rightarrow x = -\dfrac{1}{2}, x = 1$$

$$\left(-\dfrac{1}{2}, 0\right) \text{ and } (1, 0)$$

(f) y-intercept: $f(0) = 2(0)^2 - 0 - 1 = -1 \Rightarrow (0, -1)$

89. $f(x) = \dfrac{x + 2}{x - 6}$

(a) $f(3) = \dfrac{3 + 2}{3 - 6} = -\dfrac{5}{3} \neq 14$ $(3, 14)$ is not on the graph of f.

(b) $f(4) = \dfrac{4 + 2}{4 - 6} = \dfrac{6}{-2} = -3$ $(4, -3)$ is on the graph of f.

(c) Solve for x:

$$2 = \dfrac{x + 2}{x - 6}$$

$$2x - 12 = x + 2$$

$$x = 14$$

$(14, 2)$ is a point on the graph of f.

(d) The domain of f is: $\{x \mid x \neq 6\}$.

(e) x-intercepts:

$$f(x) = 0 \Rightarrow \frac{x+2}{x-6} = 0$$

$$x + 2 = 0 \Rightarrow x = -2 \Rightarrow (-2,0)$$

(f) y-intercept: $f(0) = \dfrac{0+2}{0-6} = -\dfrac{1}{3} \Rightarrow \left(0, -\dfrac{1}{3}\right)$

91. $f(x) = \dfrac{2x^2}{x^4 + 1}$

(a) $f(-1) = \dfrac{2(-1)^2}{(-1)^4 + 1} = \dfrac{2}{2} = 1$ $(-1,1)$ is on the graph of f.

(b) $f(2) = \dfrac{2(2)^2}{(2)^4 + 1} = \dfrac{8}{17}$ $\left(2, \dfrac{8}{17}\right)$ is on the graph of f.

(c)   Solve for x:

$$1 = \frac{2x^2}{x^4 + 1}$$

$$x^4 + 1 = 2x^2$$

$$x^4 - 2x^2 + 1 = 0$$

$$(x^2 - 1)^2 = 0$$

$$x^2 - 1 = 0 \Rightarrow x = \pm 1$$

$(1,1)$ and $(-1,1)$ are on the graph of f.

(d)   The domain of f is: $\{x \mid x \text{ is any real number}\}$.

(e) x-intercept:

$$f(x) = 0 \Rightarrow \frac{2x^2}{x^4 + 1} = 0$$

$$2x^2 = 0 \Rightarrow x = 0 \Rightarrow (0,0)$$

(f) y-intercept: $f(0) = \dfrac{2(0)^2}{0^4 + 1} = \dfrac{0}{0+1} = 0 \Rightarrow (0,0)$

93.   Let x represent the length of the rectangle.

Then $\dfrac{x}{2}$ represents the width of the rectangle, since the length is twice the width.

The function for the area is: $A(x) = x \cdot \dfrac{x}{2} = \dfrac{x^2}{2} = \dfrac{1}{2}x^2$

95.   Let x represent the number of hours worked.
The function for the gross salary is: $G(x) = 10x$

97.   (a) $H(1) = 20 - 4.9(1)^2 = 20 - 4.9 = 15.1$ meters

$H(1.1) = 20 - 4.9(1.1)^2 = 20 - 4.9(1.21) = 20 - 5.929 = 14.071$ meters

$H(1.2) = 20 - 4.9(1.2)^2 = 20 - 4.9(1.44) = 20 - 7.056 = 12.944$ meters

$H(1.3) = 20 - 4.9(1.3)^2 = 20 - 4.9(1.69) = 20 - 8.281 = 11.719$ meters

(b) $H(x) = 15$

   $15 = 20 - 4.9x^2$

   $-5 = -4.9x^2$

   $x^2 \approx 1.0204$

   $x \approx 1.01$ seconds

$H(x) = 10$

   $10 = 20 - 4.9x^2$

   $-10 = -4.9x^2$

   $x^2 \approx 2.0408$

   $x \approx 1.43$ seconds

$H(x) = 5$

   $5 = 20 - 4.9x^2$

   $-15 = -4.9x^2$

   $x^2 \approx 3.0612$

   $x \approx 1.75$ seconds

(c) $H(x) = 0$

   $0 = 20 - 4.9x^2$

   $-20 = -4.9x^2$

   $x^2 \approx 4.0816$

   $x \approx 2.02$ seconds

99. $h(x) = \dfrac{-32x^2}{130^2} + x$

(a) $h(100) = \dfrac{-32(100)^2}{130^2} + 100 = \dfrac{-320,000}{16,900} + 100 \approx -18.93 + 100 \approx 81.07$ feet

(b) $h(300) = \dfrac{-32(300)^2}{130^2} + 300 = \dfrac{-2,880,000}{16,900} + 300 \approx -170.41 + 300 \approx 129.59$ feet

(c) $h(500) = \dfrac{-32(500)^2}{130^2} + 500 = \dfrac{-8,000,000}{16,900} + 500 \approx -473.37 + 500 \approx 26.63$ feet

(d) Solving $h(x) = \dfrac{-32x^2}{130^2} + x = 0$

   $\dfrac{-32x^2}{130^2} + x = 0 \Rightarrow x\left(\dfrac{-32x}{130^2} + 1\right) = 0 \Rightarrow x = 0$ or $\dfrac{-32x}{130^2} + 1 = 0$

   $\dfrac{-32x}{130^2} + 1 = 0 \Rightarrow 1 = \dfrac{32x}{130^2} \Rightarrow 130^2 = 32x \Rightarrow x = \dfrac{130^2}{32} = 528.125$ feet

   Therefore, the golf ball travels 528.125 feet.

(e) $y_1 = \dfrac{-32x^2}{130^2} + x$

(f) Use INTERSECT on the graphs of $y_1 = \dfrac{-32x^2}{130^2} + x$ and $y_2 = 90$.

The ball reaches a height of 90 feet twice. The first time is when the ball has traveled approximately 115 feet, and the second time is when the ball has traveled approximately 413 feet.

(g) The ball travels approximately 275 feet before it reaches its maximum height of approximately 131.8 feet.

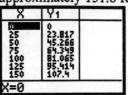

(h) The ball travels approximately 264 feet before it reaches its maximum height of approximately 132.03 feet.

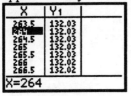

101. $C(x) = 100 + \dfrac{x}{10} + \dfrac{36,000}{x}$

(a) $C(500) = 100 + \dfrac{500}{10} + \dfrac{36,000}{500} = 100 + 50 + 72 = \$222$

(b) $C(450) = 100 + \dfrac{450}{10} + \dfrac{36,000}{450} = 100 + 45 + 80 = \$225$

(c) $C(600) = 100 + \dfrac{600}{10} + \dfrac{36,000}{600} = 100 + 60 + 60 = \$220$

(d) $C(400) = 100 + \dfrac{400}{10} + \dfrac{36,000}{400} = 100 + 40 + 90 = \$230$

103. (a) III   (b) IV   (c) I   (d) V   (e) II

105.

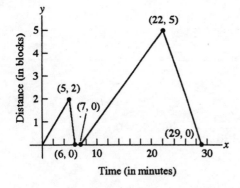

107. (a) 2 hours elapsed; Kevin was between 0 and 3 miles from home.
(b) 0.5 hours elapsed; Kevin was 3 miles from home.
(c) 0.3 hours elapsed; Kevin was between 0 and 3 miles from home.
(d) 0.2 hours elapsed; Kevin was at home.
(e) 0.9 hours elapsed; Kevin was between 0 and 2.8 miles from home.

(f)   0.3 hours elapsed; Kevin was 2.8 miles from home.
(g)   1.1 hours elapsed; Kevin was between 0 and 2.8 miles from home.
(h)   The farthest distance Kevin is from home is 3 miles.
(i)   Kevin returned home 2 times.

109. Points of the form (5, y) and of the form (x, 0) cannot be on the graph of the function.

111. No, $x = -1$ is not in the domain of g, but it is in the domain of f.

113. Answers will vary.

115. Yes. One example is $G(x) = 2$, where the domain of G is {1}.

Graphs and Functions

1.4 Properties of Functions; Library of Functions

1. $2 \leq x \leq 5$

3. $y = x^2 - 9$
   y-intercept: Let $x = 0$, then $y = 0^2 - 9 = -9$ $(0, -9)$
   x-intercepts: Let $y = 0$, then $0 = x^2 - 9 \Rightarrow x^2 = 9 \Rightarrow x = \pm 3$ $(-3, 0), (3, 0)$

5. $y = \dfrac{1}{x}$

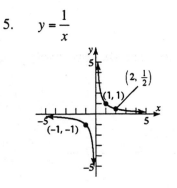

7. even, odd

9. True

11. False

13. C

15. E

17. B

19. F

21. $f(x) = x$

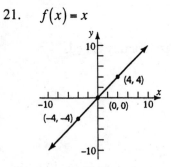

23. $f(x) = x^3$

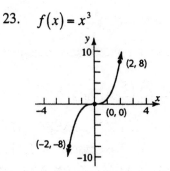

25. $f(x) = \dfrac{1}{x}$

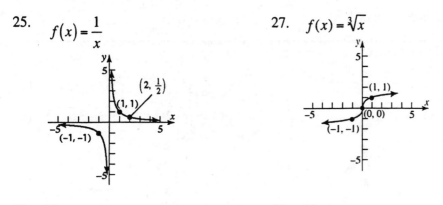

27. $f(x) = \sqrt[3]{x}$

29. Yes.

31. No

33. f is increasing on the intervals $(-8,-2)$, $(0,2)$, $(5,\infty)$.

35. Yes. The local maximum at $x = 2$ is 10.

37. f has local maxima at $x = -2$ and $x = 2$. The local maxima are 6 and 10, respectively.

39. (a) Intercepts: $(-2,0)$, $(2,0)$, and $(0,3)$.
     (b) Domain: $\{x \mid -4 \le x \le 4\}$; Range: $\{y \mid 0 \le y \le 3\}$.
     (c) Increasing: $(-2, 0)$ and $(2, 4)$; Decreasing: $(-4, -2)$ and $(0, 2)$.
     (d) Since the graph is symmetric with respect to the y-axis, the function is <u>even</u>.

41. (a) Intercepts: $(0,1)$.
     (b) Domain: $\{x \mid x \text{ is any real number}\}$; Range: $\{y \mid y > 0\}$.
     (c) Increasing: $(-\infty,\infty)$; Decreasing: never.
     (d) Since the graph is not symmetric with respect to the y-axis or the origin, the function is <u>neither</u> even nor odd.

43. (a) Intercepts: $(-\pi,0), (\pi,0)$, and $(0,0)$.
     (b) Domain: $\{x \mid -\pi \le x \le \pi\}$; Range: $\{y \mid -1 \le y \le 1\}$.
     (c) Increasing: $\left(-\dfrac{\pi}{2}, \dfrac{\pi}{2}\right)$; Decreasing: $\left(-\pi, -\dfrac{\pi}{2}\right)$ and $\left(\dfrac{\pi}{2}, \pi\right)$.
     (d) Since the graph is symmetric with respect to the origin, the function is <u>odd</u>.

45. (a) Intercepts: $\left(\dfrac{1}{2},0\right), \left(\dfrac{5}{2},0\right)$, and $\left(0,\dfrac{1}{2}\right)$.

     (b) Domain: $\{x \mid -3 \le x \le 3\}$; Range: $\{y \mid -1 \le y \le 2\}$.
     (c) Increasing: $(2, 3)$; Decreasing: $(-1, 1)$; Constant: $(-3, -1)$ and $(1, 2)$
     (d) Since the graph is not symmetric with respect to the y-axis or the origin, the function is <u>neither</u> even nor odd.

47. (a) f has a local maximum of 3 at $x = 0$.
     (b) f has a local minimum of 0 at both $x = -2$ and $x = 2$.

49.   (a) f has a local maximum of 1 at $x = \dfrac{\pi}{2}$.

(b) f has a local minimum of -1 at $x = -\dfrac{\pi}{2}$.

51. $f(x) = 4x^3$
$\qquad f(-x) = 4(-x)^3 = -4x^3$
f is odd.

53. $g(x) = -3x^2 - 5$
$\qquad g(-x) = -3(-x)^2 - 5 = -3x^2 - 5$
g is even.

55. $F(x) = \sqrt[3]{x}$
$\qquad F(-x) = \sqrt[3]{-x} = -\sqrt[3]{x}$
F is odd.

57. $f(x) = x + |x|$
$\qquad f(-x) = -x + |-x| = -x + |x|$
f is neither even nor odd.

59. $g(x) = \dfrac{1}{x^2}$
$\qquad g(-x) = \dfrac{1}{(-x)^2} = \dfrac{1}{x^2}$
g is even.

61. $h(x) = \dfrac{-x^3}{3x^2 - 9}$
$\qquad h(-x) = \dfrac{-(-x)^3}{3(-x)^2 - 9} = \dfrac{x^3}{3x^2 - 9}$
h is odd.

63. $f(x) = x^3 - 3x + 2$ on the interval $(-2,2)$
Use MAXIMUM and MINIMUM on the graph of $y_1 = x^3 - 3x + 2$.

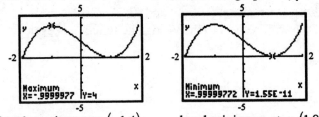

local maximum at: $(-1,4)$;   local minimum at: $(1,0)$
f is increasing on: $(-2,-1)$ and $(1,2)$; f is decreasing on: $(-1,1)$

65. $f(x) = x^5 - x^3$ on the interval $(-2,2)$
Use MAXIMUM and MINIMUM on the graph of $y_1 = x^5 - x^3$.

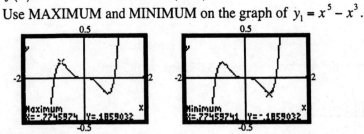

local maximum at: $(-0.77, 0.19)$;   local minimum at: $(0.77, -0.19)$
f is increasing on: $(-2,-0.77)$ and $(0.77,2)$; f is decreasing on: $(-0.77,0.77)$

67. $f(x) = -0.2x^3 - 0.6x^2 + 4x - 6$ on the interval $(-6, 4)$

Use MAXIMUM and MINIMUM on the graph of $y_1 = -0.2x^3 - 0.6x^2 + 4x - 6$.

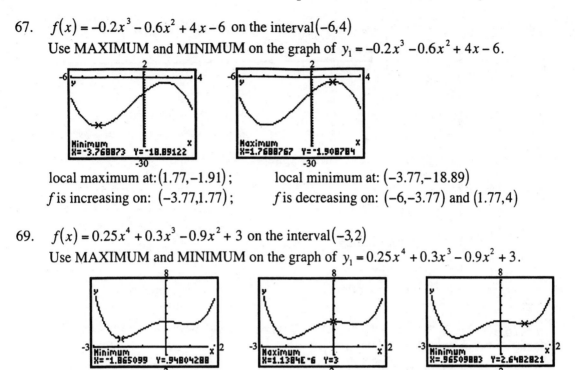

local maximum at: $(1.77, -1.91)$;   local minimum at: $(-3.77, -18.89)$

f is increasing on: $(-3.77, 1.77)$; f is decreasing on: $(-6, -3.77)$ and $(1.77, 4)$

69. $f(x) = 0.25x^4 + 0.3x^3 - 0.9x^2 + 3$ on the interval $(-3, 2)$

Use MAXIMUM and MINIMUM on the graph of $y_1 = 0.25x^4 + 0.3x^3 - 0.9x^2 + 3$.

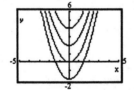

local maximum at: $(0, 3)$;   local minimum at: $(-1.87, 0.95)$, $(0.97, 2.65)$

f is increasing on: $(-1.87, 0)$ and $(0.97, 2)$; f is decreasing on: $(-3, -1.87)$ and $(0, 0.97)$

71.   Each graph is that of $y = x^2$, but shifted vertically.

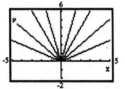

If $y = x^2 + k$, $k > 0$, the shift is up k units; if $y = x^2 + k$, $k < 0$, the shift is down $|k|$ units. The graph of $y = x^2 - 4$ is the same as the graph of $y = x^2$, but shifted down 4 units. The graph of $y = x^2 + 5$ is the graph of $y = x^2$, but shifted up 5 units.

73.   Each graph is that of $y = |x|$, but either compressed or stretched vertically.

If $y = k|x|$ and $k > 1$, the graph is stretched; if $y = k|x|$ and $0 < k < 1$, the graph is compressed. The graph of $y = \frac{1}{4}|x|$ is the same as the graph of $y = |x|$, but compressed. The graph of $y = 5|x|$ is the same as the graph of $y = |x|$, but stretched.

31

75. The graph of $y = \sqrt{-x}$ is the reflection about the y-axis of the graph of $y = \sqrt{x}$.

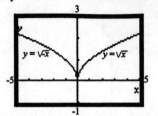

The same type of reflection occurs when graphing $y = 2x + 1$ and $y = 2(-x) + 1$.

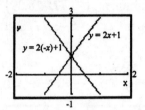

The graph of $y = f(-x)$ is the reflection about the y-axis of the graph of $y = f(x)$.

77. For the graph of $y = x^n$, n a positive even integer, as n increases, the graph of the function is narrower for $|x| > 1$ and flatter for $|x| < 1$.

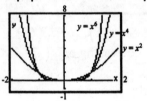

79. Answers will vary.

81. One, at most, because if f is increasing it could only cross the x-axis at most one time. The graph of f could not "turn" and cross the x-axis again or it would start to decrease.

83. The only such function is $f(x) = 0$.

Graphs and Functions

1.5   Graphing Techniques; Transformations

1.   horizontal, right   3. $-5, -2$ and 2   5.   False

7.   *B*   9.   *H*   11. *I*

13. *L*   15. *F*   17. *G*

19. $y = (x - 4)^3$ 21. $y = x^3 + 4$ 23. $y = (-x)^3 = -x^3$

25. $y = 4x^3$

27. (1) $y = \sqrt{x} + 2$
     (2) $y = -\left(\sqrt{x} + 2\right)$
     (3) $y = -\left(\sqrt{-x} + 2\right) = -\sqrt{-x} - 2$

29. (1) $y = -\sqrt{x}$
     (2) $y = -\sqrt{x} + 2$
     (3) $y = -\sqrt{x + 3} + 2$

31. c   33. c

35. $f(x) = x^2 - 1$
     Using the graph of $y = x^2$, vertically
     shift downward 1 unit.

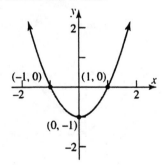

37. $g(x) = x^3 + 1$
     Using the graph of $y = x^3$, vertically
     shift upward 1 unit.

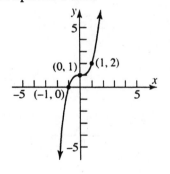

39. $h(x) = \sqrt{x-2}$

Using the graph of $y = \sqrt{x}$, horizontally shift to the right 2 units.

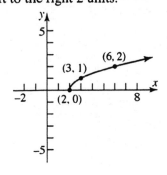

41. $f(x) = (x-1)^3 + 2$

Using the graph of $y = x^3$, horizontally shift to the right 1 unit, then vertically shift up 2 units.

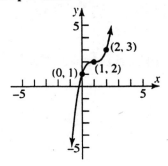

43. $g(x) = 4\sqrt{x}$

Using the graph of $y = \sqrt{x}$, vertically stretch by a factor of 4.

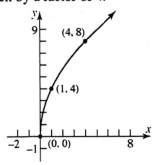

45. $h(x) = \dfrac{1}{2x} = \left(\dfrac{1}{2}\right)\left(\dfrac{1}{x}\right)$

Using the graph of $y = \dfrac{1}{x}$, vertically compress by a factor of $\dfrac{1}{2}$.

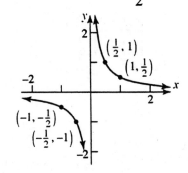

47. $f(x) = -\sqrt[3]{x}$

Reflect the graph of $y = \sqrt[3]{x}$, about the x-axis.

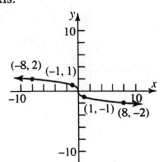

49. $g(x) = |-x|$

Reflect the graph of $y = |x|$ about the y-axis.

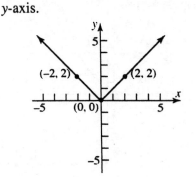

51. $h(x) = -x^3 + 2$

Reflect the graph of $y = x^3$ about the x-axis, then shift vertically upward 2 units.

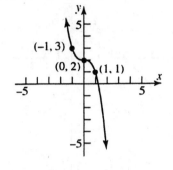

53. $f(x) = 2(x + 1)^2 - 3$

Using the graph of $y = x^2$, horizontally shift to the left 1 unit, vertically stretch by a factor of 2, and vertically shift downward 3 units.

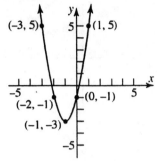

55. $g(x) = \sqrt{x - 2} + 1$

Using the graph of $y = \sqrt{x}$, horizontally shift to the right 2 units and vertically shift upward 1 unit.

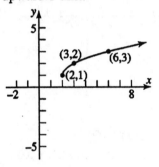

57. $h(x) = \sqrt{-x} - 2$

Reflect the graph of $y = \sqrt{x}$ about the y-axis and vertically shift downward 2 units.

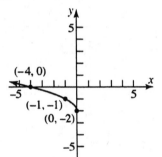

59. $f(x) = -(x + 1)^3 - 1$

Using the graph of $y = x^3$, horizontally shift to the left 1 unit, reflect the graph about the x-axis, and vertically shift downward 1 unit.

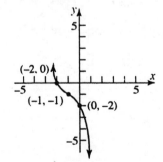

61. $g(x) = 2|1 - x| = 2|-(-1 + x)| = 2|x - 1|$

Using the graph of $y = |x|$, horizontally shift to the right 1 unit, and vertically stretch by a factor or 2.

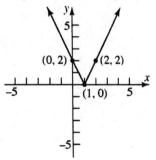

63. (a) $F(x) = f(x) + 3$
Shift up 3 units.

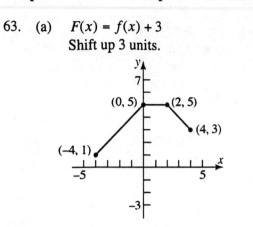

(b) $G(x) = f(x + 2)$
Shift left 2 units.

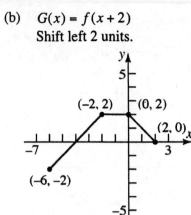

(c) $P(x) = -f(x)$
Reflect about the x-axis.

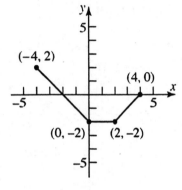

(d) $H(x) = f(x + 1) - 2$
Shift left 1 unit and shift down 2 units.

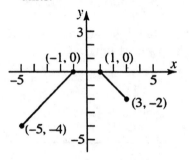

(e) $Q(x) = \dfrac{1}{2} f(x)$

Compress vertically by a factor of $\dfrac{1}{2}$.

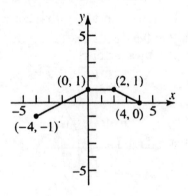

(f) $g(x) = f(-x)$
Reflect about the y-axis.

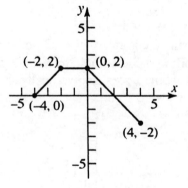

(g) $h(x) = f(2x)$

Compress horizontally by a factor of $\frac{1}{2}$.

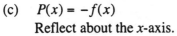

65. (a) $F(x) = f(x) + 3$
       Shift up 3 units.

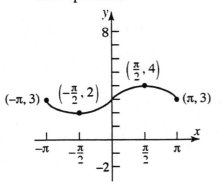

(b) $G(x) = f(x + 2)$
     Shift left 2 units.

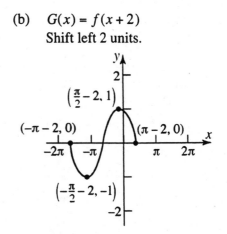

(c) $P(x) = -f(x)$
     Reflect about the x-axis.

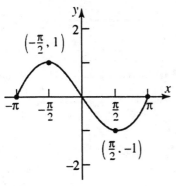

(d) $H(x) = f(x + 1) - 2$
     Shift left 1 unit and shift down 2 units.

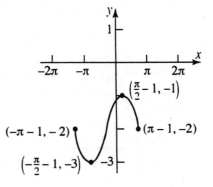

(e) $Q(x) = \dfrac{1}{2} f(x)$

Compress vertically by a factor of $\dfrac{1}{2}$.

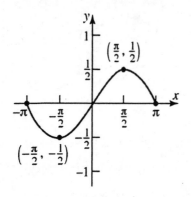

(f) $g(x) = f(-x)$
Reflect about the y-axis.

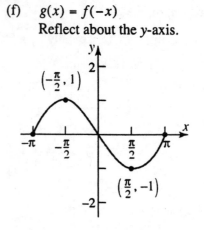

(g) $h(x) = f(2x)$

Compress horizontally by a factor of $\dfrac{1}{2}$.

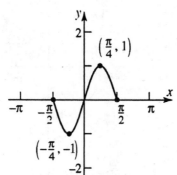

67. (a) $y = |x+1|$

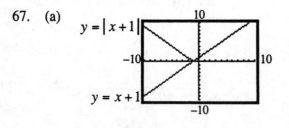

$y = x+1$

(b) $y = |4 - x^2|$

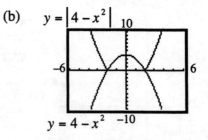

$y = 4 - x^2$

(c) $y = |x^3 + x|$

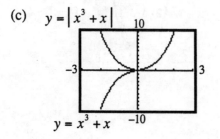

$y = x^3 + x$

(d) Any part of the graph of $y = f(x)$ that lies below the x-axis is reflected about the x-axis to obtain the graph of $y = |f(x)|$.

69.   (a) $y = |f(x)|$

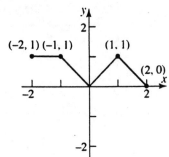

(b) $y = f(|x|)$

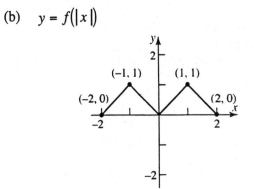

71. $f(x) = x^2 + 2x$
$f(x) = (x^2 + 2x + 1) - 1$
$f(x) = (x+1)^2 - 1$
Using $f(x) = x^2$, shift left 1 unit and shift down 1 unit.

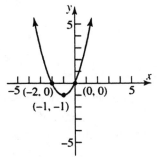

73. $f(x) = x^2 - 8x + 1$
$f(x) = (x^2 - 8x + 16) + 1 - 16$
$f(x) = (x-4)^2 - 15$
Using $f(x) = x^2$, shift right 4 units and shift down 15 units.

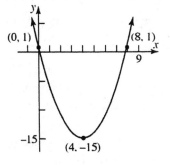

75. $f(x) = x^2 + x + 1$
$f(x) = \left(x^2 + x + \dfrac{1}{4}\right) + 1 - \dfrac{1}{4}$
$f(x) = \left(x + \dfrac{1}{2}\right)^2 + \dfrac{3}{4}$

Using $f(x) = x^2$, shift left $\dfrac{1}{2}$ unit and

shift up $\dfrac{3}{4}$ unit.

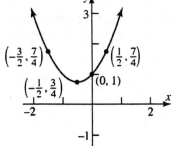

77. $y = (x - c)^2$
If $c = 0$, $y = x^2$.
If $c = 3$, $y = (x-3)^2$; shift right 3 units.
If $c = -2$, $y = (x+2)^2$; shift left 2 units.

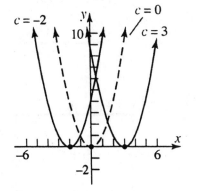

79. $F = \dfrac{9}{5}C + 32$

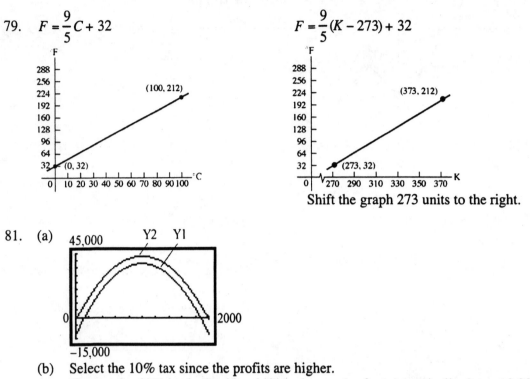

$F = \dfrac{9}{5}(K - 273) + 32$

Shift the graph 273 units to the right.

81.   (a)

(b)   Select the 10% tax since the profits are higher.

(c)   The graph of Y1 is obtained by shifting the graph of $p(x)$ vertically down 10,000 units. The graph of Y2 is obtained by multiplying the y-coordinate of the graph of $p(x)$ by 0.9. Thus, Y2 is the graph of $p(x)$ vertically compressed by a factor of 0.9.

(d)   Select the 10% tax since the graph of $Y1 = 0.9\,p(x) \geq Y2 = -0.05x^2 + 100x - 6800$ for all x in the domain.

Chapter 1

Graphs and Functions

1.6 Inverse Functions

1. The set of ordered pairs is a function because there are no ordered pairs with the same first element and different second elements.

3. Increasing on the interval $(-\infty, \infty)$.

5. $y = x$

7. False

9. (a)

Domain	Range
$200	20 hours
$300	25 hours
$350	30 hours
$425	40 hours

(b) Inverse is a function since each element in the domain corresponds to one and only one element in the range.

11. (a)

Domain	Range
	20 hours
$200	25 hours
$350	30 hours
$425	40 hours

(b) Inverse is not a function since domain element $200 corresponds to two different elements in the range.

13. (a) $\{(6, 2), (6, -3), (9, 4), (10, 1)\}$

(b) Inverse is not a function since domain element 6 corresponds to two different elements in the range.

15. (a) $\{(0, 0), (1, 1), (16, 2), (81, 3)\}$

(b) Inverse is a function since each element in the domain corresponds to one and only one element in the range.

17. Every horizontal line intersects the graph of f at exactly one point. One-to-one.

19. There are horizontal lines that intersect the graph of f at more than one point. Not one-to-one.

21. Every horizontal line intersects the graph of f at exactly one point. One-to-one.

23. Graphing the inverse:

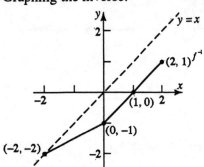

25. Graphing the inverse:

27. Graphing the inverse:

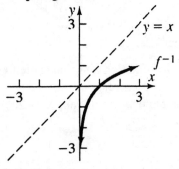

29. $f(x) = 3x + 4,$ $g(x) = \dfrac{1}{3}(x-4)$

$f(g(x)) = f\left(\dfrac{1}{3}(x-4)\right)$

$= 3\left(\dfrac{1}{3}(x-4)\right) + 4$

$= (x-4) + 4 = x$

$g(f(x)) = g(3x+4)$

$= \dfrac{1}{3}((3x+4)-4)$

$= \dfrac{1}{3}(3x) = x$

31. $f(x) = 4x - 8,$ $g(x) = \dfrac{x}{4} + 2$

$f(g(x)) = f\left(\dfrac{x}{4} + 2\right)$

$= 4\left(\dfrac{x}{4} + 2\right) - 8$

$= (x+8) - 8 = x$

$g(f(x)) = g(4x-8)$

$= \dfrac{4x-8}{4} + 2$

$= x - 2 + 2 = x$

33. $f(x) = x^3 - 8,$ $g(x) = \sqrt[3]{x+8}$

$f(g(x)) = f\left(\sqrt[3]{x+8}\right)$

$= \left(\sqrt[3]{x+8}\right)^3 - 8$

$= (x+8) - 8 = x$

$g(f(x)) = g(x^3 - 8)$

$= \sqrt[3]{(x^3 - 8) + 8}$

$= \sqrt[3]{x^3} = x$

35. $f(x) = \dfrac{1}{x}, \qquad g(x) = \dfrac{1}{x}$

$f(g(x)) = f\left(\dfrac{1}{x}\right)$

$= \dfrac{1}{\dfrac{1}{x}} = x$

$g(f(x)) = g\left(\dfrac{1}{x}\right)$

$= \dfrac{1}{\dfrac{1}{x}} = x$

37. $f(x) = \dfrac{2x+3}{x+4}, \qquad g(x) = \dfrac{4x-3}{2-x}$

$f(g(x)) = f\left(\dfrac{4x-3}{2-x}\right)$

$= \dfrac{2\left(\dfrac{4x-3}{2-x}\right) + 3}{\dfrac{4x-3}{2-x} + 4}$

$= \dfrac{\dfrac{8x-6+6-3x}{2-x}}{\dfrac{4x-3+8-4x}{2-x}}$

$= \dfrac{\dfrac{5x}{2-x}}{\dfrac{5}{2-x}}$

$= \dfrac{5x}{2-x} \cdot \dfrac{2-x}{5} = x$

$g(f(x)) = g\left(\dfrac{2x+3}{x+4}\right)$

$= \dfrac{4\left(\dfrac{2x+3}{x+4}\right) - 3}{2 - \dfrac{2x+3}{x+4}}$

$= \dfrac{\dfrac{8x+12-3x-12}{x+4}}{\dfrac{2x+8-2x-3}{x+4}}$

$= \dfrac{\dfrac{5x}{x+4}}{\dfrac{5}{x+4}}$

$= \dfrac{5x}{x+4} \cdot \dfrac{x+4}{5} = x$

39. $f(x) = 3x$

$y = 3x$

$x = 3y$ Inverse

$y = \dfrac{x}{3}$

$f^{-1}(x) = \dfrac{x}{3}$

Verify: $f\left(f^{-1}(x)\right) = f\left(\dfrac{x}{3}\right) = 3\left(\dfrac{x}{3}\right) = x$

$f^{-1}\left(f(x)\right) = f^{-1}(3x) = \dfrac{3x}{3} = x$

Domain of f = range of $f^{-1} = (-\infty, \infty)$

Range of f = domain of $f^{-1} = (-\infty, \infty)$

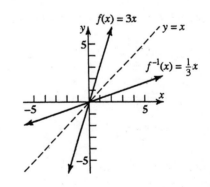

41. $f(x) = 4x + 2$

$y = 4x + 2$

$x = 4y + 2$ Inverse

$4y = x - 2$

$y = \dfrac{x-2}{4}$

$f^{-1}(x) = \dfrac{x-2}{4}$

Domain of f = range of $f^{-1} = (-\infty, \infty)$

Range of f = domain of $f^{-1} = (-\infty, \infty)$

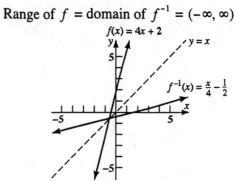

Verify: $f\left(f^{-1}(x)\right) = f\left(\dfrac{x-2}{4}\right) = 4\left(\dfrac{x-2}{4}\right) + 2 = x - 2 + 2 = x$

$f^{-1}\left(f(x)\right) = f^{-1}(4x+2) = \dfrac{(4x+2)-2}{4} = \dfrac{4x}{4} = x$

43. $f(x) = x^3 - 1$

$y = x^3 - 1$

$x = y^3 - 1$ Inverse

$y^3 = x + 1$

$y = \sqrt[3]{x+1}$

$f^{-1}(x) = \sqrt[3]{x+1}$

Domain of f = range of $f^{-1} = (-\infty, \infty)$

Range of f = domain of $f^{-1} = (-\infty, \infty)$

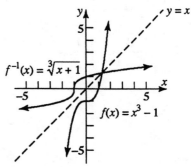

Verify: $f\left(f^{-1}(x)\right) = f\left(\sqrt[3]{x+1}\right) = \left(\sqrt[3]{x+1}\right)^3 - 1 = x + 1 - 1 = x$

$f^{-1}\left(f(x)\right) = f^{-1}(x^3 - 1) = \sqrt[3]{(x^3-1)+1} = \sqrt[3]{x^3} = x$

45. $f(x) = x^2 + 4, \quad x \geq 0$

$\qquad y = x^2 + 4 \quad x \geq 0$

$\qquad x = y^2 + 4 \quad y \geq 0 \quad$ Inverse

$\qquad y^2 = x - 4 \quad y \geq 0$

$\qquad y = \sqrt{x-4}$

$\qquad f^{-1}(x) = \sqrt{x-4}$

Verify:

$\qquad f\left(f^{-1}(x)\right) = f\left(\sqrt{x-4}\right)$

$\qquad\qquad = \left(\sqrt{x-4}\right)^2 + 4$

$\qquad\qquad = x - 4 + 4$

$\qquad\qquad = x$

$\qquad f^{-1}(f(x)) = f^{-1}\left(x^2 + 4\right)$

$\qquad\qquad = \sqrt{\left(x^2 + 4\right) - 4}$

$\qquad\qquad = \sqrt{x^2}$

$\qquad\qquad = |x|$

$\qquad\qquad = x, \, x \geq 0$

Domain of f = range of f^{-1} = $[0, \infty)$

Range of f = domain of f^{-1} = $[4, \infty)$

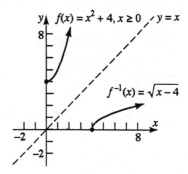

47. $f(x) = \dfrac{4}{x}$

$\qquad y = \dfrac{4}{x}$

$\qquad x = \dfrac{4}{y} \quad$ Inverse

$\qquad xy = 4$

$\qquad y = \dfrac{4}{x}$

$\qquad f^{-1}(x) = \dfrac{4}{x}$

Domain of f = range of f^{-1}

$\qquad\qquad$ = all real numbers except 0

Range of f = domain of f^{-1}

$\qquad\qquad$ = all real numbers except 0

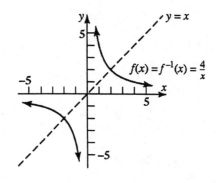

Verify: $f\left(f^{-1}(x)\right) = f\left(\dfrac{4}{x}\right) = \dfrac{4}{\dfrac{4}{x}} = 4 \cdot \left(\dfrac{x}{4}\right) = x$

$\qquad\quad f^{-1}(f(x)) = f^{-1}\left(\dfrac{4}{x}\right) = \dfrac{4}{\dfrac{4}{x}} = 4 \cdot \left(\dfrac{x}{4}\right) = x$

49. $f(x) = \dfrac{1}{x-2}$

$y = \dfrac{1}{x-2}$

$x = \dfrac{1}{y-2}$ Inverse

$x(y-2) = 1$

$xy - 2x = 1$

$xy = 2x + 1$

$y = \dfrac{2x+1}{x}$

$f^{-1}(x) = \dfrac{2x+1}{x}$

Domain of f = range of f^{-1}
= all real numbers except 2

Range of f = domain of f^{-1}
= all real numbers except 0

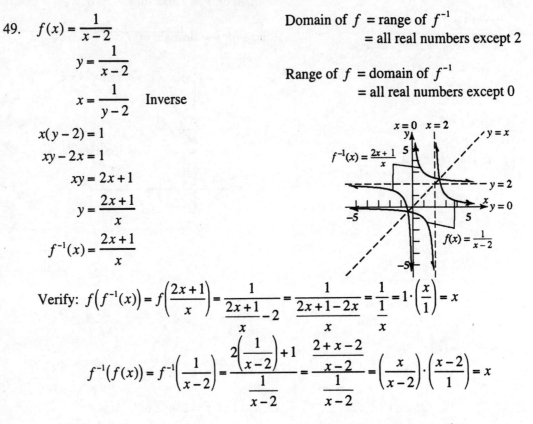

Verify: $f\left(f^{-1}(x)\right) = f\left(\dfrac{2x+1}{x}\right) = \dfrac{1}{\dfrac{2x+1}{x}-2} = \dfrac{1}{\dfrac{2x+1-2x}{x}} = \dfrac{1}{\dfrac{1}{x}} = 1 \cdot \left(\dfrac{x}{1}\right) = x$

$f^{-1}\left(f(x)\right) = f^{-1}\left(\dfrac{1}{x-2}\right) = \dfrac{2\left(\dfrac{1}{x-2}\right)+1}{\dfrac{1}{x-2}} = \dfrac{\dfrac{2+x-2}{x-2}}{\dfrac{1}{x-2}} = \left(\dfrac{x}{x-2}\right) \cdot \left(\dfrac{x-2}{1}\right) = x$

51. $f(x) = \dfrac{2}{3+x}$

$y = \dfrac{2}{3+x}$

$x = \dfrac{2}{3+y}$ Inverse

$x(3+y) = 2$

$3x + xy = 2$

$xy = 2 - 3x$

$y = \dfrac{2-3x}{x}$

$f^{-1}(x) = \dfrac{2-3x}{x}$

Domain of f = range of f^{-1}
= all real numbers except –3

Range of f = domain of f^{-1}
= all real numbers except 0

Verify: $f\left(f^{-1}(x)\right) = f\left(\dfrac{2-3x}{x}\right) = \dfrac{2}{3+\dfrac{2-3x}{x}} = \dfrac{2}{\dfrac{3x+2-3x}{x}} = \dfrac{2}{\dfrac{2}{x}} = 2 \cdot \left(\dfrac{x}{2}\right) = x$

$f^{-1}\left(f(x)\right) = f^{-1}\left(\dfrac{2}{3+x}\right) = \dfrac{2-3\left(\dfrac{2}{3+x}\right)}{\dfrac{2}{3+x}} = \dfrac{\dfrac{6+2x-6}{3+x}}{\dfrac{2}{3+x}} = \left(\dfrac{2x}{3+x}\right) \cdot \left(\dfrac{3+x}{2}\right) = x$

53. $f(x) = \dfrac{3x}{x+2}$

$y = \dfrac{3x}{x+2}$

$x = \dfrac{3y}{y+2}$ Inverse

$x(y+2) = 3y$

$xy + 2x = 3y$

$xy - 3y = -2x$

$y(x-3) = -2x$

$y = \dfrac{-2x}{x-3}$

$f^{-1}(x) = \dfrac{-2x}{x-3}$

Domain of f = range of f^{-1}
$\qquad\qquad$ = all real numbers except -2

Range of f = domain of f^{-1}
$\qquad\qquad$ = all real numbers except 3

Verify:

$$f\left(f^{-1}(x)\right) = f\left(\dfrac{-2x}{x-3}\right) = \dfrac{3\left(\dfrac{-2x}{x-3}\right)}{\dfrac{-2x}{x-3}+2}$$

$$= \dfrac{\dfrac{-6x}{x-3}}{\dfrac{-2x+2x-6}{x-3}} = \left(\dfrac{-6x}{x-3}\right)\cdot\left(\dfrac{x-3}{-6}\right) = x$$

$$f^{-1}\left(f(x)\right) = f^{-1}\left(\dfrac{3x}{x+2}\right) = \dfrac{-2\left(\dfrac{3x}{x+2}\right)}{\dfrac{3x}{x+2}-3}$$

$$= \dfrac{\dfrac{-6x}{x+2}}{\dfrac{3x-3x-6}{x+2}} = \left(\dfrac{-6x}{x+2}\right)\cdot\left(\dfrac{x+2}{-6}\right) = x$$

55. $f(x) = \dfrac{2x}{3x-1}$

$y = \dfrac{2x}{3x-1}$

$x = \dfrac{2y}{3y-1}$ Inverse

$x(3y-1) = 2y$

$3xy - x = 2y$

$3xy - 2y = x$

$y(3x-2) = x$

$y = \dfrac{x}{3x-2}$

$f^{-1}(x) = \dfrac{x}{3x-2}$

Domain of f = range of f^{-1} = all real numbers except $\dfrac{1}{3}$

Range of f = domain of f^{-1} = all real numbers except $\dfrac{2}{3}$

Verify:

$$f\left(f^{-1}(x)\right) = f\left(\dfrac{x}{3x-2}\right) = \dfrac{2\left(\dfrac{x}{3x-2}\right)}{3\left(\dfrac{x}{3x-2}\right)-1}$$

$$= \dfrac{\dfrac{2x}{3x-2}}{\dfrac{3x-3x+2}{3x-2}} = \dfrac{\dfrac{2x}{3x-2}}{\dfrac{2}{3x-2}}$$

$$= \left(\dfrac{2x}{3x-2}\right)\cdot\left(\dfrac{3x-2}{2}\right) = x$$

$$f^{-1}(f(x)) = f\left(\dfrac{2x}{3x-1}\right) = \dfrac{\dfrac{2x}{3x-1}}{3\left(\dfrac{2x}{3x-1}\right)-2} = \dfrac{\dfrac{2x}{3x-1}}{\dfrac{6x-6x+2}{3x-1}}$$

$$= \dfrac{\dfrac{2x}{3x-1}}{\dfrac{2}{3x-1}} = \left(\dfrac{2x}{3x-1}\right)\cdot\left(\dfrac{3x-1}{2}\right) = x$$

57. $f(x) = \dfrac{3x+4}{2x-3}$

$\quad y = \dfrac{3x+4}{2x-3}$

$\quad x = \dfrac{3y+4}{2y-3}$ \quad Inverse

$\quad x(2y-3) = 3y+4$

$\quad 2xy-3x = 3y+4$

$\quad 2xy-3y = 3x+4$

$\quad y(2x-3) = 3x+4$

$\quad y = \dfrac{3x+4}{2x-3}$

$\quad f^{-1}(x) = \dfrac{3x+4}{2x-3}$

Domain of f = range of f^{-1}

$\qquad$ = all real numbers except $\dfrac{3}{2}$

Range of f = domain of f^{-1}

$\qquad$ = all real numbers except $\dfrac{3}{2}$

Verify: $f\left(f^{-1}(x)\right) = f\left(\dfrac{3x+4}{2x-3}\right) = \dfrac{3\left(\dfrac{3x+4}{2x-3}\right)+4}{2\left(\dfrac{3x+4}{2x-3}\right)-3} = \dfrac{\dfrac{9x+12+8x-12}{2x-3}}{\dfrac{6x+8-6x+9}{2x-3}} = \dfrac{\dfrac{17x}{2x-3}}{\dfrac{17}{2x-3}}$

$$= \dfrac{17x}{2x-3}\cdot\dfrac{2x-3}{17} = x$$

$$f^{-1}(f(x)) = f^{-1}\left(\dfrac{3x+4}{2x-3}\right) = \dfrac{3\left(\dfrac{3x+4}{2x-3}\right)+4}{2\left(\dfrac{3x+4}{2x-3}\right)-3} = \dfrac{\dfrac{9x+12+8x-12}{2x-3}}{\dfrac{6x+8-6x+9}{2x-3}} = \dfrac{\dfrac{17x}{2x-3}}{\dfrac{17}{2x-3}}$$

$$= \dfrac{17x}{2x-3}\cdot\dfrac{2x-3}{17} = x$$

59. $f(x) = \dfrac{2x+3}{x+2}$

Domain of f = range of f^{-1}
= all real numbers except –2

$y = \dfrac{2x+3}{x+2}$

$x = \dfrac{2y+3}{y+2}$ Inverse

Range of f = domain of f^{-1}
= all real numbers except 2

$x(y+2) = 2y+3$

$xy + 2x = 2y + 3$

$xy - 2y = -2x + 3$

$y(x-2) = -2x + 3$

$y = \dfrac{-2x+3}{x-2}$

$f^{-1}(x) = \dfrac{-2x+3}{x-2}$

Verify:

$$f\left(f^{-1}(x)\right) = f\left(\dfrac{-2x+3}{x-2}\right) = \dfrac{2\left(\dfrac{-2x+3}{x-2}\right)+3}{\dfrac{-2x+3}{x-2}+2}$$

$$= \dfrac{\dfrac{-4x+6+3x-6}{x-2}}{\dfrac{-2x+3+2x-4}{x-2}}$$

$$= \dfrac{\dfrac{-x}{x-2}}{\dfrac{-1}{x-2}}$$

$$= \left(\dfrac{-x}{x-2}\right)\cdot\left(\dfrac{x-2}{-1}\right) = x$$

$$f^{-1}\left(f(x)\right) = f^{-1}\left(\dfrac{2x+3}{x+2}\right) = \dfrac{-2\left(\dfrac{2x+3}{x+2}\right)+3}{\dfrac{2x+3}{x+2}-2}$$

$$= \dfrac{\dfrac{-4x-6+3x+6}{x+2}}{\dfrac{2x+3-2x-4}{x+2}}$$

$$= \dfrac{\dfrac{-x}{x+2}}{\dfrac{-1}{x+2}}$$

$$= \left(\dfrac{-x}{x+2}\right)\cdot\left(\dfrac{x+2}{-1}\right) = x$$

61. $f(x) = \dfrac{x^2 - 4}{2x^2}, \; x > 0$

$\qquad y = \dfrac{x^2 - 4}{2x^2}, \; x > 0$

$\qquad x = \dfrac{y^2 - 4}{2y^2}, \; y > 0 \quad$ Inverse

$\qquad 2xy^2 = y^2 - 4, \; x < \dfrac{1}{2}$

$\qquad 2xy^2 - y^2 = -4, \qquad x < \dfrac{1}{2}$

$\qquad y^2(2x - 1) = -4, \qquad x < \dfrac{1}{2}$

$\qquad y^2 = \dfrac{-4}{2x - 1}, \qquad x < \dfrac{1}{2}$

$\qquad y = \sqrt{\dfrac{-4}{2x - 1}}, \qquad x < \dfrac{1}{2}$

$\qquad f^{-1}(x) = \sqrt{\dfrac{-4}{2x - 1}}, \qquad x < \dfrac{1}{2}$

Domain of f = range of $f^{-1} = (0, \infty)$

Range of f = domain of $f^{-1} = \left(-\infty, \dfrac{1}{2}\right)$

Verify:

$$f\left(f^{-1}(x)\right) = f\left(\sqrt{\dfrac{-4}{2x - 1}}\right) = \dfrac{\left(\sqrt{\dfrac{-4}{2x-1}}\right)^2 - 4}{2\left(\sqrt{\dfrac{-4}{2x-1}}\right)^2}$$

$$= \dfrac{\dfrac{-4}{2x-1} - 4}{2\left(\dfrac{-4}{2x-1}\right)} = \dfrac{\dfrac{-4 - 8x + 4}{2x-1}}{\dfrac{-8}{2x-1}}$$

$$= \left(\dfrac{-8x}{2x-1}\right) \cdot \left(\dfrac{2x-1}{-8}\right) = x$$

$$f^{-1}(f(x)) = f^{-1}\left(\dfrac{x^2 - 4}{2x^2}\right) = \sqrt{\dfrac{-4}{2\left(\dfrac{x^2-4}{2x^2}\right) - 1}} = \sqrt{\dfrac{-4}{\dfrac{x^2-4}{x^2} - 1}}$$

$$= \sqrt{\dfrac{-4}{\dfrac{x^2 - 4 - x^2}{x^2}}} = \sqrt{\dfrac{-4}{\dfrac{-4}{x^2}}} = \sqrt{(-4)\left(\dfrac{x^2}{-4}\right)}$$

$$= \sqrt{x^2} = x, \; x > 0$$

63.   (a) $f(-1) = 0$ (b) $f(1) = 2$ (c) $f^{-1}(1) = 0$ (d) $f^{-1}(2) = 1$

65. $f(x) = mx + b, \quad m \neq 0$

$\qquad y = mx + b$

$\qquad x = my + b \quad$ Inverse

$\qquad x - b = my$

$\qquad y = \dfrac{x - b}{m}$

$\qquad f^{-1}(x) = \dfrac{x - b}{m}, \quad m \neq 0$

67.   The graph of f^{-1} lies in quadrant I. Whenever (a, b) is on the graph of f, then (b, a) is on the graph of f^{-1}. Since both coordinates of (a, b) are positive, both coordinates of (b, a) are positive and it is in quadrant I.

69. $f(x) = |x|, \; x \geq 0$ is one-to-one. Thus, $f(x) = x, \; x \geq 0$ and $f^{-1}(x) = x, \; x \geq 0$.

71. (a) $H(C) = 2.15C - 10.53$

$$H = 2.15C - 10.53$$

$$H + 10.53 = 2.15C$$

$$\frac{H + 10.53}{2.15} = C$$

$$\frac{H}{2.15} + \frac{10.53}{2.15} = C$$

$$\frac{20}{43}H + \frac{1053}{215} = C$$

$$C(H) = \frac{20}{43}H + \frac{1053}{215}$$

(b) $C(26) = \frac{20}{43}(26) + \frac{1053}{215} \approx 16.99$ inches

73. $p(x) = 300 - 50x, \quad x \geq 0$

$$p = 300 - 50x$$

$$50x = 300 - p$$

$$x = \frac{300 - p}{50}$$

$$x(p) = \frac{300 - p}{50}, \quad p \leq 300$$

75. $f(x) = \dfrac{ax + b}{cx + d}$

$$y = \frac{ax + b}{cx + d}$$

$$x = \frac{ay + b}{cy + d} \quad \text{Inverse}$$

$$x(cy + d) = ay + b$$

$$cxy + dx = ay + b$$

$$cxy - ay = b - dx$$

$$y(cx - a) = b - dx$$

$$y = \frac{b - dx}{cx - a}$$

$$f^{-1}(x) = \frac{-dx + b}{cx - a}$$

Therefore, $f = f^{-1}$ provided $\dfrac{ax + b}{cx + d} = \dfrac{-dx + b}{cx - a}$, this is true if $a = -d$.

77.   Answers will vary.

79.   Not every odd function is one-to-one. Consider a function such as $f(x) = x^3 - x$.

Graphs and Functions

1.R   Chapter Review

1. $(0,0)$, $(4,2)$

(a) distance $= \sqrt{(4-0)^2 + (2-0)^2}$

$= \sqrt{16+4} = \sqrt{20} = 2\sqrt{5}$

(b) midpoint $= \left(\dfrac{0+4}{2}, \dfrac{0+2}{2}\right) = \left(\dfrac{4}{2}, \dfrac{2}{2}\right) = (2,1)$

3. $(1,-1)$, $(-2,3)$

(a) distance $= \sqrt{(-2-1)^2 + (3-(-1))^2}$

$= \sqrt{9+16} = \sqrt{25} = 5$

(b) midpoint $= \left(\dfrac{1+(-2)}{2}, \dfrac{-1+3}{2}\right)$

$= \left(\dfrac{-1}{2}, \dfrac{2}{2}\right) = \left(-\dfrac{1}{2}, 1\right)$

5. $(4,-4)$, $(4,8)$

(a) distance $= \sqrt{(4-4)^2 + (8-(-4))^2}$

$= \sqrt{0+144} = \sqrt{144} = 12$

(b) midpoint $= \left(\dfrac{4+4}{2}, \dfrac{-4+8}{2}\right)$

$= \left(\dfrac{8}{2}, \dfrac{4}{2}\right) = (4,2)$

7. $y = x^2 + 4$

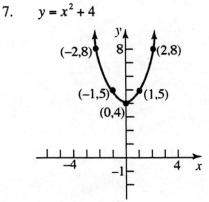

9. $2x = 3y^2$

x-intercept(s): $2x = 3(0)^2 \Rightarrow 2x = 0 \Rightarrow x = 0 \Rightarrow (0,0)$

y-intercept(s): $2(0) = 3y^2 \Rightarrow 0 = 3y^2 \Rightarrow y = 0 \Rightarrow (0,0)$

Test for symmetry:

x-axis: Replace y by $-y$: $2x = 3(-y)^2$ or $2x = 3y^2$, which is

equivalent to $2x = 3y^2$.

y-axis: Replace x by $-x$: $2(-x) = 3y^2$ or $-2x = 3y^2$,

which is not equivalent to $2x = 3y^2$.

Origin: Replace x by $-x$ and y by $-y$: $2(-x) = 3(-y)^2$ or

$-2x = 3y^2$, which is not equivalent to $2x = 3y^2$.

Therefore, the graph is symmetric with respect to the x-axis.

11. $x^2 + 4y^2 = 16$

    x-intercept(s): $x^2 + 4(0)^2 = 16 \Rightarrow x^2 = 16 \Rightarrow x = \pm 4 \Rightarrow (-4,0),(4,0)$

    y-intercept(s): $(0)^2 + 4y^2 = 16 \Rightarrow 4y^2 = 16 \Rightarrow y^2 = 4 \Rightarrow y = \pm 2 \Rightarrow (0,-2),(0,2)$

    Test for symmetry:

       x-axis: Replace y by $-y$: $x^2 + 4(-y)^2 = 16$ or $x^2 + 4y^2 = 16$,

                which is equivalent to $x^2 + 4y^2 = 16$.

       y-axis: Replace x by $-x$: $(-x)^2 + 4y^2 = 16$ or $x^2 + 4y^2 = 16$,

                which is equivalent to $x^2 + 4y^2 = 16$.

     Origin: Replace x by $-x$ and y by $-y$: $(-x)^2 + 4(-y)^2 = 16$ or $x^2 + 4y^2 = 16$,

                which is equivalent to $x^2 + 4y^2 = 16$.

    Therefore, the graph is symmetric with respect to the x-axis, the y-axis, and the origin.

13. $y = x^4 + 2x^2 + 1$

    x-intercept(s): $0 = x^4 + 2x^2 + 1 \Rightarrow 0 = (x^2 + 1)(x^2 + 1) \Rightarrow x^2 + 1 = 0 \Rightarrow x^2 = -1$

                $\Rightarrow$ no solution $\Rightarrow$ no x-intercepts

    y-intercept(s): $y = (0)^4 + 2(0)^2 + 1 = 1 \Rightarrow (0,1)$

    Test for symmetry:

      x-axis: Replace y by $-y$: $-y = x^4 + 2x^2 + 1$,

                which is not equivalent to $y = x^4 + 2x^2 + 1$.

      y-axis: Replace x by $-x$: $y = (-x)^4 + 2(-x)^2 + 1$ or $y = x^4 + 2x^2 + 1$,

                which is equivalent to $y = x^4 + 2x^2 + 1$.

     Origin: Replace x by $-x$ and y by $-y$: $-y = (-x)^4 + 2(-x)^2 + 1$ or $-y = x^4 + 2x^2 + 1$,

                which is not equivalent to $y = x^4 + 2x^2 + 1$.

    Therefore, the graph is symmetric with respect to the y-axis.

15. $x^2 + x + y^2 + 2y = 0$

    x-intercept(s): $x^2 + x + (0)^2 + 2(0) = 0 \Rightarrow x^2 + x = 0 \Rightarrow x(x+1) = 0$

                $x = 0, x = -1 \Rightarrow (-1,0),(0,0)$

    y-intercept(s): $(0)^2 + 0 + y^2 + 2y = 0 \Rightarrow y^2 + 2y = 0 \Rightarrow y(y+2) = 0$

                $y = 0, y = -2 \Rightarrow (0,-2),(0,0)$

    Test for symmetry:

      x-axis: Replace y by $-y$: $x^2 + x + (-y)^2 + 2(-y) = 0$ or $x^2 + x + y^2 - 2y = 0$,

                which is not equivalent to $x^2 + x + y^2 + 2y = 0$.

      y-axis: Replace x by $-x$: $(-x)^2 + (-x) + y^2 + 2y = 0$ or $x^2 - x + y^2 + 2y = 0$,

                which is not equivalent to $x^2 + x + y^2 + 2y = 0$.

Origin :   Replace x by $-x$ and y by $-y$: $(-x)^2 + (-x) + (-y)^2 + 2(-y) = 0$ or

$$x^2 - x + y^2 - 2y = 0, \text{ which is not equivalent to}$$

$$x^2 + x + y^2 + 2y = 0.$$

Therefore, the graph is not symmetric with respect to the x-axis, the y-axis, or the origin.

17. $(x-h)^2 + (y-k)^2 = r^2$

      $\left(x-(-2)\right)^2 + (y-3)^2 = 4^2$

       $(x+2)^2 + (y-3)^2 = 16$

19. $(x-h)^2 + (y-k)^2 = r^2$

      $\left(x-(-1)\right)^2 + \left(y-(-2)\right)^2 = 1^2$

       $(x+1)^2 + (y+2)^2 = 1$

21. $x^2 + (y-1)^2 = 4$

     $x^2 + (y-1)^2 = 2^2$

     Center: $(0,1)$

     Radius $= 2$

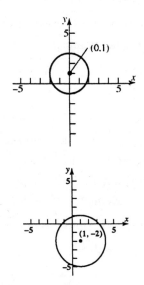

23. $x^2 + y^2 - 2x + 4y - 4 = 0$

         $x^2 - 2x + y^2 + 4y = 4$

   $(x^2 - 2x + 1) + (y^2 + 4y + 4) = 4 + 1 + 4$

         $(x-1)^2 + (y+2)^2 = 3^2$

    Center: $(1,-2)$ Radius $= 3$

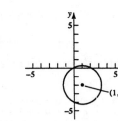

25. $3x^2 + 3y^2 - 6x + 12y = 0$

         $x^2 + y^2 - 2x + 4y = 0$

         $x^2 - 2x + y^2 + 4y = 0$

   $(x^2 - 2x + 1) + (y^2 + 4y + 4) = 1 + 4$

         $(x-1)^2 + (y+2)^2 = \left(\sqrt{5}\right)^2$

    Center: $(1,-2)$ Radius $= \sqrt{5}$

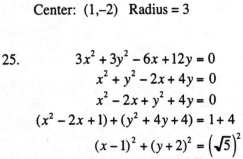

27.   This relation represents a function. Domain $= \{-1,2,4\}$; Range $= \{0,3\}$.

29. $f(x) = \dfrac{3x}{x^2 - 1}$

    (a) $f(2) = \dfrac{3(2)}{(2)^2 - 1} = \dfrac{6}{4-1} = \dfrac{6}{3} = 2$

    (b) $f(-2) = \dfrac{3(-2)}{(-2)^2 - 1} = \dfrac{-6}{4-1} = \dfrac{-6}{3} = -2$

    (c) $f(-x) = \dfrac{3(-x)}{(-x)^2 - 1} = \dfrac{-3x}{x^2 - 1}$

(d) $-f(x) = -\left(\dfrac{3x}{x^2 - 1}\right) = \dfrac{-3x}{x^2 - 1}$

(e) $f(x-2) = \dfrac{3(x-2)}{(x-2)^2 - 1} = \dfrac{3x-6}{x^2 - 4x + 4 - 1} = \dfrac{3(x-2)}{x^2 - 4x + 3}$

(f) $f(2x) = \dfrac{3(2x)}{(2x)^2 - 1} = \dfrac{6x}{4x^2 - 1}$

31. $f(x) = \sqrt{x^2 - 4}$

(a) $f(2) = \sqrt{2^2 - 4} = \sqrt{4 - 4} = \sqrt{0} = 0$

(b) $f(-2) = \sqrt{(-2)^2 - 4} = \sqrt{4 - 4} = \sqrt{0} = 0$

(c) $f(-x) = \sqrt{(-x)^2 - 4} = \sqrt{x^2 - 4}$

(d) $-f(x) = -\sqrt{x^2 - 4}$

(e) $f(x-2) = \sqrt{(x-2)^2 - 4} = \sqrt{x^2 - 4x + 4 - 4} = \sqrt{x^2 - 4x}$

(f) $f(2x) = \sqrt{(2x)^2 - 4} = \sqrt{4x^2 - 4} = \sqrt{4(x^2 - 1)} = 2\sqrt{x^2 - 1}$

33. $f(x) = \dfrac{x^2 - 4}{x^2}$

(a) $f(2) = \dfrac{2^2 - 4}{2^2} = \dfrac{4 - 4}{4} = \dfrac{0}{4} = 0$

(b) $f(-2) = \dfrac{(-2)^2 - 4}{(-2)^2} = \dfrac{4 - 4}{4} = \dfrac{0}{4} = 0$

(c) $f(-x) = \dfrac{(-x)^2 - 4}{(-x)^2} = \dfrac{x^2 - 4}{x^2}$

(d) $-f(x) = -\left(\dfrac{x^2 - 4}{x^2}\right) = \dfrac{4 - x^2}{x^2}$

(e) $f(x-2) = \dfrac{(x-2)^2 - 4}{(x-2)^2} = \dfrac{x^2 - 4x + 4 - 4}{x^2 - 4x + 4} = \dfrac{x^2 - 4x}{x^2 - 4x + 4}$

(f) $f(2x) = \dfrac{(2x)^2 - 4}{(2x)^2} = \dfrac{4x^2 - 4}{4x^2} = \dfrac{4(x^2 - 1)}{4x^2} = \dfrac{x^2 - 1}{x^2}$

35. $f(x) = \dfrac{x}{x^2 - 9}$

The denominator cannot be zero:
$$x^2 - 9 \neq 0$$
$$(x+3)(x-3) \neq 0$$
$$x \neq -3 \text{ or } 3$$
Domain: $\{x \mid x \neq -3,\ x \neq 3\}$

37. $f(x) = \sqrt{2 - x}$

The radicand must be non-negative:
$$2 - x \geq 0$$
$$x \leq 2$$
Domain: $\{x \mid x \leq 2\}$ or $(-\infty, 2]$

39. $f(x) = \dfrac{\sqrt{x}}{|x|}$

The radicand must be non-negative and the denominator cannot be zero: $x > 0$

Domain: $\{x \mid x > 0\}$ or $(0, \infty)$

41. $f(x) = \dfrac{x}{x^2 + 2x - 3}$

The denominator cannot be zero:

$x^2 + 2x - 3 \neq 0$

$(x + 3)(x - 1) \neq 0$

$x \neq -3$ or 1

Domain: $\{x \mid x \neq -3, \ x \neq 1\}$

43. $f(x) = -2x^2 + x + 1$

$\dfrac{f(x + h) - f(x)}{h} = \dfrac{-2(x + h)^2 + (x + h) + 1 - \left(-2x^2 + x + 1\right)}{h}$

$= \dfrac{-2\left(x^2 + 2xh + h^2\right) + x + h + 1 + 2x^2 - x - 1}{h}$

$= \dfrac{-2x^2 - 4xh - 2h^2 + x + h + 1 + 2x^2 - x - 1}{h}$

$= \dfrac{-4xh - 2h^2 + h}{h} = \dfrac{h(-4x - 2h + 1)}{h}$

$= -4x - 2h + 1$

45. (a) Domain: $\left\{\, x \mid -4 \leq x \leq 3 \,\right\}$ Range: $\left\{\, y \mid -3 \leq y \leq 3 \,\right\}$

(b) x-intercept: $(0,0)$; y-intercept: $(0,0)$

(c) $f(-2) = -1$

(d) $f(x) = -3$ when $x = -4$

(e) $f(x) > 0$ when $0 < x \leq 3$

(f) To graph $y = f(x - 3)$, shift the graph of f horizontally 3 units to the right.

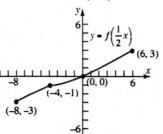

(g) To graph $y = f\left(\dfrac{1}{2}x\right)$, stretch the graph of f horizontally by a factor of 2.

(h)   To graph $y = -f(x)$, reflect the graph of f vertically about the y-axis.

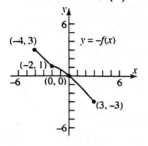

47. (a)   Domain: $\left\{ x \mid -4 \leq x \leq 4 \right\}$ Range: $\left\{ y \mid -3 \leq y \leq 1 \right\}$
     (b)   Increasing: $(-4,-1)$ and $(3,4)$;   Decreasing: $(-1, 3)$
     (c)   Local minimum $(3,-3)$;   Local maximum $(-1,1)$
     (d)   The graph is not symmetric with respect to the x-axis, the y-axis or the origin.
     (e)   The function is neither even nor odd.
     (f) x-intercepts: $(-2,0)$, $(0,0)$, $(4,0)$; y-intercept: $(0,0)$

49. $f(x) = x^3 - 4x$
$$f(-x) = (-x)^3 - 4(-x) = -x^3 + 4x = -\left(x^3 - 4x \right) = -f(x) \qquad f \text{ is odd.}$$

51. $h(x) = \dfrac{1}{x^4} + \dfrac{1}{x^2} + 1$
$$h(-x) = \frac{1}{(-x)^4} + \frac{1}{(-x)^2} + 1 = \frac{1}{x^4} + \frac{1}{x^2} + 1 = h(x) \qquad h \text{ is even.}$$

53. $G(x) = 1 - x + x^3$
$$G(-x) = 1 - (-x) + (-x)^3 = 1 + x - x^3 \neq -G(x) \text{ or } G(x)$$
G is neither even nor odd.

55. $f(x) = \dfrac{x}{1+x^2}$
$$f(-x) = \frac{-x}{1+(-x)^2} = \frac{-x}{1+x^2} = -f(x) \quad f \text{ is odd.}$$

57. $f(x) = 2x^3 - 5x + 1$ on the interval $(-3,3)$
Use MAXIMUM and MINIMUM on the graph of $y_1 = 2x^3 - 5x + 1$.

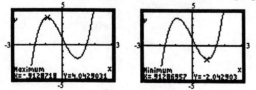

local maximum at: $(-0.91, 4.04)$;   local minimum at: $(0.91, -2.04)$
f is increasing on: $(-3, -0.91)$ and $(0.91, 3)$; f is decreasing on: $(-0.91, 0.91)$

59. $f(x) = 2x^4 - 5x^3 + 2x + 1$ on the interval $(-2,3)$

Use MAXIMUM and MINIMUM on the graph of $y_1 = 2x^4 - 5x^3 + 2x + 1$.

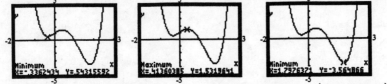

local maximum at: $(0.41, 1.53)$;   local minima at: $(-0.34, 0.54)$, $(1.80, -3.56)$

f is increasing on: $(-0.34, 0.41)$ and $(1.80, 3)$;

f is decreasing on: $(-2, -0.34)$ and $(0.41, 1.80)$

61.   (b), (c), and (d) pass the Vertical Line Test and are therefore functions.

63. $f(x) = \sqrt[3]{x}$

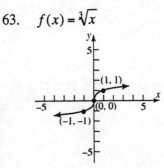

65. $F(x) = |x| - 4$

Using the graph of $y = |x|$, vertically shift the graph downward 4 units.

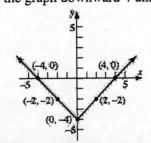

Intercepts: $(-4,0)$, $(4,0)$, $(0,-4)$
Domain: $\{x \mid x \text{ is any real number}\}$
Range: $\{y \mid y \geq -4\}$

67. $g(x) = -2|x|$

Reflect the graph of $y = |x|$ about the x-axis and vertically stretch the graph by a factor of 2.

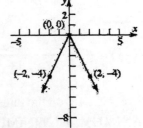

Intercepts: $(0,0)$
Domain: $\{x \mid x \text{ is any real number}\}$
Range: $\{y \mid y \leq 0\}$

69. $h(x) = \sqrt{x - 1}$

Using the graph of $y = \sqrt{x}$, horizontally shift the graph to the right 1 unit.

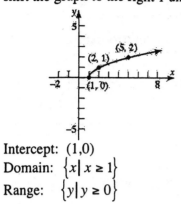

Intercept: $(1,0)$
Domain: $\{x \mid x \geq 1\}$
Range: $\{y \mid y \geq 0\}$

71. $f(x) = \sqrt{1 - x} = \sqrt{-1(x - 1)}$

Reflect the graph of $y = \sqrt{x}$ about the y-axis and horizontally shift the graph to the right 1 unit..

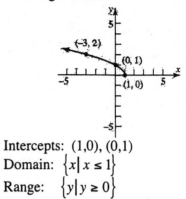

Intercepts: $(1,0)$, $(0,1)$
Domain: $\{x \mid x \leq 1\}$
Range: $\{y \mid y \geq 0\}$

73. $h(x) = (x - 1)^2 + 2$

Using the graph of $y = x^2$, horizontally shift the graph to the right 1 unit and vertically shift the graph up 2 units.

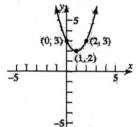

Intercepts: $(0,3)$
Domain: $\{x \mid x \text{ is any real number}\}$
Range: $\{y \mid y \geq 2\}$

75. $g(x) = 3(x - 1)^3 + 1$

Using the graph of $y = x^3$, horizontally shift the graph to the right 1 unit vertically stretch the graph by a factor of 3, and vertically shift the graph up 1 unit.

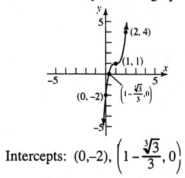

Intercepts: $(0,-2)$, $\left(1 - \frac{\sqrt[3]{3}}{3}, 0\right)$

Domain: $\{x \mid x \text{ is any real number}\}$
Range: $\{y \mid y \text{ is any real number}\}$

77. (a) The inverse is $\{(2,1),(5,3),(8,5),(10,6)\}$.

(b) The inverse is a function.

79.

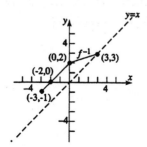

81. $f(x) = \dfrac{2x+3}{5x-2}$

$y = \dfrac{2x+3}{5x-2}$

$x = \dfrac{2y+3}{5y-2}$ Inverse

$x(5y-2) = 2y+3$

$5xy - 2x = 2y+3$

$5xy - 2y = 2x+3$

$y(5x-2) = 2x+3$

$y = \dfrac{2x+3}{5x-2}$

$f^{-1}(x) = \dfrac{2x+3}{5x-2}$

Domain of f = range of f^{-1}

= all real numbers except $\dfrac{2}{5}$.

Range of f = domain of f^{-1}

= all real numbers except $\dfrac{2}{5}$.

Check:

$$f\left(f^{-1}(x)\right) = \dfrac{2\left(\dfrac{2x+3}{5x-2}\right)+3}{5\left(\dfrac{2x+3}{5x-2}\right)-2} = \dfrac{\dfrac{2(2x+3)+3(5x-2)}{5x-2}}{\dfrac{5(2x+3)-2(5x-2)}{5x-2}}$$

$$= \dfrac{\dfrac{4x+6+15x-6}{5x-2}}{\dfrac{10x+15-10x+4}{5x-2}} = \dfrac{\dfrac{19x}{5x-2}}{\dfrac{19}{5x-2}}$$

$$= \left(\dfrac{19x}{5x-2}\right)\left(\dfrac{5x-2}{19}\right) = x$$

$$f^{-1}\left(f(x)\right) = \dfrac{2\left(\dfrac{2x+3}{5x-2}\right)+3}{5\left(\dfrac{2x+3}{5x-2}\right)-2} = x,$$

by the previous computation.

83. $f(x) = \dfrac{1}{x-1}$

$y = \dfrac{1}{x-1}$

$x = \dfrac{1}{y-1}$ Inverse

$x(y-1) = 1$

$xy - x = 1$

$xy = x+1$

$y = \dfrac{x+1}{x}$

$f^{-1}(x) = \dfrac{x+1}{x}$

Domain of f = range of f^{-1}

= all real numbers except 1

Range of f = domain of f^{-1}

= all real numbers except 0

Check:

$$f\left(f^{-1}(x)\right) = \dfrac{1}{\dfrac{x+1}{x}-1} = \dfrac{1}{\dfrac{x+1-x}{x}} = \dfrac{1}{\dfrac{1}{x}} = x$$

$$f^{-1}\left(f(x)\right) = \dfrac{\dfrac{1}{x-1}+1}{\dfrac{1}{x-1}} = \dfrac{\dfrac{1+x-1}{x-1}}{\dfrac{1}{x-1}}$$

$$= \dfrac{\dfrac{x}{x-1}}{\dfrac{1}{x-1}} = \left(\dfrac{x}{x-1}\right)\left(\dfrac{x-1}{x}\right) = x$$

85. $f(x) = \dfrac{3}{x^{1/3}}$

$y = \dfrac{3}{x^{1/3}}$

$x = \dfrac{3}{y^{1/3}}$ Inverse

$xy^{1/3} = 3$

$y^{1/3} = \dfrac{3}{x}$

$y = \dfrac{27}{x^3}$

$f^{-1}(x) = \dfrac{27}{x^3}$

Domain of f = range of f^{-1}
= all real numbers except 0
Range of f = domain of f^{-1}
= all real numbers except 0

Check:

$f\!\left(f^{-1}(x)\right) = \dfrac{3}{\left(\dfrac{27}{x^3}\right)^{1/3}} = \dfrac{3}{\dfrac{27^{1/3}}{\left(x^3\right)^{1/3}}} = \dfrac{3}{\dfrac{3}{x}} = 3\left(\dfrac{x}{3}\right) = x$

$f^{-1}\!\left(f(x)\right) = \dfrac{27}{\left(\dfrac{3}{x^{1/3}}\right)^3} = \dfrac{27}{\dfrac{3^3}{\left(x^{1/3}\right)^3}} = \dfrac{27}{\dfrac{27}{x}} = 27\left(\dfrac{x}{27}\right) = x$

87. $f(4) = -5$ gives the ordered pair $(4,-5)$. $f(0) = 3$ gives $(0,3)$.

Finding the slope: $m = \dfrac{3-(-5)}{0-4} = \dfrac{8}{-4} = -2$

Using slope-intercept form: $f(x) = -2x + 3$

89. $f(x) = \dfrac{Ax+5}{6x-2}$ and $f(1) = 4$

$\dfrac{A(1)+5}{6(1)-2} = 4$

$\dfrac{A+5}{4} = 4$

$A+5 = 16$

$A = 11$

91. Find the distance between each pair of points.

$d_{A,B} = \sqrt{(1-3)^2 + (1-4)^2} = \sqrt{4+9} = \sqrt{13}$

$d_{B,C} = \sqrt{(-2-1)^2 + (3-1)^2} = \sqrt{9+4} = \sqrt{13}$

$d_{A,C} = \sqrt{(-2-3)^2 + (3-4)^2} = \sqrt{25+1} = \sqrt{26}$

Since $AB = BC$, triangle ABC is isosceles.

93. (a) The printed region is a rectangle. Its area is given by
$A = (\text{length})(\text{width}) = (11-2x)(8.5-2x)$

$A(x) = (11-2x)(8.5-2x)$

(b) For the domain of $A(x) = (11-2x)(8.5-2x)$ recall that the dimensions of a rectangle must be non-negative.

$x \ge 0$ and $11-2x \ge 0$ and $8.5-2x \ge 0$

$x \ge 0$ and $x \le 5.5$ and $x \le 4.25$

The domain is $\{x \mid 0 \le x \le 4.25\}$.

The range of $A(x) = (11-2x)(8.5-2x)$ is given by $A(4.25) \le A \le A(0) \Rightarrow 0 \le A \le 93.5$

(c) $A(1) = (11-2(1))(8.5-2(1)) = 9 \cdot 6.5 = 58.5$ square inches

$A(1.2) = (11-2(1.2))(8.5-2(1.2)) = (8.6)(6.1) = 52.46$ square inches

$A(1.5) = (11-2(1.5))(8.5-2(1.5)) = (8)(5.5) = 44$ square inches

(d) $y_1 = (11 - 2x) * (8.5 - 2x)$

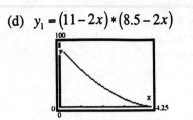

(e) Using TRACE, $A \approx 70$ when $x \approx 0.643$ inches; $A = 50$ when $x \approx 1.28$ inches

Trigonometric Functions

2.1 Angles and Their Measure

1. $C = 2\pi r$

3. standard position

5. $\dfrac{s}{t}; \dfrac{\theta}{t}$

7. True

9. False

11.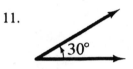

13.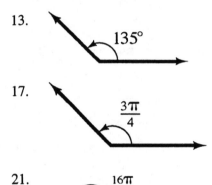

15.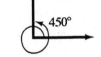

17.

19.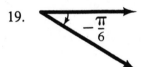

21.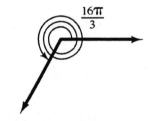

23. $40°10'25" = \left(40 + 10 \cdot \dfrac{1}{60} + 25 \cdot \dfrac{1}{60} \cdot \dfrac{1}{60}\right)° \approx (40 + 0.1667 + 0.00694)° \approx 40.17°$

25. $1°2'3" = \left(1 + 2 \cdot \dfrac{1}{60} + 3 \cdot \dfrac{1}{60} \cdot \dfrac{1}{60}\right)° \approx (1 + 0.0333 + 0.00083)° \approx 1.03°$

27. $9°9'9" = \left(9 + 9 \cdot \dfrac{1}{60} + 9 \cdot \dfrac{1}{60} \cdot \dfrac{1}{60}\right)° = (9 + 0.15 + 0.0025)° \approx 9.15°$

29. $40.32° = ?$
    $0.32° = 0.32(1°) = 0.32(60') = 19.2'$
    $\quad 0.2' = 0.2(1') = 0.2(60") = 12"$
    $40.32° = 40° + 0.32° = 40° + 19.2' = 40° + 19' + 0.2' = 40° + 19' + 12" = 40°19'12"$

31. $18.255° = ?$

$$0.255° = 0.255(1°) = 0.255(60') = 15.3'$$

$$0.3' = 0.3(1') = 0.3(60") = 18"$$

$$18.255° = 18° + 0.255° = 18° + 15.3' = 18° + 15' + 0.3' = 18° + 15' + 18" = 18°15'18"$$

33. $19.99° = ?$

$$0.99° = 0.99(1°) = 0.99(60') = 59.4'$$

$$0.4' = 0.4(1') = 0.4(60") = 24"$$

$$19.99° = 19° + 0.99° = 19° + 59.4' = 19° + 59' + 0.4' = 19° + 59' + 24" = 19°59'24"$$

35. $30° = 30 \cdot \dfrac{\pi}{180}$ radian $= \dfrac{\pi}{6}$ radian

37. $240° = 240 \cdot \dfrac{\pi}{180}$ radian $= \dfrac{4\pi}{3}$ radians

39. $-60° = -60 \cdot \dfrac{\pi}{180}$ radian $= -\dfrac{\pi}{3}$ radians

41. $180° = 180 \cdot \dfrac{\pi}{180}$ radian $= \pi$ radians

43. $-135° = -135 \cdot \dfrac{\pi}{180}$ radian $= -\dfrac{3\pi}{4}$ radians

45. $-90° = -90 \cdot \dfrac{\pi}{180}$ radian $= -\dfrac{\pi}{2}$ radians

47. $\dfrac{\pi}{3} = \dfrac{\pi}{3} \cdot \dfrac{180}{\pi}$ degrees $= 60°$

49. $-\dfrac{5\pi}{4} = -\dfrac{5\pi}{4} \cdot \dfrac{180}{\pi}$ degrees $= -225°$

51. $\dfrac{\pi}{2} = \dfrac{\pi}{2} \cdot \dfrac{180}{\pi}$ degrees $= 90°$

53. $\dfrac{\pi}{12} = \dfrac{\pi}{12} \cdot \dfrac{180}{\pi}$ degrees $= 15°$

55. $-\dfrac{\pi}{2} = -\dfrac{\pi}{2} \cdot \dfrac{180}{\pi}$ degrees $= -90°$

57. $-\dfrac{\pi}{6} = -\dfrac{\pi}{6} \cdot \dfrac{180}{\pi}$ degrees $= -30°$

59. $17° = 17 \cdot \dfrac{\pi}{180}$ radian $= \dfrac{17\pi}{180}$ radian ≈ 0.30 radian

61. $-40° = -40 \cdot \dfrac{\pi}{180}$ radian $= -\dfrac{2\pi}{9}$ radian ≈ -0.70 radian

63. $125° = 125 \cdot \dfrac{\pi}{180}$ radian $= \dfrac{25\pi}{36}$ radians ≈ 2.18 radians

65. 3.14 radians $= 3.14 \cdot \dfrac{180}{\pi}$ degrees $\approx 179.91°$

67. 2 radians $= 2 \cdot \dfrac{180}{\pi}$ degrees $\approx 114.59°$

69. 6.32 radians $= 6.32 \cdot \dfrac{180}{\pi}$ degrees $\approx 362.11°$

71. $r = 10$ meters; $\theta = \dfrac{1}{2}$ radian; $s = r\theta = 10 \cdot \dfrac{1}{2} = 5$ meters

73. $\theta = \dfrac{1}{3}$ radian; $s = 2$ feet; $\quad s = r\theta \implies r = \dfrac{s}{\theta} = \dfrac{2}{(1/3)} = 6$ feet

75. $r = 5$ miles; $s = 3$ miles; $\quad s = r\theta \implies \theta = \dfrac{s}{r} = \dfrac{3}{5} = 0.6$ radian

77. $r = 2$ inches; $\theta = 30°$; $\quad$ Convert to radians: $\quad 30° = 30 \cdot \dfrac{\pi}{180} = \dfrac{\pi}{6}$ radian

  $s = r\theta = 2 \cdot \dfrac{\pi}{6} = \dfrac{\pi}{3}$ inches

79. $r = 10$ meters; $\theta = \dfrac{1}{2}$ radian

  $A = \dfrac{1}{2}r^2\theta = \dfrac{1}{2}(10)^2 \left(\dfrac{1}{2}\right) = \dfrac{100}{4} = 25$ square meters

81. $\theta = \dfrac{1}{3}$ radian; $A = 2$ square feet

  $A = \dfrac{1}{2}r^2\theta \implies 2 = \dfrac{1}{2}r^2\left(\dfrac{1}{3}\right) = \dfrac{1}{6}r^2$

  $2 = \dfrac{1}{6}r^2$

  $12 = r^2$

  $r = \sqrt{12} \approx 3.464$ feet

83. $r = 5$ miles; $A = 3$ square miles

$$A = \frac{1}{2}r^2\theta \Rightarrow 3 = \frac{1}{2}(5)^2\theta = \frac{25}{2}\theta$$

$$3 = \frac{25}{2}\theta$$

$$\frac{6}{25} = \theta$$

$$\theta = 0.24 \ \text{radian}$$

85. $r = 2$ inches; $\theta = 30°$;   Convert to radians: $30° = 30 \cdot \dfrac{\pi}{180} = \dfrac{\pi}{6}$ radian

$$A = \frac{1}{2}r^2\theta = \frac{1}{2}(2)^2\left(\frac{\pi}{6}\right) = \frac{1}{2} \cdot 4\left(\frac{\pi}{6}\right) = \frac{\pi}{3} \approx 1.047 \ \text{square inches}$$

87. $r = 2$ feet; $\theta = \dfrac{\pi}{3}$ radians

$$s = r\theta = 2 \cdot \frac{\pi}{3} = \frac{2\pi}{3} \approx 2.094 \ \text{feet}$$

$$A = \frac{1}{2}r^2\theta = \frac{1}{2}(2)^2\left(\frac{\pi}{3}\right) = \frac{1}{2} \cdot 4\left(\frac{\pi}{3}\right) = \frac{2\pi}{3} \approx 2.094 \ \text{square feet}$$

89. $r = 12$ yards; $\theta = 70°$;   Convert to radians: $70° = 70 \cdot \dfrac{\pi}{180} = \dfrac{7\pi}{18}$ radians

$$s = r\theta = 12 \cdot \frac{7\pi}{18} \approx 14.661 \ \text{yards}$$

$$A = \frac{1}{2}r^2\theta = \frac{1}{2}(12)^2\left(\frac{7\pi}{18}\right) = \frac{1}{2} \cdot 144\left(\frac{7\pi}{18}\right) = 72\left(\frac{7\pi}{18}\right) \approx 87.965 \ \text{square yards}$$

91. In 15 minutes, $r = 6$ inches; $\theta = \dfrac{15}{60}$ rev $= \dfrac{1}{4} \cdot 360° = 90° = \dfrac{\pi}{2}$ radians

$$s = r\theta = 6 \cdot \frac{\pi}{2} = 3\pi \ \text{inches} \approx 9.42 \ \text{inches}$$

In 25 minutes, $r = 6$ inches; $\theta = \dfrac{25}{60}$ rev $= \dfrac{5}{12} \cdot 360° = 150° = \dfrac{5\pi}{6}$ radians

$$s = r\theta = 6 \cdot \frac{5\pi}{6} = 5\pi \ \text{inches} \approx 15.71 \ \text{inches}$$

93. $r = 4$ m; $\theta = 45°$;   Convert to radians: $45° = 45 \cdot \dfrac{\pi}{180} = \dfrac{\pi}{4}$ radian

$$A = \frac{1}{2}r^2\theta = \frac{1}{2}(4)^2\left(\frac{\pi}{4}\right) = \frac{1}{2} \cdot 16\left(\frac{\pi}{4}\right) = 2\pi \approx 6.283 \ \text{square meters}$$

95. $r = 30$ feet; $\theta = 135°$;   Convert to radians: $135° = 135 \cdot \dfrac{\pi}{180} = \dfrac{3\pi}{4}$ radians

$$A = \frac{1}{2}r^2\theta = \frac{1}{2}(30)^2\left(\frac{3\pi}{4}\right) = \frac{1}{2} \cdot (900)\left(\frac{3\pi}{4}\right) = \frac{2700\pi}{8} \approx 1060.29 \text{ square feet}$$

97. $r = 5$ cm; $t = 20$ seconds; $\theta = \dfrac{1}{3}$ radian

$$\omega = \frac{\theta}{t} = \frac{(1/3)}{20} = \frac{1}{3} \cdot \frac{1}{20} = \frac{1}{60} \text{ radian/sec}$$

$$v = \frac{s}{t} = \frac{r\theta}{t} = \frac{5 \cdot (1/3)}{20} = \frac{5}{3} \cdot \frac{1}{20} = \frac{1}{12} \text{ cm/sec}$$

99. $d = 26$ inches; $r = 13$ inches; $v = 35$ mi / hr

$$v = \frac{35 \text{ mi}}{\text{hr}} \cdot \frac{5280 \text{ ft}}{\text{mi}} \cdot \frac{12 \text{ in.}}{\text{ft}} \cdot \frac{1 \text{ hr}}{60 \text{ min}} = 36{,}960 \text{ in./min}$$

$$\omega = \frac{v}{r} = \frac{36{,}960 \text{ in./min}}{13 \text{ in.}} \approx 2843.08 \text{ radians/min}$$

$$\approx \frac{2843.08 \text{ rad}}{\text{min}} \cdot \frac{1 \text{ rev}}{2\pi \text{ rad}} \approx 452.5 \text{ rev/min}$$

101. $r = 3960$ miles; $\theta = 35°9' - 29°57' = 5°12' = 5.2° = 5.2 \cdot \dfrac{\pi}{180} \approx 0.09076$ radian

$$s = r\theta = 3960 \cdot 0.09076 \approx 359.4 \text{ miles}$$

103. $r = 3429.5$ miles; $\omega = 1$ rev / day $= 2\pi$ radians / day $= \dfrac{\pi}{12}$ radians / hr

$$v = r\omega = 3429.5 \cdot \frac{\pi}{12} \approx 897.8 \text{ miles/hr}$$

105. $r = 2.39 \times 10^5$ miles;

$$\omega = 1 \text{ rev/27.3 days} = 2\pi \text{ radians/27.3 days} = \frac{\pi}{12 \cdot 27.3} \text{ radians/hr}$$

$$v = r\omega = \left(2.39 \times 10^5\right) \cdot \frac{\pi}{327.6} \approx 2292 \text{ miles/hr}$$

107. $r_1 = 2$ inches; $r_2 = 8$ inches; $\omega_1 = 3$ rev / min $= 6\pi$ radians / min
    Find ω_2:

$v_1 = v_2$

$r_1\omega_1 = r_2\omega_2 \Rightarrow 2(6\pi) = 8\omega_2$

$$\omega_2 = \frac{12\pi}{8} = 1.5\pi \text{ radians/min} = \frac{1.5\pi}{2\pi} \text{ rev/min} = \frac{3}{4} \text{ rev/min}$$

109. $r = 4$ feet; $\omega = 10$ rev / min $= 20\pi$ radians / min

$$v = r\omega = 4 \cdot 20\pi = 80\pi \ \frac{\text{ft}}{\text{min}} = \frac{80\pi \text{ ft}}{\text{min}} \cdot \frac{1 \text{ mi}}{5280 \text{ ft}} \cdot \frac{60 \text{ min}}{\text{hr}} \approx 2.86 \text{ mi/hr}$$

111. $d = 8.5$ feet; $r = 4.25$ feet; $v = 9.55$ mi/hr

$$\omega = \frac{v}{r} = \frac{9.55 \text{ mi/hr}}{4.25 \text{ ft}} = \frac{9.55 \text{ mi}}{\text{hr}} \cdot \frac{1}{4.25 \text{ ft}} \cdot \frac{5280 \text{ ft}}{\text{mi}} \cdot \frac{1 \text{ hr}}{60 \text{ min}} \cdot \frac{1 \text{ rev}}{2\pi} \approx 31.47 \text{ rev/min}$$

113. The earth makes one full rotation in 24 hours. The distance traveled in 24 hours is the circumference of the earth. At the equator the circumference is $2\pi(3960)$ miles. Therefore, the linear velocity a person must travel to keep up with the sun is:

$$v = \frac{s}{t} = \frac{2\pi(3960)}{24} \approx 1037 \text{ miles / hr}$$

115. r_1 rotates at ω_1 rev/min; r_2 rotates at ω_2 rev/min

Since the linear speed of the belt connecting the pulleys is the same,

$$v = r_1\omega_1 = r_2\omega_2 \Rightarrow \frac{r_1}{r_2} = \frac{\omega_2}{\omega_1}$$

117. Answers will vary.

119. Linear speed measures the distance traveled per unit time, and angular speed measures the change in a central angle per unit time. In other words, linear speed describes distance traveled by a point located on the edge of a circle, and angular speed describes the turning rate of the circle itself.

121. Answers will vary.

Chapter 2

Trigonometric Functions

2.2 Trigonometric Functions: Unit Circle Approach

1. $a^2 + b^2 = c^2$

3. True

5. $\left(-\dfrac{1}{2}, \dfrac{\sqrt{3}}{2}\right)$

7. $1 + \dfrac{1}{2} = \dfrac{3}{2}$

9. True

11. $P = \left(\dfrac{\sqrt{3}}{2}, \dfrac{1}{2}\right) \Rightarrow x = \dfrac{\sqrt{3}}{2}, y = \dfrac{1}{2}$

$\sin t = y = \dfrac{1}{2}$

$\csc t = \dfrac{1}{y} = \dfrac{1}{\frac{1}{2}} = 2$

$\cos t = x = \dfrac{\sqrt{3}}{2}$

$\sec t = \dfrac{1}{x} = \dfrac{1}{\frac{\sqrt{3}}{2}} = \dfrac{2}{\sqrt{3}} \cdot \dfrac{\sqrt{3}}{\sqrt{3}} = \dfrac{2\sqrt{3}}{3}$

$\tan t = \dfrac{y}{x} = \dfrac{\frac{1}{2}}{\frac{\sqrt{3}}{2}} = \dfrac{1}{2} \cdot \dfrac{2}{\sqrt{3}} \cdot \dfrac{\sqrt{3}}{\sqrt{3}} = \dfrac{\sqrt{3}}{3}$

$\cot t = \dfrac{x}{y} = \dfrac{\frac{\sqrt{3}}{2}}{\frac{1}{2}} = \dfrac{\sqrt{3}}{2} \cdot \dfrac{2}{1} = \sqrt{3}$

13. $\left(-\dfrac{2}{5}, \dfrac{\sqrt{21}}{5}\right) \Rightarrow x = -\dfrac{2}{5}, y = \dfrac{\sqrt{21}}{5}$

$\sin t = y = \dfrac{\sqrt{21}}{5}$

$\csc t = \dfrac{1}{y} = \dfrac{1}{\frac{\sqrt{21}}{5}} = \dfrac{5}{\sqrt{21}} \cdot \dfrac{\sqrt{21}}{\sqrt{21}} = \dfrac{5\sqrt{21}}{21}$

$\cos t = x = -\dfrac{2}{5}$

$\sec t = \dfrac{1}{x} = \dfrac{1}{-\frac{2}{5}} = -\dfrac{5}{2}$

$\tan t = \dfrac{y}{x} = \dfrac{\frac{\sqrt{21}}{5}}{-\frac{2}{5}} = \dfrac{\sqrt{21}}{5} \cdot \left(-\dfrac{5}{2}\right) = -\dfrac{\sqrt{21}}{2}$

$\cot t = \dfrac{x}{y} = \dfrac{-\frac{2}{5}}{\frac{\sqrt{21}}{5}} = -\dfrac{2}{5} \cdot \dfrac{5}{\sqrt{21}} \cdot \dfrac{\sqrt{21}}{\sqrt{21}} = -\dfrac{2\sqrt{21}}{21}$

15. $P = \left(-\dfrac{\sqrt{2}}{2}, \dfrac{\sqrt{2}}{2}\right) \Rightarrow x = -\dfrac{\sqrt{2}}{2}, y = \dfrac{\sqrt{2}}{2}$

$\sin t = y = \dfrac{\sqrt{2}}{2}$

$\csc t = \dfrac{1}{y} = \dfrac{1}{\dfrac{\sqrt{2}}{2}} = \dfrac{2}{\sqrt{2}} \cdot \dfrac{\sqrt{2}}{\sqrt{2}} = \sqrt{2}$

$\cos t = x = -\dfrac{\sqrt{2}}{2}$

$\sec t = \dfrac{1}{x} = \dfrac{1}{-\dfrac{\sqrt{2}}{2}} = -\dfrac{2}{\sqrt{2}} \cdot \dfrac{\sqrt{2}}{\sqrt{2}} = -\sqrt{2}$

$\tan t = \dfrac{y}{x} = \dfrac{\dfrac{\sqrt{2}}{2}}{-\dfrac{\sqrt{2}}{2}} = \dfrac{\sqrt{2}}{2} \cdot \left(-\dfrac{2}{\sqrt{2}}\right) = -1$

$\cot t = \dfrac{x}{y} = \dfrac{-\dfrac{\sqrt{2}}{2}}{\dfrac{\sqrt{2}}{2}} = \left(-\dfrac{\sqrt{2}}{2}\right) \cdot \dfrac{2}{\sqrt{2}} = -1$

17. $\left(\dfrac{2\sqrt{2}}{3}, -\dfrac{1}{3}\right) \Rightarrow x = \dfrac{2\sqrt{2}}{3}, y = -\dfrac{1}{3}$

$\sin t = y = -\dfrac{1}{3}$

$\csc t = \dfrac{1}{y} = \dfrac{1}{-\dfrac{1}{3}} = -3$

$\cos t = x = \dfrac{2\sqrt{2}}{3}$

$\sec t = \dfrac{1}{x} = \dfrac{1}{\dfrac{2\sqrt{2}}{3}} = \dfrac{3}{2\sqrt{2}} \cdot \dfrac{\sqrt{2}}{\sqrt{2}} = \dfrac{3\sqrt{2}}{4}$

$\tan t = \dfrac{y}{x} = \dfrac{-\dfrac{1}{3}}{\dfrac{2\sqrt{2}}{3}} = -\dfrac{1}{3} \cdot \dfrac{3}{2\sqrt{2}} \cdot \dfrac{\sqrt{2}}{\sqrt{2}} = -\dfrac{\sqrt{2}}{4}$

$\cot t = \dfrac{x}{y} = \dfrac{\dfrac{2\sqrt{2}}{3}}{-\dfrac{1}{3}} = \dfrac{2\sqrt{2}}{3} \cdot \left(-\dfrac{3}{1}\right) = -2\sqrt{2}$

19. The point on the unit circle that corresponds to $\dfrac{11\pi}{2} = 990°$ is $(0,-1)$, thus $\sin\dfrac{11\pi}{2} = -1$.

21. The point on the unit circle that corresponds to $6\pi = 1080°$ is $(1,0)$, thus $\tan(6\pi) = \dfrac{0}{1} = 0$.

23. The point on the unit circle that corresponds to $\dfrac{11\pi}{2} = 990°$ is $(0,-1)$, thus $\csc\dfrac{11\pi}{2} = \dfrac{1}{-1} = -1$.

25. The point on the unit circle that corresponds to $-\dfrac{3\pi}{2} = -270°$ is $(0,1)$, thus $\cos\left(-\dfrac{3\pi}{2}\right) = 0$.

27. The point on the unit circle that corresponds to $-\pi = -180°$ is $(-1,0)$, thus $\sec(-\pi) = \dfrac{-1}{1} = -1$.

29. $\sin 45° + \cos 60° = \dfrac{\sqrt{2}}{2} + \dfrac{1}{2} = \dfrac{1+\sqrt{2}}{2}$

31. $\sin 90° + \tan 45° = 1 + 1 = 2$

33. $\sin 45° \cdot \cos 45° = \dfrac{\sqrt{2}}{2} \cdot \dfrac{\sqrt{2}}{2} = \dfrac{2}{4} = \dfrac{1}{2}$ 35. $\csc 45° \cdot \tan 60° = \sqrt{2} \cdot \sqrt{3} = \sqrt{6}$

37. $4 \sin 90° - 3 \tan 180° = 4 \cdot 1 - 3 \cdot 0 = 4$

39. $2 \sin \dfrac{\pi}{3} - 3 \tan \dfrac{\pi}{6} = 2 \cdot \dfrac{\sqrt{3}}{2} - 3 \cdot \dfrac{\sqrt{3}}{3} = \sqrt{3} - \sqrt{3} = 0$

41. $\sin \dfrac{\pi}{4} - \cos \dfrac{\pi}{4} = \dfrac{\sqrt{2}}{2} - \dfrac{\sqrt{2}}{2} = 0$

43. $2 \sec \dfrac{\pi}{4} + 4 \cot \dfrac{\pi}{3} = 2 \cdot \sqrt{2} + 4 \cdot \dfrac{\sqrt{3}}{3} = 2\sqrt{2} + \dfrac{4\sqrt{3}}{3}$

45. $\tan \pi - \cos 0 = 0 - 1 = -1$ 47. $\csc \dfrac{\pi}{2} + \cot \dfrac{\pi}{2} = 1 + 0 = 1$

49. The point on the unit circle that corresponds to $\theta = \dfrac{2\pi}{3} = 120°$ is $\left(-\dfrac{1}{2}, \dfrac{\sqrt{3}}{2} \right)$.

$\sin \theta = \dfrac{\sqrt{3}}{2}$ $\csc \theta = \dfrac{1}{\dfrac{\sqrt{3}}{2}} = \dfrac{2}{\sqrt{3}} \cdot \dfrac{\sqrt{3}}{\sqrt{3}} = \dfrac{2\sqrt{3}}{3}$

$\cos \theta = -\dfrac{1}{2}$ $\sec \theta = \dfrac{1}{-\dfrac{1}{2}} = -2$

$\tan \theta = \dfrac{\dfrac{\sqrt{3}}{2}}{-\dfrac{1}{2}} = \dfrac{\sqrt{3}}{2} \cdot \left(-\dfrac{2}{1} \right) = -\sqrt{3}$ $\cot \theta = \dfrac{-\dfrac{1}{2}}{\dfrac{\sqrt{3}}{2}} = -\dfrac{1}{2} \cdot \dfrac{2}{\sqrt{3}} \cdot \dfrac{\sqrt{3}}{\sqrt{3}} = -\dfrac{\sqrt{3}}{3}$

51. The point on the unit circle that corresponds to $\theta = 210° = \dfrac{7\pi}{6}$ is $\left(-\dfrac{\sqrt{3}}{2}, -\dfrac{1}{2} \right)$.

$\sin \theta = -\dfrac{1}{2}$ $\csc \theta = \dfrac{1}{-\dfrac{1}{2}} = -2$

$\cos \theta = -\dfrac{\sqrt{3}}{2}$ $\sec \theta = \dfrac{1}{-\dfrac{\sqrt{3}}{2}} = -\dfrac{2}{\sqrt{3}} \cdot \dfrac{\sqrt{3}}{\sqrt{3}} = -\dfrac{2\sqrt{3}}{3}$

$\tan \theta = \dfrac{-\dfrac{1}{2}}{-\dfrac{\sqrt{3}}{2}} = -\dfrac{1}{2} \cdot \left(-\dfrac{2}{\sqrt{3}} \right) \cdot \dfrac{\sqrt{3}}{\sqrt{3}} = \dfrac{\sqrt{3}}{3}$ $\cot \theta = \dfrac{-\dfrac{\sqrt{3}}{2}}{-\dfrac{1}{2}} = -\dfrac{\sqrt{3}}{2} \cdot \left(-\dfrac{2}{1} \right) = \sqrt{3}$

53. The point on the unit circle that corresponds to $\theta = \dfrac{3\pi}{4} = 135° $ is $\left(-\dfrac{\sqrt{2}}{2}, \dfrac{\sqrt{2}}{2}\right)$.

$$\sin\theta = \frac{\sqrt{2}}{2}$$

$$\csc\theta = \frac{1}{\dfrac{\sqrt{2}}{2}} = \frac{2}{\sqrt{2}} \cdot \frac{\sqrt{2}}{\sqrt{2}} = \sqrt{2}$$

$$\cos\theta = -\frac{\sqrt{2}}{2}$$

$$\sec\theta = \frac{1}{-\dfrac{\sqrt{2}}{2}} = -\frac{2}{\sqrt{2}} \cdot \frac{\sqrt{2}}{\sqrt{2}} = -\sqrt{2}$$

$$\tan\theta = \frac{\dfrac{\sqrt{2}}{2}}{-\dfrac{\sqrt{2}}{2}} = \frac{\sqrt{2}}{2} \cdot \left(-\frac{2}{\sqrt{2}}\right) = -1$$

$$\cot\theta = \frac{-\dfrac{\sqrt{2}}{2}}{\dfrac{\sqrt{2}}{2}} = -\frac{\sqrt{2}}{2} \cdot \frac{2}{\sqrt{2}} = -1$$

55. The point on the unit circle that corresponds to $\theta = \dfrac{8\pi}{3} = 480°$ is $\left(-\dfrac{1}{2}, \dfrac{\sqrt{3}}{2}\right)$.

$$\sin\theta = \frac{\sqrt{3}}{2}$$

$$\csc\theta = \frac{1}{\dfrac{\sqrt{3}}{2}} = \frac{2}{\sqrt{3}} \cdot \frac{\sqrt{3}}{\sqrt{3}} = \frac{2\sqrt{3}}{3}$$

$$\cos\theta = -\frac{1}{2}$$

$$\sec\theta = \frac{1}{-\dfrac{1}{2}} = -2$$

$$\tan\theta = \frac{\dfrac{\sqrt{3}}{2}}{-\dfrac{1}{2}} = \frac{\sqrt{3}}{2} \cdot \left(-\frac{2}{1}\right) = -\sqrt{3}$$

$$\cot\theta = \frac{-\dfrac{1}{2}}{\dfrac{\sqrt{3}}{2}} = -\frac{1}{2} \cdot \frac{2}{\sqrt{3}} \cdot \frac{\sqrt{3}}{\sqrt{3}} = -\frac{\sqrt{3}}{3}$$

57. The point on the unit circle that corresponds to $\theta = 405° = \dfrac{9\pi}{4}$ is $\left(\dfrac{\sqrt{2}}{2}, \dfrac{\sqrt{2}}{2}\right)$.

$$\sin\theta = \frac{\sqrt{2}}{2}$$

$$\csc\theta = \frac{1}{\dfrac{\sqrt{2}}{2}} = \frac{2}{\sqrt{2}} \cdot \frac{\sqrt{2}}{\sqrt{2}} = \sqrt{2}$$

$$\cos\theta = \frac{\sqrt{2}}{2}$$

$$\sec\theta = \frac{1}{\dfrac{\sqrt{2}}{2}} = \frac{2}{\sqrt{2}} \cdot \frac{\sqrt{2}}{\sqrt{2}} = \sqrt{2}$$

$$\tan\theta = \frac{\dfrac{\sqrt{2}}{2}}{\dfrac{\sqrt{2}}{2}} = \frac{\sqrt{2}}{2} \cdot \frac{2}{\sqrt{2}} = 1$$

$$\cot\theta = \frac{\dfrac{\sqrt{2}}{2}}{\dfrac{\sqrt{2}}{2}} = \frac{\sqrt{2}}{2} \cdot \frac{2}{\sqrt{2}} = 1$$

59. The point on the unit circle that corresponds to $\theta = -\dfrac{\pi}{6} = -30°$ is $\left(\dfrac{\sqrt{3}}{2}, -\dfrac{1}{2}\right)$.

$$\sin\theta = -\frac{1}{2} \qquad\qquad \csc\theta = \frac{1}{-\dfrac{1}{2}} = -2$$

$$\cos\theta = \frac{\sqrt{3}}{2} \qquad\qquad \sec\theta = \frac{1}{\dfrac{\sqrt{3}}{2}} = \frac{2}{\sqrt{3}} \cdot \frac{\sqrt{3}}{\sqrt{3}} = \frac{2\sqrt{3}}{3}$$

$$\tan\theta = \frac{-\dfrac{1}{2}}{\dfrac{\sqrt{3}}{2}} = -\frac{1}{2} \cdot \frac{2}{\sqrt{3}} \cdot \frac{\sqrt{3}}{\sqrt{3}} = -\frac{\sqrt{3}}{3} \qquad \cot\theta = \frac{\dfrac{\sqrt{3}}{2}}{-\dfrac{1}{2}} = \frac{\sqrt{3}}{2} \cdot \left(-\frac{2}{1}\right) = -\sqrt{3}$$

61. The point on the unit circle that corresponds to $\theta = -45° = -\dfrac{\pi}{4}$ is $\left(\dfrac{\sqrt{2}}{2}, -\dfrac{\sqrt{2}}{2}\right)$.

$$\sin\theta = -\frac{\sqrt{2}}{2} \qquad\qquad \csc\theta = \frac{1}{-\dfrac{\sqrt{2}}{2}} = -\frac{2}{\sqrt{2}} \cdot \frac{\sqrt{2}}{\sqrt{2}} = -\sqrt{2}$$

$$\cos\theta = \frac{\sqrt{2}}{2} \qquad\qquad \sec\theta = \frac{1}{\dfrac{\sqrt{2}}{2}} = \frac{2}{\sqrt{2}} \cdot \frac{\sqrt{2}}{\sqrt{2}} = \sqrt{2}$$

$$\tan\theta = \frac{-\dfrac{\sqrt{2}}{2}}{\dfrac{\sqrt{2}}{2}} = -\frac{\sqrt{2}}{2} \cdot \frac{2}{\sqrt{2}} = -1 \qquad \cot\theta = \frac{\dfrac{\sqrt{2}}{2}}{-\dfrac{\sqrt{2}}{2}} = \frac{\sqrt{2}}{2} \cdot \left(-\frac{2}{\sqrt{2}}\right) = -1$$

63. The point on the unit circle that corresponds to $\theta = \dfrac{5\pi}{2} = 450°$ is $(0, 1)$.

$$\sin\theta = 1 \qquad\qquad\qquad \csc\theta = \frac{1}{1} = 1$$

$$\cos\theta = 0 \qquad\qquad\qquad \sec\theta = \frac{1}{0}, \text{ not defined}$$

$$\tan\theta = \frac{1}{0}, \text{ not defined} \qquad \cot\theta = \frac{0}{1} = 0$$

65. The point on the unit circle that corresponds to $\theta = 720° = 4\pi$ is $(1, 0)$.

$$\sin\theta = 0 \qquad\qquad\qquad \csc\theta = \frac{1}{0}, \text{ not defined}$$

$$\cos\theta = 1 \qquad\qquad\qquad \sec\theta = \frac{1}{1} = 1$$

$$\tan\theta = \frac{0}{1} = 0 \qquad\qquad \cot\theta = \frac{1}{0}, \text{ not defined}$$

67. Set the calculator to degree mode: $\sin 28° \approx 0.47$.

69. Set the calculator to degree mode: $\tan 21° \approx 0.38$.

71. Set the calculator to degree mode: $\sec 41° = \dfrac{1}{\cos 41°} \approx 1.33$.

73. Set the calculator to radian mode: $\sin \dfrac{\pi}{10} \approx 0.31$.

75. Set the calculator to radian mode: $\tan \dfrac{5\pi}{12} \approx 3.73$.

77. Set the calculator to radian mode : $\sec \dfrac{\pi}{12} = \dfrac{1}{\cos \dfrac{\pi}{12}} \approx 1.04$.

79. Set the calculator to radian mode: $\sin 1 \approx 0.84$.

81. Set the calculator to degree mode: $\sin 1° \approx 0.02$.

83. For the point $(-3, 4)$, $x = -3$, $y = 4$, $r = \sqrt{x^2 + y^2} = \sqrt{9+16} = \sqrt{25} = 5$

$\sin\theta = \dfrac{y}{r} = \dfrac{4}{5}$ $\qquad \cos\theta = \dfrac{x}{r} = \dfrac{-3}{5} = -\dfrac{3}{5}$ $\qquad \tan\theta = \dfrac{y}{x} = \dfrac{4}{-3} = -\dfrac{4}{3}$

$\csc\theta = \dfrac{r}{y} = \dfrac{5}{4}$ $\qquad \sec\theta = \dfrac{r}{x} = \dfrac{5}{-3} = -\dfrac{5}{3}$ $\qquad \cot\theta = \dfrac{x}{y} = \dfrac{-3}{4} = -\dfrac{3}{4}$

85. For the point $(2, -3)$, $x = 2$, $y = -3$, $r = \sqrt{x^2 + y^2} = \sqrt{4+9} = \sqrt{13}$

$\sin\theta = \dfrac{y}{r} = \dfrac{-3}{\sqrt{13}} \cdot \dfrac{\sqrt{13}}{\sqrt{13}} = -\dfrac{3\sqrt{13}}{13}$ $\quad \cos\theta = \dfrac{x}{r} = \dfrac{2}{\sqrt{13}} \cdot \dfrac{\sqrt{13}}{\sqrt{13}} = \dfrac{2\sqrt{13}}{13}$ $\quad \tan\theta = \dfrac{y}{x} = \dfrac{-3}{2} = -\dfrac{3}{2}$

$\csc\theta = \dfrac{r}{y} = \dfrac{\sqrt{13}}{-3} = -\dfrac{\sqrt{13}}{3}$ $\qquad \sec\theta = \dfrac{r}{x} = \dfrac{\sqrt{13}}{2}$ $\qquad \cot\theta = \dfrac{x}{y} = \dfrac{2}{-3} = -\dfrac{2}{3}$

87. For the point $(-2, -2)$, $x = -2$, $y = -2$, $r = \sqrt{x^2 + y^2} = \sqrt{4+4} = \sqrt{8} = 2\sqrt{2}$

$\sin\theta = \dfrac{y}{r} = \dfrac{-2}{2\sqrt{2}} \cdot \dfrac{\sqrt{2}}{\sqrt{2}} = -\dfrac{\sqrt{2}}{2}$ $\quad \cos\theta = \dfrac{x}{r} = \dfrac{-2}{2\sqrt{2}} \cdot \dfrac{\sqrt{2}}{\sqrt{2}} = -\dfrac{\sqrt{2}}{2}$ $\quad \tan\theta = \dfrac{y}{x} = \dfrac{-2}{-2} = 1$

$\csc\theta = \dfrac{r}{y} = \dfrac{2\sqrt{2}}{-2} = -\sqrt{2}$ $\qquad \sec\theta = \dfrac{r}{x} = \dfrac{2\sqrt{2}}{-2} = -\sqrt{2}$ $\qquad \cot\theta = \dfrac{x}{y} = \dfrac{-2}{-2} = 1$

89. For the point $(-3, -2)$, $x = -3$, $y = -2$, $r = \sqrt{x^2 + y^2} = \sqrt{9 + 4} = \sqrt{13}$

$\sin\theta = \dfrac{y}{r} = \dfrac{-2}{\sqrt{13}} \cdot \dfrac{\sqrt{13}}{\sqrt{13}} = -\dfrac{2\sqrt{13}}{13}$ $\cos\theta = \dfrac{x}{r} = \dfrac{-3}{\sqrt{13}} \cdot \dfrac{\sqrt{13}}{\sqrt{13}} = -\dfrac{3\sqrt{13}}{13}$ $\tan\theta = \dfrac{y}{x} = \dfrac{-2}{-3} = \dfrac{2}{3}$

$\csc\theta = \dfrac{r}{y} = \dfrac{\sqrt{13}}{-2} = -\dfrac{\sqrt{13}}{2}$ $\sec\theta = \dfrac{r}{x} = \dfrac{\sqrt{13}}{-3} = -\dfrac{\sqrt{13}}{3}$ $\cot\theta = \dfrac{x}{y} = \dfrac{-3}{-2} = \dfrac{3}{2}$

91. For the point $\left(\dfrac{1}{3}, -\dfrac{1}{4}\right)$, $x = \dfrac{1}{3}$, $y = -\dfrac{1}{4}$, $r = \sqrt{x^2 + y^2} = \sqrt{\dfrac{1}{9} + \dfrac{1}{16}} = \sqrt{\dfrac{25}{144}} = \dfrac{5}{12}$

$\sin\theta = \dfrac{y}{r} = \dfrac{-\dfrac{1}{4}}{\dfrac{5}{12}} = -\dfrac{1}{4} \cdot \dfrac{12}{5} = -\dfrac{3}{5}$ $\cos\theta = \dfrac{x}{r} = \dfrac{\dfrac{1}{3}}{\dfrac{5}{12}} = \dfrac{1}{3} \cdot \dfrac{12}{5} = \dfrac{4}{5}$ $\tan\theta = \dfrac{y}{x} = \dfrac{-\dfrac{1}{4}}{\dfrac{1}{3}} = -\dfrac{1}{4} \cdot \dfrac{3}{1} = -\dfrac{3}{4}$

$\csc\theta = \dfrac{r}{y} = \dfrac{\dfrac{5}{12}}{-\dfrac{1}{4}} = \dfrac{5}{12} \cdot \left(-\dfrac{4}{1}\right) = -\dfrac{5}{3}$ $\sec\theta = \dfrac{r}{x} = \dfrac{\dfrac{5}{12}}{\dfrac{1}{3}} = \dfrac{5}{12} \cdot \dfrac{3}{1} = \dfrac{5}{4}$ $\cot\theta = \dfrac{x}{y} = \dfrac{\dfrac{1}{3}}{-\dfrac{1}{4}} = \dfrac{1}{3} \cdot \left(-\dfrac{4}{1}\right) = -\dfrac{4}{3}$

93. $\sin 45° + \sin 135° + \sin 225° + \sin 315°$

$= \sin\dfrac{\pi}{4} + \sin\dfrac{3\pi}{4} + \sin\dfrac{5\pi}{4} + \sin\dfrac{7\pi}{4}$

$= \dfrac{\sqrt{2}}{2} + \dfrac{\sqrt{2}}{2} + \left(-\dfrac{\sqrt{2}}{2}\right) + \left(-\dfrac{\sqrt{2}}{2}\right) = 0$

95. Given: $\sin\theta = 0.1 \Rightarrow$ θ in quadrant I or II

Therefore, $\theta + \pi$ is in quadrant III or IV $\Rightarrow$ $\sin(\theta + \pi) = -0.1$

97. Given: $\tan\theta = 3 \Rightarrow \theta$ in quadrant I or III

Therefore, $\theta + \pi$ is in quadrant III or I $\Rightarrow$ $\tan(\theta + \pi) = 3$

99. Given $\sin\theta = \dfrac{1}{5}$, then $\csc\theta = \dfrac{1}{\sin\theta} = \dfrac{1}{\dfrac{1}{5}} = 5$

101. $f(\theta) = \sin 60° = \dfrac{\sqrt{3}}{2}$

103. $f\left(\dfrac{\theta}{2}\right) = \sin\left(\dfrac{60°}{2}\right) = \sin 30° = \dfrac{1}{2}$

105. $[f(\theta)]^2 = [\sin 60°]^2 = \left(\dfrac{\sqrt{3}}{2}\right)^2 = \dfrac{3}{4}$

107. $f(2\theta) = \sin(2 \cdot 60°) = \sin 120° = \dfrac{\sqrt{3}}{2}$

109. $2f(\theta) = 2\sin 60° = 2 \cdot \dfrac{\sqrt{3}}{2} = \sqrt{3}$

111. $f(-\theta) = \sin(-60°) = -\dfrac{\sqrt{3}}{2}$

113. Complete the table:

θ	0.5	0.4	0.2	0.1	0.01	0.001	0.0001	0.00001
$\sin\theta$	0.4794	0.3894	0.1987	0.0998	0.0100	0.0010	0.0001	0.00001
$\dfrac{\sin\theta}{\theta}$	0.9589	0.9735	0.9933	0.9983	1.0000	1.0000	1.0000	1.0000

The ratio $\dfrac{\sin\theta}{\theta}$ approaches 1 as θ approaches 0.

115. Use the formula $R = \dfrac{v_0{}^2 \sin(2\theta)}{g}$ with $g = 32.2\,\text{ft}/\sec^2$; $\theta = 45°$; $v_0 = 100\,\text{ft}/\sec$:

$$R = \frac{100^2 \sin(2(45°))}{32.2} \approx 310.56 \text{ feet}$$

Use the formula $H = \dfrac{v_0{}^2 \sin^2\theta}{2g}$ with $g = 32.2\,\text{ft}/\sec^2$; $\theta = 45°$; $v_0 = 100\,\text{ft}/\sec$:

$$H = \frac{100^2 \sin^2(45°)}{2(32.2)} \approx 77.64 \text{ feet}$$

117. Use the formula $R = \dfrac{v_0{}^2 \sin(2\theta)}{g}$ with $g = 9.8\,\text{m}/\sec^2$; $\theta = 25°$; $v_0 = 500\,\text{m}/\sec$:

$$R = \frac{500^2 \sin(2(25°))}{9.8} \approx 19{,}542 \text{ meters}$$

Use the formula $H = \dfrac{v_0{}^2 \sin^2\theta}{2g}$ with $g = 9.8\,\text{m}/\sec^2$; $\theta = 25°$; $v_0 = 500\,\text{m}/\sec$:

$$H = \frac{500^2 \sin^2(25°)}{2(9.8)} \approx 2278 \text{ meters}$$

119. Use the formula $t = \sqrt{\dfrac{2a}{g\sin\theta\cos\theta}}$ with $g = 32\,\text{ft}/\sec^2$ and $a = 10$ feet :

(a) $t = \sqrt{\dfrac{2(10)}{32\sin(30°)\cos(30°)}} = \sqrt{\dfrac{20}{\left(32\cdot\dfrac{1}{2}\cdot\dfrac{\sqrt{3}}{2}\right)}} = \sqrt{\dfrac{20}{8\sqrt{3}}} = \sqrt{\dfrac{5}{2\sqrt{3}}} \approx 1.20 \text{ seconds}$

(b) $t = \sqrt{\dfrac{2(10)}{32\sin(45°)\cos(45°)}} = \sqrt{\dfrac{20}{\left(32\cdot\dfrac{\sqrt{2}}{2}\cdot\dfrac{\sqrt{2}}{2}\right)}} = \sqrt{\dfrac{20}{16}} = \sqrt{\dfrac{5}{4}} \approx 1.12 \text{ seconds}$

(c) $t = \sqrt{\dfrac{2(10)}{32\sin(60°)\cos(60°)}} = \sqrt{\dfrac{20}{\left(32\cdot\dfrac{\sqrt{3}}{2}\cdot\dfrac{1}{2}\right)}} = \sqrt{\dfrac{20}{8\sqrt{3}}} = \sqrt{\dfrac{5}{2\sqrt{3}}} \approx 1.20 \text{ seconds}$

121. (a) $T(30°) = 1 + \dfrac{2}{3\sin 30°} - \dfrac{1}{4\tan 30°} = 1 + \dfrac{2}{3 \cdot \dfrac{1}{2}} - \dfrac{1}{4 \cdot \dfrac{1}{\sqrt{3}}} = 1 + \dfrac{4}{3} - \dfrac{\sqrt{3}}{4} \approx 1.9$ hr

So Sally is on the paved road for $1 - \dfrac{1}{4\tan 30°} \approx 0.57$ hr.

(b) $T(45°) = 1 + \dfrac{2}{3\sin 45°} - \dfrac{1}{4\tan 45°} = 1 + \dfrac{2}{3 \cdot \dfrac{1}{\sqrt{2}}} - \dfrac{1}{4 \cdot 1} = 1 + \dfrac{2\sqrt{2}}{3} - \dfrac{1}{4} \approx 1.69$ hr

So Sally is on the paved road for $1 - \dfrac{1}{4\tan 45°} = 0.75$ hr.

(c) $T(60°) = 1 + \dfrac{2}{3\sin 60°} - \dfrac{1}{4\tan 60°} = 1 + \dfrac{2}{3 \cdot \dfrac{\sqrt{3}}{2}} - \dfrac{1}{4 \cdot \sqrt{3}}$

$= 1 + \dfrac{4}{3\sqrt{3}} - \dfrac{1}{4\sqrt{3}} \approx 1.63$ hr

So Sally is on the paved road for $1 - \dfrac{1}{4\tan 60°} \approx 0.86$ hr.

(d) $T(90°) = 1 + \dfrac{2}{3\sin 90°} - \dfrac{1}{4\tan 90°}$.

But $\tan 90°$ is undefined, so we can't use the function formula for this path.
The distance would be 2 miles in the sand and 8 miles on the road. The total time
would be: $\dfrac{2}{3} + 1 = \dfrac{5}{3} \approx 1.67$ hours.

123. (a) $R = \dfrac{\left(32^2\right)\sqrt{2}}{32} \cdot \left[\sin(2(60°)) - \cos(2(60°)) - 1\right] \approx 16.6$ ft

(b)   Graph:

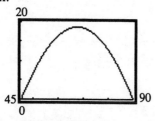

(c)   Using MAXIMUM, R is largest when $\theta \approx 67.5°$.

125–127. Answers will vary.

Trigonometric Functions

2.3   Properties of the Trigonometric Functions

1.   the set of all real numbers

3   the set of nonnegative real numbers   5. $2\pi, \pi$

7. $[-1,1]$ 9.   False

11. $\sin 405° = \sin(360° + 45°) = \sin 45° = \dfrac{\sqrt{2}}{2}$

$405° \times \dfrac{\pi}{180°}$

13. $\tan 405° = \tan(180° + 180° + 45°) = \tan 45° = 1$

15. $\csc 450° = \csc(360° + 90°) = \csc 90° = 1$

17. $\cot 390° = \cot(180° + 180° + 30°) = \cot 30° = \sqrt{3}$

19. $\cos\dfrac{33\pi}{4} = \cos\left(\dfrac{\pi}{4} + \dfrac{32\pi}{4}\right) = \cos\left(\dfrac{\pi}{4} + 8\pi\right) = \cos\left(\dfrac{\pi}{4} + 4 \cdot 2\pi\right) = \cos\dfrac{\pi}{4} = \dfrac{\sqrt{2}}{2}$

21. $\tan(21\pi) = \tan(0 + 21\pi) = \tan 0 = 0$

23. $\sec\dfrac{17\pi}{4} = \sec\left(\dfrac{\pi}{4} + \dfrac{16\pi}{4}\right) = \sec\left(\dfrac{\pi}{4} + 4\pi\right) = \sec\left(\dfrac{\pi}{4} + 2 \cdot 2\pi\right) = \sec\dfrac{\pi}{4} = \sqrt{2}$

25. $\tan\dfrac{19\pi}{6} = \tan\left(\dfrac{\pi}{6} + \dfrac{18\pi}{6}\right) = \tan\left(\dfrac{\pi}{6} + 3\pi\right) = \tan\dfrac{\pi}{6} = \dfrac{\sqrt{3}}{3}$

27. Since $\sin\theta > 0$ for points in quadrants I and II, and $\cos\theta < 0$ for points in quadrants II and III, the angle θ lies in quadrant II.

29. Since $\sin\theta < 0$ for points in quadrants III and IV, and $\tan\theta < 0$ for points in quadrants II and IV, the angle θ lies in quadrant IV.

31. Since $\cos\theta > 0$ for points in quadrants I and IV, and $\tan\theta < 0$ for points in quadrants II and IV, the angle θ lies in quadrant IV.

33. Since $\sec\theta < 0$ for points in quadrants II and III, and $\sin\theta > 0$ for points in quadrants I and II, the angle θ lies in quadrant II.

35. $\sin\theta = -\dfrac{3}{5}, \quad \cos\theta = \dfrac{4}{5}$

$$\tan\theta = \frac{\sin\theta}{\cos\theta} = \frac{-\dfrac{3}{5}}{\dfrac{4}{5}} = -\frac{3}{5}\cdot\frac{5}{4} = -\frac{3}{4}$$

$$\cot\theta = \frac{1}{\tan\theta} = -\frac{4}{3}$$

$$\sec\theta = \frac{1}{\cos\theta} = \frac{1}{\dfrac{4}{5}} = \frac{5}{4}$$

$$\csc\theta = \frac{1}{\sin\theta} = \frac{1}{-\dfrac{3}{5}} = -\frac{5}{3}$$

37. $\sin\theta = \dfrac{2\sqrt{5}}{5}, \quad \cos\theta = \dfrac{\sqrt{5}}{5}$

$$\tan\theta = \frac{\sin\theta}{\cos\theta} = \frac{\dfrac{2\sqrt{5}}{5}}{\dfrac{\sqrt{5}}{5}} = \frac{2\sqrt{5}}{5}\cdot\frac{5}{\sqrt{5}} = 2$$

$$\cot\theta = \frac{1}{\tan\theta} = \frac{1}{2}$$

$$\sec\theta = \frac{1}{\cos\theta} = \frac{1}{\dfrac{\sqrt{5}}{5}} = \frac{5}{\sqrt{5}}\cdot\frac{\sqrt{5}}{\sqrt{5}} = \sqrt{5}$$

$$\csc\theta = \frac{1}{\sin\theta} = \frac{1}{\dfrac{2\sqrt{5}}{5}} = \frac{5}{2\sqrt{5}}\cdot\frac{\sqrt{5}}{\sqrt{5}} = \frac{\sqrt{5}}{2}$$

39. $\sin\theta = \dfrac{1}{2}, \quad \cos\theta = \dfrac{\sqrt{3}}{2}$

$$\tan\theta = \frac{\sin\theta}{\cos\theta} = \frac{\dfrac{1}{2}}{\dfrac{\sqrt{3}}{2}} = \frac{1}{2}\cdot\frac{2}{\sqrt{3}}\cdot\frac{\sqrt{3}}{\sqrt{3}} = \frac{\sqrt{3}}{3}$$

$$\cot\theta = \frac{1}{\tan\theta} = \frac{1}{\dfrac{\sqrt{3}}{3}} = \frac{3}{\sqrt{3}}\cdot\frac{\sqrt{3}}{\sqrt{3}} = \sqrt{3}$$

$$\sec\theta = \frac{1}{\cos\theta} = \frac{1}{\dfrac{\sqrt{3}}{2}} = \frac{2}{\sqrt{3}}\cdot\frac{\sqrt{3}}{\sqrt{3}} = \frac{2\sqrt{3}}{3}$$

$$\csc\theta = \frac{1}{\sin\theta} = \frac{1}{\dfrac{1}{2}} = 2$$

41. $\sin\theta = -\dfrac{1}{3}, \quad \cos\theta = \dfrac{2\sqrt{2}}{3}$

$$\tan\theta = \frac{\sin\theta}{\cos\theta} = \frac{-\dfrac{1}{3}}{\dfrac{2\sqrt{2}}{3}} = -\frac{1}{3}\cdot\frac{3}{2\sqrt{2}}\cdot\frac{\sqrt{2}}{\sqrt{2}} = -\frac{\sqrt{2}}{4}$$

$$\cot\theta = \frac{1}{\tan\theta} = \frac{1}{-\dfrac{\sqrt{2}}{4}} = -\frac{4}{\sqrt{2}}\cdot\frac{\sqrt{2}}{\sqrt{2}} = -2\sqrt{2}$$

$$\sec\theta = \frac{1}{\cos\theta} = \frac{1}{\dfrac{2\sqrt{2}}{3}} = \frac{3}{2\sqrt{2}}\cdot\frac{\sqrt{2}}{\sqrt{2}} = \frac{3\sqrt{2}}{4}$$

$$\csc\theta = \frac{1}{\sin\theta} = \frac{1}{-\dfrac{1}{3}} = -3$$

43. $\sin\theta = \dfrac{12}{13},\;\; \theta$ in quadrant II

Solve for $\cos\theta$:
$$\sin^2\theta + \cos^2\theta = 1$$
$$\cos^2\theta = 1 - \sin^2\theta$$
$$\cos\theta = \pm\sqrt{1 - \sin^2\theta}$$

Since θ is in quadrant II, $\cos\theta < 0$.

$$\cos\theta = -\sqrt{1 - \sin^2\theta} = -\sqrt{1 - \left(\dfrac{12}{13}\right)^2} = -\sqrt{1 - \dfrac{144}{169}} = -\sqrt{\dfrac{25}{169}} = -\dfrac{5}{13}$$

$$\tan\theta = \dfrac{\sin\theta}{\cos\theta} = \dfrac{\dfrac{12}{13}}{-\dfrac{5}{13}} = \dfrac{12}{13}\cdot\left(-\dfrac{13}{5}\right) = -\dfrac{12}{5}$$

$$\cot\theta = \dfrac{1}{\tan\theta} = \dfrac{1}{-\dfrac{12}{5}} = -\dfrac{5}{12}$$

$$\sec\theta = \dfrac{1}{\cos\theta} = \dfrac{1}{-\dfrac{5}{13}} = -\dfrac{13}{5}$$

$$\csc\theta = \dfrac{1}{\sin\theta} = \dfrac{1}{\dfrac{12}{13}} = \dfrac{13}{12}$$

45. $\cos\theta = -\dfrac{4}{5},\;\; \theta$ in quadrant III

Solve for $\sin\theta$:
$$\sin^2\theta + \cos^2\theta = 1$$
$$\sin^2\theta = 1 - \cos^2\theta$$
$$\sin\theta = \pm\sqrt{1 - \cos^2\theta}$$

Since θ is in quadrant III, $\sin\theta < 0$.

$$\sin\theta = -\sqrt{1 - \cos^2\theta} = -\sqrt{1 - \left(-\dfrac{4}{5}\right)^2} = -\sqrt{1 - \dfrac{16}{25}} = -\sqrt{\dfrac{9}{25}} = -\dfrac{3}{5}$$

$$\tan\theta = \dfrac{\sin\theta}{\cos\theta} = \dfrac{-\dfrac{3}{5}}{-\dfrac{4}{5}} = -\dfrac{3}{5}\cdot\left(-\dfrac{5}{4}\right) = \dfrac{3}{4}$$

$$\cot\theta = \dfrac{1}{\tan\theta} = \dfrac{1}{\dfrac{3}{4}} = \dfrac{4}{3}$$

$$\sec\theta = \dfrac{1}{\cos\theta} = \dfrac{1}{-\dfrac{4}{5}} = -\dfrac{5}{4}$$

$$\csc\theta = \dfrac{1}{\sin\theta} = \dfrac{1}{-\dfrac{3}{5}} = -\dfrac{5}{3}$$

47. $\sin\theta = \dfrac{5}{13},\;\; 90° < \theta < 180° \Rightarrow \theta$ in quadrant II

Solve for $\cos\theta$:
$$\sin^2\theta + \cos^2\theta = 1$$
$$\cos^2\theta = 1 - \sin^2\theta$$
$$\cos\theta = \pm\sqrt{1 - \sin^2\theta}$$

Since θ is in quadrant II, $\cos\theta < 0$.

$$\cos\theta = -\sqrt{1 - \sin^2\theta} = -\sqrt{1 - \left(\dfrac{5}{13}\right)^2} = -\sqrt{1 - \dfrac{25}{169}} = -\sqrt{\dfrac{144}{169}} = -\dfrac{12}{13}$$

$$\tan\theta = \frac{\sin\theta}{\cos\theta} = \frac{\dfrac{5}{13}}{-\dfrac{12}{13}} = \frac{5}{13}\cdot\left(-\frac{13}{12}\right) = -\frac{5}{12}$$

$$\cot\theta = \frac{1}{\tan\theta} = \frac{1}{-\dfrac{5}{12}} = -\frac{12}{5}$$

$$\sec\theta = \frac{1}{\cos\theta} = \frac{1}{-\dfrac{12}{13}} = -\frac{13}{12}$$

$$\csc\theta = \frac{1}{\sin\theta} = \frac{1}{\dfrac{5}{13}} = \frac{13}{5}$$

49. $\cos\theta = -\dfrac{1}{3}$, $\dfrac{\pi}{2} < \theta < \pi \Rightarrow \theta$ in quadrant II

Solve for $\sin\theta$:
$$\sin^2\theta + \cos^2\theta = 1$$
$$\sin^2\theta = 1 - \cos^2\theta$$
$$\sin\theta = \pm\sqrt{1 - \cos^2\theta}$$

Since θ is in quadrant II, $\sin\theta > 0$.

$$\sin\theta = \sqrt{1 - \cos^2\theta} = \sqrt{1 - \left(-\frac{1}{3}\right)^2} = \sqrt{1 - \frac{1}{9}} = \sqrt{\frac{8}{9}} = \frac{2\sqrt{2}}{3}$$

$$\tan\theta = \frac{\sin\theta}{\cos\theta} = \frac{\dfrac{2\sqrt{2}}{3}}{-\dfrac{1}{3}} = \frac{2\sqrt{2}}{3}\cdot\left(-\frac{3}{1}\right) = -2\sqrt{2}$$

$$\cot\theta = \frac{1}{\tan\theta} = \frac{1}{-2\sqrt{2}}\cdot\frac{\sqrt{2}}{\sqrt{2}} = -\frac{\sqrt{2}}{4}$$

$$\sec\theta = \frac{1}{\cos\theta} = \frac{1}{-\dfrac{1}{3}} = -3$$

$$\csc\theta = \frac{1}{\sin\theta} = \frac{1}{\dfrac{2\sqrt{2}}{3}} = \frac{3}{2\sqrt{2}}\cdot\frac{\sqrt{2}}{\sqrt{2}} = \frac{3\sqrt{2}}{4}$$

51. $\sin\theta = \dfrac{2}{3}$, $\tan\theta < 0 \Rightarrow \theta$ in quadrant II

Solve for $\cos\theta$:
$$\sin^2\theta + \cos^2\theta = 1$$
$$\cos^2\theta = 1 - \sin^2\theta$$
$$\cos\theta = \pm\sqrt{1 - \sin^2\theta}$$

Since θ is in quadrant II, $\cos\theta < 0$.

$$\cos\theta = -\sqrt{1 - \sin^2\theta} = -\sqrt{1 - \left(\frac{2}{3}\right)^2} = -\sqrt{1 - \frac{4}{9}} = -\sqrt{\frac{5}{9}} = -\frac{\sqrt{5}}{3}$$

$$\tan\theta = \frac{\sin\theta}{\cos\theta} = \frac{\dfrac{2}{3}}{-\dfrac{\sqrt{5}}{3}} = \frac{2}{3}\cdot\left(-\frac{3}{\sqrt{5}}\right)\cdot\frac{\sqrt{5}}{\sqrt{5}} = -\frac{2\sqrt{5}}{5}$$

$$\cot\theta = \frac{1}{\tan\theta} = \frac{1}{-\dfrac{2\sqrt{5}}{5}} = -\frac{5}{2\sqrt{5}}\cdot\frac{\sqrt{5}}{\sqrt{5}} = -\frac{\sqrt{5}}{2}$$

$$\sec\theta = \frac{1}{\cos\theta} = \frac{1}{-\dfrac{\sqrt{5}}{3}} = -\frac{3}{\sqrt{5}}\cdot\frac{\sqrt{5}}{\sqrt{5}} = -\frac{3\sqrt{5}}{5}$$

$$\csc\theta = \frac{1}{\sin\theta} = \frac{1}{\dfrac{2}{3}} = \frac{3}{2}$$

53. $\sec\theta = 2, \quad \sin\theta < 0 \Rightarrow \theta$ in quadrant IV

Solve for $\cos\theta$:
$$\cos\theta = \frac{1}{\sec\theta} = \frac{1}{2}$$

Solve for $\sin\theta$:
$$\sin^2\theta + \cos^2\theta = 1$$
$$\sin^2\theta = 1 - \cos^2\theta$$
$$\sin\theta = \pm\sqrt{1 - \cos^2\theta}$$

$$\sin\theta = -\sqrt{1 - \cos^2\theta} = -\sqrt{1 - \left(\frac{1}{2}\right)^2} = -\sqrt{1 - \frac{1}{4}} = -\sqrt{\frac{3}{4}} = -\frac{\sqrt{3}}{2}$$

$$\tan\theta = \frac{\sin\theta}{\cos\theta} = \frac{-\frac{\sqrt{3}}{2}}{\frac{1}{2}} = -\frac{\sqrt{3}}{2} \cdot \frac{2}{1} = -\sqrt{3} \qquad \cot\theta = \frac{1}{\tan\theta} = \frac{1}{-\sqrt{3}} \cdot \frac{\sqrt{3}}{\sqrt{3}} = -\frac{\sqrt{3}}{3}$$

$$\csc\theta = \frac{1}{\sin\theta} = \frac{1}{-\frac{\sqrt{3}}{2}} = -\frac{2}{\sqrt{3}} \cdot \frac{\sqrt{3}}{\sqrt{3}} = -\frac{2\sqrt{3}}{3}$$

55. $\tan\theta = \frac{3}{4}, \quad \sin\theta < 0 \Rightarrow \theta$ in quadrant III

Solve for $\sec\theta$:
$$\sec^2\theta = 1 + \tan^2\theta$$
$$\sec\theta = \pm\sqrt{1 + \tan^2\theta}$$

Since θ is in quadrant III, $\sec\theta < 0$.

$$\sec\theta = -\sqrt{1 + \tan^2\theta} = -\sqrt{1 + \left(\frac{3}{4}\right)^2} = -\sqrt{1 + \frac{9}{16}} = -\sqrt{\frac{25}{16}} = -\frac{5}{4}$$

$$\cos\theta = \frac{1}{\sec\theta} = \frac{1}{-\frac{5}{4}} = -\frac{4}{5}$$

$$\sin\theta = -\sqrt{1 - \cos^2\theta} = -\sqrt{1 - \left(-\frac{4}{5}\right)^2} = -\sqrt{1 - \frac{16}{25}} = -\sqrt{\frac{9}{25}} = -\frac{3}{5}$$

$$\csc\theta = \frac{1}{\sin\theta} = \frac{1}{-\frac{3}{5}} = -\frac{5}{3} \qquad \cot\theta = \frac{1}{\tan\theta} = \frac{1}{\frac{3}{4}} = \frac{4}{3}$$

57. $\tan\theta = -\frac{1}{3}, \quad \sin\theta > 0 \Rightarrow \theta$ in quadrant II

Solve for $\sec\theta$:
$$\sec^2\theta = 1 + \tan^2\theta$$
$$\sec\theta = \pm\sqrt{1 + \tan^2\theta}$$

Since θ is in quadrant II, $\sec\theta < 0$.

$$\sec\theta = -\sqrt{1+\tan^2\theta} = -\sqrt{1+\left(-\frac{1}{3}\right)^2} = -\sqrt{1+\frac{1}{9}} = -\sqrt{\frac{10}{9}} = -\frac{\sqrt{10}}{3}$$

$$\cos\theta = \frac{1}{\sec\theta} = \frac{1}{-\dfrac{\sqrt{10}}{3}} = -\frac{3}{\sqrt{10}}\cdot\frac{\sqrt{10}}{\sqrt{10}} = -\frac{3\sqrt{10}}{10}$$

$\sin\theta > 0$ was given.

$$\sin\theta = \sqrt{1-\cos^2\theta} = \sqrt{1-\left(-\frac{3\sqrt{10}}{10}\right)^2} = \sqrt{1-\frac{90}{100}} = \sqrt{\frac{10}{100}} = \frac{\sqrt{10}}{10}$$

$$\csc\theta = \frac{1}{\sin\theta} = \frac{1}{\dfrac{\sqrt{10}}{10}} = \frac{10}{\sqrt{10}}\cdot\frac{\sqrt{10}}{\sqrt{10}} = \sqrt{10} \qquad\qquad \cot\theta = \frac{1}{\tan\theta} = \frac{1}{-\dfrac{1}{3}} = -3$$

59. $\sin(-60°) = -\sin 60° = -\dfrac{\sqrt{3}}{2}$ 　　　　61. $\tan(-30°) = -\tan 30° = -\dfrac{\sqrt{3}}{3}$

63. $\sec(-60°) = \sec 60° = 2$ 　　　　65. $\sin(-90°) = -\sin 90° = -1$

67. $\tan\left(-\dfrac{\pi}{4}\right) = -\tan\dfrac{\pi}{4} = -1$ 　　　　69. $\cos\left(-\dfrac{\pi}{4}\right) = \cos\dfrac{\pi}{4} = \dfrac{\sqrt{2}}{2}$

71. $\tan(-\pi) = -\tan\pi = 0$ 　　　　73. $\csc\left(-\dfrac{\pi}{4}\right) = -\csc\dfrac{\pi}{4} = -\sqrt{2}$

75. $\sec\left(-\dfrac{\pi}{6}\right) = \sec\dfrac{\pi}{6} = \dfrac{2\sqrt{3}}{3}$ 　　　　77. $\sin^2 40° + \cos^2 40° = 1$

79. $\sin 80°\csc 80° = \sin 80°\cdot\dfrac{1}{\sin 80°} = 1$ 　　81. $\tan 40° - \dfrac{\sin 40°}{\cos 40°} = \tan 40° - \tan 40° = 0$

83. $\cos 400°\cdot\sec 40° = \cos(40°+360°)\cdot\sec 40° = \cos 40°\cdot\sec 40° = \cos 40°\cdot\dfrac{1}{\cos 40°} = 1$

85. $\sin\left(-\dfrac{\pi}{12}\right)\csc\dfrac{25\pi}{12} = -\sin\dfrac{\pi}{12}\csc\dfrac{25\pi}{12} = -\sin\dfrac{\pi}{12}\csc\left(\dfrac{\pi}{12}+\dfrac{24\pi}{12}\right)$

$$= -\sin\dfrac{\pi}{12}\csc\left(\dfrac{\pi}{12}+2\pi\right) = -\sin\dfrac{\pi}{12}\csc\dfrac{\pi}{12} = -\sin\dfrac{\pi}{12}\cdot\dfrac{1}{\sin\dfrac{\pi}{12}} = -1$$

87. $\dfrac{\sin(-20°)}{\cos 380°} + \tan 200° = \dfrac{-\sin 20°}{\cos(20°+360°)} + \tan(20°+180°)$

$$= \dfrac{-\sin 20°}{\cos 20°} + \tan 20° = -\tan 20° + \tan 20° = 0$$

89.   If $\sin\theta = 0.3$, then $\sin\theta + \sin(\theta + 2\pi) + \sin(\theta + 4\pi) = 0.3 + 0.3 + 0.3 = 0.9$

91.   If $\tan\theta = 3$, then $\tan\theta + \tan(\theta + \pi) + \tan(\theta + 2\pi) = 3 + 3 + 3 = 9$

93. $\sin 1° + \sin 2° + \sin 3° + \cdots + \sin 357° + \sin 358° + \sin 359°$
       $= \sin 1° + \sin 2° + \sin 3° + \cdots + \sin(360° - 3°) + \sin(360° - 2°) + \sin(360° - 1°)$
       $= \sin 1° + \sin 2° + \sin 3° + \cdots + \sin(-3°) + \sin(-2°) + \sin(-1°)$
       $= \sin 1° + \sin 2° + \sin 3° + \cdots - \sin 3° - \sin 2° - \sin 2° = \sin 180° = 0$

95.   The domain of the sine function is the set of all real numbers.

97. $f(\theta) = \tan\theta$ is not defined for numbers that are odd multiples of $\frac{\pi}{2}$.

99. $f(\theta) = \sec\theta$ is not defined for numbers that are odd multiples of $\frac{\pi}{2}$.

101.   The range of the sine function is the set of all real numbers between -1 and 1, inclusive.

103.   The range of the tangent function is the set of all real numbers.

105.   The range of the secant function is the set of all real number greater than or equal to 1 and all real numbers less than or equal to -1.

107.   The sine function is odd because $\sin(-\theta) = -\sin\theta$. Its graph is symmetric with respect to the origin.

109.   The tangent function is odd because $\tan(-\theta) = -\tan\theta$. Its graph is symmetric with respect to the origin.

111.   The secant function is even because $\sec(-\theta) = \sec\theta$. Its graph is symmetric with respect to the y-axis.

113.   (a) $f(-a) = -f(a) = -\frac{1}{3}$

       (b) $f(a) + f(a + 2\pi) + f(a + 4\pi) = f(a) + f(a) + f(a) = \frac{1}{3} + \frac{1}{3} + \frac{1}{3} = 1$

115.   (a) $f(-a) = -f(a) = -2$
       (b) $f(a) + f(a + \pi) + f(a + 2\pi) = f(a) + f(a) + f(a) = 2 + 2 + 2 = 6$

117.   (a) $f(-a) = f(a) = -4$
       (b) $f(a) + f(a + 2\pi) + f(a + 4\pi) = f(a) + f(a) + f(a) = -4 + (-4) + (-4) = -12$

119. Since $\tan\theta = \dfrac{500}{1500} = \dfrac{1}{3} = \dfrac{y}{x}$, for $0 < \theta < \dfrac{\pi}{2}$. $r^2 = x^2 + y^2 = 9 + 1 = 10 \Rightarrow r = \sqrt{10}$.

Thus, $\sin\theta = \dfrac{1}{\sqrt{10}}$

$T = 5 - \dfrac{5}{3 \cdot \dfrac{1}{3}} + \dfrac{5}{\dfrac{1}{\sqrt{10}}} = 5 - 5 + 5\sqrt{10} = 5\sqrt{10} \approx 15.8$ minutes

121. Let $P = (x, y)$ be the point on the unit circle that corresponds to an angle θ.

Consider the equation $\tan\theta = \dfrac{y}{x} = a$. Then $y = ax$. Now $x^2 + y^2 = 1$, so $x^2 + a^2 x^2 = 1$.

Thus, $x = \pm\dfrac{1}{\sqrt{1 + a^2}}$ and $y = \pm\dfrac{a}{\sqrt{1 + a^2}}$; that is, for any real number a, there is a point

$P = (x, y)$ on the unit circle for which $\tan\theta = a$. In other words, $-\infty < \tan\theta < \infty$, and the range of the tangent function is the set of all real numbers.

123. Suppose there is a number p, $0 < p < 2\pi$, for which $\sin(\theta + p) = \sin\theta$ for all θ. If

$\theta = 0$, then $\sin(0 + p) = \sin p = \sin 0 = 0$; so that $p = \pi$. If $\theta = \dfrac{\pi}{2}$, then $\sin\left(\dfrac{\pi}{2} + p\right) = \sin\left(\dfrac{\pi}{2}\right)$.

But $p = \pi$. Thus, $\sin\left(\dfrac{3\pi}{2}\right) = -1 = \sin\left(\dfrac{\pi}{2}\right) = 1$, or $-1 = 1$. This is impossible. The smallest

positive number p for which $\sin(\theta + p) = \sin\theta$ for all θ is therefore $p = 2\pi$.

125. $\sec\theta = \dfrac{1}{\cos\theta}$: since $\cos\theta$ has period 2π, so does $\sec\theta$.

127. If $P = (a, b)$ is the point on the unit circle corresponding to θ, then $Q = (-a, -b)$ is the point on

the unit circle corresponding to $\theta + \pi$. Thus, $\tan(\theta + \pi) = \dfrac{-b}{-a} = \dfrac{b}{a} = \tan\theta$. If there exists a

number p, $0 < p < \pi$, for which $\tan(\theta + p) = \tan\theta$ for all θ, then $\theta = 0 \Rightarrow \tan(p) = \tan(0) = 0$.

But this means that p is a multiple of π. Since no multiple of π exists in the interval $(0, \pi)$, this is impossible. Therefore, the period of $f(\theta) = \tan\theta$ is π.

129. Let $P = (a, b)$ be the point on the unit circle corresponding to θ.

Then $\csc\theta = \dfrac{1}{b} = \dfrac{1}{\sin\theta}$; $\sec\theta = \dfrac{1}{a} = \dfrac{1}{\cos\theta}$; $\cot\theta = \dfrac{a}{b} = \dfrac{1}{\dfrac{b}{a}} = \dfrac{1}{\tan\theta}$.

131. $(\sin\theta\cos\phi)^2 + (\sin\theta\sin\phi)^2 + \cos^2\theta$

$= \sin^2\theta\cos^2\phi + \sin^2\theta\sin^2\phi + \cos^2\theta$

$= \sin^2\theta(\cos^2\phi + \sin^2\phi) + \cos^2\theta$

$= \sin^2\theta + \cos^2\theta$

$= 1$

133–135. Answers will vary.

Trigonometric Functions

2.4   Graphs of the Sine and Cosine Functions

1. $y = 3x^2$
   Using the graph of $y = x^2$, vertically stretch the graph by a factor of 3.

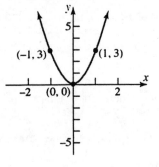

3. $1; ..., -\dfrac{3\pi}{2}, \dfrac{\pi}{2}, \dfrac{5\pi}{2}, \dfrac{9\pi}{2}, ...$

5. $3; \dfrac{2\pi}{6} = \dfrac{\pi}{3}$

7.   False

9.   0

11.   The graph of $y = \sin x$ is increasing for $-\dfrac{\pi}{2} < x < \dfrac{\pi}{2}$.

13.   The largest value of $y = \sin x$ is 1.

15. $\sin x = 0$ when $x = 0, \pi, 2\pi$.

17. $\sin x = 1$ when $x = -\dfrac{3\pi}{2}, \dfrac{\pi}{2}$; $\sin x = -1$ when $x = -\dfrac{\pi}{2}, \dfrac{3\pi}{2}$.

19.   B, C, F

21. $y = 3\sin x$; The graph of $y = \sin x$ is stretched vertically by a factor of 3.

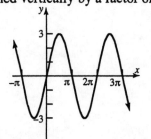

23. $y = -\cos x$; The graph of $y = \cos x$ is reflected across the x-axis.

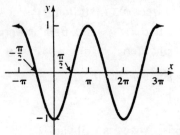

25. $y = \sin x - 1$; The graph of $y = \sin x$ is shifted down 1 unit.

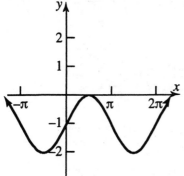

27. $y = \sin(x - \pi)$; The graph of $y = \sin x$ is shifted right π units.

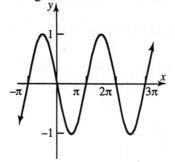

29. $y = \sin(\pi x)$; The graph of $y = \sin x$ is compressed horizontally by a factor of $\dfrac{1}{\pi}$.

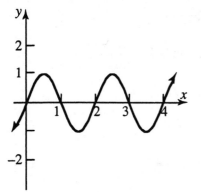

31. $y = 2\sin x + 2$; The graph of $y = \sin x$ is stretched vertically by a factor of 2 and shifted up 2 units.

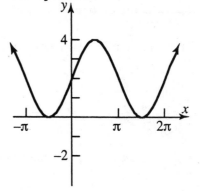

33. $y = 4\cos(2x)$; The graph of $y = \cos x$ is compressed horizontally by a factor of $\dfrac{1}{2}$, then stretched vertically by a factor of 4.

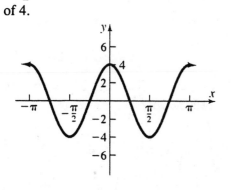

35. $y = -2\sin x + 2$; The graph of $y = \sin x$ is stretched vertically by a factor of 2, reflected across the x-axis, then shifted up 2 units.

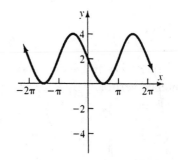

37. $y = 2\sin x$

This is in the form $y = A\sin(\omega x)$ where $A = 2$ and $\omega = 1$.

Thus, the amplitude is $|A| = |2| = 2$ and the period is $T = \dfrac{2\pi}{\omega} = \dfrac{2\pi}{1} = 2\pi$.

39. $y = -4\cos(2x)$

This is in the form $y = A\cos(\omega x)$ where $A = -4$ and $\omega = 2$.

Thus, the amplitude is $|A| = |-4| = 4$ and the period is $T = \dfrac{2\pi}{\omega} = \dfrac{2\pi}{2} = \pi$.

41. $y = 6\sin(\pi x)$

This is in the form $y = A\sin(\omega x)$ where $A = 6$ and $\omega = \pi$.

Thus, the amplitude is $|A| = |6| = 6$ and the period is $T = \dfrac{2\pi}{\omega} = \dfrac{2\pi}{\pi} = 2$.

43. $y = -\dfrac{1}{2}\cos\left(\dfrac{3}{2}x\right)$

This is in the form $y = A\cos(\omega x)$ where $A = -\dfrac{1}{2}$ and $\omega = \dfrac{3}{2}$.

Thus, the amplitude is $|A| = \left|-\dfrac{1}{2}\right| = \dfrac{1}{2}$ and the period is $T = \dfrac{2\pi}{\omega} = \dfrac{2\pi}{\dfrac{3}{2}} = \dfrac{4\pi}{3}$.

45. $y = \dfrac{5}{3}\sin\left(-\dfrac{2\pi}{3}x\right) = -\dfrac{5}{3}\sin\left(\dfrac{2\pi}{3}x\right)$

This is in the form $y = A\sin(\omega x)$ where $A = -\dfrac{5}{3}$ and $\omega = \dfrac{2\pi}{3}$.

Thus, the amplitude is $|A| = \left|-\dfrac{5}{3}\right| = \dfrac{5}{3}$ and the period is $T = \dfrac{2\pi}{\omega} = \dfrac{2\pi}{\dfrac{2\pi}{3}} = 3$.

47. F   49. A   51. H   53. C

55. J   57. A   59. B

61. $y = 5\sin(4x)$ $A = 5;\ \ T = \dfrac{\pi}{2}$ 63. $y = 5\cos(\pi x)$ $A = 5;\ \ T = 2$

65. $y = -2\cos(2\pi x)$ $A = -2;\ T = 1$ 67. $y = -4\sin\left(\dfrac{1}{2}x\right)$ $A = -4;\ T = 4\pi$

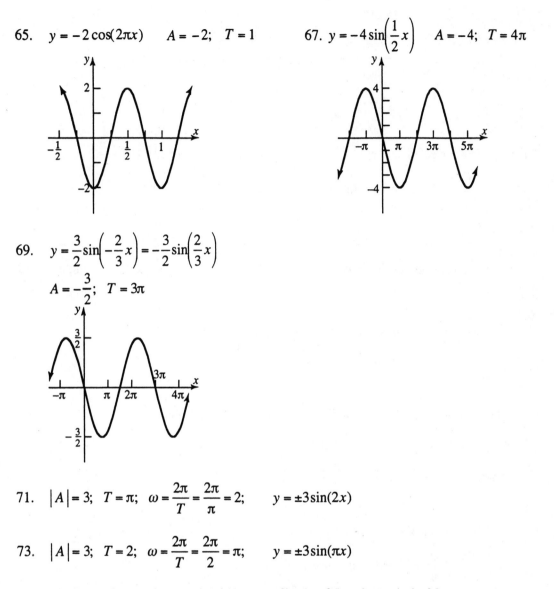

69. $y = \dfrac{3}{2}\sin\left(-\dfrac{2}{3}x\right) = -\dfrac{3}{2}\sin\left(\dfrac{2}{3}x\right)$

$A = -\dfrac{3}{2};\ T = 3\pi$

71. $|A| = 3;\ T = \pi;\ \omega = \dfrac{2\pi}{T} = \dfrac{2\pi}{\pi} = 2;\qquad y = \pm 3\sin(2x)$

73. $|A| = 3;\ T = 2;\ \omega = \dfrac{2\pi}{T} = \dfrac{2\pi}{2} = \pi;\qquad y = \pm 3\sin(\pi x)$

75. The graph is a cosine graph with an amplitude of 5 and a period of 8.

Find ω: $8 = \dfrac{2\pi}{\omega} \Rightarrow 8\omega = 2\pi \Rightarrow \omega = \dfrac{2\pi}{8} = \dfrac{\pi}{4}$

The equation is: $y = 5\cos\left(\dfrac{\pi}{4}x\right)$.

77. The graph is a reflected cosine graph with an amplitude of 3 and a period of 4π.

Find ω: $4\pi = \dfrac{2\pi}{\omega} \Rightarrow 4\pi\omega = 2\pi \Rightarrow \omega = \dfrac{2\pi}{4\pi} = \dfrac{1}{2}$

The equation is: $y = -3\cos\left(\dfrac{1}{2}x\right)$.

89

79.   The graph is a sine graph with an amplitude of $\frac{3}{4}$ and a period of 1.

Find ω: $1 = \frac{2\pi}{\omega} \Rightarrow \omega = 2\pi$

The equation is: $y = \frac{3}{4}\sin(2\pi x)$.

81.   The graph is a reflected sine graph with an amplitude of 1 and a period of $\frac{4\pi}{3}$.

Find ω: $\frac{4\pi}{3} = \frac{2\pi}{\omega} \Rightarrow 4\pi\omega = 6\pi \Rightarrow \omega = \frac{6\pi}{4\pi} = \frac{3}{2}$

The equation is: $y = -\sin\left(\frac{3}{2}x\right)$.

83.   The graph is a reflected cosine graph, shifted up 1 unit, with an amplitude of 1 and a period of $\frac{3}{2}$.

Find ω: $\frac{3}{2} = \frac{2\pi}{\omega} \Rightarrow 3\omega = 4\pi \Rightarrow \omega = \frac{4\pi}{3}$

The equation is: $y = -\cos\left(\frac{4\pi}{2}x\right) + 1$

85.   The graph is a sine graph with an amplitude of 3 and a period of 4.

Find ω: $4 = \frac{2\pi}{\omega} \Rightarrow 4\omega = 2\pi \Rightarrow \omega = \frac{2\pi}{4} = \frac{\pi}{2}$

The equation is: $y = 3\sin\left(\frac{\pi}{2}x\right)$.

87.   The graph is a reflected cosine graph with an amplitude of 4 and a period of $\frac{2\pi}{3}$.

Find ω: $\frac{2\pi}{3} = \frac{2\pi}{\omega} \Rightarrow 2\pi\omega = 6\pi \Rightarrow \omega = \frac{6\pi}{2\pi} = 3$

The equation is: $y = -4\cos(3x)$.

89. $I = 220\sin(60\pi t),\ t \geq 0$

Period: $T = \frac{2\pi}{\omega} = \frac{2\pi}{60\pi} = \frac{1}{30}$

Amplitude: $|A| = |220| = 220$

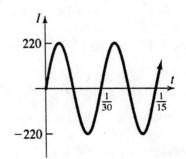

91. $V = 220\sin(120\pi t)$

   (a)   Amplitude: $|A| = |220| = 220$

   Period: $T = \dfrac{2\pi}{\omega} = \dfrac{2\pi}{120\pi} = \dfrac{1}{60}$

   (b), (e)

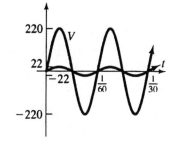

   (c) $V = IR$

   $220\sin(120\pi t) = 10I$

   $22\sin(120\pi t) = I$

   (d)   Amplitude: $|A| = |22| = 22$

   Period: $T = \dfrac{2\pi}{\omega} = \dfrac{2\pi}{120\pi} = \dfrac{1}{60}$

93. (a) $P = \dfrac{V^2}{R} = \dfrac{\left(V_0\sin(2\pi f)t\right)^2}{R} = \dfrac{V_0^2\sin^2(2\pi f)t}{R} = \dfrac{V_0^2}{R}\sin^2(2\pi ft)$

   (b)   The graph is the reflected cosine graph translated up a distance equivalent to the amplitude. The period is $\dfrac{1}{2f}$, so $\omega = 4\pi f$. The amplitude is $\dfrac{1}{2}\cdot\dfrac{V_0^2}{R} = \dfrac{V_0^2}{2R}$.

   The equation is: $P = -\dfrac{V_0^2}{2R}\cos(4\pi f)t + \dfrac{V_0^2}{2R} = \dfrac{V_0^2}{R}\dfrac{1}{2}\left(1 - \cos(4\pi f)t\right)$

   (c)   Comparing the formulas:

   $\sin^2(2\pi ft) = \dfrac{1}{2}\left(1 - \cos(4\pi ft)\right)$

95. $y = |\cos x|, \quad -2\pi \le x \le 2\pi$

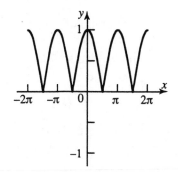

97–101.   Answers will vary.

Trigonometric Functions

2.5   Graphs of the Tangent, Cotangent, Cosecant, and Secant Functions

1. $x = 4$

3.   origin; $x = \ldots, -\dfrac{3\pi}{2}, -\dfrac{\pi}{2}, \dfrac{\pi}{2}, \dfrac{3\pi}{2}, \ldots$

5. $y = \cos x$

7.   0

9.   1

11. $\sec x = 1$ for $x = -2\pi, 0, 2\pi;$ $\sec x = -1$ for $x = -\pi, \pi$

13. $y = \sec x$ has vertical asymptotes for $x = -\dfrac{3\pi}{2}, -\dfrac{\pi}{2}, \dfrac{\pi}{2}, \dfrac{3\pi}{2}$

15. $y = \tan x$ has vertical asymptotes for $x = -\dfrac{3\pi}{2}, -\dfrac{\pi}{2}, \dfrac{\pi}{2}, \dfrac{3\pi}{2}$

17.   D

19.   B

21. $y = -\sec x$; The graph of $y = \sec x$ is reflected across the x-axis.

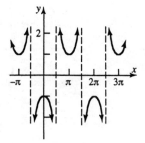

23. $y = \sec\left(x - \dfrac{\pi}{2}\right)$; The graph of $y = \sec x$ is shifted right $\dfrac{\pi}{2}$ units.

25. $y = \tan(x - \pi)$; The graph of $y = \tan x$ is shifted right π units.

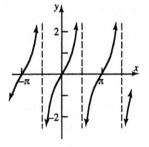

27. $y = 3\tan(2x)$; The graph of $y = \tan x$ is compressed horizontally by a factor of $\dfrac{1}{2}$ and stretched vertically by a factor of 3.

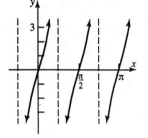

29. $y = \sec(2x)$; The graph of $y = \sec x$ is compressed horizontally by a factor of $\dfrac{1}{2}$.

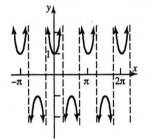

31. $y = \cot(\pi x)$; The graph of $y = \cot x$ is compressed horizontally by a factor of $\dfrac{1}{\pi}$.

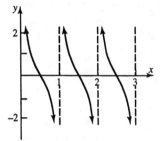

33. $y = -3\tan(4x)$; The graph of $y = \tan x$ is compressed horizontally by a factor of $\dfrac{1}{4}$, stretched vertically by a factor of 3 and reflected across the x-axis.

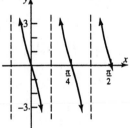

35. $y = 2\sec\left(\dfrac{1}{2}x\right)$; The graph of $y = \sec x$ is stretched horizontally by a factor of 2, and stretched vertically by a factor of 2.

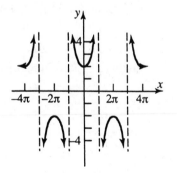

37. $y = -3\csc\left(x + \dfrac{\pi}{4}\right)$; The graph of $y = \csc x$ is shifted left $\dfrac{\pi}{4}$ units, stretched vertically by a factor of 3 and reflected across the x-axis.

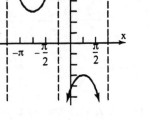

39. $y = \dfrac{1}{2}\cot\left(x - \dfrac{\pi}{4}\right)$; The graph of $y = \cot x$ is shifted right $\dfrac{\pi}{4}$ units and compressed vertically by a factor of $\dfrac{1}{2}$.

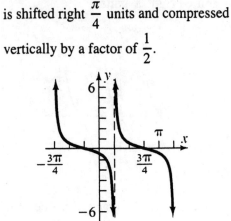

41. (a) Consider the length of the line segment in two sections, x, the portion across the hall that is 3 feet wide and y, the portion across that hall that is 4 feet wide. Then,

$$\cos\theta = \frac{3}{x} \ \Rightarrow \ x = \frac{3}{\cos\theta} \quad \text{and} \quad \sin\theta = \frac{4}{y} \ \Rightarrow \ y = \frac{4}{\sin\theta}$$

$$L = x + y = \frac{3}{\cos\theta} + \frac{4}{\sin\theta}$$

(b) Graph:

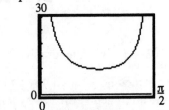

(c) Use MINIMUM to find the least value: L is least when $\theta = 0.83$.

(d) $L \approx \dfrac{3}{\cos(0.83)} + \dfrac{4}{\sin(0.83)} \approx 9.86 \text{ feet}$. Note that rounding up will result in a ladder that won't fit around the corner. Answers will vary.

Trigonometric Functions

2.6   Phase Shift; Sinusoidal Curve Fitting

1.   phase shift

3. $y = 4\sin(2x - \pi)$

 Amplitude : $|A| = |4| = 4$

 Period: $T = \dfrac{2\pi}{\omega} = \dfrac{2\pi}{2} = \pi$

 Phase Shift: $\dfrac{\phi}{\omega} = \dfrac{\pi}{2}$

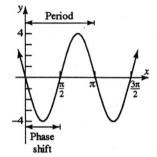

5. $y = 2\cos\left(3x + \dfrac{\pi}{2}\right)$

 Amplitude : $|A| = |2| = 2$

 Period : $T = \dfrac{2\pi}{\omega} = \dfrac{2\pi}{3}$

 Phase Shift : $\dfrac{\phi}{\omega} = \dfrac{-\dfrac{\pi}{2}}{3} = -\dfrac{\pi}{6}$

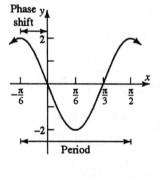

7. $y = -3\sin\left(2x + \dfrac{\pi}{2}\right)$

 Amplitude : $|A| = |-3| = 3$

 Period : $T = \dfrac{2\pi}{\omega} = \dfrac{2\pi}{2} = \pi$

 Phase Shift : $\dfrac{\phi}{\omega} = \dfrac{-\dfrac{\pi}{2}}{2} = -\dfrac{\pi}{4}$

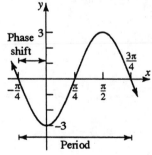

9. $y = 4\sin(\pi x + 2)$

Amplitude: $|A| = |4| = 4$

Period: $T = \dfrac{2\pi}{\omega} = \dfrac{2\pi}{\pi} = 2$

Phase Shift: $\dfrac{\phi}{\omega} = \dfrac{-2}{\pi} = -\dfrac{2}{\pi}$

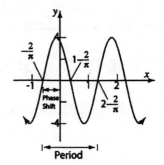

11. $y = 3\cos(\pi x - 2)$

Amplitude: $|A| = |3| = 3$

Period: $T = \dfrac{2\pi}{\omega} = \dfrac{2\pi}{\pi} = 2$

Phase Shift: $\dfrac{\phi}{\omega} = \dfrac{2}{\pi}$

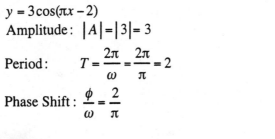

13. $y = 3\sin\left(-2x + \dfrac{\pi}{2}\right) = 3\sin\left(-\left(2x - \dfrac{\pi}{2}\right)\right)$

$\qquad\qquad = -3\sin\left(2x - \dfrac{\pi}{2}\right)$

Amplitude: $|A| = |-3| = 3$

Period: $T = \dfrac{2\pi}{\omega} = \dfrac{2\pi}{2} = \pi$

Phase Shift: $\dfrac{\phi}{\omega} = \dfrac{\frac{\pi}{2}}{2} = \dfrac{\pi}{4}$

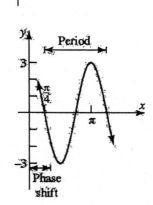

15. $|A| = 2;\;\; T = \pi;\;\; \dfrac{\phi}{\omega} = \dfrac{1}{2};\;\; \omega = \dfrac{2\pi}{T} = \dfrac{2\pi}{\pi} = 2;\;\; \dfrac{\phi}{\omega} = \dfrac{\phi}{2} = \dfrac{1}{2} \Rightarrow \phi = 1$

$y = \pm 2\sin(2x - 1) = \pm 2\sin\left[2\left(x - \dfrac{1}{2}\right)\right]$

17. $|A| = 3;\;\; T = 3\pi;\;\; \dfrac{\phi}{\omega} = -\dfrac{1}{3};\;\; \omega = \dfrac{2\pi}{T} = \dfrac{2\pi}{3\pi} = \dfrac{2}{3};$

$\dfrac{\phi}{\omega} = \dfrac{\phi}{\frac{2}{3}} = -\dfrac{1}{3} \Rightarrow \phi = -\dfrac{1}{3} \cdot \dfrac{2}{3} = -\dfrac{2}{9}$

$y = \pm 3\sin\left(\dfrac{2}{3}x + \dfrac{2}{9}\right) = \pm 3\sin\left[\dfrac{2}{3}\left(x + \dfrac{1}{3}\right)\right]$

19. $I = 120\sin\left(30\pi t - \dfrac{\pi}{3}\right), \quad t \ge 0$

Period : $T = \dfrac{2\pi}{\omega} = \dfrac{2\pi}{30\pi} = \dfrac{1}{15}$

Amplitude : $|A| = |120| = 120$

Phase Shift : $\dfrac{\phi}{\omega} = \dfrac{\frac{\pi}{3}}{30\pi} = \dfrac{1}{90}$

21. (a)   Draw a scatter diagram:

(b)   Amplitude : $A = \dfrac{56.0 - 24.2}{2} = \dfrac{31.8}{2} = 15.9$

Vertical Shift : $\dfrac{56.0 + 24.2}{2} = \dfrac{80.2}{2} = 40.1$

$\omega = \dfrac{2\pi}{12} = \dfrac{\pi}{6}$

Phase shift (use $y = 24.2$, $x = 1$):

$24.2 = 15.9\sin\left(\dfrac{\pi}{6}\cdot 1 - \phi\right) + 40.1$

$-15.9 = 15.9\sin\left(\dfrac{\pi}{6} - \phi\right)$

$-1 = \sin\left(\dfrac{\pi}{6} - \phi\right)$

$-\dfrac{\pi}{2} = \dfrac{\pi}{6} - \phi$

$\phi = \dfrac{2\pi}{3}$

Thus, $y = 15.9\sin\left(\dfrac{\pi}{6}x - \dfrac{2\pi}{3}\right) + 40.1$.

(c)

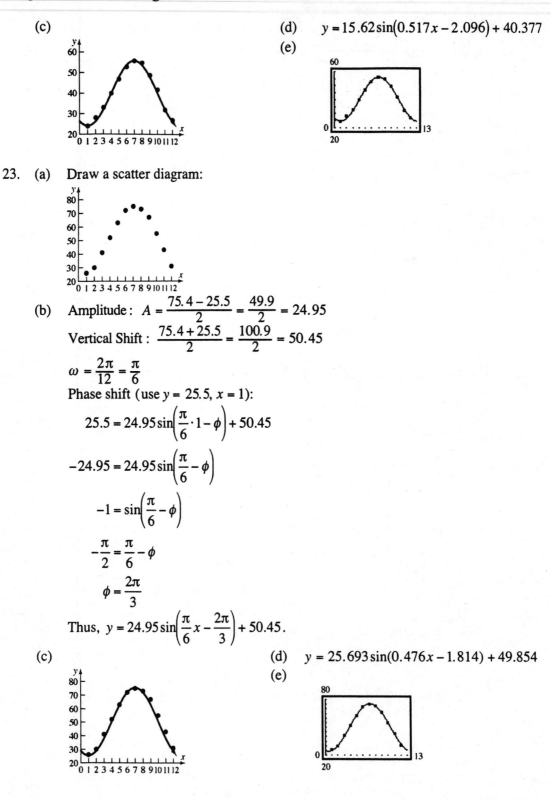

(d) $y = 15.62\sin(0.517x - 2.096) + 40.377$

(e)

23.   (a)   Draw a scatter diagram:

(b)   Amplitude : $A = \dfrac{75.4 - 25.5}{2} = \dfrac{49.9}{2} = 24.95$

Vertical Shift : $\dfrac{75.4 + 25.5}{2} = \dfrac{100.9}{2} = 50.45$

$\omega = \dfrac{2\pi}{12} = \dfrac{\pi}{6}$

Phase shift (use $y = 25.5$, $x = 1$):

$25.5 = 24.95\sin\left(\dfrac{\pi}{6} \cdot 1 - \phi\right) + 50.45$

$-24.95 = 24.95\sin\left(\dfrac{\pi}{6} - \phi\right)$

$-1 = \sin\left(\dfrac{\pi}{6} - \phi\right)$

$-\dfrac{\pi}{2} = \dfrac{\pi}{6} - \phi$

$\phi = \dfrac{2\pi}{3}$

Thus, $y = 24.95\sin\left(\dfrac{\pi}{6}x - \dfrac{2\pi}{3}\right) + 50.45$.

(c)

(d) $y = 25.693\sin(0.476x - 1.814) + 49.854$

(e)

25. (a) $3.6333 + 12.5 = 16.1333$ hours which is at 4:08 PM.

(b) Amplitude: $A = \dfrac{8.2 - (-0.6)}{2} = \dfrac{8.8}{2} = 4.4$

Vertical Shift: $\dfrac{8.2 + (-0.6)}{2} = \dfrac{7.6}{2} = 3.8$

$\omega = \dfrac{2\pi}{12.5} = \dfrac{\pi}{6.25}$

Phase shift (use $y = -0.6$, $x = 10.1333$):

$-0.6 = 4.4 \sin\left(\dfrac{\pi}{6.25} \cdot 10.1333 - \phi\right) + 3.8$

$-4.4 = 4.4 \sin\left(\dfrac{\pi}{6.25} \cdot 10.1333 - \phi\right)$

$-1 = \sin\left(\dfrac{10.1333\pi}{6.25} - \phi\right)$

$-\dfrac{\pi}{2} = \dfrac{10.1333\pi}{6.25} - \phi \Rightarrow \phi \approx 6.6643$

Thus, $y = 4.4 \sin\left(\dfrac{\pi}{6.25} x - 6.6643\right) + 3.8$

(c)

(d) $y = 4.4 \sin\left(\dfrac{\pi}{6.25}(16.1333) - 6.6643\right) + 3.8 \approx 8.2$ feet

27. (a) Amplitude: $A = \dfrac{12.75 - 10.583}{2} = \dfrac{2.167}{2} = 1.0835$

Vertical Shift: $\dfrac{12.75 + 10.583}{2} = \dfrac{23.333}{2} = 11.6665$

$\omega = \dfrac{2\pi}{365}$

Phase shift (use $y = 10.583$, $x = 355$):

$10.583 = 1.0835 \sin\left(\dfrac{2\pi}{365} \cdot 355 - \phi\right) + 11.6665$

$-1.0835 = 1.0835 \sin\left(\dfrac{2\pi}{365} \cdot 355 - \phi\right)$

$-1 = \sin\left(\dfrac{710\pi}{365} - \phi\right)$

$-\dfrac{\pi}{2} = \dfrac{710\pi}{365} - \phi \Rightarrow \phi \approx 7.6818$

Thus, $y = 1.0835 \sin\left(\dfrac{2\pi}{365} x - 7.6818\right) + 11.6665$.

(b) $y = 1.0835 \sin\left(\dfrac{2\pi}{365}(91) - 7.6818\right) + 11.6665 \approx 11.85$ hours

(c)

(d)   Answers will vary.

29. (a)   Amplitude : $A = \dfrac{16.233 - 5.45}{2} = \dfrac{10.783}{2} = 5.3915$

Vertical Shift : $\dfrac{16.233 + 5.45}{2} = \dfrac{21.683}{2} = 10.8415$

$\omega = \dfrac{2\pi}{365}$

Phase shift (use $y = 5.45$, $x = 355$):

$$5.45 = 5.3915 \sin\left(\dfrac{2\pi}{365} \cdot 355 - \phi\right) + 10.8415$$

$$-5.3915 = 5.3915 \sin\left(\dfrac{2\pi}{365} \cdot 355 - \phi\right)$$

$$-1 = \sin\left(\dfrac{710\pi}{365} - \phi\right)$$

$$-\dfrac{\pi}{2} = \dfrac{710\pi}{365} - \phi$$

$$\phi \approx 7.6818$$

Thus, $y = 5.3915 \sin\left(\dfrac{2\pi}{365} x - 7.6818\right) + 10.8415$.

(b) $y = 5.3915 \sin\left(\dfrac{2\pi}{365}(91) - 7.6818\right) + 10.8415 \approx 11.74$ hours

(c)

(d)   Answers will vary.

31.   Answers will vary.

Trigonometric Functions

2.R   Chapter Review

1. $135° = 135 \cdot \dfrac{\pi}{180}$ radian $= \dfrac{3\pi}{4}$ radians

3. $18° = 18 \cdot \dfrac{\pi}{180}$ radian $= \dfrac{\pi}{10}$ radian

5. $\dfrac{3\pi}{4} = \dfrac{3\pi}{4} \cdot \dfrac{180}{\pi}$ degrees $= 135°$

7. $-\dfrac{5\pi}{2} = -\dfrac{5\pi}{2} \cdot \dfrac{180}{\pi}$ degrees $= -450°$

9. $\tan\dfrac{\pi}{4} - \sin\dfrac{\pi}{6} = 1 - \dfrac{1}{2} = \dfrac{1}{2}$

11. $3\sin 45° - 4\tan\dfrac{\pi}{6} = 3 \cdot \dfrac{\sqrt{2}}{2} - 4 \cdot \dfrac{\sqrt{3}}{3} = \dfrac{3\sqrt{2}}{2} - \dfrac{4\sqrt{3}}{3}$

13. $6\cos\dfrac{3\pi}{4} + 2\tan\left(-\dfrac{\pi}{3}\right) = 6\left(-\dfrac{\sqrt{2}}{2}\right) + 2\left(-\sqrt{3}\right) = -3\sqrt{2} - 2\sqrt{3}$

15. $\sec\left(-\dfrac{\pi}{3}\right) - \cot\left(-\dfrac{5\pi}{4}\right) = \sec\dfrac{\pi}{3} + \cot\dfrac{5\pi}{4} = 2 + 1 = 3$

17. $\tan\pi + \sin\pi = 0 + 0 = 0$

19. $\cos 540° - \tan(-45°) = -1 - (-1) = -1 + 1 = 0$

21. $\sin^2 20° + \dfrac{1}{\sec^2 20°} = \sin^2 20° + \cos^2 20° = 1$

23. $\sec 50° \cdot \cos 50° = \dfrac{1}{\cos 50°} \cdot \cos 50° = 1$

25. $\sec^2 20° - \tan^2 20° = \tan^2 20° + 1 - \tan^2 20° = 1$

27. $\sin(-40°) \cdot \csc(40°) = -\sin(40°) \cdot \dfrac{1}{\sin(40°)} = -1$

29. $\cos(410°) \cdot \sec(-50°) = \cos(360°+50°) \cdot \sec(50°) = \cos(50°) \cdot \dfrac{1}{\cos(50°)} = 1$

31. $\sin\theta = \dfrac{4}{5}$, θ acute $\Rightarrow \theta$ in quadrant I

Solve for $\cos\theta$:

$$\sin^2\theta + \cos^2\theta = 1$$
$$\cos^2\theta = 1 - \sin^2\theta$$
$$\cos\theta = \pm\sqrt{1 - \sin^2\theta}$$

Since θ is in quadrant I, $\cos\theta > 0$.

$$\cos\theta = \sqrt{1 - \sin^2\theta} = \sqrt{1 - \left(\dfrac{4}{5}\right)^2} = \sqrt{1 - \dfrac{16}{25}} = \sqrt{\dfrac{9}{25}} = \dfrac{3}{5}$$

$$\tan\theta = \dfrac{\sin\theta}{\cos\theta} = \dfrac{\frac{4}{5}}{\frac{3}{5}} = \dfrac{4}{5} \cdot \dfrac{5}{3} = \dfrac{4}{3} \qquad \cot\theta = \dfrac{1}{\tan\theta} = \dfrac{1}{\frac{4}{3}} = \dfrac{3}{4}$$

$$\sec\theta = \dfrac{1}{\cos\theta} = \dfrac{1}{\frac{3}{5}} = \dfrac{5}{3} \qquad\qquad \csc\theta = \dfrac{1}{\sin\theta} = \dfrac{1}{\frac{4}{5}} = \dfrac{5}{4}$$

33. $\tan\theta = \dfrac{12}{5}$, $\sin\theta < 0 \Rightarrow \theta$ in quadrant III

Solve for $\sec\theta$:

$$\sec^2\theta = \tan^2\theta + 1$$
$$\sec\theta = \pm\sqrt{\tan^2\theta + 1}$$

Since θ is in quadrant III, $\sec\theta < 0$.

$$\sec\theta = -\sqrt{\tan^2\theta + 1} = -\sqrt{\left(\dfrac{12}{5}\right)^2 + 1} = -\sqrt{\dfrac{144}{25} + 1} = -\sqrt{\dfrac{169}{25}} = -\dfrac{13}{5}$$

$$\cos\theta = \dfrac{1}{\sec\theta} = \dfrac{1}{-\frac{13}{5}} = -\dfrac{5}{13}$$

Solve for $\sin\theta$:

$$\sin^2\theta + \cos^2\theta = 1$$
$$\sin^2\theta = 1 - \cos^2\theta$$
$$\sin\theta = \pm\sqrt{1 - \cos^2\theta}$$

Since θ is in quadrant III, $\sin\theta < 0$.

$$\sin\theta = -\sqrt{1 - \cos^2\theta} = -\sqrt{1 - \left(-\dfrac{5}{13}\right)^2} = -\sqrt{1 - \dfrac{25}{169}} = -\sqrt{\dfrac{144}{169}} = -\dfrac{12}{13}$$

$$\cot\theta = \frac{1}{\tan\theta} = \frac{1}{\dfrac{12}{5}} = \frac{5}{12} \qquad\qquad \csc\theta = \frac{1}{\sin\theta} = \frac{1}{-\dfrac{12}{13}} = -\frac{13}{12}$$

35. $\sec\theta = -\dfrac{5}{4}, \quad \tan\theta < 0 \Rightarrow \theta$ in quadrant II

Solve for $\tan\theta$:
$$\tan^2\theta + 1 = \sec^2\theta$$
$$\tan\theta = \pm\sqrt{\sec^2\theta - 1}$$

Since θ is in quadrant II, $\tan\theta < 0$.

$$\tan\theta = -\sqrt{\sec^2\theta - 1} = -\sqrt{\left(-\frac{5}{4}\right)^2 - 1} = -\sqrt{\frac{25}{16} - 1} = -\sqrt{\frac{9}{16}} = -\frac{3}{4}$$

$$\cos\theta = \frac{1}{\sec\theta} = \frac{1}{-\dfrac{5}{4}} = -\frac{4}{5}$$

Solve for $\sin\theta$:
$$\sin^2\theta + \cos^2\theta = 1$$
$$\sin^2\theta = 1 - \cos^2\theta$$
$$\sin\theta = \pm\sqrt{1 - \cos^2\theta}$$

Since θ is in quadrant II, $\sin\theta > 0$.

$$\sin\theta = \sqrt{1 - \cos^2\theta} = \sqrt{1 - \left(-\frac{4}{5}\right)^2} = \sqrt{1 - \frac{16}{25}} = \sqrt{\frac{9}{25}} = \frac{3}{5}$$

$$\cot\theta = \frac{1}{\tan\theta} = \frac{1}{-\dfrac{1}{4}} = -\frac{4}{3} \qquad\qquad \csc\theta = \frac{1}{\sin\theta} = \frac{1}{\dfrac{3}{5}} = \frac{5}{3}$$

37. $\sin\theta = \dfrac{12}{13}, \quad \theta$ in quadrant II

Solve for $\cos\theta$:
$$\sin^2\theta + \cos^2\theta = 1$$
$$\cos^2\theta = 1 - \sin^2\theta$$
$$\cos\theta = \pm\sqrt{1 - \sin^2\theta}$$

Since θ is in quadrant II, $\cos\theta < 0$.

$$\cos\theta = -\sqrt{1 - \sin^2\theta} = -\sqrt{1 - \left(\frac{12}{13}\right)^2} = -\sqrt{1 - \frac{144}{169}} = -\sqrt{\frac{25}{169}} = -\frac{5}{13}$$

$$\tan\theta = \frac{\sin\theta}{\cos\theta} = \frac{\dfrac{12}{13}}{-\dfrac{5}{13}} = \frac{12}{13}\cdot\left(-\frac{13}{5}\right) = -\frac{12}{5} \qquad\qquad \cot\theta = \frac{1}{\tan\theta} = \frac{1}{-\dfrac{12}{5}} = -\frac{5}{12}$$

$$\sec\theta = \frac{1}{\cos\theta} = \frac{1}{-\dfrac{5}{13}} = -\frac{13}{5} \qquad\qquad \csc\theta = \frac{1}{\sin\theta} = \frac{1}{\dfrac{12}{13}} = \frac{13}{12}$$

39. $\sin\theta = -\dfrac{5}{13}, \quad \dfrac{3\pi}{2} < \theta < 2\pi \Rightarrow \theta$ in quadrant IV

Solve for $\cos\theta$:
$$\sin^2\theta + \cos^2\theta = 1$$
$$\cos^2\theta = 1 - \sin^2\theta$$
$$\cos\theta = \pm\sqrt{1 - \sin^2\theta}$$

Since θ is in quadrant IV, $\cos\theta > 0$.

$$\cos\theta = \sqrt{1 - \sin^2\theta} = \sqrt{1 - \left(-\dfrac{5}{13}\right)^2} = \sqrt{1 - \dfrac{25}{169}} = \sqrt{\dfrac{144}{169}} = \dfrac{12}{13}$$

$$\tan\theta = \dfrac{\sin\theta}{\cos\theta} = \dfrac{-\dfrac{5}{13}}{\dfrac{12}{13}} = -\dfrac{5}{13}\cdot\left(\dfrac{13}{12}\right) = -\dfrac{5}{12} \qquad \cot\theta = \dfrac{1}{\tan\theta} = \dfrac{1}{-\dfrac{5}{12}} = -\dfrac{12}{5}$$

$$\sec\theta = \dfrac{1}{\cos\theta} = \dfrac{1}{\dfrac{12}{13}} = \dfrac{13}{12} \qquad\qquad \csc\theta = \dfrac{1}{\sin\theta} = \dfrac{1}{-\dfrac{5}{13}} = -\dfrac{13}{5}$$

41. $\tan\theta = \dfrac{1}{3}, \quad 180° < \theta < 270° \Rightarrow \theta$ in quadrant III

Solve for $\sec\theta$:
$$\sec^2\theta = \tan^2\theta + 1$$
$$\sec\theta = \pm\sqrt{\tan^2\theta + 1}$$

Since θ is in quadrant III, $\sec\theta < 0$.

$$\sec\theta = -\sqrt{\tan^2\theta + 1} = -\sqrt{\left(\dfrac{1}{3}\right)^2 + 1} = -\sqrt{\dfrac{1}{9} + 1} = -\sqrt{\dfrac{10}{9}} = -\dfrac{\sqrt{10}}{3}$$

$$\cos\theta = \dfrac{1}{\sec\theta} = \dfrac{1}{-\dfrac{\sqrt{10}}{3}} = -\dfrac{3}{\sqrt{10}}\cdot\dfrac{\sqrt{10}}{\sqrt{10}} = -\dfrac{3\sqrt{10}}{10}$$

Solve for $\sin\theta$:
$$\sin^2\theta + \cos^2\theta = 1$$
$$\sin^2\theta = 1 - \cos^2\theta$$
$$\sin\theta = \pm\sqrt{1 - \cos^2\theta}$$

Since θ is in quadrant III, $\sin\theta < 0$.

$$\sin\theta = -\sqrt{1 - \cos^2\theta} = -\sqrt{1 - \left(-\dfrac{3}{\sqrt{10}}\right)^2} = -\sqrt{1 - \dfrac{9}{10}} = -\sqrt{\dfrac{1}{10}} = -\dfrac{1}{\sqrt{10}}\cdot\dfrac{\sqrt{10}}{\sqrt{10}} = -\dfrac{\sqrt{10}}{10}$$

$$\cot\theta = \dfrac{1}{\tan\theta} = \dfrac{1}{\dfrac{1}{3}} = 3 \qquad\qquad \csc\theta = \dfrac{1}{\sin\theta} = \dfrac{1}{-\dfrac{1}{\sqrt{10}}} = -\sqrt{10}$$

43. $\sec\theta = 3$, $\dfrac{3\pi}{2} < \theta < 2\pi \Rightarrow \theta$ in quadrant IV

Solve for $\tan\theta$:

$$\tan^2\theta + 1 = \sec^2\theta$$

$$\tan\theta = \pm\sqrt{\sec^2\theta - 1}$$

Since θ is in quadrant IV, $\tan\theta < 0$.

$$\tan\theta = -\sqrt{\sec^2\theta - 1} = -\sqrt{3^2 - 1} = -\sqrt{9 - 1} = -\sqrt{8} = -2\sqrt{2}$$

$$\cos\theta = \frac{1}{\sec\theta} = \frac{1}{3}$$

Solve for $\sin\theta$:

$$\sin^2\theta + \cos^2\theta = 1$$

$$\sin^2\theta = 1 - \cos^2\theta$$

$$\sin\theta = \pm\sqrt{1 - \cos^2\theta}$$

Since θ is in quadrant IV, $\sin\theta < 0$.

$$\sin\theta = -\sqrt{1 - \cos^2\theta} = -\sqrt{1 - \left(\frac{1}{3}\right)^2} = -\sqrt{1 - \frac{1}{9}} = -\sqrt{\frac{8}{9}} = -\frac{\sqrt{8}}{3} = -\frac{2\sqrt{2}}{3}$$

$$\cot\theta = \frac{1}{\tan\theta} = \frac{1}{-2\sqrt{2}} \cdot \frac{\sqrt{2}}{\sqrt{2}} = -\frac{\sqrt{2}}{4}$$

$$\csc\theta = \frac{1}{\sin\theta} = \frac{1}{-\dfrac{2\sqrt{2}}{3}} = -\frac{3}{2\sqrt{2}} \cdot \frac{\sqrt{2}}{\sqrt{2}} = -\frac{3\sqrt{2}}{4}$$

45. $\cot\theta = -2$, $\dfrac{\pi}{2} < \theta < \pi \Rightarrow \theta$ in quadrant II

Solve for $\csc\theta$:

$$\csc^2\theta = \cot^2\theta + 1$$

$$\csc\theta = \pm\sqrt{\cot^2\theta + 1}$$

Since θ is in quadrant II, $\csc\theta > 0$.

$$\csc\theta = \sqrt{\cot^2\theta + 1} = \sqrt{(-2)^2 + 1} = \sqrt{4 + 1} = \sqrt{5}$$

$$\sin\theta = \frac{1}{\csc\theta} = \frac{1}{\sqrt{5}} \cdot \frac{\sqrt{5}}{\sqrt{5}} = \frac{\sqrt{5}}{5}$$

Solve for $\cos\theta$:

$$\sin^2\theta + \cos^2\theta = 1$$

$$\cos^2\theta = 1 - \sin^2\theta$$

$$\cos\theta = \pm\sqrt{1 - \sin^2\theta}$$

Since θ is in quadrant II, $\cos\theta < 0$.

$$\cos\theta = -\sqrt{1 - \sin^2\theta} = -\sqrt{1 - \left(\frac{1}{\sqrt{5}}\right)^2} = -\sqrt{1 - \frac{1}{5}} = -\sqrt{\frac{4}{5}} = -\frac{2}{\sqrt{5}} \cdot \frac{\sqrt{5}}{\sqrt{5}} = -\frac{2\sqrt{5}}{5}$$

$$\tan\theta = \frac{1}{\cot\theta} = \frac{1}{-2} = -\frac{1}{2}$$

$$\sec\theta = \frac{1}{\cos\theta} = \frac{1}{-\dfrac{2}{\sqrt{5}}} = -\frac{\sqrt{5}}{2}$$

47. $y = 2\sin(4x)$ The graph of $y = \sin x$ is stretched vertically by a factor of 2 and compressed horizontally by a factor of $\dfrac{1}{4}$.

49. $y = -2\cos\left(x + \dfrac{\pi}{2}\right)$ The graph of $y = \cos x$ is shifted $\dfrac{\pi}{2}$ units to the left, stretched vertically by a factor of 2, and reflected across the x-axis.

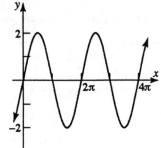

51. $y = \tan(x + \pi)$ The graph of $y = \tan x$ is shifted π units to the left.

53. $y = -2\tan(3x)$ The graph of $y = \tan x$ is stretched vertically by a factor of 2, reflected across the x-axis, and compressed horizontally by a factor of $\dfrac{1}{3}$.

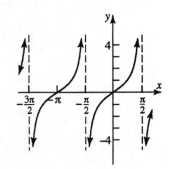

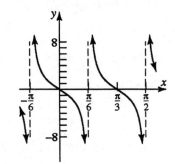

55. $y = \cot\left(x + \dfrac{\pi}{4}\right)$ The graph of $y = \cot x$ is shifted $\dfrac{\pi}{4}$ units to the left.

57. $y = \sec\left(x - \dfrac{\pi}{4}\right)$ The graph of $y = \sec x$ is shifted $\dfrac{\pi}{4}$ units to the right.

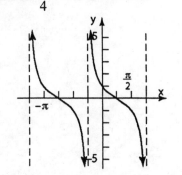

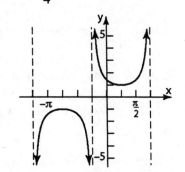

59. $y = 4\cos x$

Amplitude $= |4| = 4$

Period $= 2\pi$

61. $y = -8\sin\left(\dfrac{\pi}{2}x\right)$

Amplitude $= |-8| = 8$

Period $= \dfrac{2\pi}{\dfrac{\pi}{2}} = 4$

63. $y = 4\sin(3x)$

Amplitude: $|A| = |4| = 4$

Period: $T = \dfrac{2\pi}{\omega} = \dfrac{2\pi}{3}$

Phase Shift: $\dfrac{\phi}{\omega} = \dfrac{0}{3} = 0$

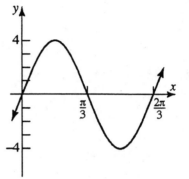

65. $y = 2\sin(2x - \pi)$

Amplitude: $|A| = |2| = 2$

Period: $T = \dfrac{2\pi}{\omega} = \dfrac{2\pi}{2} = \pi$

Phase Shift: $\dfrac{\phi}{\omega} = \dfrac{\pi}{2} = \dfrac{\pi}{2}$

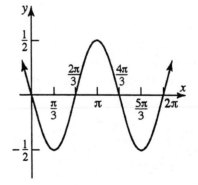

67. $y = \dfrac{1}{2}\sin\left(\dfrac{3}{2}x - \pi\right)$

Amplitude: $|A| = \left|\dfrac{1}{2}\right| = \dfrac{1}{2}$

Period: $T = \dfrac{2\pi}{\omega} = \dfrac{2\pi}{\dfrac{3}{2}} = \dfrac{4\pi}{3}$

Phase Shift: $\dfrac{\phi}{\omega} = \dfrac{\pi}{\dfrac{3}{2}} = \dfrac{2\pi}{3}$

69. $y = -\dfrac{2}{3}\cos(\pi x - 6)$

Amplitude: $|A| = \left|-\dfrac{2}{3}\right| = \dfrac{2}{3}$

Period: $T = \dfrac{2\pi}{\omega} = \dfrac{2\pi}{\pi} = 2$

Phase Shift: $\dfrac{\phi}{\omega} = \dfrac{6}{\pi}$

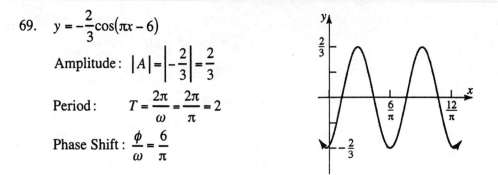

71. The graph is a cosine graph with an amplitude of 5 and a period of 8π.

Find ω: $8\pi = \dfrac{2\pi}{\omega} \Rightarrow 8\pi\omega = 2\pi \Rightarrow \omega = \dfrac{2\pi}{8\pi} = \dfrac{1}{4}$

The equation is: $y = 5\cos\left(\dfrac{1}{4}x\right)$.

73. The graph is a reflected cosine graph with an amplitude of 6 and a period of 8.

Find ω: $8 = \dfrac{2\pi}{\omega} \Rightarrow 8\omega = 2\pi \Rightarrow \omega = \dfrac{2\pi}{8} = \dfrac{\pi}{4}$

The equation is: $y = -6\cos\left(\dfrac{\pi}{4}x\right)$.

75. Use calculator in radian mode: $\sin\dfrac{\pi}{8} \approx 0.38$

77. θ in quadrant III $\Rightarrow \sin\theta < 0$, $\cos\theta < 0$, $\sec\theta < 0$, $\csc\theta < 0$, $\tan\theta > 0$, and $\cot\theta > 0$.

79. $P = \left(-\dfrac{1}{3}, \dfrac{2\sqrt{2}}{3}\right) \Rightarrow x = -\dfrac{1}{3},\ y = \dfrac{2\sqrt{2}}{3}$

$\sin t = y = \dfrac{2\sqrt{2}}{3}$
$\qquad\qquad\qquad$
$\csc t = \dfrac{1}{y} = \dfrac{1}{\dfrac{2\sqrt{2}}{3}} = \dfrac{3}{2\sqrt{2}} \cdot \dfrac{\sqrt{2}}{\sqrt{2}} = \dfrac{3\sqrt{2}}{4}$

$\cos t = x = -\dfrac{1}{3}$
$\qquad\qquad\qquad$
$\sec t = \dfrac{1}{x} = \dfrac{1}{-\dfrac{1}{3}} = -3$

$\tan t = \dfrac{y}{x} = \dfrac{\dfrac{2\sqrt{2}}{3}}{-\dfrac{1}{3}} = \left(\dfrac{2\sqrt{2}}{3}\right)\cdot\left(-\dfrac{3}{1}\right) = -2\sqrt{2}$
$\qquad$
$\cot t = \dfrac{x}{y} = \dfrac{-\dfrac{1}{3}}{\dfrac{2\sqrt{2}}{3}} = \left(-\dfrac{1}{3}\right)\cdot\dfrac{3}{2\sqrt{2}} \cdot \dfrac{\sqrt{2}}{\sqrt{2}} = -\dfrac{\sqrt{2}}{4}$

81. The domain of $y = \sec x$ is $\left\{x \mid x \text{ is any real number, except odd multiples of } \dfrac{\pi}{2}\right\}$.

The range of $y = \sec x$ is $\{y \mid y < -1 \text{ or } y > 1\}$.

83. $r = 2$ feet, $\theta = 30° \implies \theta = \dfrac{\pi}{6}$

$s = r\theta = 2 \cdot \dfrac{\pi}{6} = \dfrac{\pi}{3}$ feet

$A = \dfrac{1}{2} \cdot r^2\theta = \dfrac{1}{2} \cdot (2)^2 \cdot \dfrac{\pi}{6} = \dfrac{\pi}{3}$ square feet

85. $v = 180$ mi/hr, $d = \dfrac{1}{2}$ mile $\implies r = \dfrac{1}{4} = 0.25$ mile

$\omega = \dfrac{v}{r} = \dfrac{180 \text{ mi/hr}}{0.25 \text{ mi}} = 720 \text{ rad/hr} = \dfrac{720 \text{ rad}}{\text{hr}} \cdot \dfrac{1 \text{ rev}}{2\pi \text{ rad}} = \dfrac{360 \text{ rev}}{\pi \text{ hr}} \approx 114.6 \text{ rev/hr}$

87. Since there are two lights on opposite sides and the light is seen every 5 seconds, the beacon makes 1 revolution every 10 seconds.

$\omega = \dfrac{1 \text{ rev}}{10 \text{ sec}} \cdot \dfrac{2\pi \text{ radians}}{1 \text{ rev}} = \dfrac{\pi}{5}$ radian/second

89. $E(t) = 120\sin(120\pi t)$, $t \geq 0$

(a) The maximum value of E is the amplitude, which is 120.

(b) Period $= \dfrac{2\pi}{120\pi} = \dfrac{1}{60}$ second

(c) Graphing:

91. (a) Draw a scatter diagram:

(b) Amplitude: $A = \dfrac{90 - 51}{2} = \dfrac{39}{2} = 19.5$

Vertical Shift : $\dfrac{90 + 51}{2} = \dfrac{141}{2} = 70.5$

$\omega = \dfrac{2\pi}{12} = \dfrac{\pi}{6}$

Phase shift (use $y = 51$, $x = 1$):

$$51 = 19.5\sin\left(\frac{\pi}{6}\cdot 1 - \phi\right) + 70.5$$

$$-19.5 = 19.5\sin\left(\frac{\pi}{6} - \phi\right)$$

$$-1 = \sin\left(\frac{\pi}{6} - \phi\right)$$

$$-\frac{\pi}{2} = \frac{\pi}{6} - \phi$$

$$\phi = \frac{2\pi}{3}$$

Thus, $y = 19.5\sin\left(\frac{\pi}{6}x - \frac{2\pi}{3}\right) + 70.5$.

(c)

(d) $y = 19.518\sin(0.541x - 2.283) + 71.01$

(e)

93. (a)   Amplitude: $A = \dfrac{13.367 - 9.667}{2} = \dfrac{3.7}{2} = 1.85$

Vertical Shift: $\dfrac{13.367 + 9.667}{2} = \dfrac{23.034}{2} = 11.517$

$$\omega = \frac{2\pi}{365}$$

Phase shift (use $y = 9.667$, $x = 355$):

$$9.667 = 1.85\sin\left(\frac{2\pi}{365}\cdot 355 - \phi\right) + 11.517$$

$$-1.85 = 1.85\sin\left(\frac{2\pi}{365}\cdot 355 - \phi\right)$$

$$-1 = \sin\left(\frac{710\pi}{365} - \phi\right)$$

$$-\frac{\pi}{2} = \frac{710\pi}{365} - \phi$$

$$\phi \approx 7.6818$$

Thus, $y = 1.85\sin\left(\dfrac{2\pi}{365}x - 7.6818\right) + 11.517$.

(b) $y = 1.85\sin\left(\dfrac{2\pi}{365}(91) - 7.6818\right) + 11.517 \approx 11.83$ hours

(c)

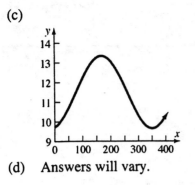

(d)   Answers will vary.

Trigonometric Functions

2.CR Cumulative Review

1. $2x^2 + x - 1 = 0$
   $(2x - 1)(x + 1) = 0$
   $x = \dfrac{1}{2}$ or $x = -1$

3. radius = 4, center $(0, -2)$
   Using $(x - h)^2 + (y - k)^2 = r^2$
   $(x - 0)^2 + (y - (-2))^2 = 4^2$
   $$x^2 + (y + 2)^2 = 16$$
   $$x^2 + y^2 + 4y + 4 = 16$$
   $$x^2 + y^2 + 4y - 12 = 0$$

5. $x^2 + y^2 - 2x + 4y - 4 = 0$
   $x^2 - 2x + 1 + y^2 + 4y + 4 = 4 + 1 + 4$
   $(x - 1)^2 + (y + 2)^2 = 9$
   $(x - 1)^2 + (y + 2)^2 = 3^2$
   This equation yields a circle with radius 3 and center $(1, -2)$.

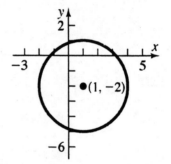

7. (a) $y = x^2$

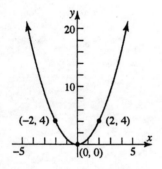

(b) $y = x^3$

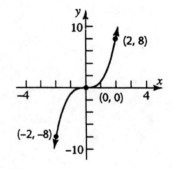

(c) $y = \sqrt{x}$

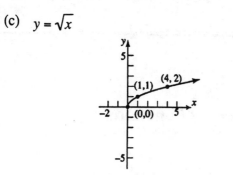

(d) $y = \sqrt[3]{x}$

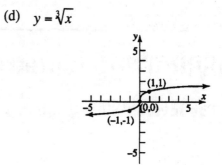

(e) $y = \sin x$

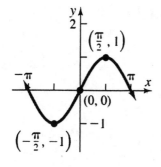

(f) $y = \tan x$

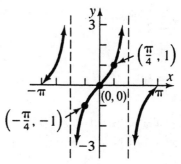

9. $\left(\sin 14°\right)^2 + \left(\cos 14°\right)^2 - 3 = 1 - 3 = -2$

11. $\tan\dfrac{\pi}{4} - 3\cos\dfrac{\pi}{6} + \csc\dfrac{\pi}{6} = 1 - 3\left(\dfrac{\sqrt{3}}{2}\right) + 2 = 3 - \dfrac{3\sqrt{3}}{2} = \dfrac{6 - 3\sqrt{3}}{2}$

Chapter 3

Analytic Trigonometry

3.1 The Inverse Sine, Cosine, and Tangent Functions

1. Domain $\{x \mid x \text{ is any real number}\}$, Range $\{y \mid -1 \le y \le 1\}$

3. False

5. $1; \dfrac{\sqrt{3}}{2}$

7. $x = \sin y$

9. $\dfrac{\pi}{5}$

11. True

13. $\sin^{-1} 0$

   We are finding the angle θ, $-\dfrac{\pi}{2} \le \theta \le \dfrac{\pi}{2}$, whose sine equals 0.

   $$\sin\theta = 0 \qquad -\dfrac{\pi}{2} \le \theta \le \dfrac{\pi}{2}$$
   $$\theta = 0$$
   $$\sin^{-1} 0 = 0$$

15. $\sin^{-1}(-1)$

   We are finding the angle θ, $-\dfrac{\pi}{2} \le \theta \le \dfrac{\pi}{2}$, whose sine equals -1.

   $$\sin\theta = -1 \qquad -\dfrac{\pi}{2} \le \theta \le \dfrac{\pi}{2}$$
   $$\theta = -\dfrac{\pi}{2}$$
   $$\sin^{-1}(-1) = -\dfrac{\pi}{2}$$

17. $\tan^{-1} 0$

   We are finding the angle θ, $-\dfrac{\pi}{2} < \theta < \dfrac{\pi}{2}$, whose tangent equals 0.

   $$\tan\theta = 0 \qquad -\dfrac{\pi}{2} < \theta < \dfrac{\pi}{2}$$
   $$\theta = 0$$
   $$\tan^{-1} 0 = 0$$

19. $\sin^{-1} \dfrac{\sqrt{2}}{2}$

We are finding the angle θ, $-\dfrac{\pi}{2} \le \theta \le \dfrac{\pi}{2}$, whose sine equals $\dfrac{\sqrt{2}}{2}$.

$$\sin\theta = \dfrac{\sqrt{2}}{2} \qquad -\dfrac{\pi}{2} \le \theta \le \dfrac{\pi}{2}$$

$$\theta = \dfrac{\pi}{4}$$

$$\sin^{-1} \dfrac{\sqrt{2}}{2} = \dfrac{\pi}{4}$$

21. $\tan^{-1} \sqrt{3}$

We are finding the angle θ, $-\dfrac{\pi}{2} < \theta < \dfrac{\pi}{2}$, whose tangent equals $\sqrt{3}$.

$$\tan\theta = \sqrt{3} \qquad -\dfrac{\pi}{2} < \theta < \dfrac{\pi}{2}$$

$$\theta = \dfrac{\pi}{3}$$

$$\tan^{-1} \sqrt{3} = \dfrac{\pi}{3}$$

23. $\cos^{-1}\left(-\dfrac{\sqrt{3}}{2}\right)$

We are finding the angle θ, $0 \le \theta \le \pi$, whose cosine equals $-\dfrac{\sqrt{3}}{2}$.

$$\cos\theta = -\dfrac{\sqrt{3}}{2} \qquad 0 \le \theta \le \pi$$

$$\theta = \dfrac{5\pi}{6}$$

$$\cos^{-1}\left(-\dfrac{\sqrt{3}}{2}\right) = \dfrac{5\pi}{6}$$

25. $\sin^{-1} 0.1 \approx 0.10$

27. $\tan^{-1} 5 \approx 1.37$

29. $\cos^{-1} \dfrac{7}{8} \approx 0.51$

31. $\tan^{-1}(-0.4) \approx -0.38$

33. $\sin^{-1}(-0.12) \approx -0.12$

35. $\cos^{-1} \dfrac{\sqrt{2}}{3} \approx 1.08$

37. $\sin\left[\sin^{-1}(0.54)\right] = 0.54$

39. $\cos^{-1}\left[\cos\left(\dfrac{4\pi}{5}\right)\right] = \dfrac{4\pi}{5}$

41. $\tan\left[\tan^{-1}(-3.5)\right] = -3.5$

43. $\sin^{-1}\left[\sin\left(-\dfrac{3\pi}{7}\right)\right] = -\dfrac{3\pi}{7}$

45. Yes, $\sin^{-1}\left[\sin\left(-\dfrac{\pi}{6}\right)\right] = -\dfrac{\pi}{6}$, since $\sin^{-1}[\sin(x)] = x$ where $-\dfrac{\pi}{2} \le x \le \dfrac{\pi}{2}$

    and $-\dfrac{\pi}{6}$ is in the restricted domain of $f(x) = \sin(x)$.

47. No, $\sin\left[\sin^{-1}(2)\right] \ne 2$. since $\sin\left[\sin^{-1}(x)\right] = x$ where $-1 \le x \le 1$
    and 2 is not in the domain of $f(x) = \sin^{-1}(x)$.

49. No, $\cos^{-1}\left[\cos\left(-\dfrac{\pi}{6}\right)\right] \ne -\dfrac{\pi}{6}$, since $\cos^{-1}[\cos(x)] = x$ where $0 \le x \le \pi$

    and $-\dfrac{\pi}{6}$ is not in the restricted domain of $f(x) = \cos(x)$.

51. Yes, $\cos\left[\cos^{-1}\left(-\dfrac{1}{2}\right)\right] = -\dfrac{1}{2}$, since $\cos\left[\cos^{-1}(x)\right] = x$ where $-1 \le x \le 1$

    and $-\dfrac{1}{2}$ is in the domain of $f(x) = \cos^{-1}(x)$.

53. Yes, $\tan^{-1}\left[\tan\left(-\dfrac{\pi}{3}\right)\right] = -\dfrac{\pi}{3}$, since $\tan^{-1}[\tan(x)] = x$ where $-\dfrac{\pi}{2} < x < \dfrac{\pi}{2}$

    and $-\dfrac{\pi}{3}$ is in the restricted domain of $f(x) = \tan(x)$.

55. Yes, $\tan\left[\tan^{-1}(2)\right] = 2$, since $\tan\left[\tan^{-1}(x)\right] = x$ where $-\infty < x < \infty$.

57. Note that $\theta = 29°45' = 29.75$ degrees.

    (a) $D = 24 \cdot \left[1 - \dfrac{\cos^{-1}\left(\tan\left(23.5 \cdot \dfrac{\pi}{180}\right) \tan\left(29.75 \cdot \dfrac{\pi}{180}\right)\right)}{\pi}\right] \approx 13.92$ hours

    (b) $D = 24 \cdot \left[1 - \dfrac{\cos^{-1}\left(\tan\left(0 \cdot \dfrac{\pi}{180}\right) \tan\left(29.75 \cdot \dfrac{\pi}{180}\right)\right)}{\pi}\right] \approx 12$ hours

(c) $D = 24 \cdot \left[1 - \dfrac{\cos^{-1}\left(\tan\left(22.8 \cdot \dfrac{\pi}{180}\right)\tan\left(29.75 \cdot \dfrac{\pi}{180}\right)\right)}{\pi} \right] \approx 13.85$ hours

59.   Note that $\theta = 21°18' = 21.3$ degrees.

(a) $D = 24 \cdot \left(1 - \dfrac{\cos^{-1}\left(\tan\left(23.5 \cdot \dfrac{\pi}{180}\right)\tan\left(21.3 \cdot \dfrac{\pi}{180}\right)\right)}{\pi} \right) \approx 13.30$ hours

(b) $D = 24 \cdot \left(1 - \dfrac{\cos^{-1}\left(\tan\left(0 \cdot \dfrac{\pi}{180}\right)\tan\left(21.3 \cdot \dfrac{\pi}{180}\right)\right)}{\pi} \right) \approx 12$ hours

(c) $D = 24 \cdot \left(1 - \dfrac{\cos^{-1}\left(\tan\left(22.8 \cdot \dfrac{\pi}{180}\right)\tan\left(21.3 \cdot \dfrac{\pi}{180}\right)\right)}{\pi} \right) \approx 13.26$ hours

61.   (a) $D = 24 \cdot \left(1 - \dfrac{\cos^{-1}\left(\tan\left(23.5 \cdot \dfrac{\pi}{180}\right)\tan\left(0 \cdot \dfrac{\pi}{180}\right)\right)}{\pi} \right) \approx 12$ hours

(b) $D = 24 \cdot \left(1 - \dfrac{\cos^{-1}\left(\tan\left(0 \cdot \dfrac{\pi}{180}\right)\tan\left(0 \cdot \dfrac{\pi}{180}\right)\right)}{\pi} \right) \approx 12$ hours

(c) $D = 24 \cdot \left(1 - \dfrac{\cos^{-1}\left(\tan\left(22.8 \cdot \dfrac{\pi}{180}\right)\tan\left(0 \cdot \dfrac{\pi}{180}\right)\right)}{\pi} \right) \approx 12$ hours

(d)   There are approximately 12 hours of daylight every day at the equator.

63. At the latitude of Cadillac Mountain, the effective radius of the earth is 2710 miles.

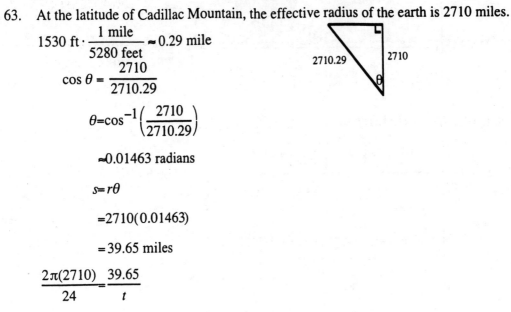

$$1530 \text{ ft} \cdot \frac{1 \text{ mile}}{5280 \text{ feet}} \approx 0.29 \text{ mile}$$

$$\cos \theta = \frac{2710}{2710.29}$$

$$\theta = \cos^{-1}\left(\frac{2710}{2710.29}\right)$$

$$\approx 0.01463 \text{ radians}$$

$$s = r\theta$$

$$= 2710(0.01463)$$

$$= 39.65 \text{ miles}$$

$$\frac{2\pi(2710)}{24} = \frac{39.65}{t}$$

$$t \approx 0.05589 \text{ hour} \approx 3.35 \text{ minutes}$$

Analytic Trigonometry

3.2   The Inverse Trigonometric Functions (Continued)

1.   Domain $\left\{ x \middle| x \neq (2n+1) \cdot \dfrac{\pi}{2}, n \text{ is any integer} \right\}$, Range $\left\{ y \middle| |y| \geq 1 \right\}$

3. $-\dfrac{2}{\sqrt{5}}$

5. $\dfrac{\sqrt{2}}{2}$

7.   True

9. $\cos\left(\sin^{-1} \dfrac{\sqrt{2}}{2} \right)$

Find the angle θ, $-\dfrac{\pi}{2} \leq \theta \leq \dfrac{\pi}{2}$, whose sine equals $\dfrac{\sqrt{2}}{2}$.

$$\sin\theta = \dfrac{\sqrt{2}}{2} \qquad -\dfrac{\pi}{2} \leq \theta \leq \dfrac{\pi}{2}$$

$$\theta = \dfrac{\pi}{4}$$

$$\cos\left(\sin^{-1} \dfrac{\sqrt{2}}{2} \right) = \cos\dfrac{\pi}{4} = \dfrac{\sqrt{2}}{2}$$

11. $\tan\left(\cos^{-1}\left(-\dfrac{\sqrt{3}}{2} \right) \right)$

Find the angle θ, $0 \leq \theta \leq \pi$, whose cosine equals $-\dfrac{\sqrt{3}}{2}$.

$$\cos\theta = -\dfrac{\sqrt{3}}{2} \qquad 0 \leq \theta \leq \pi$$

$$\theta = \dfrac{5\pi}{6}$$

$$\tan\left(\cos^{-1}\left(-\dfrac{\sqrt{3}}{2} \right) \right) = \tan\dfrac{5\pi}{6} = -\dfrac{\sqrt{3}}{3}$$

13. $\sec\left(\cos^{-1}\dfrac{1}{2}\right)$

Find the angle θ, $0 \le \theta \le \pi$, whose cosine equals $\dfrac{1}{2}$.

$$\cos\theta = \frac{1}{2} \quad 0 \le \theta \le \pi$$

$$\theta = \frac{\pi}{3}$$

$$\sec\left(\cos^{-1}\frac{1}{2}\right) = \sec\frac{\pi}{3} = 2$$

15. $\csc\left(\tan^{-1}1\right)$

Find the angle θ, $-\dfrac{\pi}{2} < \theta < \dfrac{\pi}{2}$, whose tangent equals 1.

$$\tan\theta = 1 \quad -\frac{\pi}{2} < \theta < \frac{\pi}{2}$$

$$\theta = \frac{\pi}{4}$$

$$\csc\left(\tan^{-1}1\right) = \csc\frac{\pi}{4} = \sqrt{2}$$

17. $\sin\left(\tan^{-1}(-1)\right)$

Find the angle θ, $-\dfrac{\pi}{2} < \theta < \dfrac{\pi}{2}$, whose tangent equals -1.

$$\tan\theta = -1 \quad -\frac{\pi}{2} < \theta < \frac{\pi}{2}$$

$$\theta = -\frac{\pi}{4}$$

$$\sin\left(\tan^{-1}(-1)\right) = \sin\left(-\frac{\pi}{4}\right) = -\frac{\sqrt{2}}{2}$$

19. $\sec\left(\sin^{-1}\left(-\dfrac{1}{2}\right)\right)$

Find the angle θ, $-\dfrac{\pi}{2} \le \theta \le \dfrac{\pi}{2}$, whose sine equals $-\dfrac{1}{2}$.

$$\sin\theta = -\frac{1}{2} \quad -\frac{\pi}{2} \le \theta \le \frac{\pi}{2}$$

$$\theta = -\frac{\pi}{6}$$

$$\sec\left(\sin^{-1}\left(-\frac{1}{2}\right)\right) = \sec\left(-\frac{\pi}{6}\right) = \frac{2\sqrt{3}}{3}$$

21. $\cos^{-1}\left(\cos\dfrac{5\pi}{4}\right) = \cos^{-1}\left(-\dfrac{\sqrt{2}}{2}\right)$

Find the angle θ, $0 \le \theta \le \pi$, whose cosine equals $-\dfrac{\sqrt{2}}{2}$.

$$\cos\theta = -\dfrac{\sqrt{2}}{2} \qquad 0 \le \theta \le \pi$$

$$\theta = \dfrac{3\pi}{4}$$

$$\cos^{-1}\left(\cos\dfrac{5\pi}{4}\right) = \dfrac{3\pi}{4}$$

23. $\sin^{-1}\left(\sin\left(-\dfrac{7\pi}{6}\right)\right) = \sin^{-1}\dfrac{1}{2}$

Find the angle θ, $-\dfrac{\pi}{2} \le \theta \le \dfrac{\pi}{2}$, whose sine equals $\dfrac{1}{2}$.

$$\sin\theta = \dfrac{1}{2} \qquad -\dfrac{\pi}{2} \le \theta \le \dfrac{\pi}{2}$$

$$\theta = \dfrac{\pi}{6}$$

$$\sin^{-1}\left(\sin\left(-\dfrac{7\pi}{6}\right)\right) = \dfrac{\pi}{6}$$

25. $\tan\left(\sin^{-1}\dfrac{1}{3}\right)$

Let $\theta = \sin^{-1}\dfrac{1}{3}$. Since $\sin\theta = \dfrac{1}{3}$ and $-\dfrac{\pi}{2} \le \theta \le \dfrac{\pi}{2}$, θ is in quadrant I and we can let $y = 1$ and $r = 3$.
Solve for x:

$$x^2 + 1 = 9$$

$$x^2 = 8$$

$$x = \pm\sqrt{8} = \pm2\sqrt{2}$$

Since θ is in quadrant I, $x = 2\sqrt{2}$.

$$\tan\left(\sin^{-1}\dfrac{1}{2}\right) = \tan\theta = \dfrac{y}{x} = \dfrac{1}{2\sqrt{2}}\dfrac{\sqrt{2}}{\sqrt{2}} = \dfrac{\sqrt{2}}{4}$$

27. $\sec\left(\tan^{-1}\dfrac{1}{2}\right)$

Let $\theta = \tan^{-1}\dfrac{1}{2}$. Since $\tan\theta = \dfrac{1}{2}$ and $-\dfrac{\pi}{2} < \theta < \dfrac{\pi}{2}$, θ is in quadrant I and we can let $x = 2$ and $y = 1$.

Solve for r:

$2^2 + 1 = r^2$

$r^2 = 5$

$r = \sqrt{5}$

θ is in quadrant I.

$$\sec\left(\tan^{-1}\frac{1}{2}\right) = \sec\theta = \frac{r}{x} = \frac{\sqrt{5}}{2}$$

29. $\cot\left(\sin^{-1}\left(-\frac{\sqrt{2}}{3}\right)\right)$

Let $\theta = \sin^{-1}\left(-\frac{\sqrt{2}}{3}\right)$. Since $\sin\theta = -\frac{\sqrt{2}}{3}$ and $-\frac{\pi}{2} \le \theta \le \frac{\pi}{2}$, θ is in quadrant IV and we can

let $y = -\sqrt{2}$ and $r = 3$.

Solve for x:

$x^2 + 2 = 9$

$x^2 = 7$

$x = \pm\sqrt{7}$

Since θ is in quadrant IV, $x = \sqrt{7}$.

$$\cot\left(\sin^{-1}\left(-\frac{\sqrt{2}}{3}\right)\right) = \cot\theta = \frac{x}{y} = \frac{\sqrt{7}}{-\sqrt{2}}\frac{\sqrt{2}}{\sqrt{2}} = -\frac{\sqrt{14}}{2}$$

31. $\sin\left(\tan^{-1}(-3)\right)$

Let $\theta = \tan^{-1}(-3)$. Since $\tan\theta = -3$ and $-\frac{\pi}{2} < \theta < \frac{\pi}{2}$, θ is in quadrant IV and we can

let $x = 1$ and $y = -3$.

Solve for r:

$1 + 9 = r^2$

$r^2 = 10$

$r = \sqrt{10}$

θ is in quadrant IV.

$$\sin\left(\tan^{-1}(-3)\right) = \sin\theta = \frac{y}{r} = \frac{-3}{\sqrt{10}}\frac{\sqrt{10}}{\sqrt{10}} = -\frac{3\sqrt{10}}{10}$$

33. $\sec\left(\sin^{-1}\frac{2\sqrt{5}}{5}\right)$

Let $\theta = \sin^{-1}\frac{2\sqrt{5}}{5}$. Since $\sin\theta = \frac{2\sqrt{5}}{5}$ and $-\frac{\pi}{2} \le \theta \le \frac{\pi}{2}$, θ is in quadrant I and we can

let $y = 2\sqrt{5}$ and $r = 5$.

Solve for x:

$x^2 + 20 = 25$

$\qquad x^2 = 5$

$\qquad x = \pm\sqrt{5}$

Since θ is in quadrant I, $x = \sqrt{5}$.

$$\sec\left(\sin^{-1}\left(\frac{2\sqrt{5}}{5}\right)\right) = \sec\theta = \frac{r}{x} = \frac{5}{\sqrt{5}}\cdot\frac{\sqrt{5}}{\sqrt{5}} = \sqrt{5}$$

35. $\quad \sin^{-1}\left(\cos\frac{3\pi}{4}\right) = \sin^{-1}\left(-\frac{\sqrt{2}}{2}\right) = -\frac{\pi}{4}$

37. $\quad \cot^{-1}\sqrt{3}$

We are finding the angle θ, $0 < \theta < \pi$, whose cotangent equals $\sqrt{3}$.

$\qquad \cot\theta = \sqrt{3} \qquad 0 < \theta < \pi$

$\qquad\quad \theta = \frac{\pi}{6}$

$\cot^{-1}\sqrt{3} = \frac{\pi}{6}$

39. $\quad \csc^{-1}(-1)$

We are finding the angle θ, $-\frac{\pi}{2} \le \theta \le \frac{\pi}{2}$, $\theta \ne 0$, whose cosecant equals -1.

$\qquad \csc\theta = -1 \qquad -\frac{\pi}{2} \le \theta \le \frac{\pi}{2}, \ \theta \ne 0$

$\qquad\quad \theta = -\frac{\pi}{2}$

$\csc^{-1}(-1) = -\frac{\pi}{2}$

41. $\quad \sec^{-1}\frac{2\sqrt{3}}{3}$

We are finding the angle θ, $0 \le \theta \le \pi$, $\theta \ne \frac{\pi}{2}$, whose secant equals $\frac{2\sqrt{3}}{3}$.

$\qquad \sec\theta = \frac{2\sqrt{3}}{3} \qquad 0 \le \theta \le \pi, \ \theta \ne \frac{\pi}{2}$

$\qquad\quad \theta = \frac{\pi}{6}$

$\sec^{-1}\frac{2\sqrt{3}}{3} = \frac{\pi}{6}$

43. $\cot^{-1}\left(-\dfrac{\sqrt{3}}{3}\right)$

We are finding the angle θ, $0 < \theta < \pi$, whose cotangent equals $-\dfrac{\sqrt{3}}{3}$.

$$\cot\theta = -\dfrac{\sqrt{3}}{3} \quad 0 < \theta < \pi$$

$$\theta = \dfrac{2\pi}{3}$$

$$\cot^{-1}\left(-\dfrac{\sqrt{3}}{3}\right) = \dfrac{2\pi}{3}$$

45. $\sec^{-1} 4 = \cos^{-1}\dfrac{1}{4}$

We are finding the angle θ, $0 \le \theta \le \pi$, whose cosine equals $\dfrac{1}{4}$.

$$\cos\theta = \dfrac{1}{4} \implies \theta \text{ in quadrant I}$$

The calculator yields $\theta = \cos^{-1}\dfrac{1}{4} \approx 1.32$, which is an angle in quadrant I. Therefore, $\sec^{-1}(4) \approx 1.32$.

47. $\cot^{-1} 2 = \tan^{-1}\dfrac{1}{2}$

We are finding the angle θ, $0 \le \theta \le \pi$, whose tangent equals $\dfrac{1}{2}$.

$$\tan\theta = \dfrac{1}{2} \implies \theta \text{ in quadrant I}$$

The calculator yields $\theta = \tan^{-1}\dfrac{1}{2} \approx 0.46$, which is an angle in quadrant I. Therefore, $\cot^{-1}(2) \approx 0.46$.

49. $\csc^{-1}(-3) = \sin^{-1}\left(-\dfrac{1}{3}\right)$

We are finding the angle θ, $-\dfrac{\pi}{2} \le \theta \le \dfrac{\pi}{2}$, whose sine equals $-\dfrac{1}{3}$.

$$\sin\theta = -\dfrac{1}{3} \implies \theta \text{ in quadrant IV}$$

The calculator yields $\theta = \sin^{-1}\left(-\dfrac{1}{3}\right) \approx -0.34$, which is an angle in quadrant IV. Therefore $\csc^{-1}(-3) \approx -0.34$.

51. $\cot^{-1}\left(-\sqrt{5}\right) = \tan^{-1}\left(-\frac{1}{\sqrt{5}}\right)$

We are finding the angle θ, $0 \le \theta \le \pi$, whose tangent equals $-\frac{1}{\sqrt{5}}$.

$$\tan\theta = -\frac{1}{\sqrt{5}} \Rightarrow \theta \text{ in quadrant II}$$

The calculator yields $\tan^{-1}\left(-\frac{1}{\sqrt{5}}\right) \approx -0.42$, which is an angle in quadrant IV.

Since θ is in quadrant II, $\theta \approx -0.42 + \pi \approx 2.72$.

Therefore, $\cot^{-1}\left(-\sqrt{5}\right) \approx 2.72$.

53. $\csc^{-1}\left(-\frac{3}{2}\right) = \sin^{-1}\left(-\frac{2}{3}\right)$

We are finding the angle θ, $-\frac{\pi}{2} \le \theta \le \frac{\pi}{2}$, $\theta \ne 0$, whose sine equals $-\frac{2}{3}$.

$$\sin\theta = -\frac{2}{3} \Rightarrow \theta \text{ in quadrant IV}$$

The calculator yields $\sin^{-1}\left(-\frac{2}{3}\right) \approx -0.73$, which is an angle in quadrant IV.

Therefore, $\csc^{-1}\left(-\frac{3}{2}\right) \approx -0.73$

55. $\cot^{-1}\left(-\frac{3}{2}\right) = \tan^{-1}\left(-\frac{2}{3}\right)$

We are finding the angle θ, $0 \le \theta \le \pi$, whose tangent equals $-\frac{2}{3}$.

$$\tan\theta = -\frac{2}{3} \Rightarrow \theta \text{ in quadrant II}$$

The calculator yields $\tan^{-1}\left(-\frac{2}{3}\right) \approx -0.59$, which is an angle in quadrant IV.

Since θ is in quadrant II, $\theta \approx -0.59 + \pi \approx 2.55$.

Therefore, $\cot^{-1}\left(-\frac{3}{2}\right) \approx 2.55$

57. $y = \cot^{-1} x$

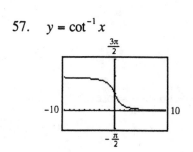

59. $y = \csc^{-1} x$

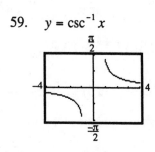

61. Answers will vary.

Analytic Trigonometry

3.3 Trigonometric Identities

1. True

3. identity, conditional

5. 0

7. True

9. $\tan\theta \cdot \csc\theta = \dfrac{\sin\theta}{\cos\theta} \cdot \dfrac{1}{\sin\theta} = \dfrac{1}{\cos\theta}$

11. $\dfrac{\cos\theta}{1-\sin\theta} \cdot \dfrac{1+\sin\theta}{1+\sin\theta} = \dfrac{\cos\theta(1+\sin\theta)}{1-\sin^2\theta} = \dfrac{\cos\theta(1+\sin\theta)}{\cos^2\theta} = \dfrac{1+\sin\theta}{\cos\theta}$

13. $\dfrac{\sin\theta+\cos\theta}{\cos\theta} + \dfrac{\cos\theta-\sin\theta}{\sin\theta} = \dfrac{\sin^2\theta+\sin\theta\cos\theta+\cos\theta(\cos\theta-\sin\theta)}{\sin\theta\cos\theta}$

    $= \dfrac{\sin^2\theta+\sin\theta\cos\theta+\cos^2\theta-\cos\theta\sin\theta}{\sin\theta\cos\theta} = \dfrac{\sin^2\theta+\cos^2\theta+\sin\theta\cos\theta-\cos\theta\sin\theta}{\sin\theta\cos\theta}$

    $= \dfrac{1}{\sin\theta\cos\theta}$

15. $\dfrac{(\sin\theta+\cos\theta)(\sin\theta+\cos\theta)-1}{\sin\theta\cos\theta} = \dfrac{\sin^2\theta+2\sin\theta\cos\theta+\cos^2\theta-1}{\sin\theta\cos\theta}$

    $= \dfrac{\sin^2\theta+\cos^2\theta+2\sin\theta\cos\theta-1}{\sin\theta\cos\theta} = \dfrac{1+2\sin\theta\cos\theta-1}{\sin\theta\cos\theta} = \dfrac{2\sin\theta\cos\theta}{\sin\theta\cos\theta} = 2$

17. $\dfrac{3\sin^2\theta+4\sin\theta+1}{\sin^2\theta+2\sin\theta+1} = \dfrac{(3\sin\theta+1)(\sin\theta+1)}{(\sin\theta+1)(\sin\theta+1)} = \dfrac{3\sin\theta+1}{\sin\theta+1}$

19. $\csc\theta \cdot \cos\theta = \dfrac{1}{\sin\theta} \cdot \cos\theta = \dfrac{\cos\theta}{\sin\theta} = \cot\theta$

21. $1+\tan^2(-\theta) = 1+(-\tan\theta)^2 = 1+\tan^2\theta = \sec^2\theta$

23. $\cos\theta(\tan\theta+\cot\theta) = \cos\theta\left(\dfrac{\sin\theta}{\cos\theta}+\dfrac{\cos\theta}{\sin\theta}\right) = \cos\theta\left(\dfrac{\sin^2\theta+\cos^2\theta}{\cos\theta\sin\theta}\right) = \dfrac{1}{\sin\theta} = \csc\theta$

25. $\tan\theta\cot\theta - \cos^2\theta = \tan\theta \cdot \dfrac{1}{\tan\theta} - \cos^2\theta = 1-\cos^2\theta = \sin^2\theta$

27. $(\sec\theta-1)(\sec\theta+1) = \sec^2\theta-1 = \tan^2\theta$

29. $(\sec\theta + \tan\theta)(\sec\theta - \tan\theta) = \sec^2\theta - \tan^2\theta = 1$

31. $\cos^2\theta(1 + \tan^2\theta) = \cos^2\theta \cdot \sec^2\theta = \cos^2\theta \cdot \dfrac{1}{\cos^2\theta} = 1$

33. $(\sin\theta + \cos\theta)^2 + (\sin\theta - \cos\theta)^2$
$= \sin^2\theta + 2\sin\theta\cos\theta + \cos^2\theta + \sin^2\theta - 2\sin\theta\cos\theta + \cos^2\theta$
$= 2\sin^2\theta + 2\cos^2\theta = 2(\sin^2\theta + \cos^2\theta) = 2\cdot 1 = 2$

35. $\sec^4\theta - \sec^2\theta = \sec^2\theta(\sec^2\theta - 1) = (\tan^2\theta + 1)\tan^2\theta = \tan^4\theta + \tan^2\theta$

37. $\sec\theta - \tan\theta = \dfrac{1}{\cos\theta} - \dfrac{\sin\theta}{\cos\theta} = \left(\dfrac{1 - \sin\theta}{\cos\theta}\right) \cdot \left(\dfrac{1 + \sin\theta}{1 + \sin\theta}\right) = \dfrac{1 - \sin^2\theta}{\cos\theta(1 + \sin\theta)}$
$= \dfrac{\cos^2\theta}{\cos\theta(1 + \sin\theta)} = \dfrac{\cos\theta}{1 + \sin\theta}$

39. $3\sin^2\theta + 4\cos^2\theta = 3\sin^2\theta + 3\cos^2\theta + \cos^2\theta = 3(\sin^2\theta + \cos^2\theta) + \cos^2\theta$
$= 3\cdot 1 + \cos^2\theta = 3 + \cos^2\theta$

41. $1 - \dfrac{\cos^2\theta}{1 + \sin\theta} = 1 - \dfrac{1 - \sin^2\theta}{1 + \sin\theta} = 1 - \dfrac{(1 - \sin\theta)(1 + \sin\theta)}{1 + \sin\theta} = 1 - 1 + \sin\theta = \sin\theta$

43. $\dfrac{1 + \tan\theta}{1 - \tan\theta} = \dfrac{1 + \dfrac{1}{\cot\theta}}{1 - \dfrac{1}{\cot\theta}} = \dfrac{\dfrac{\cot\theta + 1}{\cot\theta}}{\dfrac{\cot\theta - 1}{\cot\theta}} = \dfrac{\cot\theta + 1}{\cot\theta} \cdot \dfrac{\cot\theta}{\cot\theta - 1} = \dfrac{\cot\theta + 1}{\cot\theta - 1}$

45. $\dfrac{\sec\theta}{\csc\theta} + \dfrac{\sin\theta}{\cos\theta} = \dfrac{\dfrac{1}{\cos\theta}}{\dfrac{1}{\sin\theta}} + \dfrac{\sin\theta}{\cos\theta} = \dfrac{\sin\theta}{\cos\theta} + \dfrac{\sin\theta}{\cos\theta} = \tan\theta + \tan\theta = 2\tan\theta$

47. $\dfrac{1 + \sin\theta}{1 - \sin\theta} = \dfrac{1 + \dfrac{1}{\csc\theta}}{1 - \dfrac{1}{\csc\theta}} = \dfrac{\dfrac{\csc\theta + 1}{\csc\theta}}{\dfrac{\csc\theta - 1}{\csc\theta}} = \dfrac{\csc\theta + 1}{\csc\theta} \cdot \dfrac{\csc\theta}{\csc\theta - 1} = \dfrac{\csc\theta + 1}{\csc\theta - 1}$

49. $\dfrac{1 - \sin\theta}{\cos\theta} + \dfrac{\cos\theta}{1 - \sin\theta} = \dfrac{(1 - \sin\theta)^2 + \cos^2\theta}{\cos\theta(1 - \sin\theta)} = \dfrac{1 - 2\sin\theta + \sin^2\theta + \cos^2\theta}{\cos\theta(1 - \sin\theta)}$
$= \dfrac{1 - 2\sin\theta + 1}{\cos\theta(1 - \sin\theta)} = \dfrac{2 - 2\sin\theta}{\cos\theta(1 - \sin\theta)} = \dfrac{2(1 - \sin\theta)}{\cos\theta(1 - \sin\theta)} = \dfrac{2}{\cos\theta} = 2\sec\theta$

51. $\dfrac{\sin\theta}{\sin\theta - \cos\theta} = \dfrac{\sin\theta}{\sin\theta - \cos\theta} \cdot \dfrac{\dfrac{1}{\sin\theta}}{\dfrac{1}{\sin\theta}} = \dfrac{1}{1 - \dfrac{\cos\theta}{\sin\theta}} = \dfrac{1}{1 - \cot\theta}$

53. $(\sec\theta - \tan\theta)^2 = \sec^2\theta - 2\sec\theta\tan\theta + \tan^2\theta = \dfrac{1}{\cos^2\theta} - 2\cdot\dfrac{1}{\cos\theta}\cdot\dfrac{\sin\theta}{\cos\theta} + \dfrac{\sin^2\theta}{\cos^2\theta}$

$= \dfrac{1 - 2\sin\theta + \sin^2\theta}{\cos^2\theta} = \dfrac{(1-\sin\theta)(1-\sin\theta)}{1-\sin^2\theta} = \dfrac{(1-\sin\theta)(1-\sin\theta)}{(1-\sin\theta)(1+\sin\theta)} = \dfrac{1-\sin\theta}{1+\sin\theta}$

55. $\dfrac{\cos\theta}{1-\tan\theta} + \dfrac{\sin\theta}{1-\cot\theta} = \dfrac{\cos\theta}{1-\dfrac{\sin\theta}{\cos\theta}} + \dfrac{\sin\theta}{1-\dfrac{\cos\theta}{\sin\theta}} = \dfrac{\cos\theta}{\dfrac{\cos\theta-\sin\theta}{\cos\theta}} + \dfrac{\sin\theta}{\dfrac{\sin\theta-\cos\theta}{\sin\theta}}$

$= \dfrac{\cos^2\theta}{\cos\theta-\sin\theta} + \dfrac{\sin^2\theta}{\sin\theta-\cos\theta} = \dfrac{\cos^2\theta - \sin^2\theta}{\cos\theta-\sin\theta}$

$= \dfrac{(\cos\theta-\sin\theta)(\cos\theta+\sin\theta)}{\cos\theta-\sin\theta} = \cos\theta + \sin\theta = \sin\theta + \cos\theta$

57. $\tan\theta + \dfrac{\cos\theta}{1+\sin\theta} = \dfrac{\sin\theta}{\cos\theta} + \dfrac{\cos\theta}{1+\sin\theta} = \dfrac{\sin\theta(1+\sin\theta) + \cos^2\theta}{\cos\theta(1+\sin\theta)}$

$= \dfrac{\sin\theta + \sin^2\theta + \cos^2\theta}{\cos\theta(1+\sin\theta)} = \dfrac{\sin\theta + 1}{\cos\theta(1+\sin\theta)} = \dfrac{1}{\cos\theta} = \sec\theta$

59. $\dfrac{\tan\theta + \sec\theta - 1}{\tan\theta - \sec\theta + 1} = \dfrac{\tan\theta + (\sec\theta-1)}{\tan\theta - (\sec\theta-1)} \cdot \dfrac{\tan\theta + (\sec\theta-1)}{\tan\theta + (\sec\theta-1)}$

$= \dfrac{\tan^2\theta + 2\tan\theta(\sec\theta-1) + \sec^2\theta - 2\sec\theta + 1}{\tan^2\theta - (\sec^2\theta - 2\sec\theta + 1)}$

$= \dfrac{\sec^2\theta - 1 + 2\tan\theta(\sec\theta-1) + \sec^2\theta - 2\sec\theta + 1}{\sec^2\theta - 1 - \sec^2\theta + 2\sec\theta - 1}$

$= \dfrac{2\sec^2\theta - 2\sec\theta + 2\tan\theta(\sec\theta-1)}{2\sec\theta - 2}$

$= \dfrac{2\sec\theta(\sec\theta-1) + 2\tan\theta(\sec\theta-1)}{2\sec\theta - 2}$

$= \dfrac{2(\sec\theta-1)(\sec\theta+\tan\theta)}{2(\sec\theta-1)} = \sec\theta + \tan\theta = \tan\theta + \sec\theta$

61. $\dfrac{\tan\theta - \cot\theta}{\tan\theta + \cot\theta} = \dfrac{\dfrac{\sin\theta}{\cos\theta} - \dfrac{\cos\theta}{\sin\theta}}{\dfrac{\sin\theta}{\cos\theta} + \dfrac{\cos\theta}{\sin\theta}} = \dfrac{\dfrac{\sin^2\theta - \cos^2\theta}{\cos\theta\sin\theta}}{\dfrac{\sin^2\theta + \cos^2\theta}{\cos\theta\sin\theta}} = \dfrac{\sin^2\theta - \cos^2\theta}{1} = \sin^2\theta - \cos^2\theta$

63. $\dfrac{\tan\theta - \cot\theta}{\tan\theta + \cot\theta} + 1 = \dfrac{\dfrac{\sin\theta}{\cos\theta} - \dfrac{\cos\theta}{\sin\theta}}{\dfrac{\sin\theta}{\cos\theta} + \dfrac{\cos\theta}{\sin\theta}} + 1 = \dfrac{\dfrac{\sin^2\theta - \cos^2\theta}{\cos\theta\sin\theta}}{\dfrac{\sin^2\theta + \cos^2\theta}{\cos\theta\sin\theta}} + 1 = \dfrac{\sin^2\theta - \cos^2\theta}{1} + 1$

$= \sin^2\theta - \cos^2\theta + 1 = \sin^2\theta + (1 - \cos^2\theta) = \sin^2\theta + \sin^2\theta = 2\sin^2\theta$

65. $\dfrac{\sec\theta+\tan\theta}{\cot\theta+\cos\theta}=\dfrac{\dfrac{1}{\cos\theta}+\dfrac{\sin\theta}{\cos\theta}}{\dfrac{\cos\theta}{\sin\theta}+\cos\theta}=\dfrac{\dfrac{1+\sin\theta}{\cos\theta}}{\dfrac{\cos\theta+\cos\theta\sin\theta}{\sin\theta}}=\dfrac{1+\sin\theta}{\cos\theta}\cdot\dfrac{\sin\theta}{\cos\theta(1+\sin\theta)}$

$=\dfrac{\sin\theta}{\cos\theta}\cdot\dfrac{1}{\cos\theta}=\tan\theta\sec\theta$

67. $\dfrac{1-\tan^2\theta}{1+\tan^2\theta}+1=\dfrac{1-\tan^2\theta+1+\tan^2\theta}{1+\tan^2\theta}=\dfrac{2}{\sec^2\theta}=2\cdot\dfrac{1}{\sec^2\theta}=2\cos^2\theta$

69. $\dfrac{\sec\theta-\csc\theta}{\sec\theta\csc\theta}=\dfrac{\dfrac{1}{\cos\theta}-\dfrac{1}{\sin\theta}}{\dfrac{1}{\cos\theta}\cdot\dfrac{1}{\sin\theta}}=\dfrac{\dfrac{\sin\theta-\cos\theta}{\cos\theta\sin\theta}}{\dfrac{1}{\cos\theta\sin\theta}}=\sin\theta-\cos\theta$

71. $\sec\theta-\cos\theta-\sin\theta\tan\theta=\dfrac{1}{\cos\theta}-\cos\theta-\sin\theta\cdot\dfrac{\sin\theta}{\cos\theta}=\dfrac{1-\cos^2\theta-\sin^2\theta}{\cos\theta}$

$=\dfrac{\sin^2\theta-\sin^2\theta}{\cos\theta}=0$

73. $\dfrac{1}{1-\sin\theta}+\dfrac{1}{1+\sin\theta}=\dfrac{1+\sin\theta+1-\sin\theta}{(1-\sin\theta)(1+\sin\theta)}=\dfrac{2}{1-\sin^2\theta}=\dfrac{2}{\cos^2\theta}=2\sec^2\theta$

75. $\dfrac{\sec\theta}{1-\sin\theta}=\left(\dfrac{\sec\theta}{1-\sin\theta}\right)\cdot\left(\dfrac{1+\sin\theta}{1+\sin\theta}\right)=\dfrac{\sec\theta(1+\sin\theta)}{1-\sin^2\theta}=\dfrac{\sec\theta(1+\sin\theta)}{\cos^2\theta}$

$=\dfrac{1}{\cos\theta}\cdot\dfrac{1+\sin\theta}{\cos^2\theta}=\dfrac{1+\sin\theta}{\cos^3\theta}$

77. $\dfrac{(\sec\theta-\tan\theta)^2+1}{\csc\theta(\sec\theta-\tan\theta)}=\dfrac{\sec^2\theta-2\sec\theta\tan\theta+\tan^2\theta+1}{\csc\theta(\sec\theta-\tan\theta)}=\dfrac{2\sec^2\theta-2\sec\theta\tan\theta}{\csc\theta(\sec\theta-\tan\theta)}$

$=\dfrac{2\sec\theta(\sec\theta-\tan\theta)}{\csc\theta(\sec\theta-\tan\theta)}=\dfrac{2\sec\theta}{\csc\theta}=\dfrac{2\cdot\dfrac{1}{\cos\theta}}{\dfrac{1}{\sin\theta}}=2\cdot\dfrac{1}{\cos\theta}\cdot\dfrac{\sin\theta}{1}=2\tan\theta$

79. $\dfrac{\sin\theta+\cos\theta}{\cos\theta}-\dfrac{\sin\theta-\cos\theta}{\sin\theta}=\dfrac{\sin\theta}{\cos\theta}+\dfrac{\cos\theta}{\cos\theta}-\dfrac{\sin\theta}{\sin\theta}+\dfrac{\cos\theta}{\sin\theta}=\dfrac{\sin\theta}{\cos\theta}+1-1+\dfrac{\cos\theta}{\sin\theta}$

$=\dfrac{\sin^2\theta+\cos^2\theta}{\cos\theta\sin\theta}=\dfrac{1}{\cos\theta\sin\theta}=\sec\theta\csc\theta$

81. $\dfrac{\sin^3\theta+\cos^3\theta}{\sin\theta+\cos\theta}=\dfrac{(\sin\theta+\cos\theta)(\sin^2\theta-\sin\theta\cos\theta+\cos^2\theta)}{\sin\theta+\cos\theta}=1-\sin\theta\cos\theta$

83. $\dfrac{\cos^2\theta-\sin^2\theta}{1-\tan^2\theta}=\dfrac{\cos^2\theta-\sin^2\theta}{1-\dfrac{\sin^2\theta}{\cos^2\theta}}=\dfrac{\cos^2\theta-\sin^2\theta}{\dfrac{\cos^2\theta-\sin^2\theta}{\cos^2\theta}}=\cos^2\theta$

85. $\dfrac{(2\cos^2\theta - 1)^2}{\cos^4\theta - \sin^4\theta} = \dfrac{\left[2\cos^2\theta - (\sin^2\theta + \cos^2\theta)\right]^2}{(\cos^2\theta - \sin^2\theta)(\cos^2\theta + \sin^2\theta)}$

$= \dfrac{(\cos^2\theta - \sin^2\theta)^2}{(\cos^2\theta - \sin^2\theta)(\cos^2\theta + \sin^2\theta)} = \dfrac{\cos^2\theta - \sin^2\theta}{\cos^2\theta + \sin^2\theta}$

$= \cos^2\theta - \sin^2\theta = 1 - \sin^2\theta - \sin^2\theta = 1 - 2\sin^2\theta$

87. $\dfrac{1 + \sin\theta + \cos\theta}{1 + \sin\theta - \cos\theta} = \dfrac{(1 + \sin\theta) + \cos\theta}{(1 + \sin\theta) - \cos\theta} \cdot \dfrac{(1 + \sin\theta) + \cos\theta}{(1 + \sin\theta) + \cos\theta}$

$= \dfrac{1 + 2\sin\theta + \sin^2\theta + 2\cos\theta(1 + \sin\theta) + \cos^2\theta}{1 + 2\sin\theta + \sin^2\theta - \cos^2\theta}$

$= \dfrac{1 + 2\sin\theta + \sin^2\theta + 2\cos\theta(1 + \sin\theta) + (1 - \sin^2\theta)}{1 + 2\sin\theta + \sin^2\theta - (1 - \sin^2\theta)}$

$= \dfrac{2 + 2\sin\theta + 2\cos\theta(1 + \sin\theta)}{2\sin\theta + 2\sin^2\theta} = \dfrac{2(1 + \sin\theta) + 2\cos\theta(1 + \sin\theta)}{2\sin\theta(1 + \sin\theta)}$

$= \dfrac{2(1 + \sin\theta)(1 + \cos\theta)}{2\sin\theta(1 + \sin\theta)} = \dfrac{1 + \cos\theta}{\sin\theta}$

89. $(a\sin\theta + b\cos\theta)^2 + (a\cos\theta - b\sin\theta)^2$

$= a^2\sin^2\theta + 2ab\sin\theta\cos\theta + b^2\cos^2\theta + a^2\cos^2\theta - 2ab\sin\theta\cos\theta + b^2\sin^2\theta$

$= a^2(\sin^2\theta + \cos^2\theta) + b^2(\sin^2\theta + \cos^2\theta) = a^2 + b^2$

91. $\dfrac{\tan\alpha + \tan\beta}{\cot\alpha + \cot\beta} = \dfrac{\tan\alpha + \tan\beta}{\dfrac{1}{\tan\alpha} + \dfrac{1}{\tan\beta}} = \dfrac{\tan\alpha + \tan\beta}{\dfrac{\tan\beta + \tan\alpha}{\tan\alpha\,\tan\beta}}$

$= (\tan\alpha + \tan\beta) \cdot \left(\dfrac{\tan\alpha\,\tan\beta}{\tan\alpha + \tan\beta}\right) = \tan\alpha\,\tan\beta$

93. $(\sin\alpha + \cos\beta)^2 + (\cos\beta + \sin\alpha)(\cos\beta - \sin\alpha)$

$= \sin^2\alpha + 2\sin\alpha\cos\beta + \cos^2\beta + \cos^2\beta - \sin^2\alpha$

$= 2\sin\alpha\cos\beta + 2\cos^2\beta = 2\cos\beta(\sin\alpha + \cos\beta)$

95. $\ln|\sec\theta| = \ln\left|\dfrac{1}{\cos\theta}\right| = \ln\left|\cos\theta\right|^{-1} = -\ln|\cos\theta|$

97. $\ln|1 + \cos\theta| + \ln|1 - \cos\theta| = \ln\left(|1 + \cos\theta| \cdot |1 - \cos\theta|\right) = \ln|1 - \cos^2\theta|$

$= \ln\left|\sin^2\theta\right| = 2\ln|\sin\theta|$

99. Show that $\sec\left(\tan^{-1}v\right) = \sqrt{1 + v^2}$.

Let $\alpha = \tan^{-1}v$. Then $\tan\alpha = v,\ -\dfrac{\pi}{2} < \alpha < \dfrac{\pi}{2}$.

$\sec\left(\tan^{-1}v\right) = \sec\alpha = \sqrt{1 + \tan^2\alpha} = \sqrt{1 + v^2}$

101. Show that $\tan\left(\cos^{-1}v\right) = \dfrac{\sqrt{1-v^2}}{v}$.

   Let $\alpha = \cos^{-1}v$. Then $\cos\alpha = v,\ 0 \le \alpha \le \pi$.

   $\tan\left(\cos^{-1}v\right) = \tan\alpha = \dfrac{\sin\alpha}{\cos\alpha} = \dfrac{\sqrt{1-\cos^2\alpha}}{\cos\alpha} = \dfrac{\sqrt{1-v^2}}{v}$

103. Show that $\cos\left(\sin^{-1}v\right) = \sqrt{1-v^2}$.

   Let $\alpha = \sin^{-1}v$. Then $\sin\alpha = v,\ -\dfrac{\pi}{2} \le \alpha \le \dfrac{\pi}{2}$.

   $\cos\left(\sin^{-1}v\right) = \cos\alpha = \sqrt{1-\sin^2\alpha} = \sqrt{1-v^2}$

105–107.   Answers will vary.

Analytic Trigonometry

3.4 Sum and Difference Formulas

1. $\sqrt{(5-2)^2+(1-(-3))^2}=\sqrt{3^2+4^2}$
   $=\sqrt{9+16}=\sqrt{25}=5$

3. (a) $\dfrac{\sqrt{2}}{2}\cdot\dfrac{1}{2}=\dfrac{\sqrt{2}}{4}$

   (b) $1-\dfrac{1}{2}=\dfrac{1}{2}$

5.   –

7. False

9. $\sin\dfrac{5\pi}{12}=\sin\left(\dfrac{3\pi}{12}+\dfrac{2\pi}{12}\right)=\sin\dfrac{\pi}{4}\cdot\cos\dfrac{\pi}{6}+\cos\dfrac{\pi}{4}\cdot\sin\dfrac{\pi}{6}=\dfrac{\sqrt{2}}{2}\cdot\dfrac{\sqrt{3}}{2}+\dfrac{\sqrt{2}}{2}\cdot\dfrac{1}{2}$
   $=\dfrac{1}{4}\left(\sqrt{6}+\sqrt{2}\right)$

11. $\cos\dfrac{7\pi}{12}=\cos\left(\dfrac{4\pi}{12}+\dfrac{3\pi}{12}\right)=\cos\dfrac{\pi}{3}\cdot\cos\dfrac{\pi}{4}-\sin\dfrac{\pi}{3}\cdot\sin\dfrac{\pi}{4}=\dfrac{1}{2}\cdot\dfrac{\sqrt{2}}{2}-\dfrac{\sqrt{3}}{2}\cdot\dfrac{\sqrt{2}}{2}$
    $=\dfrac{1}{4}\left(\sqrt{2}-\sqrt{6}\right)$

13. $\cos165°=\cos(120°+45°)=\cos120°\cdot\cos45°-\sin120°\cdot\sin45°$
    $=-\dfrac{1}{2}\cdot\dfrac{\sqrt{2}}{2}-\dfrac{\sqrt{3}}{2}\cdot\dfrac{\sqrt{2}}{2}=-\dfrac{1}{4}\left(\sqrt{2}+\sqrt{6}\right)$

15. $\tan15°=\tan(45°-30°)=\dfrac{\tan45°-\tan30°}{1+\tan45°\cdot\tan30°}=\dfrac{1-\dfrac{\sqrt{3}}{3}}{1+1\cdot\dfrac{\sqrt{3}}{3}}=\dfrac{\dfrac{3-\sqrt{3}}{3}}{\dfrac{3+\sqrt{3}}{3}}$
    $=\left(\dfrac{3-\sqrt{3}}{3+\sqrt{3}}\right)\cdot\left(\dfrac{3-\sqrt{3}}{3-\sqrt{3}}\right)=\dfrac{9-6\sqrt{3}+3}{9-3}=\dfrac{12-6\sqrt{3}}{6}=\dfrac{6\left(2-\sqrt{3}\right)}{6}=2-\sqrt{3}$

17. $\sin\dfrac{17\pi}{12}=\sin\left(\dfrac{15\pi}{12}+\dfrac{2\pi}{12}\right)=\sin\dfrac{5\pi}{4}\cdot\cos\dfrac{\pi}{6}+\cos\dfrac{5\pi}{4}\cdot\sin\dfrac{\pi}{6}=-\dfrac{\sqrt{2}}{2}\cdot\dfrac{\sqrt{3}}{2}+\left(-\dfrac{\sqrt{2}}{2}\right)\cdot\dfrac{1}{2}$
    $=-\dfrac{1}{4}\left(\sqrt{6}+\sqrt{2}\right)$

19. $\sec\left(-\dfrac{\pi}{12}\right) = \dfrac{1}{\cos\left(-\dfrac{\pi}{12}\right)} = \dfrac{1}{\cos\left(\dfrac{3\pi}{12} - \dfrac{4\pi}{12}\right)} = \dfrac{1}{\cos\dfrac{\pi}{4}\cdot\cos\dfrac{\pi}{3} + \sin\dfrac{\pi}{4}\cdot\sin\dfrac{\pi}{3}}$

$= \dfrac{1}{\dfrac{\sqrt{2}}{2}\cdot\dfrac{1}{2} + \dfrac{\sqrt{2}}{2}\cdot\dfrac{\sqrt{3}}{2}} = \dfrac{1}{\dfrac{\sqrt{2}+\sqrt{6}}{4}} = \left(\dfrac{4}{\sqrt{2}+\sqrt{6}}\right)\cdot\left(\dfrac{\sqrt{2}-\sqrt{6}}{\sqrt{2}-\sqrt{6}}\right)$

$= \dfrac{4\left(\sqrt{2}-\sqrt{6}\right)}{2-6} = \dfrac{4\left(\sqrt{2}-\sqrt{6}\right)}{-4} = -\left(\sqrt{2}-\sqrt{6}\right) = \sqrt{6} - \sqrt{2}$

21. $\sin 20°\cdot\cos 10° + \cos 20°\cdot\sin 10° = \sin(20° + 10°) = \sin 30° = \dfrac{1}{2}$

23. $\cos 70°\cdot\cos 20° - \sin 70°\cdot\sin 20° = \cos(70° + 20°) = \cos 90° = 0$

25. $\dfrac{\tan 20° + \tan 25°}{1 - (\tan 20°)(\tan 25°)} = \tan(20° + 25°) = \tan 45° = 1$

$\dfrac{\tan 20°}{1 - (\tan(20°))}$

27. $\sin\dfrac{\pi}{12}\cdot\cos\dfrac{7\pi}{12} - \cos\dfrac{\pi}{12}\cdot\sin\dfrac{7\pi}{12} = \sin\left(\dfrac{\pi}{12} - \dfrac{7\pi}{12}\right) = \sin\left(-\dfrac{6\pi}{12}\right) = \sin\left(-\dfrac{\pi}{2}\right) = -1$

29. $\cos\dfrac{\pi}{12}\cdot\cos\dfrac{5\pi}{12} + \sin\dfrac{5\pi}{12}\cdot\sin\dfrac{\pi}{12} = \cos\left(\dfrac{\pi}{12} - \dfrac{5\pi}{12}\right) = \cos\left(-\dfrac{4\pi}{12}\right) = \cos\left(-\dfrac{\pi}{3}\right) = \cos\dfrac{\pi}{3} = \dfrac{1}{2}$

31. $\sin\alpha = \dfrac{3}{5},\ 0 < \alpha < \dfrac{\pi}{2};$ $\cos\beta = \dfrac{2\sqrt{5}}{5},\ -\dfrac{\pi}{2} < \beta < 0$

$x^2 + 3^2 = 5^2,\ x > 0$
    $x^2 = 25 - 9 = 16,\ x > 0$
        $x = 4$
    $\cos\alpha = \dfrac{4}{5},\ \tan\alpha = \dfrac{3}{4}$

$\left(2\sqrt{5}\right)^2 + y^2 = 5^2,\ y < 0$
    $y^2 = 25 - 20 = 5,\ y < 0$
        $y = -\sqrt{5}$
    $\sin\beta = -\dfrac{\sqrt{5}}{5},\ \tan\beta = \dfrac{-\sqrt{5}}{2\sqrt{5}} = -\dfrac{1}{2}$

(a) $\sin(\alpha + \beta) = \sin\alpha\cos\beta + \cos\alpha\sin\beta = \dfrac{3}{5}\cdot\dfrac{2\sqrt{5}}{5} + \dfrac{4}{5}\cdot\left(-\dfrac{\sqrt{5}}{5}\right) = \dfrac{6\sqrt{5} - 4\sqrt{5}}{25} = \dfrac{2\sqrt{5}}{25}$

(b) $\cos(\alpha + \beta) = \cos\alpha\cos\beta - \sin\alpha\sin\beta = \dfrac{4}{5}\cdot\dfrac{2\sqrt{5}}{5} - \dfrac{3}{5}\cdot\left(-\dfrac{\sqrt{5}}{5}\right) = \dfrac{8\sqrt{5} + 3\sqrt{5}}{25} = \dfrac{11\sqrt{5}}{25}$

(c) $\sin(\alpha - \beta) = \sin\alpha\cos\beta - \cos\alpha\sin\beta = \dfrac{3}{5}\cdot\dfrac{2\sqrt{5}}{5} - \dfrac{4}{5}\cdot\left(-\dfrac{\sqrt{5}}{5}\right) = \dfrac{6\sqrt{5} + 4\sqrt{5}}{25}$

$= \dfrac{10\sqrt{5}}{25} = \dfrac{2\sqrt{5}}{5}$

(d) $\tan(\alpha - \beta) = \dfrac{\tan\alpha - \tan\beta}{1 + \tan\alpha\cdot\tan\beta} = \dfrac{\dfrac{3}{4} - \left(-\dfrac{1}{2}\right)}{1 + \left(\dfrac{3}{4}\right)\left(-\dfrac{1}{2}\right)} = \dfrac{\dfrac{5}{4}}{\dfrac{5}{8}} = 2$

33. $\tan\alpha = -\dfrac{4}{3}, \ \dfrac{\pi}{2} < \alpha < \pi;$ $\cos\beta = \dfrac{1}{2}, \ 0 < \beta < \dfrac{\pi}{2}$

$r^2 = (-3)^2 + 4^2 = 25$ $1^2 + y^2 = 2^2, \ y > 0$

$r = 5$ $y^2 = 4 - 1 = 3, \ y > 0$

$\sin\alpha = \dfrac{4}{5}, \ \cos\alpha = \dfrac{-3}{5} = -\dfrac{3}{5}$ $y = \sqrt{3}$

$\sin\beta = \dfrac{\sqrt{3}}{2}, \ \tan\beta = \dfrac{\sqrt{3}}{1} = \sqrt{3}$

(a) $\sin(\alpha + \beta) = \sin\alpha\cos\beta + \cos\alpha\sin\beta = \left(\dfrac{4}{5}\right)\cdot\left(\dfrac{1}{2}\right) + \left(-\dfrac{3}{5}\right)\cdot\left(\dfrac{\sqrt{3}}{2}\right) = \dfrac{4 - 3\sqrt{3}}{10}$

(b) $\cos(\alpha + \beta) = \cos\alpha\cos\beta - \sin\alpha\sin\beta = \left(-\dfrac{3}{5}\right)\cdot\left(\dfrac{1}{2}\right) - \left(\dfrac{4}{5}\right)\cdot\left(\dfrac{\sqrt{3}}{2}\right) = \dfrac{-3 - 4\sqrt{3}}{10}$

(c) $\sin(\alpha - \beta) = \sin\alpha\cos\beta - \cos\alpha\sin\beta = \left(\dfrac{4}{5}\right)\cdot\left(\dfrac{1}{2}\right) - \left(-\dfrac{3}{5}\right)\cdot\left(\dfrac{\sqrt{3}}{2}\right) = \dfrac{4 + 3\sqrt{3}}{10}$

(d) $\tan(\alpha - \beta) = \dfrac{\tan\alpha - \tan\beta}{1 + \tan\alpha\tan\beta} = \dfrac{-\dfrac{4}{3} - \sqrt{3}}{1 + \left(-\dfrac{4}{3}\right)\cdot\sqrt{3}} = \dfrac{\dfrac{-4 - 3\sqrt{3}}{3}}{\dfrac{3 - 4\sqrt{3}}{3}} = \left(\dfrac{-4 - 3\sqrt{3}}{3 - 4\sqrt{3}}\right)\cdot\left(\dfrac{3 + 4\sqrt{3}}{3 + 4\sqrt{3}}\right)$

$= \dfrac{-48 - 25\sqrt{3}}{-39} = \dfrac{48 + 25\sqrt{3}}{39}$

35. $\sin\alpha = \dfrac{5}{13}, \ -\dfrac{3\pi}{2} < \alpha < -\pi;$ $\tan\beta = -\sqrt{3}, \ \dfrac{\pi}{2} < \beta < \pi$

$$x^2 + 5^2 = 13^2, \ x < 0$$
$$x^2 = 169 - 25 = 144, \ x < 0$$
$$x = -12$$
$$\cos\alpha = \frac{-12}{13} = -\frac{12}{13}, \ \tan\alpha = -\frac{5}{12}$$

$$r^2 = (-1)^2 + \sqrt{3}^2 = 4$$
$$r = 2$$
$$\sin\beta = \frac{\sqrt{3}}{2}, \quad \cos\beta = \frac{-1}{2} = -\frac{1}{2}$$

(a) $\sin(\alpha + \beta) = \sin\alpha\cos\beta + \cos\alpha\sin\beta = \left(\frac{5}{13}\right)\cdot\left(-\frac{1}{2}\right) + \left(-\frac{12}{13}\right)\cdot\left(\frac{\sqrt{3}}{2}\right) = \dfrac{-5 - 12\sqrt{3}}{26}$

(b) $\cos(\alpha + \beta) = \cos\alpha\cos\beta - \sin\alpha\sin\beta = \left(-\frac{12}{13}\right)\cdot\left(-\frac{1}{2}\right) - \left(\frac{5}{13}\right)\cdot\left(\frac{\sqrt{3}}{2}\right) = \dfrac{12 - 5\sqrt{3}}{26}$

(c) $\sin(\alpha - \beta) = \sin\alpha\cos\beta - \cos\alpha\sin\beta = \left(\frac{5}{13}\right)\cdot\left(-\frac{1}{2}\right) - \left(-\frac{12}{13}\right)\cdot\left(\frac{\sqrt{3}}{2}\right) = \dfrac{-5 + 12\sqrt{3}}{26}$

(d) $\tan(\alpha - \beta) = \dfrac{\tan\alpha - \tan\beta}{1 + \tan\alpha\tan\beta} = \dfrac{-\dfrac{5}{12} - \left(-\sqrt{3}\right)}{1 + \left(-\dfrac{5}{12}\right)\cdot\left(-\sqrt{3}\right)} = \dfrac{\dfrac{-5 + 12\sqrt{3}}{12}}{\dfrac{12 + 5\sqrt{3}}{12}}$

$$= \left(\frac{-5 + 12\sqrt{3}}{12 + 5\sqrt{3}}\right)\cdot\left(\frac{12 - 5\sqrt{3}}{12 - 5\sqrt{3}}\right) = \dfrac{-240 + 169\sqrt{3}}{69}$$

37. $\sin\theta = \frac{1}{3}, \quad \theta$ in quadrant II

(a) $\cos\theta = -\sqrt{1 - \sin^2\theta} = -\sqrt{1 - \left(\frac{1}{3}\right)^2} = -\sqrt{1 - \frac{1}{9}} = -\sqrt{\frac{8}{9}} = -\dfrac{2\sqrt{2}}{3}$

(b) $\sin\left(\theta + \frac{\pi}{6}\right) = \sin\theta\cdot\cos\frac{\pi}{6} + \cos\theta\cdot\sin\frac{\pi}{6} = \left(\frac{1}{3}\right)\left(\frac{\sqrt{3}}{2}\right) + \left(-\frac{2\sqrt{2}}{3}\right)\left(\frac{1}{2}\right) = \dfrac{\sqrt{3} - 2\sqrt{2}}{6}$

(c) $\cos\left(\theta - \frac{\pi}{3}\right) = \cos\theta\cdot\cos\frac{\pi}{3} + \sin\theta\cdot\sin\frac{\pi}{3} = \left(-\frac{2\sqrt{2}}{3}\right)\left(\frac{1}{2}\right) + \left(\frac{1}{3}\right)\left(\frac{\sqrt{3}}{2}\right) = \dfrac{-2\sqrt{2} + \sqrt{3}}{6}$

(d) $\tan\left(\theta + \frac{\pi}{4}\right) = \dfrac{\tan\theta + \tan\frac{\pi}{4}}{1 - \tan\theta\cdot\tan\frac{\pi}{4}} = \dfrac{-\dfrac{1}{2\sqrt{2}} + 1}{1 - \left(-\dfrac{1}{2\sqrt{2}}\right)\cdot 1} = \dfrac{\dfrac{-1 + 2\sqrt{2}}{2\sqrt{2}}}{\dfrac{2\sqrt{2} + 1}{2\sqrt{2}}}$

$$= \left(\frac{2\sqrt{2} - 1}{2\sqrt{2} + 1}\right)\cdot\left(\frac{2\sqrt{2} - 1}{2\sqrt{2} - 1}\right) = \dfrac{8 - 4\sqrt{2} + 1}{8 - 1} = \dfrac{9 - 4\sqrt{2}}{7}$$

39. $\sin\left(\frac{\pi}{2} + \theta\right) = \sin\frac{\pi}{2}\cdot\cos\theta + \cos\frac{\pi}{2}\cdot\sin\theta = 1\cdot\cos\theta + 0\cdot\sin\theta = \cos\theta$

41. $\sin(\pi - \theta) = \sin\pi\cdot\cos\theta - \cos\pi\cdot\sin\theta = 0\cdot\cos\theta - (-1)\sin\theta = \sin\theta$

43. $\sin(\pi + \theta) = \sin\pi\cdot\cos\theta + \cos\pi\cdot\sin\theta = 0\cdot\cos\theta + (-1)\sin\theta = -\sin\theta$

45. $\tan(\pi - \theta) = \dfrac{\tan\pi - \tan\theta}{1 + \tan\pi \cdot \tan\theta} = \dfrac{0 - \tan\theta}{1 + 0 \cdot \tan\theta} = \dfrac{-\tan\theta}{1} = -\tan\theta$

47. $\sin\left(\dfrac{3\pi}{2} + \theta\right) = \sin\dfrac{3\pi}{2} \cdot \cos\theta + \cos\dfrac{3\pi}{2} \cdot \sin\theta = -1 \cdot \cos\theta + 0 \cdot \sin\theta = -\cos\theta$

49. $\sin(\alpha + \beta) + \sin(\alpha - \beta) = \sin\alpha\cos\beta + \cos\alpha\sin\beta + \sin\alpha\cos\beta - \cos\alpha\sin\beta$
    $= 2\sin\alpha\cos\beta$

51. $\dfrac{\sin(\alpha + \beta)}{\sin\alpha\cos\beta} = \dfrac{\sin\alpha\cos\beta + \cos\alpha\sin\beta}{\sin\alpha\cos\beta} = \dfrac{\sin\alpha\cos\beta}{\sin\alpha\cos\beta} + \dfrac{\cos\alpha\sin\beta}{\sin\alpha\cos\beta} = 1 + \cot\alpha\tan\beta$

53. $\dfrac{\cos(\alpha + \beta)}{\cos\alpha\cos\beta} = \dfrac{\cos\alpha\cos\beta - \sin\alpha\sin\beta}{\cos\alpha\cos\beta} = \dfrac{\cos\alpha\cos\beta}{\cos\alpha\cos\beta} - \dfrac{\sin\alpha\sin\beta}{\cos\alpha\cos\beta} = 1 - \tan\alpha\tan\beta$

55. $\dfrac{\sin(\alpha + \beta)}{\sin(\alpha - \beta)} = \dfrac{\sin\alpha\cos\beta + \cos\alpha\sin\beta}{\sin\alpha\cos\beta - \cos\alpha\sin\beta} = \dfrac{\dfrac{\sin\alpha\cos\beta}{\cos\alpha\cos\beta} + \dfrac{\cos\alpha\sin\beta}{\cos\alpha\cos\beta}}{\dfrac{\sin\alpha\cos\beta}{\cos\alpha\cos\beta} - \dfrac{\cos\alpha\sin\beta}{\cos\alpha\cos\beta}} = \dfrac{\tan\alpha + \tan\beta}{\tan\alpha - \tan\beta}$

57. $\cot(\alpha + \beta) = \dfrac{\cos(\alpha + \beta)}{\sin(\alpha + \beta)} = \dfrac{\cos\alpha\cos\beta - \sin\alpha\sin\beta}{\sin\alpha\cos\beta + \cos\alpha\sin\beta}$

    $= \dfrac{\dfrac{\cos\alpha\cos\beta}{\sin\alpha\sin\beta} - \dfrac{\sin\alpha\sin\beta}{\sin\alpha\sin\beta}}{\dfrac{\sin\alpha\cos\beta}{\sin\alpha\sin\beta} + \dfrac{\cos\alpha\sin\beta}{\sin\alpha\sin\beta}} = \dfrac{\cot\alpha\cot\beta - 1}{\cot\beta + \cot\alpha}$

59. $\sec(\alpha + \beta) = \dfrac{1}{\cos(\alpha + \beta)} = \dfrac{1}{\cos\alpha\cos\beta - \sin\alpha\sin\beta}$

    $= \dfrac{\dfrac{1}{\sin\alpha\sin\beta}}{\dfrac{\cos\alpha\cos\beta}{\sin\alpha\sin\beta} - \dfrac{\sin\alpha\sin\beta}{\sin\alpha\sin\beta}} = \dfrac{\csc\alpha\csc\beta}{\cot\alpha\cot\beta - 1}$

61. $\sin(\alpha - \beta)\sin(\alpha + \beta) = (\sin\alpha\cos\beta - \cos\alpha\sin\beta)(\sin\alpha\cos\beta + \cos\alpha\sin\beta)$
    $= \sin^2\alpha\cos^2\beta - \cos^2\alpha\sin^2\beta = \sin^2\alpha(1 - \sin^2\beta) - (1 - \sin^2\alpha)\sin^2\beta$
    $= \sin^2\alpha - \sin^2\alpha\sin^2\beta - \sin^2\beta + \sin^2\alpha\sin^2\beta = \sin^2\alpha - \sin^2\beta$

63. $\sin(\theta + k\pi) = \sin\theta \cdot \cos k\pi + \cos\theta \cdot \sin k\pi = \sin\theta(-1)^k + \cos\theta \cdot 0 = (-1)^k \sin\theta$, k any integer

65. $\sin\left(\sin^{-1}\dfrac{1}{2} + \cos^{-1}0\right) = \sin\left(\dfrac{\pi}{6} + \dfrac{\pi}{2}\right) = \sin\left(\dfrac{2\pi}{3}\right) = \dfrac{\sqrt{3}}{2}$

67. $\sin\left[\sin^{-1}\dfrac{3}{5} - \cos^{-1}\left(-\dfrac{4}{5}\right)\right]$

Let $\alpha = \sin^{-1}\dfrac{3}{5}$ and $\beta = \cos^{-1}\left(-\dfrac{4}{5}\right)$. α is in quadrant I; β is in quadrant II.

Then $\sin\alpha = \dfrac{3}{5},\ 0 \le \alpha \le \dfrac{\pi}{2},\ \cos\beta = -\dfrac{4}{5},\ \dfrac{\pi}{2} \le \beta \le \pi$.

$\cos\alpha = \sqrt{1 - \sin^2\alpha} = \sqrt{1 - \left(\dfrac{3}{5}\right)^2} = \sqrt{1 - \dfrac{9}{25}} = \sqrt{\dfrac{16}{25}} = \dfrac{4}{5}$

$\sin\beta = \sqrt{1 - \cos^2\beta} = \sqrt{1 - \left(-\dfrac{4}{5}\right)^2} = \sqrt{1 - \dfrac{16}{25}} = \sqrt{\dfrac{9}{25}} = \dfrac{3}{5}$

$\sin\left[\sin^{-1}\dfrac{3}{5} - \cos^{-1}\left(-\dfrac{4}{5}\right)\right] = \sin(\alpha - \beta) = \sin\alpha\cos\beta - \cos\alpha\sin\beta$

$= \left(\dfrac{3}{5}\right)\cdot\left(-\dfrac{4}{5}\right) - \left(\dfrac{4}{5}\right)\cdot\left(\dfrac{3}{5}\right) = -\dfrac{12}{25} - \dfrac{12}{25} = -\dfrac{24}{25}$

69. $\cos\left(\tan^{-1}\dfrac{4}{3} + \cos^{-1}\dfrac{5}{13}\right)$

Let $\alpha = \tan^{-1}\dfrac{4}{3}$ and $\beta = \cos^{-1}\dfrac{5}{13}$. α is in quadrant I; β is in quadrant I.

Then $\tan\alpha = \dfrac{4}{3},\ 0 < \alpha < \dfrac{\pi}{2},\ \cos\beta = \dfrac{5}{13},\ 0 \le \beta \le \dfrac{\pi}{2}$.

$\sec\alpha = \sqrt{1 + \tan^2\alpha} = \sqrt{1 + \left(\dfrac{4}{3}\right)^2} = \sqrt{1 + \dfrac{16}{9}} = \sqrt{\dfrac{25}{9}} = \dfrac{5}{3};\quad \cos\alpha = \dfrac{3}{5}$

$\sin\alpha = \sqrt{1 - \cos^2\alpha} = \sqrt{1 - \left(\dfrac{3}{5}\right)^2} = \sqrt{1 - \dfrac{9}{25}} = \sqrt{\dfrac{16}{25}} = \dfrac{4}{5}$

$\sin\beta = \sqrt{1 - \cos^2\beta} = \sqrt{1 - \left(\dfrac{5}{13}\right)^2} = \sqrt{1 - \dfrac{25}{169}} = \sqrt{\dfrac{144}{169}} = \dfrac{12}{13}$

$\cos\left(\tan^{-1}\dfrac{4}{3} + \cos^{-1}\dfrac{5}{13}\right) = \cos(\alpha + \beta) = \cos\alpha\cos\beta - \sin\alpha\sin\beta$

$= \left(\dfrac{3}{5}\right)\cdot\left(\dfrac{5}{13}\right) - \left(\dfrac{4}{5}\right)\cdot\left(\dfrac{12}{13}\right) = \dfrac{15}{65} - \dfrac{48}{65} = -\dfrac{33}{65}$

71. $\cos\left(\sin^{-1}\dfrac{5}{13} - \tan^{-1}\dfrac{3}{4}\right)$

Let $\alpha = \sin^{-1}\dfrac{5}{13}$ and $\beta = \tan^{-1}\dfrac{3}{4}$. α is in quadrant I; β is in quadrant I.

Then $\sin\alpha = \dfrac{5}{13},\ 0 \le \alpha \le \dfrac{\pi}{2}$, and $\tan\beta = \dfrac{3}{4},\ 0 < \beta < \dfrac{\pi}{2}$.

$$\cos\alpha = \sqrt{1 - \sin^2\alpha} = \sqrt{1 - \left(\frac{5}{13}\right)^2} = \sqrt{1 - \frac{25}{169}} = \sqrt{\frac{144}{169}} = \frac{12}{13}$$

$$\sec\beta = \sqrt{1 + \tan^2\beta} = \sqrt{1 + \left(\frac{3}{4}\right)^2} = \sqrt{1 + \frac{9}{16}} = \sqrt{\frac{25}{16}} = \frac{5}{4}; \quad \cos\beta = \frac{4}{5}$$

$$\sin\beta = \sqrt{1 - \cos^2\beta} = \sqrt{1 - \left(\frac{4}{5}\right)^2} = \sqrt{1 - \frac{16}{25}} = \sqrt{\frac{9}{25}} = \frac{3}{5}$$

$$\cos\left[\sin^{-1}\frac{5}{13} - \tan^{-1}\frac{3}{4}\right] = \cos(\alpha - \beta)$$

$$= \cos\alpha\cos\beta + \sin\alpha\sin\beta = \frac{12}{13}\cdot\frac{4}{5} + \frac{5}{13}\cdot\frac{3}{5} = \frac{48}{65} + \frac{15}{65} = \frac{63}{65}$$

73. $\tan\left(\sin^{-1}\frac{3}{5} + \frac{\pi}{6}\right)$

Let $\alpha = \sin^{-1}\frac{3}{5}$. α is in quadrant I.

Then $\sin\alpha = \frac{3}{5}$, $0 \le \alpha \le \frac{\pi}{2}$.

$$\cos\alpha = \sqrt{1 - \sin^2\alpha} = \sqrt{1 - \left(\frac{3}{5}\right)^2} = \sqrt{1 - \frac{9}{25}} = \sqrt{\frac{16}{25}} = \frac{4}{5}$$

$$\tan\alpha = \frac{\sin\alpha}{\cos\alpha} = \frac{\frac{3}{5}}{\frac{4}{5}} = \frac{3}{5}\cdot\frac{5}{4} = \frac{3}{4}$$

$$\tan\left(\sin^{-1}\frac{3}{5} + \frac{\pi}{6}\right) = \frac{\tan\left(\sin^{-1}\frac{3}{5}\right) + \tan\frac{\pi}{6}}{1 - \tan\left(\sin^{-1}\frac{3}{5}\right)\cdot\tan\frac{\pi}{6}} = \frac{\frac{3}{4} + \frac{\sqrt{3}}{3}}{1 - \frac{3}{4}\cdot\frac{\sqrt{3}}{3}}$$

$$= \frac{\frac{9 + 4\sqrt{3}}{12}}{\frac{12 - 3\sqrt{3}}{12}} = \left(\frac{9 + 4\sqrt{3}}{12}\right)\left(\frac{12}{12 - 3\sqrt{3}}\right) = \left(\frac{9 + 4\sqrt{3}}{12 - 3\sqrt{3}}\right)\left(\frac{12 + 3\sqrt{3}}{12 + 3\sqrt{3}}\right)$$

$$= \frac{108 + 75\sqrt{3} + 36}{144 - 27} = \frac{144 + 75\sqrt{3}}{117} = \frac{48 + 25\sqrt{3}}{39}$$

75. $\tan\left(\sin^{-1}\frac{4}{5} + \cos^{-1}1\right)$

Let $\alpha = \sin^{-1}\frac{4}{5}$ and $\beta = \cos^{-1}1$; α is in quadrant I.

Then $\sin\alpha = \frac{4}{5}$, $0 \le \alpha \le \frac{\pi}{2}$ and $\cos\beta = 1$, $0 \le \beta \le \pi$.

$\cos\beta = 1, \ 0 \le \beta \le \pi \Rightarrow \beta = 0 \ \Rightarrow \cos^{-1}1 = 0$

$\cos\alpha = \sqrt{1 - \sin^2\alpha} = \sqrt{1 - \left(\dfrac{4}{5}\right)^2} = \sqrt{1 - \dfrac{16}{25}} = \sqrt{\dfrac{9}{25}} = \dfrac{3}{5}$

$\tan\alpha = \dfrac{\sin\alpha}{\cos\alpha} = \dfrac{\dfrac{4}{5}}{\dfrac{3}{5}} = \dfrac{4}{5}\cdot\dfrac{5}{3} = \dfrac{4}{3}$

$\tan\left(\sin^{-1}\dfrac{4}{5} + \cos^{-1}1\right) = \dfrac{\tan\left(\sin^{-1}\dfrac{4}{5}\right) + \tan\left(\cos^{-1}1\right)}{1 - \tan\left(\sin^{-1}\dfrac{4}{5}\right)\tan\left(\cos^{-1}1\right)} = \dfrac{\dfrac{4}{3} + 0}{1 - \dfrac{4}{3}\cdot 0} = \dfrac{\dfrac{4}{3}}{1} = \dfrac{4}{3}$

77. $\cos\left(\cos^{-1}u + \sin^{-1}v\right)$

Let $\alpha = \cos^{-1}u$ and $\beta = \sin^{-1}v$.

Then $\cos\alpha = u, \ 0 \le \alpha \le \pi$, and $\sin\beta = v, \ -\dfrac{\pi}{2} \le \beta \le \dfrac{\pi}{2}$

$\sin\alpha = \sqrt{1 - \cos^2\alpha} = \sqrt{1 - u^2}$

$\cos\beta = \sqrt{1 - \sin^2\beta} = \sqrt{1 - v^2}$

$\cos\left(\cos^{-1}u + \sin^{-1}v\right) = \cos(\alpha + \beta) = \cos\alpha\cos\beta - \sin\alpha\sin\beta = u\sqrt{1 - v^2} - v\sqrt{1 - u^2}$

79. $\sin\left(\tan^{-1}u - \sin^{-1}v\right)$

Let $\alpha = \tan^{-1}u$ and $\beta = \sin^{-1}v$.

Then $\tan\alpha = u, \ -\dfrac{\pi}{2} < \alpha < \dfrac{\pi}{2}$, and $\sin\beta = v, \ -\dfrac{\pi}{2} \le \beta \le \dfrac{\pi}{2}$

$\sec\alpha = \sqrt{\tan^2\alpha + 1} = \sqrt{u^2 + 1}; \quad \cos\alpha = \dfrac{1}{\sqrt{u^2 + 1}}$

$\sin\alpha = \sqrt{1 - \cos^2\alpha} = \sqrt{1 - \dfrac{1}{u^2 + 1}} = \sqrt{\dfrac{u^2 + 1 - 1}{u^2 + 1}} = \sqrt{\dfrac{u^2}{u^2 + 1}} = \dfrac{u}{\sqrt{u^2 + 1}}$

$\cos\beta = \sqrt{1 - \sin^2\beta} = \sqrt{1 - v^2}$

$\sin\left(\tan^{-1}u - \sin^{-1}v\right) = \sin(\alpha - \beta) = \sin\alpha\cos\beta - \cos\alpha\sin\beta$

$= \dfrac{u}{\sqrt{u^2 + 1}}\cdot\sqrt{1 - v^2} - \dfrac{1}{\sqrt{u^2 + 1}}\cdot v = \dfrac{u\sqrt{1 - v^2} - v}{\sqrt{u^2 + 1}}$

81. $\tan\left(\sin^{-1}u - \cos^{-1}v\right)$

Let $\alpha = \sin^{-1}u$ and $\beta = \cos^{-1}v$.

Then $\sin\alpha = u, \ -\dfrac{\pi}{2} \le \alpha \le \dfrac{\pi}{2}$, and $\cos\beta = v, \ 0 \le \beta \le \pi$

$\cos\alpha = \sqrt{1 - \sin^2\alpha} = \sqrt{1 - u^2}; \quad \tan\alpha = \dfrac{\sin\alpha}{\cos\alpha} = \dfrac{u}{\sqrt{1 - u^2}}$

$\sin\beta = \sqrt{1 - \cos^2\beta} = \sqrt{1 - v^2}; \quad \tan\beta = \dfrac{\sin\beta}{\cos\beta} = \dfrac{\sqrt{1 - v^2}}{v}$

$$\tan\left(\sin^{-1}u - \cos^{-1}v\right) = \tan(\alpha - \beta) = \frac{\tan\alpha - \tan\beta}{1 + \tan\alpha\tan\beta} = \frac{\dfrac{u}{\sqrt{1-u^2}} - \dfrac{\sqrt{1-v^2}}{v}}{1 + \dfrac{u}{\sqrt{1-u^2}} \cdot \dfrac{\sqrt{1-v^2}}{v}}$$

$$= \frac{\dfrac{uv - \sqrt{1-u^2}\sqrt{1-v^2}}{v\sqrt{1-u^2}}}{\dfrac{v\sqrt{1-u^2} + u\sqrt{1-v^2}}{v\sqrt{1-u^2}}} = \frac{uv - \sqrt{1-u^2}\sqrt{1-v^2}}{v\sqrt{1-u^2} + u\sqrt{1-v^2}}$$

83.   Show that $\sin^{-1}v + \cos^{-1}v = \dfrac{\pi}{2}$.

Let $\alpha = \sin^{-1}v$ and $\beta = \cos^{-1}v$.

Then $\sin\alpha = v = \cos\beta$, and since $\sin\alpha = \cos\left(\dfrac{\pi}{2} - \alpha\right)$, $\cos\left(\dfrac{\pi}{2} - \alpha\right) = \cos\beta$.

If $v \geq 0$, then $0 \leq \alpha \leq \dfrac{\pi}{2}$, so that $\left(\dfrac{\pi}{2} - \alpha\right)$ and β both lie in the interval $\left[0, \dfrac{\pi}{2}\right]$.

If $v < 0$, then $-\dfrac{\pi}{2} \leq \alpha < 0$, so that $\left(\dfrac{\pi}{2} - \alpha\right)$ and β both lie in the interval $\left(\dfrac{\pi}{2}, \pi\right]$. Either

way, $\cos\left(\dfrac{\pi}{2} - \alpha\right) = \cos\beta$ implies $\dfrac{\pi}{2} - \alpha = \beta$, or $\alpha + \beta = \dfrac{\pi}{2}$. Thus, $\sin^{-1}v + \cos^{-1}v = \dfrac{\pi}{2}$.

85.   Show that $\tan^{-1}\left(\dfrac{1}{v}\right) = \dfrac{\pi}{2} - \tan^{-1}v$, if $v > 0$.

Let $\alpha = \tan^{-1}\left(\dfrac{1}{v}\right)$ and $\beta = \tan^{-1}v$. Because $\dfrac{1}{v}$ must be defined, $v \neq 0$ and so $\alpha, \beta \neq 0$.

Then $\tan\alpha = \dfrac{1}{v} = \dfrac{1}{\tan\beta} = \cot\beta$, and since $\tan\alpha = \cot\left(\dfrac{\pi}{2} - \alpha\right)$, $\cot\left(\dfrac{\pi}{2} - \alpha\right) = \cot\beta$.

Because $v > 0$, $0 < \alpha < \dfrac{\pi}{2}$ and so $\dfrac{\pi}{2} - \alpha$ and β both lie in the interval $\left(0, \dfrac{\pi}{2}\right)$.

Then, $\cot\left(\dfrac{\pi}{2} - \alpha\right) = \cot\beta$ implies $\dfrac{\pi}{2} - \alpha = \beta$ or $\alpha = \dfrac{\pi}{2} - \beta$.

Thus, $\tan^{-1}\left(\dfrac{1}{v}\right) = \dfrac{\pi}{2} - \tan^{-1}v$, if $v > 0$.

87. $\sin\left(\sin^{-1}v + \cos^{-1}v\right) = \sin\left(\sin^{-1}v\right)\cos\left(\cos^{-1}v\right) + \cos\left(\sin^{-1}v\right)\sin\left(\cos^{-1}v\right)$

$= v \cdot v + \sqrt{1-v^2}\sqrt{1-v^2} = v^2 + 1 - v^2 = 1$

89. $\dfrac{\sin(x+h) - \sin x}{h} = \dfrac{\sin x\cos h + \cos x\sin h - \sin x}{h} = \dfrac{\cos x\sin h - \sin x + \sin x\cos h}{h}$

$= \dfrac{\cos x\sin h - \sin x(1 - \cos h)}{h} = \cos x \cdot \left(\dfrac{\sin h}{h}\right) - \sin x \cdot \left(\dfrac{1 - \cos h}{h}\right)$

91. $\tan\left(\dfrac{\pi}{2}-\theta\right)=\dfrac{\tan\dfrac{\pi}{2}-\tan\theta}{1+\tan\dfrac{\pi}{2}\cdot\tan\theta}$. This is impossible because $\tan\dfrac{\pi}{2}$ is undefined.

$\tan\left(\dfrac{\pi}{2}-\theta\right)=\dfrac{\sin\left(\dfrac{\pi}{2}-\theta\right)}{\cos\left(\dfrac{\pi}{2}-\theta\right)}=\dfrac{\cos\theta}{\sin\theta}=\cot\theta$

93. $\tan\theta=\tan\left(\theta_2-\theta_1\right)=\dfrac{\tan\theta_2-\tan\theta_1}{1+\tan\theta_2\tan\theta_1}=\dfrac{m_2-m_1}{1+m_2 m_1}$

95. The first step in the derivation, $\tan\left(\theta+\dfrac{\pi}{2}\right)=\dfrac{\tan\theta+\tan\dfrac{\pi}{2}}{1-\tan\theta\cdot\tan\dfrac{\pi}{2}}$, is impossible because

$\tan\dfrac{\pi}{2}$ is undefined.

Analytic Trigonometry

3.5 Double-angle and Half-angle Formulas

1. $\sin^2\theta,\ 2\cos^2\theta,\ 2\sin^2\theta$ 3. $\sin\theta$

5. False

7. $\sin\theta = \dfrac{3}{5},\ 0 < \theta < \dfrac{\pi}{2};$ thus, $0 < \dfrac{\theta}{2} < \dfrac{\pi}{4} \Rightarrow \dfrac{\theta}{2}$ is in quadrant I.

    $y = 3,\ r = 5$

    $x^2 + 3^2 = 5^2,\ x > 0 \Rightarrow x^2 = 25 - 9 = 16,\ x > 0 \Rightarrow x = 4$

    $\cos\theta = \dfrac{4}{5}$

    (a) $\sin(2\theta) = 2\sin\theta\cos\theta = 2 \cdot \dfrac{3}{5} \cdot \dfrac{4}{5} = \dfrac{24}{25}$

    (b) $\cos(2\theta) = \cos^2\theta - \sin^2\theta = \left(\dfrac{4}{5}\right)^2 - \left(\dfrac{3}{5}\right)^2 = \dfrac{16}{25} - \dfrac{9}{25} = \dfrac{7}{25}$

    (c) $\sin\dfrac{\theta}{2} = \sqrt{\dfrac{1 - \cos\theta}{2}} = \sqrt{\dfrac{1 - \dfrac{4}{5}}{2}} = \sqrt{\dfrac{\dfrac{1}{5}}{2}} = \sqrt{\dfrac{1}{10}} = \dfrac{1}{\sqrt{10}} \dfrac{\sqrt{10}}{\sqrt{10}} = \dfrac{\sqrt{10}}{10}$

    (d) $\cos\dfrac{\theta}{2} = \sqrt{\dfrac{1 + \cos\theta}{2}} = \sqrt{\dfrac{1 + \dfrac{4}{5}}{2}} = \sqrt{\dfrac{\dfrac{9}{5}}{2}} = \sqrt{\dfrac{9}{10}} = \dfrac{3}{\sqrt{10}} \dfrac{\sqrt{10}}{\sqrt{10}} = \dfrac{3\sqrt{10}}{10}$

9. $\tan\theta = \dfrac{4}{3},\ \pi < \theta < \dfrac{3\pi}{2};$ thus, $\dfrac{\pi}{2} < \dfrac{\theta}{2} < \dfrac{3\pi}{4} \Rightarrow \dfrac{\theta}{2}$ is in quadrant II.

    $x = -3,\ y = -4$

    $r^2 = (-3)^2 + (-4)^2 = 9 + 16 = 25 \Rightarrow r = 5$

    $\sin\theta = -\dfrac{4}{5},\ \cos\theta = -\dfrac{3}{5}$

    (a) $\sin(2\theta) = 2\sin\theta\cos\theta = 2 \cdot \left(-\dfrac{4}{5}\right) \cdot \left(-\dfrac{3}{5}\right) = \dfrac{24}{25}$

    (b) $\cos(2\theta) = \cos^2\theta - \sin^2\theta = \left(-\dfrac{3}{5}\right)^2 - \left(-\dfrac{4}{5}\right)^2 = \dfrac{9}{25} - \dfrac{16}{25} = -\dfrac{7}{25}$

142

(c) $\sin\dfrac{\theta}{2} = \sqrt{\dfrac{1-\cos\theta}{2}} = \sqrt{\dfrac{1-\left(-\dfrac{3}{5}\right)}{2}} = \sqrt{\dfrac{\dfrac{8}{5}}{2}} = \sqrt{\dfrac{4}{5}} = \dfrac{2}{\sqrt{5}}\dfrac{\sqrt{5}}{\sqrt{5}} = \dfrac{2\sqrt{5}}{5}$

(d) $\cos\dfrac{\theta}{2} = -\sqrt{\dfrac{1+\cos\theta}{2}} = -\sqrt{\dfrac{1+\left(-\dfrac{3}{5}\right)}{2}} = -\sqrt{\dfrac{\dfrac{2}{5}}{2}} = -\sqrt{\dfrac{1}{5}} = -\dfrac{1}{\sqrt{5}}\dfrac{\sqrt{5}}{\sqrt{5}} = -\dfrac{\sqrt{5}}{5}$

11. $\cos\theta = -\dfrac{\sqrt{6}}{3}$, $\dfrac{\pi}{2} < \theta < \pi$;   thus, $\dfrac{\pi}{4} < \dfrac{\theta}{2} < \dfrac{\pi}{2} \Rightarrow$ $\dfrac{\theta}{2}$ is in quadrant I.

$x = -\sqrt{6}$, $r = 3$

$(-\sqrt{6})^2 + y^2 = 3^2 \Rightarrow y^2 = 9 - 6 = 3 \Rightarrow y = \sqrt{3}$

$\sin\theta = \dfrac{\sqrt{3}}{3}$

(a) $\sin(2\theta) = 2\sin\theta\cos\theta = 2\cdot\left(\dfrac{\sqrt{3}}{3}\right)\cdot\left(-\dfrac{\sqrt{6}}{3}\right) = -\dfrac{2\sqrt{18}}{9} = -\dfrac{6\sqrt{2}}{9} = -\dfrac{2\sqrt{2}}{3}$

(b) $\cos(2\theta) = \cos^2\theta - \sin^2\theta = \left(-\dfrac{\sqrt{6}}{3}\right)^2 - \left(\dfrac{\sqrt{3}}{3}\right)^2 = \dfrac{6}{9} - \dfrac{3}{9} = \dfrac{3}{9} = \dfrac{1}{3}$

(c) $\sin\dfrac{\theta}{2} = \sqrt{\dfrac{1-\cos\theta}{2}} = \sqrt{\dfrac{1-\left(-\dfrac{\sqrt{6}}{3}\right)}{2}} = \sqrt{\dfrac{\dfrac{3+\sqrt{6}}{3}}{2}} = \sqrt{\dfrac{3+\sqrt{6}}{6}}$

(d) $\cos\dfrac{\theta}{2} = \sqrt{\dfrac{1+\cos\theta}{2}} = \sqrt{\dfrac{1+\left(-\dfrac{\sqrt{6}}{3}\right)}{2}} = \sqrt{\dfrac{\dfrac{3-\sqrt{6}}{3}}{2}} = \sqrt{\dfrac{3-\sqrt{6}}{6}}$

13. $\sec\theta = 3$, $\sin\theta > 0 \Rightarrow 0 < \theta < \dfrac{\pi}{2}$;   thus, $0 < \dfrac{\theta}{2} < \dfrac{\pi}{4} \Rightarrow \dfrac{\theta}{2}$ is in quadrant I.

$\cos\theta = \dfrac{1}{3}$, $x = 1$, $r = 3$

$1^2 + y^2 = 3^2 \Rightarrow y^2 = 9 - 1 = 8 \Rightarrow y = 2\sqrt{2}$

$\sin\theta = \dfrac{2\sqrt{2}}{3}$

(a) $\sin(2\theta) = 2\sin\theta\cos\theta = 2\cdot\dfrac{2\sqrt{2}}{3}\cdot\dfrac{1}{3} = \dfrac{4\sqrt{2}}{9}$

(b) $\cos(2\theta) = \cos^2\theta - \sin^2\theta = \left(\dfrac{1}{3}\right)^2 - \left(\dfrac{2\sqrt{2}}{3}\right)^2 = \dfrac{1}{9} - \dfrac{8}{9} = -\dfrac{7}{9}$

(c) $\sin\dfrac{\theta}{2} = \sqrt{\dfrac{1-\cos\theta}{2}} = \sqrt{\dfrac{1-\frac{1}{3}}{2}} = \sqrt{\dfrac{\frac{2}{3}}{2}} = \sqrt{\dfrac{1}{3}} = \dfrac{1}{\sqrt{3}} = \dfrac{\sqrt{3}}{\sqrt{3}} = \dfrac{\sqrt{3}}{3}$

(d) $\cos\dfrac{\theta}{2} = \sqrt{\dfrac{1+\cos\theta}{2}} = \sqrt{\dfrac{1+\frac{1}{3}}{2}} = \sqrt{\dfrac{\frac{4}{3}}{2}} = \sqrt{\dfrac{2}{3}} = \dfrac{\sqrt{2}}{\sqrt{3}} = \dfrac{\sqrt{2}}{\sqrt{3}}\dfrac{\sqrt{3}}{\sqrt{3}} = \dfrac{\sqrt{6}}{3}$

15. $\cot\theta = -2,\ \sec\theta < 0 \Rightarrow \dfrac{\pi}{2} < \theta < \pi$; thus, $\dfrac{\pi}{4} < \dfrac{\theta}{2} < \dfrac{\pi}{2} \Rightarrow \dfrac{\theta}{2}$ is in quadrant I.

$x = -2,\ y = 1$

$r^2 = (-2)^2 + 1^2 = 4 + 1 = 5 \ \Rightarrow \ r = \sqrt{5}$

$\sin\theta = \dfrac{1}{\sqrt{5}} = \dfrac{\sqrt{5}}{5},\quad \cos\theta = -\dfrac{2}{\sqrt{5}} = -\dfrac{2\sqrt{5}}{5}$

(a) $\sin(2\theta) = 2\sin\theta\cos\theta = 2\cdot\left(\dfrac{\sqrt{5}}{5}\right)\cdot\left(-\dfrac{2\sqrt{5}}{5}\right) = -\dfrac{20}{25} = -\dfrac{4}{5}$

(b) $\cos(2\theta) = \cos^2\theta - \sin^2\theta = \left(-\dfrac{2\sqrt{5}}{5}\right)^2 - \left(\dfrac{\sqrt{5}}{5}\right)^2 = \dfrac{20}{25} - \dfrac{5}{25} = \dfrac{15}{25} = \dfrac{3}{5}$

(c) $\sin\dfrac{\theta}{2} = \sqrt{\dfrac{1-\cos\theta}{2}} = \sqrt{\dfrac{1-\left(-\frac{2\sqrt{5}}{5}\right)}{2}} = \sqrt{\dfrac{\frac{5+2\sqrt{5}}{5}}{2}} = \sqrt{\dfrac{5+2\sqrt{5}}{10}}$

(d) $\cos\dfrac{\theta}{2} = \sqrt{\dfrac{1+\cos\theta}{2}} = \sqrt{\dfrac{1+\left(-\frac{2\sqrt{5}}{5}\right)}{2}} = \sqrt{\dfrac{\frac{5-2\sqrt{5}}{5}}{2}} = \sqrt{\dfrac{5-2\sqrt{5}}{10}}$

17. $\tan\theta = -3,\ \sin\theta < 0 \Rightarrow \dfrac{3\pi}{2} < \theta < 2\pi$; thus, $\dfrac{3\pi}{4} < \dfrac{\theta}{2} < \pi \Rightarrow \dfrac{\theta}{2}$ is in quadrant II.

$x = 1,\ y = -3$

$r^2 = 1^2 + (-3)^2 = 1 + 9 = 10 \ \Rightarrow \ r = \sqrt{10}$

$\sin\theta = \dfrac{-3}{\sqrt{10}} = -\dfrac{3\sqrt{10}}{10},\quad \cos\theta = \dfrac{1}{\sqrt{10}} = \dfrac{\sqrt{10}}{10}$

(a) $\sin(2\theta) = 2\sin\theta\cos\theta = 2\cdot\left(-\dfrac{3\sqrt{10}}{10}\right)\cdot\left(\dfrac{\sqrt{10}}{10}\right) = -\dfrac{6}{10} = -\dfrac{3}{5}$

(b) $\cos(2\theta) = \cos^2\theta - \sin^2\theta = \left(\dfrac{\sqrt{10}}{10}\right)^2 - \left(-\dfrac{3\sqrt{10}}{10}\right)^2 = \dfrac{10}{100} - \dfrac{90}{100} = -\dfrac{80}{100} = -\dfrac{4}{5}$

(c) $\sin\dfrac{\theta}{2} = \sqrt{\dfrac{1-\cos\theta}{2}} = \sqrt{\dfrac{1-\dfrac{\sqrt{10}}{10}}{2}} = \sqrt{\dfrac{\dfrac{10-\sqrt{10}}{10}}{2}} = \sqrt{\dfrac{10-\sqrt{10}}{20}} = \dfrac{1}{2}\sqrt{\dfrac{10-\sqrt{10}}{5}}$

(d) $\cos\dfrac{\theta}{2} = -\sqrt{\dfrac{1+\cos\theta}{2}} = -\sqrt{\dfrac{1+\dfrac{\sqrt{10}}{10}}{2}} = -\sqrt{\dfrac{\dfrac{10+\sqrt{10}}{10}}{2}} = -\sqrt{\dfrac{10+\sqrt{10}}{20}} = -\dfrac{1}{2}\sqrt{\dfrac{10+\sqrt{10}}{5}}$

19. $\sin 22.5° = \sin\left(\dfrac{45°}{2}\right) = \sqrt{\dfrac{1-\cos 45°}{2}} = \sqrt{\dfrac{1-\dfrac{\sqrt{2}}{2}}{2}} = \sqrt{\dfrac{2-\sqrt{2}}{4}} = \dfrac{\sqrt{2-\sqrt{2}}}{2}$

21. $\tan\dfrac{7\pi}{8} = \tan\left(\dfrac{\dfrac{7\pi}{4}}{2}\right) = -\sqrt{\dfrac{1-\cos\dfrac{7\pi}{4}}{1+\cos\dfrac{7\pi}{4}}} = -\sqrt{\dfrac{1-\dfrac{\sqrt{2}}{2}}{1+\dfrac{\sqrt{2}}{2}}} = -\sqrt{\left(\dfrac{2-\sqrt{2}}{2+\sqrt{2}}\right)\cdot\left(\dfrac{2-\sqrt{2}}{2-\sqrt{2}}\right)}$

$= -\sqrt{\dfrac{\left(2-\sqrt{2}\right)^2}{2}} = -\left(\dfrac{2-\sqrt{2}}{\sqrt{2}}\right) = -\left(\sqrt{2}-1\right) = 1-\sqrt{2}$

23. $\cos 165° = \cos\left(\dfrac{330°}{2}\right) = -\sqrt{\dfrac{1+\cos 330°}{2}} = -\sqrt{\dfrac{1+\dfrac{\sqrt{3}}{2}}{2}} = -\sqrt{\dfrac{2+\sqrt{3}}{4}} = -\dfrac{\sqrt{2+\sqrt{3}}}{2}$

25. $\sec\dfrac{15\pi}{8} = \dfrac{1}{\cos\dfrac{15\pi}{8}} = \dfrac{1}{\cos\left(\dfrac{\dfrac{15\pi}{4}}{2}\right)} = \dfrac{1}{\sqrt{\dfrac{1+\cos\dfrac{15\pi}{4}}{2}}} = \dfrac{1}{\sqrt{\dfrac{1+\dfrac{\sqrt{2}}{2}}{2}}} = \dfrac{1}{\sqrt{\dfrac{2+\sqrt{2}}{4}}}$

$= \left(\dfrac{2}{\sqrt{2+\sqrt{2}}}\right)\cdot\left(\dfrac{\sqrt{2+\sqrt{2}}}{\sqrt{2+\sqrt{2}}}\right) = \left(\dfrac{2\sqrt{2+\sqrt{2}}}{2+\sqrt{2}}\right)\cdot\left(\dfrac{2-\sqrt{2}}{2-\sqrt{2}}\right)$

$= \dfrac{2\left(2-\sqrt{2}\right)\sqrt{2+\sqrt{2}}}{2} = \left(2-\sqrt{2}\right)\sqrt{2+\sqrt{2}}$

27. $\sin\left(-\dfrac{\pi}{8}\right) = \sin\left(\dfrac{\left(-\dfrac{\pi}{4}\right)}{2}\right) = -\sqrt{\dfrac{1-\cos\left(-\dfrac{\pi}{4}\right)}{2}} = -\sqrt{\dfrac{1-\dfrac{\sqrt{2}}{2}}{2}} = -\sqrt{\dfrac{2-\sqrt{2}}{4}} = -\dfrac{\sqrt{2-\sqrt{2}}}{2}$

29. $\sin^4\theta = \left(\sin^2\theta\right)^2 = \left(\dfrac{1-\cos(2\theta)}{2}\right)^2 = \dfrac{1}{4}\left(1-2\cos(2\theta)+\cos^2(2\theta)\right)$

$= \dfrac{1}{4} - \dfrac{1}{2}\cos(2\theta) + \dfrac{1}{4}\cos^2(2\theta) = \dfrac{1}{4} - \dfrac{1}{2}\cos(2\theta) + \dfrac{1}{4}\left(\dfrac{1+\cos(4\theta)}{2}\right)$

$= \dfrac{1}{4} - \dfrac{1}{2}\cos(2\theta) + \dfrac{1}{8} + \dfrac{1}{8}\cos(4\theta) = \dfrac{3}{8} - \dfrac{1}{2}\cos(2\theta) + \dfrac{1}{8}\cos(4\theta)$

31. $\sin(4\theta) = \sin(2(2\theta)) = 2\sin(2\theta)\cos(2\theta) = 2(2\sin\theta\cos\theta)\left(1-2\sin^2\theta\right)$

$= \cos\theta\left(4\sin\theta - 8\sin^3\theta\right)$

33. Use the results of problem 31 to help solve the problem:
$\sin(5\theta) = \sin(4\theta + \theta) = \sin(4\theta)\cos\theta + \cos(4\theta)\sin\theta$

$= \cos\theta\left(4\sin\theta - 8\sin^3\theta\right)\cos\theta + \cos(2(2\theta))\sin\theta$

$= \cos^2\theta\left(4\sin\theta - 8\sin^3\theta\right) + \left(1-2\sin^2(2\theta)\right)\sin\theta$

$= \left(1-\sin^2\theta\right)\left(4\sin\theta - 8\sin^3\theta\right) + \sin\theta\left(1-2(2\sin\theta\cos\theta)^2\right)$

$= 4\sin\theta - 12\sin^3\theta + 8\sin^5\theta + \sin\theta\left(1-8\sin^2\theta\cos^2\theta\right)$

$= 4\sin\theta - 12\sin^3\theta + 8\sin^5\theta + \sin\theta - 8\sin^3\theta\left(1-\sin^2\theta\right)$

$= 5\sin\theta - 12\sin^3\theta + 8\sin^5\theta - 8\sin^3\theta + 8\sin^5\theta$

$= 5\sin\theta - 20\sin^3\theta + 16\sin^5\theta$

35. $\cos^4\theta - \sin^4\theta = \left(\cos^2\theta + \sin^2\theta\right)\left(\cos^2\theta - \sin^2\theta\right) = 1\cdot\cos(2\theta) = \cos(2\theta)$

37. $\cot(2\theta) = \dfrac{1}{\tan(2\theta)} = \dfrac{1}{\dfrac{2\tan\theta}{1-\tan^2\theta}} = \dfrac{1-\tan^2\theta}{2\tan\theta} = \dfrac{1-\dfrac{1}{\cot^2\theta}}{\dfrac{2}{\cot\theta}} = \dfrac{\dfrac{\cot^2\theta-1}{\cot^2\theta}}{\dfrac{2}{\cot\theta}} = \dfrac{\cot^2\theta-1}{2\cot\theta}$

39. $\sec(2\theta) = \dfrac{1}{\cos(2\theta)} = \dfrac{1}{2\cos^2\theta-1} = \dfrac{1}{\dfrac{2}{\sec^2\theta}-1} = \dfrac{1}{\dfrac{2-\sec^2\theta}{\sec^2\theta}} = \dfrac{\sec^2\theta}{2-\sec^2\theta}$

41. $\cos^2(2\theta) - \sin^2(2\theta) = \cos(2(2\theta)) = \cos(4\theta)$

43. $\dfrac{\cos(2\theta)}{1+\sin(2\theta)} = \dfrac{\cos^2\theta - \sin^2\theta}{1+2\sin\theta\cos\theta} = \dfrac{(\cos\theta - \sin\theta)(\cos\theta + \sin\theta)}{\cos^2\theta + \sin^2\theta + 2\sin\theta\cos\theta}$

$= \dfrac{(\cos\theta - \sin\theta)(\cos\theta + \sin\theta)}{(\cos\theta + \sin\theta)(\cos\theta + \sin\theta)} = \dfrac{\cos\theta - \sin\theta}{\cos\theta + \sin\theta} = \dfrac{\dfrac{\cos\theta}{\sin\theta} - \dfrac{\sin\theta}{\sin\theta}}{\dfrac{\cos\theta}{\sin\theta} + \dfrac{\sin\theta}{\sin\theta}} = \dfrac{\cot\theta - 1}{\cot\theta + 1}$

45. $\sec^2\left(\dfrac{\theta}{2}\right) = \dfrac{1}{\cos^2\left(\dfrac{\theta}{2}\right)} = \dfrac{1}{\dfrac{1+\cos\theta}{2}} = \dfrac{2}{1+\cos\theta}$

47. $\cot^2\left(\dfrac{\theta}{2}\right) = \dfrac{1}{\tan^2\left(\dfrac{\theta}{2}\right)} = \dfrac{1}{\dfrac{1-\cos\theta}{1+\cos\theta}} = \dfrac{1+\cos\theta}{1-\cos\theta} = \dfrac{1+\dfrac{1}{\sec\theta}}{1-\dfrac{1}{\sec\theta}} = \dfrac{\dfrac{\sec\theta+1}{\sec\theta}}{\dfrac{\sec\theta-1}{\sec\theta}} = \dfrac{\sec\theta+1}{\sec\theta-1}$

49. $\dfrac{1-\tan^2\dfrac{\theta}{2}}{1+\tan^2\dfrac{\theta}{2}} = \dfrac{1-\dfrac{1-\cos\theta}{1+\cos\theta}}{1+\dfrac{1-\cos\theta}{1+\cos\theta}} = \dfrac{\dfrac{1+\cos\theta-(1-\cos\theta)}{1+\cos\theta}}{\dfrac{1+\cos\theta+1-\cos\theta}{1+\cos\theta}} = \dfrac{2\cos\theta}{2} = \cos\theta$

51. $\dfrac{\sin(3\theta)}{\sin\theta} - \dfrac{\cos(3\theta)}{\cos\theta} = \dfrac{\sin(3\theta)\cos\theta - \cos(3\theta)\sin\theta}{\sin\theta\cos\theta} = \dfrac{\sin(3\theta-\theta)}{\sin\theta\cos\theta} = \dfrac{\sin 2\theta}{\sin\theta\cos\theta} = \dfrac{2\sin\theta\cos\theta}{\sin\theta\cos\theta} = 2$

53. $\tan(3\theta) = \tan(2\theta+\theta) = \dfrac{\tan(2\theta)+\tan\theta}{1-\tan(2\theta)\tan\theta} = \dfrac{\dfrac{2\tan\theta}{1-\tan^2\theta}+\tan\theta}{1-\dfrac{2\tan\theta}{1-\tan^2\theta}\cdot\tan\theta}$

$= \dfrac{\dfrac{2\tan\theta+\tan\theta-\tan^3\theta}{1-\tan^2\theta}}{\dfrac{1-\tan^2\theta-2\tan^2\theta}{1-\tan^2\theta}} = \dfrac{3\tan\theta-\tan^3\theta}{1-3\tan^2\theta}$

55. $\dfrac{1}{2}\cdot\left(\ln|1-\cos(2\theta)|-\ln 2\right) = \dfrac{1}{2}\cdot\ln\left|\dfrac{1-\cos 2\theta}{2}\right| = \ln\left(\left|\dfrac{1-\cos(2\theta)}{2}\right|^{1/2}\right) = \ln\left(\left|\sin^2\theta\right|^{1/2}\right) = \ln|\sin\theta|$

57. $\sin\left(2\sin^{-1}\dfrac{1}{2}\right) = \sin\left(2\left(\dfrac{\pi}{6}\right)\right) = \sin\dfrac{\pi}{3} = \dfrac{\sqrt{3}}{2}$

59. $\cos\left(2\sin^{-1}\dfrac{3}{5}\right) = 1-2\sin^2\left(\sin^{-1}\dfrac{3}{5}\right) = 1-2\left(\dfrac{3}{5}\right)^2 = 1-2\left(\dfrac{9}{25}\right) = 1-\dfrac{18}{25} = \dfrac{7}{25}$

61. $\tan\left[2\cos^{-1}\left(-\dfrac{3}{5}\right)\right]$

Let $\alpha = \cos^{-1}\left(-\dfrac{3}{5}\right)$. α is in quadrant II.

Then $\cos\alpha = -\dfrac{3}{5}$, $\dfrac{\pi}{2} \le \alpha \le \pi$.

$$\sec\alpha = -\frac{5}{3}; \quad \tan\alpha = -\sqrt{\sec^2\alpha - 1} = -\sqrt{\left(-\frac{5}{3}\right)^2 - 1} = -\sqrt{\frac{25}{9} - 1} = -\sqrt{\frac{16}{9}} = -\frac{4}{3}$$

$$\tan\left[2\cos^{-1}\left(-\frac{3}{5}\right)\right] = \tan 2\alpha = \frac{2\tan\alpha}{1-\tan^2\alpha} = \frac{2\left(-\frac{4}{3}\right)}{1-\left(-\frac{4}{3}\right)^2} = \frac{-\frac{8}{3}}{1-\frac{16}{9}} = \frac{-\frac{8}{3}}{-\frac{7}{9}} = \left(-\frac{8}{3}\right)\cdot\left(-\frac{9}{7}\right) = \frac{24}{7}$$

63. $\sin\left(2\cos^{-1}\frac{4}{5}\right)$

Let $\alpha = \cos^{-1}\frac{4}{5}$. α is in quadrant I.

Then $\cos\alpha = \frac{4}{5}, \ 0 \le \alpha \le \frac{\pi}{2}$.

$$\sin\alpha = \sqrt{1-\cos^2\alpha} = \sqrt{1-\left(\frac{4}{5}\right)^2} = \sqrt{1-\frac{16}{25}} = \sqrt{\frac{9}{25}} = \frac{3}{5}$$

$$\sin\left[2\cos^{-1}\frac{4}{5}\right] = \sin 2\alpha = 2\sin\alpha\cos\alpha = 2\cdot\frac{3}{5}\cdot\frac{4}{5} = \frac{24}{25}$$

65. $\sin^2\left[\frac{1}{2}\cdot\cos^{-1}\frac{3}{5}\right] = \dfrac{1-\cos\left(\cos^{-1}\frac{3}{5}\right)}{2} = \dfrac{1-\frac{3}{5}}{2} = \dfrac{\frac{2}{5}}{2} = \frac{1}{5}$

67. $\sec\left(2\tan^{-1}\frac{3}{4}\right)$

Let $\alpha = \tan^{-1}\left(\frac{3}{4}\right)$. α is in quadrant I.

Then $\tan\alpha = \frac{3}{4}, \ 0 < \alpha < \frac{\pi}{2}$.

$$\sec\alpha = \sqrt{\tan^2\alpha + 1} = \sqrt{\left(\frac{3}{4}\right)^2 + 1} = \sqrt{\frac{9}{16} + 1} = \sqrt{\frac{25}{16}} = \frac{5}{4}; \quad \cos\alpha = \frac{4}{5}$$

$$\sec\left[2\tan^{-1}\frac{3}{4}\right] = \sec(2\alpha) = \frac{1}{\cos(2\alpha)} = \frac{1}{2\cos^2\alpha - 1} = \frac{1}{2\left(\frac{4}{5}\right)^2 - 1} = \frac{1}{2\cdot\left(\frac{16}{25}\right) - 1} = \frac{1}{\frac{7}{25}} = \frac{25}{7}$$

69. $\sin(2\theta) = 2\sin\theta\cos\theta = \dfrac{2\sin\theta}{\cos\theta}\cdot\dfrac{\cos^2\theta}{1} = \dfrac{2\cdot\frac{\sin\theta}{\cos\theta}}{\frac{1}{\cos^2\theta}} = \dfrac{2\tan\theta}{\sec^2\theta} = \dfrac{2\tan\theta}{1+\tan^2\theta}\cdot\dfrac{4}{4}$

$$= \frac{4(2\tan\theta)}{4+(2\tan\theta)^2} = \frac{4x}{4+x^2}$$

71. $\dfrac{1}{2} \cdot \sin^2 x + C = -\dfrac{1}{4} \cdot \cos(2x)$

$C = -\dfrac{1}{4} \cdot \cos(2x) - \dfrac{1}{2} \cdot \sin^2 x = -\dfrac{1}{4} \cdot \left(\cos(2x) + 2\sin^2 x \right)$

$= -\dfrac{1}{4} \cdot \left(1 - 2\sin^2 x + 2\sin^2 x \right) = -\dfrac{1}{4} \cdot (1)$

$= -\dfrac{1}{4}$

73.
$$z = \tan\left(\dfrac{\alpha}{2} \right)$$

$$z = \dfrac{1 - \cos\alpha}{\sin\alpha}$$

$$z \sin\alpha = 1 - \cos\alpha$$

$$z \sin\alpha = 1 - \sqrt{1 - \sin^2\alpha}$$

$$z \sin\alpha - 1 = -\sqrt{1 - \sin^2\alpha}$$

$$z^2 \sin^2\alpha - 2z\sin\alpha + 1 = 1 - \sin^2\alpha$$

$$z^2 \sin^2\alpha + \sin^2\alpha = 2z\sin\alpha$$

$$\sin^2\alpha(z^2 + 1) = 2z\sin\alpha$$

$$\sin\alpha(z^2 + 1) = 2z$$

$$\sin\alpha = \dfrac{2z}{z^2 + 1}$$

75. Let b represent the base of the triangle.

$\cos\dfrac{\theta}{2} = \dfrac{h}{s} \Rightarrow h = s\cos\dfrac{\theta}{2}$ and $\sin\dfrac{\theta}{2} = \dfrac{(b/2)}{s} \Rightarrow b = 2s\sin\dfrac{\theta}{2}$

$A = \dfrac{1}{2}b \cdot h = \dfrac{1}{2} \cdot \left(2s\sin\dfrac{\theta}{2} \right)\left(s\cos\dfrac{\theta}{2} \right) = s^2 \sin\dfrac{\theta}{2}\cos\dfrac{\theta}{2} = \dfrac{1}{2} \cdot s^2 \sin\theta$

77. $f(x) = \sin^2 x = \dfrac{1 - \cos(2x)}{2}$

Starting with the graph of $y = \cos x$,
compress horizontally by a factor of 2,
reflect across the x-axis, shift 1 unit up,
and shrink vertically by a factor of 2.

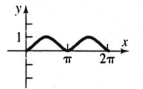

79. $\sin\dfrac{\pi}{24} = \sin\left(\dfrac{\dfrac{\pi}{12}}{2}\right) = \sqrt{\dfrac{1-\cos\dfrac{\pi}{12}}{2}} = \sqrt{\dfrac{1-\left(\dfrac{1}{4}\left(\sqrt{6}+\sqrt{2}\right)\right)}{2}} = \sqrt{\dfrac{1}{2}-\dfrac{1}{8}\left(\sqrt{6}+\sqrt{2}\right)}$

$= \sqrt{\dfrac{8-2\left(\sqrt{6}+\sqrt{2}\right)}{16}} = \dfrac{\sqrt{8-2\left(\sqrt{6}+\sqrt{2}\right)}}{4} = \dfrac{\sqrt{2\left(4-\left(\sqrt{6}+\sqrt{2}\right)\right)}}{4} = \dfrac{\sqrt{2}}{4}\sqrt{4-\sqrt{6}-\sqrt{2}}$

$\cos\dfrac{\pi}{24} = \cos\left(\dfrac{\dfrac{\pi}{12}}{2}\right) = \sqrt{\dfrac{1+\cos\dfrac{\pi}{12}}{2}} = \sqrt{\dfrac{1+\left(\dfrac{1}{4}\left(\sqrt{6}+\sqrt{2}\right)\right)}{2}} = \sqrt{\dfrac{1}{2}+\dfrac{1}{8}\left(\sqrt{6}+\sqrt{2}\right)}$

$= \sqrt{\dfrac{8+2\left(\sqrt{6}+\sqrt{2}\right)}{16}} = \dfrac{\sqrt{8+2\left(\sqrt{6}+\sqrt{2}\right)}}{4} = \dfrac{\sqrt{2\left(4+\sqrt{6}+\sqrt{2}\right)}}{4} = \dfrac{\sqrt{2}}{4}\sqrt{4+\sqrt{6}+\sqrt{2}}$

81. $\sin^3\theta + \sin^3(\theta+120°) + \sin^3(\theta+240°)$

$= \sin^3\theta + \left(\sin\theta\cos(120°)+\cos\theta\sin(120°)\right)^3 + \left(\sin\theta\cos(240°)+\cos\theta\sin(240°)\right)^3$

$= \sin^3\theta + \left(-\dfrac{1}{2}\cdot\sin\theta+\dfrac{\sqrt{3}}{2}\cdot\cos\theta\right)^3 + \left(-\dfrac{1}{2}\cdot\sin\theta-\dfrac{\sqrt{3}}{2}\cdot\cos\theta\right)^3$

$= \sin^3\theta + \dfrac{1}{8}\cdot\left(-\sin^3\theta+3\sqrt{3}\sin^2\theta\cos\theta-9\sin\theta\cos^2\theta+3\sqrt{3}\cos^3\theta\right)$

$\qquad -\dfrac{1}{8}\left(\sin^3\theta+3\sqrt{3}\sin^2\theta\cos\theta+9\sin\theta\cos^2\theta+3\sqrt{3}\cos^3\theta\right)$

$= \sin^3\theta - \dfrac{1}{8}\cdot\sin^3\theta+\dfrac{3\sqrt{3}}{8}\cdot\sin^2\theta\cos\theta-\dfrac{9}{8}\cdot\sin\theta\cos^2\theta+\dfrac{3\sqrt{3}}{8}\cdot\cos^3\theta$

$\qquad -\dfrac{1}{8}\cdot\sin^3\theta-\dfrac{3\sqrt{3}}{8}\cdot\sin^2\theta\cos\theta-\dfrac{9}{8}\cdot\sin\theta\cos^2\theta-\dfrac{3\sqrt{3}}{8}\cdot\cos^3\theta$

$= \dfrac{3}{4}\cdot\sin^3\theta-\dfrac{9}{4}\cdot\sin\theta\cos^2\theta = \dfrac{3}{4}\cdot\left(\sin^3\theta-3\sin\theta\left(1-\sin^2\theta\right)\right)$

$= \dfrac{3}{4}\cdot\left(\sin^3\theta-3\sin\theta+3\sin^3\theta\right) = \dfrac{3}{4}\cdot\left(4\sin^3\theta-3\sin\theta\right) = -\dfrac{3}{4}\cdot\sin(3\theta)$

(See the formula for $\sin(3\theta)$ on page 214 of the text.)

83. (a) $R(\theta) = \dfrac{v_0^2\sqrt{2}}{16}\cos\theta(\sin\theta-\cos\theta) = \dfrac{v_0^2\sqrt{2}}{16}(\cos\theta\sin\theta-\cos^2\theta)$

$= \dfrac{v_0^2\sqrt{2}}{16}\cdot\dfrac{1}{2}(2\cos\theta\sin\theta-2\cos^2\theta) = \dfrac{v_0^2\sqrt{2}}{32}\left(\sin 2\theta-2\left(\dfrac{1+\cos 2\theta}{2}\right)\right)$

$= \dfrac{v_0^2\sqrt{2}}{32}(\sin(2\theta)-1-\cos(2\theta)) = \dfrac{v_0^2\sqrt{2}}{32}(\sin(2\theta)-\cos(2\theta)-1)$

(b)

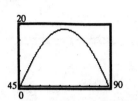

(c)   Using the MAXIMUM feature on the calculator:
R has the largest value when $\theta \approx 67.5°$.

85.   Answers will vary.

Analytic Trigonometry

3.6   Product-to-Sum and Sum-to-Product Formulas

For Problems 1–9, use the formulas:

$$\sin\alpha\sin\beta = \frac{1}{2}\cdot\left[\cos(\alpha-\beta)-\cos(\alpha+\beta)\right] \qquad \cos\alpha\cos\beta = \frac{1}{2}\cdot\left[\cos(\alpha-\beta)+\cos(\alpha+\beta)\right]$$

$$\sin\alpha\cos\beta = \frac{1}{2}\cdot\left[\sin(\alpha+\beta)+\sin(\alpha-\beta)\right]$$

---

1. $\sin(4\theta)\sin(2\theta) = \dfrac{1}{2}\cdot\left[\cos(4\theta-2\theta)-\cos(4\theta+2\theta)\right] = \dfrac{1}{2}\cdot\left[\cos(2\theta)-\cos(6\theta)\right]$

3. $\sin(4\theta)\cos(2\theta) = \dfrac{1}{2}\cdot\left[\sin(4\theta+2\theta)+\sin(4\theta-2\theta)\right] = \dfrac{1}{2}\cdot\left[\sin(6\theta)+\sin(2\theta)\right]$

5. $\cos(3\theta)\cos(5\theta) = \dfrac{1}{2}\cdot\left[\cos(3\theta-5\theta)+\cos(3\theta+5\theta)\right] = \dfrac{1}{2}\cdot\left[\cos(-2\theta)+\cos(8\theta)\right]$

   $= \dfrac{1}{2}\cdot\left[\cos(2\theta)+\cos(8\theta)\right]$

7. $\sin\theta\sin(2\theta) = \dfrac{1}{2}\cdot\left[\cos(\theta-2\theta)-\cos(\theta+2\theta)\right] = \dfrac{1}{2}\cdot\left[\cos(-\theta)-\cos(3\theta)\right]$

   $= \dfrac{1}{2}\cdot\left[\cos\theta-\cos(3\theta)\right]$

9. $\sin\dfrac{3\theta}{2}\cos\dfrac{\theta}{2} = \dfrac{1}{2}\cdot\left[\sin\left(\dfrac{3\theta}{2}+\dfrac{\theta}{2}\right)+\sin\left(\dfrac{3\theta}{2}-\dfrac{\theta}{2}\right)\right] = \dfrac{1}{2}\cdot\left[\sin(2\theta)+\sin\theta\right]$

For Problems 11–17, use the formulas:

$$\sin\alpha + \sin\beta = 2\sin\left(\frac{\alpha+\beta}{2}\right)\cos\left(\frac{\alpha-\beta}{2}\right) \qquad \sin\alpha - \sin\beta = 2\sin\left(\frac{\alpha-\beta}{2}\right)\cos\left(\frac{\alpha+\beta}{2}\right)$$

$$\cos\alpha + \cos\beta = 2\cos\left(\frac{\alpha+\beta}{2}\right)\cos\left(\frac{\alpha-\beta}{2}\right) \qquad \cos\alpha - \cos\beta = -2\sin\left(\frac{\alpha+\beta}{2}\right)\sin\left(\frac{\alpha-\beta}{2}\right)$$

---

11. $\sin(4\theta) - \sin(2\theta) = 2\sin\left(\dfrac{4\theta-2\theta}{2}\right)\cos\left(\dfrac{4\theta+2\theta}{2}\right) = 2\sin\theta\cos(3\theta)$

13. $\cos(2\theta) + \cos(4\theta) = 2\cos\left(\dfrac{2\theta + 4\theta}{2}\right)\cos\left(\dfrac{2\theta - 4\theta}{2}\right) = 2\cos(3\theta)\cos(-\theta) = 2\cos(3\theta)\cos\theta$

15. $\sin\theta + \sin(3\theta) = 2\sin\left(\dfrac{\theta + 3\theta}{2}\right)\cos\left(\dfrac{\theta - 3\theta}{2}\right) = 2\sin(2\theta)\cos(-\theta) = 2\sin(2\theta)\cos\theta$

17. $\cos\dfrac{\theta}{2} - \cos\dfrac{3\theta}{2} = -2\sin\left(\dfrac{\dfrac{\theta}{2} + \dfrac{3\theta}{2}}{2}\right)\sin\left(\dfrac{\dfrac{\theta}{2} - \dfrac{3\theta}{2}}{2}\right) = -2\sin\theta\sin\left(-\dfrac{\theta}{2}\right) = -2\sin\theta\left(-\sin\dfrac{\theta}{2}\right) = 2\sin\theta\sin\dfrac{\theta}{2}$

19. $\dfrac{\sin\theta + \sin(3\theta)}{2\sin(2\theta)} = \dfrac{2\sin(2\theta)\cos(-\theta)}{2\sin(2\theta)} = \cos(-\theta) = \cos\theta$

21. $\dfrac{\sin(4\theta) + \sin(2\theta)}{\cos(4\theta) + \cos(2\theta)} = \dfrac{2\sin(3\theta)\cos\theta}{2\cos(3\theta)\cos\theta} = \dfrac{\sin(3\theta)}{\cos(3\theta)} = \tan(3\theta)$

23. $\dfrac{\cos\theta - \cos(3\theta)}{\sin\theta + \sin(3\theta)} = \dfrac{-2\sin(2\theta)\sin(-\theta)}{2\sin(2\theta)\cos(-\theta)} = \dfrac{-(-\sin\theta)}{\cos\theta} = \tan\theta$

25. $\sin\theta[\sin\theta + \sin(3\theta)] = \sin\theta[2\sin(2\theta)\cos(-\theta)] = \cos\theta[2\sin(2\theta)\sin\theta]$

$= \cos\theta\left[2 \cdot \dfrac{1}{2}(\cos\theta - \cos(3\theta))\right] = \cos\theta(\cos\theta - \cos(3\theta))$

27. $\dfrac{\sin(4\theta) + \sin(8\theta)}{\cos(4\theta) + \cos(8\theta)} = \dfrac{2\sin(6\theta)\cos(-2\theta)}{2\cos(6\theta)\cos(-2\theta)} = \dfrac{\sin(6\theta)}{\cos(6\theta)} = \tan(6\theta)$

29. $\dfrac{\sin(4\theta) + \sin(8\theta)}{\sin(4\theta) - \sin(8\theta)} = \dfrac{2\sin(6\theta)\cos(-2\theta)}{2\sin(-2\theta)\cos(6\theta)} = \dfrac{\sin(6\theta)\cos(2\theta)}{-\sin(2\theta)\cos(6\theta)}$

$= -\tan(6\theta)\cot(2\theta) = -\dfrac{\tan(6\theta)}{\tan(2\theta)}$

31. $\dfrac{\sin\alpha + \sin\beta}{\sin\alpha - \sin\beta} = \dfrac{2\sin\left(\dfrac{\alpha + \beta}{2}\right)\cos\left(\dfrac{\alpha - \beta}{2}\right)}{2\sin\left(\dfrac{\alpha - \beta}{2}\right)\cos\left(\dfrac{\alpha + \beta}{2}\right)} = \tan\left(\dfrac{\alpha + \beta}{2}\right)\cot\left(\dfrac{\alpha - \beta}{2}\right)$

33. $\dfrac{\sin\alpha + \sin\beta}{\cos\alpha + \cos\beta} = \dfrac{2\sin\left(\dfrac{\alpha + \beta}{2}\right)\cos\left(\dfrac{\alpha - \beta}{2}\right)}{2\cos\left(\dfrac{\alpha + \beta}{2}\right)\cos\left(\dfrac{\alpha - \beta}{2}\right)} = \tan\left(\dfrac{\alpha + \beta}{2}\right)$

35. $1 + \cos(2\theta) + \cos(4\theta) + \cos(6\theta) = \cos 0 + \cos(6\theta) + \cos(2\theta) + \cos(4\theta)$

$= 2\cos(3\theta)\cos(-3\theta) + 2\cos(3\theta)\cos(-\theta) = 2\cos^2(3\theta) + 2\cos(3\theta)\cos\theta$

$= 2\cos(3\theta)(\cos(3\theta) + \cos\theta) = 2\cos(3\theta)2\cos(2\theta)\cos\theta$

$= 4\cos\theta\cos(2\theta)\cos(3\theta)$

37. (a) $y = \sin[2\pi(852)t] + \sin[2\pi(1209)t]$

$$= 2\sin\left(\frac{2\pi(852)t + 2\pi(1209)t}{2}\right)\cos\left(\frac{2\pi(852)t - 2\pi(1209)t}{2}\right)$$

$$= 2\sin(2061\pi t)\cos(-357\pi t)$$

$$= 2\sin(2061\pi t)\cos(357\pi t)$$

(b) The maximum value of y is 2.

(c)

39. $\sin(2\alpha) + \sin(2\beta) + \sin(2\gamma)$

$$= 2\sin\left(\frac{2\alpha + 2\beta}{2}\right)\cos\left(\frac{2\alpha - 2\beta}{2}\right) + \sin(2\gamma)$$

$$= 2\sin(\alpha + \beta)\cos(\alpha - \beta) + 2\sin\gamma\cos\gamma$$

$$= 2\sin(\pi - \gamma)\cos(\alpha - \beta) + 2\sin\gamma\cos\gamma$$

$$= 2\sin\gamma\cos(\alpha - \beta) + 2\sin\gamma\cos\gamma = 2\sin\gamma[\cos(\alpha - \beta) + \cos\gamma]$$

$$= 2\sin\gamma\left(2\cos\left(\frac{\alpha - \beta + \gamma}{2}\right)\cos\left(\frac{\alpha - \beta - \gamma}{2}\right)\right)$$

$$= 4\sin\gamma\cos\left(\frac{\pi}{2} - \beta\right)\cos\left(\alpha - \frac{\pi}{2}\right) = 4\sin\gamma\sin\beta\sin\alpha$$

$$= 4\sin\alpha\sin\beta\sin\gamma$$

41. Add the sum formulas for $\sin(\alpha + \beta)$ and $\sin(\alpha - \beta)$ and solve for $\sin\alpha\cos\beta$:

$$\sin(\alpha + \beta) = \sin\alpha\cos\beta + \cos\alpha\sin\beta$$

$$\sin(\alpha - \beta) = \sin\alpha\cos\beta - \cos\alpha\sin\beta$$

$$\sin(\alpha + \beta) + \sin(\alpha - \beta) = 2\sin\alpha\cos\beta$$

$$\sin\alpha\cos\beta = \frac{1}{2}\cdot[\sin(\alpha + \beta) + \sin(\alpha - \beta)]$$

43. $2\cos\left(\dfrac{\alpha + \beta}{2}\right)\cos\left(\dfrac{\alpha - \beta}{2}\right) = 2\cdot\dfrac{1}{2}\left[\cos\left(\dfrac{\alpha + \beta}{2} - \dfrac{\alpha - \beta}{2}\right) + \cos\left(\dfrac{\alpha + \beta}{2} + \dfrac{\alpha - \beta}{2}\right)\right]$

$$= \cos\left(\frac{2\beta}{2}\right) + \cos\left(\frac{2\alpha}{2}\right) = \cos\beta + \cos\alpha$$

Therefore, $\cos\alpha + \cos\beta = 2\cos\left(\dfrac{\alpha + \beta}{2}\right)\cos\left(\dfrac{\alpha - \beta}{2}\right)$

Chapter 3

Analytic Trigonometry

3.7 Trigonometric Equations (I)

1. $3x - 5 = -x + 1$

$4x = 6$

$x = \dfrac{6}{4} = \dfrac{3}{2}$

The solution set is $\left\{ \dfrac{3}{2} \right\}$.

3. $\dfrac{\pi}{6}, \dfrac{5\pi}{6}$

5. False

7. $2\sin\theta + 3 = 2$

$2\sin\theta = -1 \Rightarrow \sin\theta = -\dfrac{1}{2}$

$\theta = \dfrac{7\pi}{6} + 2k\pi$ or $\theta = \dfrac{11\pi}{6} + 2k\pi$, k is any integer

The solutions on the interval $0 \le \theta < 2\pi$ are $\theta = \dfrac{7\pi}{6}, \dfrac{11\pi}{6}$.

9. $4\cos^2\theta = 1$

$\cos^2\theta = \dfrac{1}{4} \Rightarrow \cos\theta = \pm\dfrac{1}{2}$

$\theta = \dfrac{\pi}{3} + k\pi$ or $\theta = \dfrac{2\pi}{3} + k\pi$, k is any integer

The solutions on the interval $0 \le \theta < 2\pi$ are $\theta = \dfrac{\pi}{3}, \dfrac{2\pi}{3}, \dfrac{4\pi}{3}, \dfrac{5\pi}{3}$.

11. $2\sin^2\theta - 1 = 0$

$2\sin^2\theta = 1 \Rightarrow \sin^2\theta = \dfrac{1}{2} \Rightarrow \sin\theta = \pm\sqrt{\dfrac{1}{2}} = \pm\dfrac{\sqrt{2}}{2}$

$\theta = \dfrac{\pi}{4} + k\pi$ or $\theta = \dfrac{3\pi}{4} + k\pi$, k is any integer

The solutions on the interval $0 \le \theta < 2\pi$ are $\theta = \dfrac{\pi}{4}, \dfrac{3\pi}{4}, \dfrac{5\pi}{4}, \dfrac{7\pi}{4}$.

13. $\sin(3\theta) = -1$

$3\theta = \dfrac{3\pi}{2} + 2k\pi \implies \theta = \dfrac{\pi}{2} + \dfrac{2k\pi}{3}$, k is any integer

The solutions on the interval $0 \le \theta < 2\pi$ are $\theta = \dfrac{\pi}{2}, \dfrac{7\pi}{6}, \dfrac{11\pi}{6}$.

15. $\cos(2\theta) = -\dfrac{1}{2}$

$2\theta = \dfrac{2\pi}{3} + 2k\pi \implies \theta = \dfrac{\pi}{3} + k\pi$, k is any integer

$2\theta = \dfrac{4\pi}{3} + 2k\pi \implies \theta = \dfrac{2\pi}{3} + k\pi$, k is any integer

The solutions on the interval $0 \le \theta < 2\pi$ are $\theta = \dfrac{\pi}{3}, \dfrac{2\pi}{3}, \dfrac{4\pi}{3}, \dfrac{5\pi}{3}$.

17. $\sec\left(\dfrac{3\theta}{2}\right) = -2$

$\dfrac{3\theta}{2} = \dfrac{2\pi}{3} + 2k\pi \implies \theta = \dfrac{4\pi}{9} + \dfrac{4k\pi}{3}$, k is any integer

$\dfrac{3\theta}{2} = \dfrac{4\pi}{3} + 2k\pi \implies \theta = \dfrac{8\pi}{9} + \dfrac{4k\pi}{3}$, k is any integer

The solutions on the interval $0 \le \theta < 2\pi$ are $\theta = \dfrac{4\pi}{9}, \dfrac{8\pi}{9}, \dfrac{16\pi}{9}$

19. $2\sin\theta + 1 = 0 \implies 2\sin\theta = -1 \implies \sin\theta = -\dfrac{1}{2}$

$\theta = \dfrac{7\pi}{6} + 2k\pi$ or $\theta = \dfrac{11\pi}{6} + 2k\pi$, k is any integer

The solutions on the interval $0 \le \theta < 2\pi$ are $\theta = \dfrac{7\pi}{6}, \dfrac{11\pi}{6}$.

21. $\tan\theta + 1 = 0 \implies \tan\theta = -1$

$\theta = \dfrac{3\pi}{4} + k\pi$, k is any integer

The solutions on the interval $0 \le \theta < 2\pi$ are $\theta = \dfrac{3\pi}{4}, \dfrac{7\pi}{4}$.

23. $4\sec\theta + 6 = -2 \implies 4\sec\theta = -8 \implies \sec\theta = -2$

$\theta = \dfrac{2\pi}{3} + 2k\pi$ or $\theta = \dfrac{4\pi}{3} + 2k\pi$, k is any integer

The solutions on the interval $0 \le \theta < 2\pi$ are $\theta = \dfrac{2\pi}{3}, \dfrac{4\pi}{3}$.

25. $3\sqrt{2}\cos\theta + 2 = -1 \implies 3\sqrt{2}\cos\theta = -3 \implies \cos\theta = -\dfrac{1}{\sqrt{2}} = -\dfrac{\sqrt{2}}{2}$

$\theta = \dfrac{3\pi}{4} + 2k\pi$ or $\theta = \dfrac{5\pi}{4} + 2k\pi$, k is any integer

The solutions on the interval $0 \le \theta < 2\pi$ are $\theta = \dfrac{3\pi}{4}, \dfrac{5\pi}{4}$.

27. $\cos\left(2\theta - \dfrac{\pi}{2}\right) = -1$

$2\theta - \dfrac{\pi}{2} = \pi + 2k\pi \;\;\Rightarrow\;\; 2\theta = \dfrac{3\pi}{2} + 2k\pi \;\;\Rightarrow\;\; \theta = \dfrac{3\pi}{4} + k\pi, \; k \text{ is any integer}$

The solutions on the interval $0 \le \theta < 2\pi$ are $\theta = \dfrac{3\pi}{4}, \dfrac{7\pi}{4}$.

29. $\tan\left(\dfrac{\theta}{2} + \dfrac{\pi}{3}\right) = 1$

$\dfrac{\theta}{2} + \dfrac{\pi}{3} = \dfrac{\pi}{4} + k\pi \;\;\Rightarrow\;\; \dfrac{\theta}{2} = -\dfrac{\pi}{12} + k\pi \;\;\Rightarrow\;\; \theta = -\dfrac{\pi}{6} + 2k\pi, \; k \text{ is any integer}$

The solution on the interval $0 \le \theta < 2\pi$ is $\theta = \dfrac{11\pi}{6}$.

31. $\sin\theta = \dfrac{1}{2}$

$\theta = \dfrac{\pi}{6} + 2k\pi \text{ or } \theta = \dfrac{5\pi}{6} + 2k\pi, \; k \text{ is any integer}$

Six solutions are $\theta = \dfrac{\pi}{6}, \dfrac{5\pi}{6}, \dfrac{13\pi}{6}, \dfrac{17\pi}{6}, \dfrac{25\pi}{6}, \dfrac{29\pi}{6}$.

33. $\tan\theta = -\dfrac{\sqrt{3}}{3}$

$\theta = \dfrac{5\pi}{6} + k\pi, \; k \text{ is any integer}$

Six solutions are $\theta = \dfrac{5\pi}{6}, \dfrac{11\pi}{6}, \dfrac{17\pi}{6}, \dfrac{23\pi}{6}, \dfrac{29\pi}{6}, \dfrac{35\pi}{6}$.

35. $\cos\theta = 0$

$\theta = \dfrac{\pi}{2} + 2k\pi \text{ or } \theta = \dfrac{3\pi}{2} + 2k\pi, \; k \text{ is any integer}$

Six solutions are $\theta = \dfrac{\pi}{2}, \dfrac{3\pi}{2}, \dfrac{5\pi}{2}, \dfrac{7\pi}{2}, \dfrac{9\pi}{2}, \dfrac{11\pi}{2}$.

37. $\cos(2\theta) = -\dfrac{1}{2}$

$2\theta = \dfrac{2\pi}{3} + 2k\pi \;\;\Rightarrow\;\; \theta = \dfrac{\pi}{3} + k\pi, \; k \text{ is any integer}$

$2\theta = \dfrac{4\pi}{3} + 2k\pi \;\;\Rightarrow\;\; \theta = \dfrac{2\pi}{3} + k\pi, \; k \text{ is any integer}$

Six solutions are $\theta = \dfrac{\pi}{3}, \dfrac{2\pi}{3}, \dfrac{4\pi}{3}, \dfrac{5\pi}{3}, \dfrac{7\pi}{3}, \dfrac{8\pi}{3}$.

39. $\sin\dfrac{\theta}{2} = -\dfrac{\sqrt{3}}{2}$

$\dfrac{\theta}{2} = \dfrac{4\pi}{3} + 2k\pi \;\Rightarrow\; \theta = \dfrac{8\pi}{3} + 4k\pi$, k is any integer

$\dfrac{\theta}{2} = \dfrac{5\pi}{3} + 2k\pi \;\Rightarrow\; \theta = \dfrac{10\pi}{3} + 4k\pi$, k is any integer

Six solutions are $\theta = \dfrac{8\pi}{3}, \dfrac{10\pi}{3}, \dfrac{20\pi}{3}, \dfrac{22\pi}{3}, \dfrac{32\pi}{3}, \dfrac{34\pi}{3}$.

41.

Thus, $\theta \approx 0.41$ or $\theta \approx \pi - 0.41 \approx 2.73$.
The solution set is $\{0.41,\ 2.73\}$.

43. $\tan\theta = 5$

$\theta = \tan^{-1}(5) \approx 1.37$

Thus, $\theta \approx 1.37$ or $\theta \approx \pi + 1.37 \approx 4.51$.
The solution set is $\{1.37,\ 4.51\}$.

45. $\cos\theta = -0.9$

$\theta = \cos^{-1}(-0.9) \approx 2.69$

Thus, $\theta \approx 2.69$ or $\theta \approx 2\pi - 2.69 \approx 3.59$.
The solution set is $\{2.69,\ 3.69\}$.

47. $\sec\theta = -4$

$\cos\theta = -\dfrac{1}{4}$

$\theta = \cos^{-1}\left(-\dfrac{1}{4}\right) \approx 1.82$

Thus, $\theta \approx 1.82$ or $\theta \approx 2\pi - 1.82 \approx 4.46$.
The solution set is $\{1.82,\ 4.46\}$.

49. $5\tan\theta + 9 = 0$

$5\tan\theta = -9$

$\tan\theta = -\dfrac{9}{5}$

$\theta = \tan^{-1}\left(-\dfrac{9}{5}\right) \approx -1.064$

Thus, $\theta \approx -1.064 + \pi \approx 2.08$ or
$\theta \approx -1.064 + 2\pi \approx 5.22$.
The solution set is $\{2.08,\ 5.22\}$.

51. $3\sin\theta - 2 = 0$

$3\sin\theta = 2$

$\sin\theta = \dfrac{2}{3}$

$\theta = \sin^{-1}\left(\dfrac{2}{3}\right) \approx 0.73$

Thus, $\theta \approx 0.73$ or $\theta \approx \pi - 0.73 \approx 2.41$.
The solution set is $\{0.73,\ 2.41\}$

53. $f(x) = 3\sin x$

(a) $f(x) = \dfrac{3}{2} \Rightarrow 3\sin x = \dfrac{3}{2}$

$3\sin x = \dfrac{3}{2}$

$\sin x = \dfrac{1}{2}$

$x = \dfrac{\pi}{6} + 2k\pi$ or $x = \dfrac{5\pi}{6} + 2k\pi$, k any integer

(b) $f(x) > \dfrac{3}{2} \Rightarrow 3\sin x > \dfrac{3}{2}$

$3\sin x > \dfrac{3}{2} \Rightarrow \sin x > \dfrac{1}{2}$

Graphing $y_1 = \sin x$ and $y_2 = \dfrac{1}{2}$ on the interval $[0, 2\pi)$ and using INTERSECT, we can

see that $y_1 > y_2$ for $\dfrac{\pi}{6} < x < \dfrac{5\pi}{6}$.

55. $f(x) = 4\tan x$

(a) $f(x) = -4 \Rightarrow 4\tan x = -4$

$4\tan x = -4$

$\tan x = -1$

$x = -\dfrac{\pi}{4} + k\pi,\ k$ any integer

(b) $f(x) < -4 \Rightarrow 4\tan x < -4$

$4\tan x < -4 \Rightarrow \tan x < -1$

Graphing $y_1 = \tan x$ and $y_2 = -1$ on the interval $\left(-\dfrac{\pi}{2}, \dfrac{\pi}{2}\right)$ and using INTERSECT,

we can see that $y_1 < y_2$ for $-\dfrac{\pi}{2} < x < -\dfrac{\pi}{4}$.

57. $h(t) = 125\sin\left(0.157t - \dfrac{\pi}{2}\right) + 125$

(a) Solve $h(t) = 125\sin\left(0.157t - \dfrac{\pi}{2}\right) + 125 = 125$ on the interval $[0,40]$.

$$125\sin\left(0.157t - \dfrac{\pi}{2}\right) + 125 = 125$$

$$125\sin\left(0.157t - \dfrac{\pi}{2}\right) = 0$$

$$\sin\left(0.157t - \dfrac{\pi}{2}\right) = 0$$

$$0.157t - \dfrac{\pi}{2} = k\pi,\ k \text{ any integer}$$

$$0.157t = k\pi + \dfrac{\pi}{2},\ k \text{ any integer}$$

$$t = \dfrac{(k\pi + \pi/2)}{0.157},\ k \text{ any integer}$$

For $k = 0$, $t = \dfrac{0 + \pi/2}{0.157} \approx 10.01$ seconds. For $k = 1$, $t = \dfrac{\pi + \pi/2}{0.157} \approx 30.02$ seconds.

For $k = 2$, $t = \dfrac{2\pi + \pi/2}{0.157} \approx 50.03$ seconds.

So during the first 40 seconds, an individual on the Ferris Wheel is exactly 125 feet above the ground when $t \approx 10.01$ seconds and again when $t \approx 30.02$ seconds.

(b) Solve $h(t) = 125\sin\left(0.157t - \dfrac{\pi}{2}\right) + 125 = 250$ on the interval $[0,80]$.

$$125\sin\left(0.157t - \dfrac{\pi}{2}\right) + 125 = 250$$

$$125\sin\left(0.157t - \dfrac{\pi}{2}\right) = 125$$

$$\sin\left(0.157t - \dfrac{\pi}{2}\right) = 1$$

$$0.157t - \dfrac{\pi}{2} = \dfrac{\pi}{2} + 2k\pi,\ k \text{ any integer}$$

$$0.157t = \pi + 2k\pi,\ k \text{ any integer}$$

$$t = \dfrac{\pi + 2k\pi}{0.157},\ k \text{ any integer}$$

For $k = 0$, $t = \dfrac{\pi}{0.157} \approx 20.01$ seconds. For $k = 1$, $t = \dfrac{3\pi}{0.157} \approx 60.03$ seconds.

For $k = 5$, $t = \dfrac{5\pi}{0.157} \approx 100.01$ seconds.

So during the first 80 seconds, an individual on the Ferris Wheel is exactly 250 feet above the ground when $t \approx 20.01$ seconds and again when $t \approx 60.030$ seconds.

(c)   Solve $h(t) = 125\sin\left(0.157t - \dfrac{\pi}{2}\right) + 125 > 125$ on the interval $[0,40]$.

$$125\sin\left(0.157t - \frac{\pi}{2}\right) + 125 > 125$$

$$125\sin\left(0.157t - \frac{\pi}{2}\right) > 0 \Rightarrow \sin\left(0.157t - \frac{\pi}{2}\right) > 0$$

Graphing $y_1 = \sin\left(0.157x - \dfrac{\pi}{2}\right)$ and $y_2 = 0$ on the interval $[0,40]$ and using

INTERSECT, we can see that $y_1 > y_2$ for $10.01 < x < 30.02$.

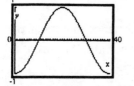

So during the first 40 seconds, an individual on the Ferris Wheel is more than 125 feet above the ground between 10.01 seconds and 30.02 seconds.

59. $d(x) = 70\sin(0.65x) + 150$

(a) $d(0) = 70\sin(0.65(0)) + 150 = 70\sin(0) + 150 = 150$ miles.

(b)   Solve $d(x) = 70\sin(0.65x) + 150 = 100$ on the interval $[0,20]$.

$$70\sin(0.65x) + 150 = 100$$

$$70\sin(0.65x) = -50$$

$$\sin(0.65x) = -\frac{5}{7}$$

$$0.65x = \sin^{-1}\left(-\frac{5}{7}\right)$$

$$x = \frac{\sin^{-1}(-5/7)}{0.65} \approx \frac{3.94 + 2k\pi}{0.65} \text{ or } \frac{5.49 + 2k\pi}{0.65}, \ k \text{ any integer}$$

For $k = 0$, $x \approx \dfrac{3.94 + 0}{0.65} \approx 6.06$ minutes or $x \approx \dfrac{5.49 + 0}{0.65} \approx 8.44$ minutes.

For $k = 1$, $x \approx \dfrac{3.94 + 2\pi}{0.65} \approx 15.72$ minutes or $x \approx \dfrac{5.49 + 2\pi}{0.65} \approx 18.11$ minutes.

For $k = 2$, $x \approx \dfrac{3.94 + 4\pi}{0.65} \approx 25.39$ minutes or $x \approx \dfrac{5.49 + 4\pi}{0.65} \approx 27.78$ minutes.

So during the first 20 minutes in the holding pattern, the plane is exactly 100 miles from the airport when $x \approx 6.06$ minutes, $x \approx 8.44$ minutes, $x \approx 15.72$ minutes, and $x \approx 18.11$ minutes.

(c)   Solve $d(x) = 70\sin(0.65x) + 150 > 100$ on the interval $[0,20]$.

$$70\sin(0.65x) + 150 > 100$$

$$70\sin(0.65x) > -50 \Rightarrow \sin(0.65x) > -\frac{5}{7}$$

Graphing $y_1 = \sin(0.65x)$ and $y_2 = -\dfrac{5}{7}$ on the interval $[0,20]$ and using INTERSECT, we can see that $y_1 > y_2$ for $0 < x < 6.06$, $8.44 < x < 15.72$ and $18.11 < x < 20$.

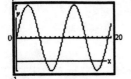

So during the first 20 minutes in the holding pattern, the plane is more than 100 miles from the airport when $0 < x < 6.06$ minutes, when $8.44 < x < 15.72$ minutes and when $18.11 < x < 20$ minutes.

(d)   The minimum value of $\sin(0.65x)$ is -1. Thus, the least distance that the plane is from the airport is $70(-1) + 150 = 80$ miles. The plane is never within 70 miles of the airport while in the holding pattern.

61. $\dfrac{\sin 40^\circ}{\sin \theta_2} = 1.33$

     $\sin 40^\circ = 1.33 \sin \theta_2$

     $\sin \theta_2 = \dfrac{\sin 40^\circ}{1.33} \approx 0.4833$

       $\theta_2 = \sin^{-1}(0.4833) \approx 28.90^\circ$

63.   Calculate the index of refraction for each:

   $\theta_1 = 10^\circ,\ \theta_2 = 7^\circ 45' = 7.75^\circ$ $\dfrac{\sin \theta_1}{\sin \theta_2} = \dfrac{\sin 10^\circ}{\sin 7.75^\circ} \approx 1.2877$

   $\theta_1 = 20^\circ,\ \theta_2 = 15^\circ 30' = 15.5^\circ$ $\dfrac{\sin \theta_1}{\sin \theta_2} = \dfrac{\sin 20^\circ}{\sin 15.5^\circ} \approx 1.2798$

   $\theta_1 = 30^\circ,\ \theta_2 = 22^\circ 30' = 22.5^\circ$ $\dfrac{\sin \theta_1}{\sin \theta_2} = \dfrac{\sin 30^\circ}{\sin 22.5^\circ} \approx 1.3066$

   $\theta_1 = 40^\circ,\ \theta_2 = 29^\circ 0' = 29^\circ$ $\dfrac{\sin \theta_1}{\sin \theta_2} = \dfrac{\sin 40^\circ}{\sin 29^\circ} \approx 1.3259$

   $\theta_1 = 50^\circ,\ \theta_2 = 35^\circ 0' = 35^\circ$ $\dfrac{\sin \theta_1}{\sin \theta_2} = \dfrac{\sin 50^\circ}{\sin 35^\circ} \approx 1.3356$

   $\theta_1 = 60^\circ,\ \theta_2 = 40^\circ 30' = 40.5^\circ$ $\dfrac{\sin \theta_1}{\sin \theta_2} = \dfrac{\sin 60^\circ}{\sin 40.5^\circ} \approx 1.3335$

   $\theta_1 = 70^\circ,\ \theta_2 = 45^\circ 30' = 45.5^\circ$ $\dfrac{\sin \theta_1}{\sin \theta_2} = \dfrac{\sin 70^\circ}{\sin 45.5^\circ} \approx 1.3175$

   $\theta_1 = 80^\circ,\ \theta_2 = 50^\circ 0' = 50^\circ$ $\dfrac{\sin \theta_1}{\sin \theta_2} = \dfrac{\sin 80^\circ}{\sin 50^\circ} \approx 1.2856$

The results range from 1.28 to 1.34 and are surprisingly close to Snell's Law.

65. Calculate the index of refraction:

$\theta_1 = 40°$, $\theta_2 = 26°$ $\dfrac{\sin\theta_1}{\sin\theta_2} = \dfrac{\sin 40°}{\sin 26°} \approx 1.47$

67. If θ is the original angle of incidence and ϕ is the angle of refraction, then $\dfrac{\sin\theta}{\sin\phi} = n_2$. The angle of incidence of the emerging beam is also ϕ, and the index of refraction is $\dfrac{1}{n_2}$. Thus, θ is the angle of refraction of the emerging beam. The two beams are parallel since the original angle of incidence and the angle of refraction of the emerging beam are equal.

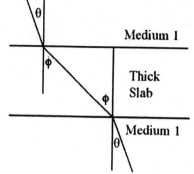

Analytic Trigonometry

3.8   Trigonometric Equations (II)

1.
$$4x^2 - x - 5 = 0$$
$$(4x-5)(x+1) = 0$$
$$4x - 5 = 0 \Rightarrow x = \frac{5}{4}$$
$$x + 1 = 0 \Rightarrow x = -1$$
The solution set is $\left\{-1, \dfrac{4}{5}\right\}$.

3.
$$2\cos^2\theta + \cos\theta = 0$$
$$\cos\theta(2\cos\theta + 1) = 0$$
$$\cos\theta = 0 \Rightarrow \theta = \frac{\pi}{2}, \frac{3\pi}{2}$$
or $2\cos\theta + 1 = 0$
$$\cos\theta = -\frac{1}{2} \Rightarrow \theta = \frac{2\pi}{3}, \frac{4\pi}{3}$$
The solution set is $\left\{\dfrac{\pi}{2}, \dfrac{2\pi}{3}, \dfrac{4\pi}{3}, \dfrac{3\pi}{2}\right\}$.

5.
$$2\sin^2\theta - \sin\theta - 1 = 0$$
$$(2\sin\theta + 1)(\sin\theta - 1) = 0$$
$$2\sin\theta + 1 = 0$$
$$\sin\theta = -\frac{1}{2} \Rightarrow \theta = \frac{7\pi}{6}, \frac{11\pi}{6}$$
or $\sin\theta - 1 = 0$
$$\sin\theta = 1 \Rightarrow \theta = \frac{\pi}{2}$$
The solution set is $\left\{\dfrac{\pi}{2}, \dfrac{7\pi}{6}, \dfrac{11\pi}{6}\right\}$.

7.
$$(\tan\theta - 1)(\sec\theta - 1) = 0$$
$$\tan\theta - 1 = 0$$
$$\tan\theta = 1 \Rightarrow \theta = \frac{\pi}{4}, \frac{5\pi}{4}$$
or $\sec\theta - 1 = 0$
$$\sec\theta = 1 \Rightarrow \theta = 0$$
The solution set is $\left\{0, \dfrac{\pi}{4}, \dfrac{5\pi}{4}\right\}$.

9.
$$\sin^2\theta - \cos^2\theta = 1 + \cos\theta$$
$$\left(1 - \cos^2\theta\right) - \cos^2\theta = 1 + \cos\theta$$
$$1 - 2\cos^2\theta = 1 + \cos\theta$$
$$2\cos^2\theta + \cos\theta = 0$$
$$\cos\theta(2\cos\theta + 1) = 0$$
$$\cos\theta = 0 \Rightarrow \theta = \frac{\pi}{2}, \frac{3\pi}{2}$$
$$\text{or } 2\cos\theta + 1 = 0$$
$$\cos\theta = -\frac{1}{2} \Rightarrow \theta = \frac{2\pi}{3}, \frac{4\pi}{3} \quad \sec\theta = 1 \Rightarrow \theta = 0$$

The solution set is $\left\{\dfrac{\pi}{2}, \dfrac{2\pi}{3}, \dfrac{4\pi}{3}, \dfrac{3\pi}{2}\right\}$.

11.
$$\sin^2\theta = 6(\cos\theta + 1)$$
$$1 - \cos^2\theta = 6\cos\theta + 6$$
$$\cos^2\theta + 6\cos\theta + 5 = 0$$
$$(\cos\theta + 5)(\cos\theta + 1) = 0$$
$$\cos\theta + 5 =$$
$$\cos\theta = -5, \text{ which is impossible}$$
$$\text{or } \cos\theta + 1 = 0$$
$$\cos\theta = -1 \Rightarrow \theta = \pi$$
The solution set is $\{\pi\}$.

13.
$$\cos(2\theta) + 6\sin^2\theta = 4$$
$$1 - 2\sin^2\theta + 6\sin^2\theta = 4$$
$$4\sin^2\theta = 3$$
$$\sin^2\theta = \frac{3}{4}$$
$$\sin\theta = \pm\sqrt{\frac{3}{4}}$$
$$\sin\theta = \pm\frac{\sqrt{3}}{2} \Rightarrow \theta = \frac{\pi}{3}, \frac{2\pi}{3}, \frac{4\pi}{3}, \frac{5\pi}{3}$$

$+4\sin^2\theta + 3 = 0$

The solution set is $\left\{0, \dfrac{\pi}{3}, \dfrac{2\pi}{3}, \dfrac{4\pi}{3}, \dfrac{5\pi}{3}\right\}$.

15. $\cos\theta = \sin\theta$

$\dfrac{\sin\theta}{\cos\theta} = 1$

$\tan\theta = 1 \Rightarrow \theta = \dfrac{\pi}{4}, \dfrac{5\pi}{4}$

The solution set is $\left\{\dfrac{\pi}{4}, \dfrac{5\pi}{4}\right\}$.

17. $\tan\theta = 2\sin\theta$

$\dfrac{\sin\theta}{\cos\theta} = 2\sin\theta$

$\sin\theta = 2\sin\theta\cos\theta$

$0 = 2\sin\theta\cos\theta - \sin\theta$

$0 = \sin\theta(2\cos\theta - 1)$

$2\cos\theta - 1 = 0$

$\cos\theta = \dfrac{1}{2} \Rightarrow \theta = \dfrac{\pi}{3}, \dfrac{5\pi}{3}$

or $\sin\theta = 0 \Rightarrow \theta = 0, \pi$

The solution set is $\left\{0, \dfrac{\pi}{3}, \pi, \dfrac{5\pi}{3}\right\}$.

19. $\sin\theta = \csc\theta$

$\sin\theta = \dfrac{1}{\sin\theta}$

$\sin^2\theta = 1$

$\sin\theta = \pm 1 \Rightarrow \theta = \dfrac{\pi}{2}, \dfrac{3\pi}{2}$

The solution set is $\left\{\dfrac{\pi}{2}, \dfrac{3\pi}{2}\right\}$.

21. $\cos(2\theta) = \cos\theta$

$2\cos^2\theta - 1 = \cos\theta$

$2\cos^2\theta - \cos\theta - 1 = 0$

$(2\cos\theta + 1)(\cos\theta - 1) = 0$

$2\cos\theta + 1 = 0$

$\cos\theta = -\dfrac{1}{2} \Rightarrow \theta = \dfrac{2\pi}{3}, \dfrac{4\pi}{3}$

or $\cos\theta - 1 = 0$

$\cos\theta = 1 \Rightarrow \theta = 0$

The solution set is $\left\{0, \dfrac{2\pi}{3}, \dfrac{4\pi}{3}\right\}$.

23. $\sin(2\theta) + \sin(4\theta) = 0$

$\sin(2\theta) + 2\sin(2\theta)\cos(2\theta) = 0$

$\sin(2\theta)\big(1 + 2\cos(2\theta)\big) = 0$

$1 + 2\cos(2\theta) = 0$

$\cos(2\theta) = -\dfrac{1}{2} \Rightarrow 2\theta = \dfrac{2\pi}{3} + 2k\pi \Rightarrow \theta = \dfrac{\pi}{3} + k\pi$

$2\theta = \dfrac{4\pi}{3} + 2k\pi \Rightarrow \theta = \dfrac{2\pi}{3} + k\pi$

or $\sin(2\theta) = 0 \Rightarrow 2\theta = 0 + k\pi \Rightarrow \theta = \dfrac{k\pi}{2}$

The solution set is $\left\{0, \dfrac{\pi}{3}, \dfrac{\pi}{2}, \dfrac{2\pi}{3}, \pi, \dfrac{4\pi}{3}, \dfrac{3\pi}{2}, \dfrac{5\pi}{3}\right\}$.

25. $\cos(4\theta) - \cos(6\theta) = 0$

$-2\sin(5\theta)\sin(-\theta) = 0$

$2\sin(5\theta)\sin\theta = 0$

$\sin(5\theta) = 0 \Rightarrow 5\theta = 0 + k\pi \Rightarrow \theta = \dfrac{k\pi}{5}$

or $\sin\theta = 0 \Rightarrow \theta = 0 + k\pi$

The solution set is $\left\{0, \dfrac{\pi}{5}, \dfrac{2\pi}{5}, \dfrac{3\pi}{5}, \dfrac{4\pi}{5}, \pi, \dfrac{6\pi}{5}, \dfrac{7\pi}{5}, \dfrac{8\pi}{5}, \dfrac{9\pi}{5}\right\}$.

27. $1 + \sin\theta = 2\cos^2\theta$

$1 + \sin\theta = 2(1 - \sin^2\theta)$

$2\sin^2\theta + \sin\theta - 1 = 0$

$(2\sin\theta - 1)(\sin\theta + 1) = 0$

$2\sin\theta - 1 = 0$

$\sin\theta = \dfrac{1}{2} \Rightarrow \theta = \dfrac{\pi}{6}, \dfrac{5\pi}{6}$

or $\sin\theta + 1 = 0$

$\sin\theta = -1 \Rightarrow \theta = \dfrac{3\pi}{2}$

The solution set is $\left\{\dfrac{\pi}{6}, \dfrac{5\pi}{6}, \dfrac{3\pi}{2}\right\}$.

29. $2\sin^2\theta - 5\sin\theta + 3 = 0$

$(\sin\theta - 1)(2\sin\theta - 3) = 0$

$\sin\theta - 1 = 0$

$\sin\theta = 1 \Rightarrow \theta = \dfrac{\pi}{2}$

or $2\sin\theta - 3 = 0$

$\sin\theta = \dfrac{3}{2}$, which is impossible

The solution set is $\left\{\dfrac{\pi}{2}\right\}$.

31.
$$3(1 - \cos\theta) = \sin^2\theta$$
$$3 - 3\cos\theta = 1 - \cos^2\theta$$
$$\cos^2\theta - 3\cos\theta + 2 = 0$$
$$(\cos\theta - 1)(\cos\theta - 2) = 0$$
$$\cos\theta - 1 = 0$$
$$\cos\theta = 1 \Rightarrow \theta = 0$$
or $\cos\theta - 2 = 0$
$$\cos\theta = 2, \text{ which is impossible}$$
The solution set is $\{0\}$.

33.
$$\tan^2\theta = \frac{3}{2}\sec\theta$$
$$\sec^2\theta - 1 = \frac{3}{2}\sec\theta$$
$$2\sec^2\theta - 2 = 3\sec\theta$$
$$2\sec^2\theta - 3\sec\theta - 2 = 0$$
$$(2\sec\theta + 1)(\sec\theta - 2) = 0$$
$$2\sec\theta + 1 = 0$$
$$\sec\theta = -\frac{1}{2}$$
$$\cos\theta = -2, \text{ which is impossible}$$
or $\sec\theta - 2 = 0$
$$\sec\theta = 2 \Rightarrow \theta = \frac{\pi}{3}, \frac{5\pi}{3}$$
The solution set is $\left\{\dfrac{\pi}{3}, \dfrac{5\pi}{3}\right\}$.

35.
$$3 - \sin\theta = \cos(2\theta)$$
$$3 - \sin\theta = 1 - 2\sin^2\theta$$
$$2\sin^2\theta - \sin\theta + 2 = 0$$
This is a quadratic equation in $\sin\theta$.
The discriminant is $b^2 - 4ac = (-1)^2 - 4(2)(2) = 1 - 16 = -15 < 0$.
The equation has no real solutions.

37.
$$\sec^2\theta + \tan\theta = 0$$
$$\tan^2\theta + 1 + \tan\theta = 0$$
$$\tan^2\theta + \tan\theta + 1 = 0$$
This is a quadratic equation in $\tan\theta$.
The discriminant is $b^2 - 4ac = 1^2 - 4(1)(1) = 1 - 4 = -3 < 0$.
The equation has no real solutions.

39. $\sin\theta - \sqrt{3}\cos\theta = 1$
Divide each side by 2:
$\frac{1}{2}\sin\theta - \frac{\sqrt{3}}{2}\cos\theta = \frac{1}{2}$

Rewrite using the difference of two angles formula where $\phi = \frac{\pi}{3}$, so $\cos\phi = \frac{1}{2}$ and $\sin\phi = \frac{\sqrt{3}}{2}$.

$$\sin\theta\cos\phi - \cos\theta\sin\phi = \frac{1}{2}$$

$$\sin(\theta - \phi) = \frac{1}{2}$$

$$\theta - \phi = \frac{\pi}{6} \quad \text{or} \quad \theta - \phi = \frac{5\pi}{6}$$

$$\theta - \frac{\pi}{3} = \frac{\pi}{6} \quad \text{or} \quad \theta - \frac{\pi}{3} = \frac{5\pi}{6}$$

$$\theta = \frac{\pi}{2} \quad \text{or} \quad \theta = \frac{7\pi}{6}$$

The solution set is $\left\{\frac{\pi}{2}, \frac{7\pi}{6}\right\}$.

41.
$$\tan(2\theta) + 2\sin\theta = 0$$

$$\frac{\sin(2\theta)}{\cos(2\theta)} + 2\sin\theta = 0$$

$$\frac{\sin(2\theta) + 2\sin\theta\cos(2\theta)}{\cos(2\theta)} = 0$$

$$2\sin\theta\cos\theta + 2\sin\theta(2\cos^2\theta - 1) = 0$$

$$2\sin\theta(\cos\theta + 2\cos^2\theta - 1) = 0$$

$$2\sin\theta(2\cos^2\theta + \cos\theta - 1) = 0$$

$$2\sin\theta(2\cos\theta - 1)(\cos\theta + 1) = 0$$

$$2\cos\theta - 1 = 0$$

$$\cos\theta = \frac{1}{2} \Rightarrow \theta = \frac{\pi}{3}, \frac{5\pi}{3}$$

or $2\sin\theta = 0$

$$\sin\theta = 0 \Rightarrow \theta = 0, \pi$$

or $\cos\theta + 1 = 0$

$$\cos\theta = -1 \Rightarrow \theta = \pi$$

The solution set is $\left\{0, \frac{\pi}{3}, \pi, \frac{5\pi}{3}\right\}$.

43.
$$\sin\theta + \cos\theta = \sqrt{2}$$

Divide each side by $\sqrt{2}$.

$$\frac{1}{\sqrt{2}}\sin\theta + \frac{1}{\sqrt{2}}\cos\theta = 1$$

Rewrite in the sum of two angles form where $\phi = \dfrac{\pi}{4}$, so $\cos\phi = \dfrac{1}{\sqrt{2}}$ and $\sin\phi = \dfrac{1}{\sqrt{2}}$.

$$\sin\theta\cos\phi + \cos\theta\sin\phi = 1$$

$$\sin(\theta + \phi) = 1$$

$$\theta + \phi = \frac{\pi}{2}$$

$$\theta + \frac{\pi}{4} = \frac{\pi}{2} \Rightarrow \theta = \frac{\pi}{4}$$

The solution set is $\left\{\dfrac{\pi}{4}\right\}$.

45. Use INTERSECT to solve by graphing $y_1 = \cos x$, $y_2 = e^x$.

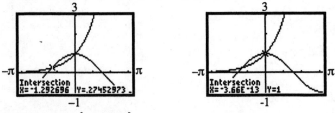

The solution set is $\{-1.29, 0\}$.

47. Use INTERSECT to solve by graphing $y_1 = 2\sin x$, $y_2 = 0.7x$.

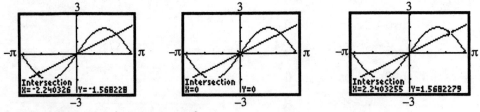

The solution set is $\{-2.24, 0, 2.24\}$.

49. Use INTERSECT to solve by graphing $y_1 = \cos x$, $y_2 = x^2$.

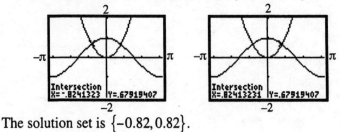

The solution set is $\{-0.82, 0.82\}$.

51. $x + 5\cos x = 0$
Find the intersection of
$y_1 = x + 5\cos x$ and $y_2 = 0$:

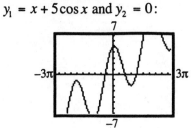

The solution set is $\{-1.31, 1.98, 3.84\}$.

53. $22x - 17\sin x = 3$
Find the intersection of
$y_1 = 22x - 17\sin x$ and $y_2 = 3$:

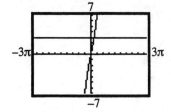

The solution set is $\{0.52\}$.

55. $\sin x + \cos x = x$
Find the intersection of
$y_1 = \sin x + \cos x$ and $y_2 = x$:

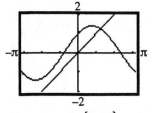

The solution set is $\{1.26\}$.

57. $x^2 - 2\cos x = 0$
Find the intersection of
$y_1 = x^2 - 2\cos x$ and $y_2 = 0$:

The solution set is $\{-1.02, 1.02\}$.

59. $x^2 - 2\sin(2x) = 3x$
Find the intersection of
$y_1 = x^2 - 2\sin 2x$ and $y_2 = 3x$:

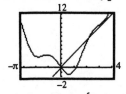

The solution set is $\{0, 2.15\}$.

61. $6\sin x - e^x = 2, \ x > 0$
Find the intersection of
$y_1 = 6\sin x - e^x$ and $y_2 = 2$:

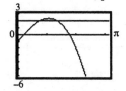

The solution set is $\{0.76, 1.35\}$.

63. (a) $\cos(2\theta) + \cos\theta = 0, \ 0° < \theta < 90°$
$2\cos^2\theta - 1 + \cos\theta = 0$
$2\cos^2\theta + \cos\theta - 1 = 0$
$(2\cos\theta - 1)(\cos\theta + 1) = 0$
$2\cos\theta - 1 = 0$

$$\cos\theta = \frac{1}{2} \Rightarrow \theta = 60°, 300°$$

or $\cos\theta + 1 = 0$

$$\cos\theta = -1 \Rightarrow \theta = 180°$$

The solution is $60°$.

(b) $\cos(2\theta) + \cos\theta = 0, \quad 0° < \theta < 90°$

$$2\cos\left(\frac{3\theta}{2}\right)\cos\left(\frac{\theta}{2}\right) = 0$$

$$\cos\left(\frac{3\theta}{2}\right) = 0 \Rightarrow \frac{3\theta}{2} = 90° \Rightarrow \theta = 60°$$

$$\text{or } \frac{3\theta}{2} = 270° \Rightarrow \theta = 180°$$

$$\text{or } \cos\left(\frac{\theta}{2}\right) = 0 \Rightarrow \frac{\theta}{2} = 90° \Rightarrow \theta = 180°$$

$$\text{or } \frac{\theta}{2} = 270° \Rightarrow \theta = 540°$$

The solution is 60°.

(c) $A(60°) = 16\sin(60°)(\cos(60°) + 1) = 16 \cdot \frac{\sqrt{3}}{2}\left(\frac{1}{2} + 1\right) = 12\sqrt{3} \text{ in}^2 \approx 20.78 \text{ in}^2$

(d)   Graph and use the MAXIMUM feature:

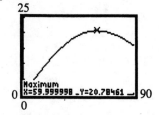

The maximum area is approximately 20.78 in^2 when the angle is 60°.

65. Graph:

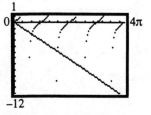

The first two positive solutions are 2.03 and 4.91.

67. (a) $R(\theta) = 107 \Rightarrow \dfrac{(34.8)^2 \sin(2\theta)}{9.8} = 107$

$$\sin(2\theta) = \frac{107(9.8)}{(34.8)^2} \approx 0.8659$$

$$2\theta = \sin^{-1}(0.8659) \approx 59.98° \text{ or } 120.02°$$

$$\theta \approx 29.99° \text{ or } 60.01°$$

(b)   The maximum distance occurs when $\sin(2\theta)$ is greatest. That is, when $\sin(2\theta) = 1$.
        But $\sin(2\theta) = 1$ when $2\theta = 90° \Rightarrow \theta = 45°$.

The maximum distance is

$$R\left(45^\circ\right) = \frac{\left(34.8\right)^2 \sin\left(2 \cdot 45^\circ\right)}{9.8} = \frac{\left(34.8\right)^2 \sin\left(90^\circ\right)}{9.8} \approx 123.58 \text{ meters}$$

(c)   Graph: $y_1 = \dfrac{\left(34.8\right)^2 \sin\left(2x\right)}{9.8}$

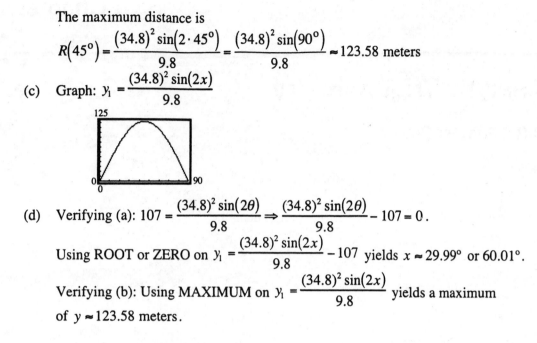

(d)   Verifying (a): $107 = \dfrac{\left(34.8\right)^2 \sin\left(2\theta\right)}{9.8} \Rightarrow \dfrac{\left(34.8\right)^2 \sin\left(2\theta\right)}{9.8} - 107 = 0$.

Using ROOT or ZERO on $y_1 = \dfrac{\left(34.8\right)^2 \sin\left(2x\right)}{9.8} - 107$ yields $x \approx 29.99^\circ$ or 60.01°.

Verifying (b): Using MAXIMUM on $y_1 = \dfrac{\left(34.8\right)^2 \sin\left(2x\right)}{9.8}$ yields a maximum

of $y \approx 123.58$ meters.

Analytic Trigonometry

3.R   Chapter Review

1. $\sin^{-1}1$

Find the angle θ, $-\dfrac{\pi}{2} \le \theta \le \dfrac{\pi}{2}$, whose sine equals 1.

$$\sin\theta = 1 \quad -\frac{\pi}{2} \le \theta \le \frac{\pi}{2}$$

$$\theta = \frac{\pi}{2} \Rightarrow \sin^{-1}1 = \frac{\pi}{2}$$

3. $\tan^{-1}1$

Find the angle θ, $-\dfrac{\pi}{2} < \theta < \dfrac{\pi}{2}$, whose tangent equals 1.

$$\tan\theta = 1 \quad -\frac{\pi}{2} < \theta < \frac{\pi}{2}$$

$$\theta = \frac{\pi}{4} \Rightarrow \tan^{-1}1 = \frac{\pi}{4}$$

5. $\cos^{-1}\left(-\dfrac{\sqrt{3}}{2}\right)$

Find the angle θ, $0 \le \theta \le \pi$, whose cosine equals $-\dfrac{\sqrt{3}}{2}$.

$$\cos\theta = -\frac{\sqrt{3}}{2} \quad 0 \le \theta \le \pi$$

$$\theta = \frac{5\pi}{6} \Rightarrow \cos^{-1}\left(-\frac{\sqrt{3}}{2}\right) = \frac{5\pi}{6}$$

7. $\sec^{-1}\sqrt{2}$

Find the angle θ, $0 \le \theta \le \pi$, whose secant equals $\sqrt{2}$.

$$\sec\theta = \sqrt{2} \quad 0 \le \theta \le \pi$$

$$\theta = \frac{\pi}{4} \Rightarrow \sec^{-1}\sqrt{2} = \frac{\pi}{4}$$

9. $\tan\left(\sin^{-1}\left(-\dfrac{\sqrt{3}}{2}\right)\right)$

Find the angle θ, $-\dfrac{\pi}{2} \le \theta \le \dfrac{\pi}{2}$, whose sine equals $-\dfrac{\sqrt{3}}{2}$.

$$\sin\theta = -\dfrac{\sqrt{3}}{2} \qquad -\dfrac{\pi}{2} \le \theta \le \dfrac{\pi}{2}$$

$$\theta = -\dfrac{\pi}{3} \Rightarrow \tan\left(\sin^{-1}\left(-\dfrac{\sqrt{3}}{2}\right)\right) = \tan\left(-\dfrac{\pi}{3}\right) = -\sqrt{3}$$

11. $\sec\left(\tan^{-1}\dfrac{\sqrt{3}}{3}\right)$

Find the angle θ, $-\dfrac{\pi}{2} < \theta < \dfrac{\pi}{2}$, whose tangent is $\dfrac{\sqrt{3}}{3}$

$$\tan\theta = \dfrac{\sqrt{3}}{3}, \qquad -\dfrac{\pi}{2} < \theta < \dfrac{\pi}{2}$$

$$\theta = \dfrac{\pi}{6} \Rightarrow \sec\left(\tan^{-1}\dfrac{\sqrt{3}}{3}\right) = \sec\dfrac{\pi}{6} = \dfrac{2\sqrt{3}}{3}$$

13. $\sin\left(\tan^{-1}\dfrac{3}{4}\right)$

Since $\tan\theta = \dfrac{3}{4}$, $-\dfrac{\pi}{2} < \theta < \dfrac{\pi}{2}$, let $x = 4$ and $y = 3$.

Solve for r:

$16 + 9 = r^2 \Rightarrow r^2 = 25 \Rightarrow r = 5$

θ is in quadrant I.

$$\sin\left(\tan^{-1}\dfrac{3}{4}\right) = \sin\theta = \dfrac{y}{r} = \dfrac{3}{5}$$

15. $\tan\left(\sin^{-1}\left(-\dfrac{4}{5}\right)\right)$

Since $\sin\theta = -\dfrac{4}{5}$, $-\dfrac{\pi}{2} \le \theta \le \dfrac{\pi}{2}$, let $y = -4$ and $r = 5$.

Solve for x:

$x^2 + 16 = 25 \Rightarrow x^2 = 9 \Rightarrow x = \pm 3$

Since θ is in quadrant IV, $x = 3$.

$$\tan\left(\sin^{-1}\left(-\dfrac{4}{5}\right)\right) = \tan\theta = \dfrac{y}{x} = \dfrac{-4}{3} = -\dfrac{4}{3}$$

17. $\sin^{-1}\left(\cos\dfrac{2\pi}{3}\right) = \sin^{-1}\left(-\dfrac{1}{2}\right) = -\dfrac{\pi}{6}$

19. $\tan^{-1}\left(\tan\dfrac{7\pi}{4}\right) = \tan^{-1}(-1) = -\dfrac{\pi}{4}$

21. $\tan\theta\cot\theta - \sin^2\theta = \tan\theta \cdot \dfrac{1}{\tan\theta} - \sin^2\theta = 1 - \sin^2\theta = \cos^2\theta$

23. $\cos^2\theta(1 + \tan^2\theta) = \cos^2\theta \cdot \sec^2\theta = \cos^2\theta \cdot \dfrac{1}{\cos^2\theta} = 1$

25. $4\cos^2\theta + 3\sin^2\theta = \cos^2\theta + 3\cos^2\theta + 3\sin^2\theta = \cos^2\theta + 3(\cos^2\theta + \sin^2\theta)$
$= \cos^2\theta + 3 \cdot 1 = \cos^2\theta + 3 = 3 + \cos^2\theta$

27. $\dfrac{1 - \cos\theta}{\sin\theta} + \dfrac{\sin\theta}{1 - \cos\theta} = \dfrac{(1 - \cos\theta)^2 + \sin^2\theta}{\sin\theta(1 - \cos\theta)} = \dfrac{1 - 2\cos\theta + \cos^2\theta + \sin^2\theta}{\sin\theta(1 - \cos\theta)}$
$= \dfrac{1 - 2\cos\theta + 1}{\sin\theta(1 - \cos\theta)} = \dfrac{2 - 2\cos\theta}{\sin\theta(1 - \cos\theta)} = \dfrac{2(1 - \cos\theta)}{\sin\theta(1 - \cos\theta)} = \dfrac{2}{\sin\theta} = 2\csc\theta$

29. $\dfrac{\cos\theta}{\cos\theta - \sin\theta} = \dfrac{\cos\theta}{\cos\theta - \sin\theta} \cdot \left(\dfrac{\frac{1}{\cos\theta}}{\frac{1}{\cos\theta}}\right) = \dfrac{1}{1 - \dfrac{\sin\theta}{\cos\theta}} = \dfrac{1}{1 - \tan\theta}$

31. $\dfrac{\csc\theta}{1 + \csc\theta} = \dfrac{\frac{1}{\sin\theta}}{1 + \frac{1}{\sin\theta}} = \dfrac{\frac{1}{\sin\theta}}{\frac{\sin\theta + 1}{\sin\theta}} = \left(\dfrac{1}{1 + \sin\theta}\right) \cdot \left(\dfrac{1 - \sin\theta}{1 - \sin\theta}\right) = \dfrac{1 - \sin\theta}{1 - \sin^2\theta} = \dfrac{1 - \sin\theta}{\cos^2\theta}$

33. $\csc\theta - \sin\theta = \dfrac{1}{\sin\theta} - \sin\theta = \dfrac{1 - \sin^2\theta}{\sin\theta} = \dfrac{\cos^2\theta}{\sin\theta} = \cos\theta \cdot \dfrac{\cos\theta}{\sin\theta} = \cos\theta\cot\theta$

35. $\dfrac{1 - \sin\theta}{\sec\theta} = \cos\theta(1 - \sin\theta) = \cos\theta(1 - \sin\theta) \cdot \dfrac{1 + \sin\theta}{1 + \sin\theta} = \dfrac{\cos\theta(1 - \sin^2\theta)}{1 + \sin\theta} = \dfrac{\cos\theta(\cos^2\theta)}{1 + \sin\theta} = \dfrac{\cos^3\theta}{1 + \sin\theta}$

37. $\cot\theta - \tan\theta = \dfrac{\cos\theta}{\sin\theta} - \dfrac{\sin\theta}{\cos\theta} = \dfrac{\cos^2\theta - \sin^2\theta}{\sin\theta\cos\theta} = \dfrac{1 - \sin^2\theta - \sin^2\theta}{\sin\theta\cos\theta} = \dfrac{1 - 2\sin^2\theta}{\sin\theta\cos\theta}$

39. $\dfrac{\cos(\alpha + \beta)}{\cos\alpha\sin\beta} = \dfrac{\cos\alpha\cos\beta - \sin\alpha\sin\beta}{\cos\alpha\sin\beta} = \dfrac{\cos\alpha\cos\beta}{\cos\alpha\sin\beta} - \dfrac{\sin\alpha\sin\beta}{\cos\alpha\sin\beta} = \cot\beta - \tan\alpha$

41. $\dfrac{\cos(\alpha - \beta)}{\cos\alpha\cos\beta} = \dfrac{\cos\alpha\cos\beta + \sin\alpha\sin\beta}{\cos\alpha\cos\beta} = \dfrac{\cos\alpha\cos\beta}{\cos\alpha\cos\beta} + \dfrac{\sin\alpha\sin\beta}{\cos\alpha\cos\beta} = 1 + \tan\alpha\tan\beta$

43. $(1 + \cos\theta)\left(\tan\dfrac{\theta}{2}\right) = (1 + \cos\theta) \cdot \dfrac{\sin\theta}{1 + \cos\theta} = \sin\theta$

45. $2\cot\theta\cot(2\theta) = 2 \cdot \dfrac{\cos\theta}{\sin\theta} \cdot \dfrac{\cos(2\theta)}{\sin(2\theta)} = \dfrac{2\cos\theta(\cos^2\theta - \sin^2\theta)}{\sin\theta(2\sin\theta\cos\theta)} = \dfrac{\cos^2\theta - \sin^2\theta}{\sin^2\theta} = \cot^2\theta - 1$

47. $1 - 8\sin^2\theta\cos^2\theta = 1 - 2(2\sin\theta\cos\theta)^2 = 1 - 2\sin^2(2\theta) = \cos(4\theta)$

49. $\dfrac{\sin(2\theta)+\sin(4\theta)}{\cos(2\theta)+\cos(4\theta)}=\dfrac{2\sin(3\theta)\cos(-\theta)}{2\cos(3\theta)\cos(-\theta)}=\dfrac{\sin(3\theta)}{\cos(3\theta)}=\tan(3\theta)$

51. $\dfrac{\cos(2\theta)-\cos(4\theta)}{\cos(2\theta)+\cos(4\theta)}-\tan\theta\tan(3\theta)=\dfrac{-2\sin(3\theta)\sin(-\theta)}{2\cos(3\theta)\cos(-\theta)}-\tan\theta\tan(3\theta)$

$=\dfrac{2\sin(3\theta)\sin\theta}{2\cos(3\theta)\cos\theta}-\tan\theta\tan(3\theta)=\tan(3\theta)\tan\theta-\tan\theta\tan(3\theta)=0$

53. $\sin165°=\sin(120°+45°)=\sin120°\cdot\cos45°+\cos120°\cdot\sin45°$

$=\left(\dfrac{\sqrt3}{2}\right)\cdot\left(\dfrac{\sqrt2}{2}\right)+\left(-\dfrac12\right)\cdot\left(\dfrac{\sqrt2}{2}\right)=\dfrac14\left(\sqrt6-\sqrt2\right)$

55. $\cos\dfrac{5\pi}{12}=\cos\left(\dfrac{3\pi}{12}+\dfrac{2\pi}{12}\right)=\cos\dfrac{\pi}{4}\cdot\cos\dfrac{\pi}{6}-\sin\dfrac{\pi}{4}\cdot\sin\dfrac{\pi}{6}=\dfrac{\sqrt2}{2}\cdot\dfrac{\sqrt3}{2}-\dfrac{\sqrt2}{2}\cdot\dfrac12=\dfrac14\left(\sqrt6-\sqrt2\right)$

57. $\cos80°\cdot\cos20°+\sin80°\cdot\sin20°=\cos(80°-20°)=\cos60°=\dfrac12$

59. $\tan\dfrac{\pi}{8}=\tan\left(\dfrac{\frac{\pi}{4}}{2}\right)=\sqrt{\dfrac{1-\cos\frac{\pi}{4}}{1+\cos\frac{\pi}{4}}}=\sqrt{\dfrac{1-\frac{\sqrt2}{2}}{1+\frac{\sqrt2}{2}}}=\sqrt{\left(\dfrac{2-\sqrt2}{2+\sqrt2}\right)\cdot\left(\dfrac{2-\sqrt2}{2-\sqrt2}\right)}$

$=\sqrt{\dfrac{\left(2-\sqrt2\right)^2}{2}}=\left(\dfrac{2-\sqrt2}{\sqrt2}\right)\cdot\dfrac{\sqrt2}{\sqrt2}=\dfrac{2\sqrt2-2}{2}=\sqrt2-1$

61. $\sin\alpha=\dfrac45,\ 0<\alpha<\dfrac{\pi}{2};\qquad \sin\beta=\dfrac{5}{13},\ \dfrac{\pi}{2}<\beta<\pi$

$\cos\alpha=\dfrac35,\ \tan\alpha=\dfrac43,\ \cos\beta=-\dfrac{12}{13},\ \tan\beta=-\dfrac{5}{12},\quad 0<\dfrac{\alpha}{2}<\dfrac{\pi}{4},\ \dfrac{\pi}{4}<\dfrac{\beta}{2}<\dfrac{\pi}{2}$

(a) $\sin(\alpha+\beta)=\sin\alpha\cos\beta+\cos\alpha\sin\beta=\left(\dfrac45\right)\cdot\left(-\dfrac{12}{13}\right)+\left(\dfrac35\right)\cdot\left(\dfrac{5}{13}\right)=\dfrac{-48+15}{65}=-\dfrac{33}{65}$

(b) $\cos(\alpha+\beta)=\cos\alpha\cos\beta-\sin\alpha\sin\beta=\left(\dfrac35\right)\cdot\left(-\dfrac{12}{13}\right)-\left(\dfrac45\right)\cdot\left(\dfrac{5}{13}\right)=\dfrac{-36-20}{65}=-\dfrac{56}{65}$

(c) $\sin(\alpha-\beta)=\sin\alpha\cos\beta-\cos\alpha\sin\beta=\left(\dfrac45\right)\cdot\left(-\dfrac{12}{13}\right)-\left(\dfrac35\right)\cdot\left(\dfrac{5}{13}\right)=\dfrac{-48-15}{65}=-\dfrac{63}{65}$

(d) $\tan(\alpha+\beta)=\dfrac{\tan\alpha+\tan\beta}{1-\tan\alpha\tan\beta}=\dfrac{\frac43+\left(-\frac{5}{12}\right)}{1-\left(\frac43\right)\cdot\left(-\frac{5}{12}\right)}=\dfrac{\frac{11}{12}}{\frac{14}{9}}=\dfrac{11}{12}\cdot\dfrac{9}{14}=\dfrac{33}{56}$

(e) $\sin(2\alpha)=2\sin\alpha\cos\alpha=2\cdot\dfrac45\cdot\dfrac35=\dfrac{24}{25}$

(f) $\cos(2\beta)=\cos^2\beta-\sin^2\beta=\left(-\dfrac{12}{13}\right)^2-\left(\dfrac{5}{13}\right)^2=\dfrac{144}{169}-\dfrac{25}{169}=\dfrac{119}{169}$

(g) $\sin\dfrac{\beta}{2} = \sqrt{\dfrac{1-\cos\beta}{2}} = \sqrt{\dfrac{1-\left(-\dfrac{12}{13}\right)}{2}} = \sqrt{\dfrac{\dfrac{25}{13}}{2}} = \sqrt{\dfrac{25}{26}} = \dfrac{5}{\sqrt{26}} = \dfrac{5\sqrt{26}}{26}$

(h) $\cos\dfrac{\alpha}{2} = \sqrt{\dfrac{1+\cos\alpha}{2}} = \sqrt{\dfrac{1+\dfrac{3}{5}}{2}} = \sqrt{\dfrac{\dfrac{8}{5}}{2}} = \sqrt{\dfrac{4}{5}} = \dfrac{2}{\sqrt{5}} = \dfrac{2\sqrt{5}}{5}$

63. $\sin\alpha = -\dfrac{3}{5},\ \pi < \alpha < \dfrac{3\pi}{2};\qquad \cos\beta = \dfrac{12}{13},\ \dfrac{3\pi}{2} < \beta < 2\pi$

$\cos\alpha = -\dfrac{4}{5},\ \tan\alpha = \dfrac{3}{4},\ \sin\beta = -\dfrac{5}{13},\ \tan\beta = -\dfrac{5}{12},\ \dfrac{\pi}{2} < \dfrac{\alpha}{2} < \dfrac{3\pi}{4},\ \dfrac{3\pi}{4} < \dfrac{\beta}{2} < \pi$

(a) $\sin(\alpha+\beta) = \sin\alpha\cos\beta + \cos\alpha\sin\beta = \left(-\dfrac{3}{5}\right)\cdot\left(\dfrac{12}{13}\right) + \left(-\dfrac{4}{5}\right)\cdot\left(-\dfrac{5}{13}\right) = \dfrac{-36+20}{65} = -\dfrac{16}{65}$

(b) $\cos(\alpha+\beta) = \cos\alpha\cos\beta - \sin\alpha\sin\beta = \left(-\dfrac{4}{5}\right)\cdot\left(\dfrac{12}{13}\right) - \left(-\dfrac{3}{5}\right)\cdot\left(-\dfrac{5}{13}\right) = \dfrac{-48-15}{65} = -\dfrac{63}{65}$

(c) $\sin(\alpha-\beta) = \sin\alpha\cos\beta - \cos\alpha\sin\beta = \left(-\dfrac{3}{5}\right)\cdot\left(\dfrac{12}{13}\right) - \left(-\dfrac{4}{5}\right)\cdot\left(-\dfrac{5}{13}\right) = \dfrac{-36-20}{65} = -\dfrac{56}{65}$

(d) $\tan(\alpha+\beta) = \dfrac{\tan\alpha + \tan\beta}{1 - \tan\alpha\tan\beta} = \dfrac{\dfrac{3}{4}+\left(-\dfrac{5}{12}\right)}{1-\left(\dfrac{3}{4}\right)\cdot\left(-\dfrac{5}{12}\right)} = \dfrac{\dfrac{1}{3}}{\dfrac{21}{16}} = \dfrac{1}{3}\cdot\dfrac{16}{21} = \dfrac{16}{63}$

(e) $\sin(2\alpha) = 2\sin\alpha\cos\alpha = 2\cdot\left(-\dfrac{3}{5}\right)\cdot\left(-\dfrac{4}{5}\right) = \dfrac{24}{25}$

(f) $\cos(2\beta) = \cos^2\beta - \sin^2\beta = \left(\dfrac{12}{13}\right)^2 - \left(-\dfrac{5}{13}\right)^2 = \dfrac{144}{169} - \dfrac{25}{169} = \dfrac{119}{169}$

(g) $\sin\dfrac{\beta}{2} = \sqrt{\dfrac{1-\cos\beta}{2}} = \sqrt{\dfrac{1-\dfrac{12}{13}}{2}} = \sqrt{\dfrac{\dfrac{1}{13}}{2}} = \sqrt{\dfrac{1}{26}} = \dfrac{1}{\sqrt{26}} = \dfrac{\sqrt{26}}{26}$

(h) $\cos\dfrac{\alpha}{2} = -\sqrt{\dfrac{1+\cos\alpha}{2}} = -\sqrt{\dfrac{1+\left(-\dfrac{4}{5}\right)}{2}} = -\sqrt{\dfrac{\dfrac{1}{5}}{2}} = -\sqrt{\dfrac{1}{10}} = -\dfrac{1}{\sqrt{10}} = -\dfrac{\sqrt{10}}{10}$

65. $\tan\alpha = \dfrac{3}{4},\ \pi < \alpha < \dfrac{3\pi}{2};\qquad \tan\beta = \dfrac{12}{5},\ 0 < \beta < \dfrac{\pi}{2}$

$\sin\alpha = -\dfrac{3}{5},\ \cos\alpha = -\dfrac{4}{5},\ \sin\beta = \dfrac{12}{13},\ \cos\beta = \dfrac{5}{13},\ \dfrac{\pi}{2} < \dfrac{\alpha}{2} < \dfrac{3\pi}{4},\ 0 < \dfrac{\beta}{2} < \dfrac{\pi}{4}$

(a) $\sin(\alpha+\beta) = \sin\alpha\cos\beta + \cos\alpha\sin\beta = \left(-\dfrac{3}{5}\right)\cdot\left(\dfrac{5}{13}\right) + \left(-\dfrac{4}{5}\right)\cdot\left(\dfrac{12}{13}\right) = \dfrac{-15-48}{65} = -\dfrac{63}{65}$

(b) $\cos(\alpha+\beta) = \cos\alpha\cos\beta - \sin\alpha\sin\beta = \left(-\dfrac{4}{5}\right)\cdot\left(\dfrac{5}{13}\right) - \left(-\dfrac{3}{5}\right)\cdot\left(\dfrac{12}{13}\right) = \dfrac{-20+36}{65} = \dfrac{16}{65}$

(c) $\sin(\alpha-\beta) = \sin\alpha\cos\beta - \cos\alpha\sin\beta = \left(-\dfrac{3}{5}\right)\cdot\left(\dfrac{5}{13}\right) - \left(-\dfrac{4}{5}\right)\cdot\left(\dfrac{12}{13}\right) = \dfrac{-15+48}{65} = \dfrac{33}{65}$

(d) $\tan(\alpha + \beta) = \dfrac{\tan\alpha + \tan\beta}{1 - \tan\alpha\tan\beta} = \dfrac{\dfrac{3}{4} + \dfrac{12}{5}}{1 - \left(\dfrac{3}{4}\right)\cdot\left(\dfrac{12}{5}\right)} = \dfrac{\dfrac{15 + 48}{20}}{-\dfrac{4}{5}} = \left(\dfrac{63}{20}\right)\cdot\left(-\dfrac{5}{4}\right) = -\dfrac{63}{16}$

(e) $\sin(2\alpha) = 2\sin\alpha\cos\alpha = 2\cdot\left(-\dfrac{3}{5}\right)\cdot\left(-\dfrac{4}{5}\right) = \dfrac{24}{25}$

(f) $\cos(2\beta) = \cos^2\beta - \sin^2\beta = \left(\dfrac{5}{13}\right)^2 - \left(\dfrac{12}{13}\right)^2 = \dfrac{25}{169} - \dfrac{144}{169} = -\dfrac{119}{169}$

(g) $\sin\dfrac{\beta}{2} = \sqrt{\dfrac{1 - \cos\beta}{2}} = \sqrt{\dfrac{1 - \dfrac{5}{13}}{2}} = \sqrt{\dfrac{\dfrac{8}{13}}{2}} = \sqrt{\dfrac{4}{13}} = \dfrac{2}{\sqrt{13}} = \dfrac{2\sqrt{13}}{13}$

(h) $\cos\dfrac{\alpha}{2} = -\sqrt{\dfrac{1 + \cos\alpha}{2}} = -\sqrt{\dfrac{1 + \left(-\dfrac{4}{5}\right)}{2}} = -\sqrt{\dfrac{\dfrac{1}{5}}{2}} = -\sqrt{\dfrac{1}{10}} = -\dfrac{1}{\sqrt{10}} = -\dfrac{\sqrt{10}}{10}$

67. $\sec\alpha = 2,\ -\dfrac{\pi}{2} < \alpha < 0;\qquad \sec\beta = 3,\ \dfrac{3\pi}{2} < \beta < 2\pi$

$\sin\alpha = -\dfrac{\sqrt{3}}{2},\ \cos\alpha = \dfrac{1}{2},\ \tan\alpha = -\sqrt{3},\ \sin\beta = -\dfrac{2\sqrt{2}}{3},\ \cos\beta = \dfrac{1}{3},\ \tan\beta = -2\sqrt{2},$

$-\dfrac{\pi}{4} < \dfrac{\alpha}{2} < 0,\quad \dfrac{3\pi}{4} < \dfrac{\beta}{2} < \pi$

(a) $\sin(\alpha + \beta) = \sin\alpha\cos\beta + \cos\alpha\sin\beta = \left(-\dfrac{\sqrt{3}}{2}\right)\cdot\left(\dfrac{1}{3}\right) + \left(\dfrac{1}{2}\right)\cdot\left(-\dfrac{2\sqrt{2}}{3}\right) = \dfrac{-\sqrt{3} - 2\sqrt{2}}{6}$

(b) $\cos(\alpha + \beta) = \cos\alpha\cos\beta - \sin\alpha\sin\beta = \left(\dfrac{1}{2}\right)\cdot\left(\dfrac{1}{3}\right) - \left(-\dfrac{\sqrt{3}}{2}\right)\cdot\left(-\dfrac{2\sqrt{2}}{3}\right) = \dfrac{1 - 2\sqrt{6}}{6}$

(c) $\sin(\alpha - \beta) = \sin\alpha\cos\beta - \cos\alpha\sin\beta = \left(-\dfrac{\sqrt{3}}{2}\right)\cdot\left(\dfrac{1}{3}\right) - \left(\dfrac{1}{2}\right)\cdot\left(-\dfrac{2\sqrt{2}}{3}\right) = \dfrac{-\sqrt{3} + 2\sqrt{2}}{6}$

(d) $\tan(\alpha + \beta) = \dfrac{\tan\alpha + \tan\beta}{1 - \tan\alpha\tan\beta} = \dfrac{-\sqrt{3} + \left(-2\sqrt{2}\right)}{1 - \left(-\sqrt{3}\right)\left(-2\sqrt{2}\right)} = \left(\dfrac{-\sqrt{3} - 2\sqrt{2}}{1 - 2\sqrt{6}}\right)\cdot\left(\dfrac{1 + 2\sqrt{6}}{1 + 2\sqrt{6}}\right)$

$= \dfrac{-9\sqrt{3} - 8\sqrt{2}}{-23} = \dfrac{9\sqrt{3} + 8\sqrt{2}}{23}$

(e) $\sin(2\alpha) = 2\sin\alpha\cos\alpha = 2\cdot\left(-\dfrac{\sqrt{3}}{2}\right)\cdot\left(\dfrac{1}{2}\right) = -\dfrac{\sqrt{3}}{2}$

(f) $\cos(2\beta) = \cos^2\beta - \sin^2\beta = \left(\dfrac{1}{3}\right)^2 - \left(-\dfrac{2\sqrt{2}}{3}\right)^2 = \dfrac{1}{9} - \dfrac{8}{9} = -\dfrac{7}{9}$

(g) $\sin\dfrac{\beta}{2} = \sqrt{\dfrac{1 - \cos\beta}{2}} = \sqrt{\dfrac{1 - \dfrac{1}{3}}{2}} = \sqrt{\dfrac{\dfrac{2}{3}}{2}} = \sqrt{\dfrac{1}{3}} = \dfrac{1}{\sqrt{3}} = \dfrac{\sqrt{3}}{3}$

(h) $\cos\dfrac{\alpha}{2} = \sqrt{\dfrac{1 + \cos\alpha}{2}} = \sqrt{\dfrac{1 + \dfrac{1}{2}}{2}} = \sqrt{\dfrac{\dfrac{3}{2}}{2}} = \sqrt{\dfrac{3}{4}} = \dfrac{\sqrt{3}}{2}$

69. $\sin\alpha = -\dfrac{2}{3}$, $\pi < \alpha < \dfrac{3\pi}{2}$; $\cos\beta = -\dfrac{2}{3}$, $\pi < \beta < \dfrac{3\pi}{2}$

$\cos\alpha = -\dfrac{\sqrt{5}}{3}$, $\tan\alpha = \dfrac{2\sqrt{5}}{5}$, $\sin\beta = -\dfrac{\sqrt{5}}{3}$, $\tan\beta = \dfrac{\sqrt{5}}{2}$, $\dfrac{\pi}{2} < \dfrac{\alpha}{2} < \dfrac{3\pi}{4}$, $\dfrac{\pi}{2} < \dfrac{\beta}{2} < \dfrac{3\pi}{4}$

(a) $\sin(\alpha + \beta) = \sin\alpha\cos\beta + \cos\alpha\sin\beta = \left(-\dfrac{2}{3}\right)\cdot\left(-\dfrac{2}{3}\right) + \left(-\dfrac{\sqrt{5}}{3}\right)\cdot\left(-\dfrac{\sqrt{5}}{3}\right) = \dfrac{4+5}{9} = 1$

(b) $\cos(\alpha + \beta) = \cos\alpha\cos\beta - \sin\alpha\sin\beta = \left(-\dfrac{\sqrt{5}}{3}\right)\cdot\left(-\dfrac{2}{3}\right) - \left(-\dfrac{2}{3}\right)\cdot\left(-\dfrac{\sqrt{5}}{3}\right) = \dfrac{2\sqrt{5}-2\sqrt{5}}{9} = 0$

(c) $\sin(\alpha - \beta) = \sin\alpha\cos\beta - \cos\alpha\sin\beta = \left(-\dfrac{2}{3}\right)\cdot\left(-\dfrac{2}{3}\right) - \left(-\dfrac{\sqrt{5}}{3}\right)\cdot\left(-\dfrac{\sqrt{5}}{3}\right) = \dfrac{4-5}{9} = -\dfrac{1}{9}$

(d) $\tan(\alpha + \beta) = \dfrac{\tan\alpha + \tan\beta}{1 - \tan\alpha\tan\beta} = \dfrac{\dfrac{2\sqrt{5}}{5} + \dfrac{\sqrt{5}}{2}}{1 - \left(\dfrac{2\sqrt{5}}{5}\right)\cdot\left(\dfrac{\sqrt{5}}{2}\right)} = \dfrac{\dfrac{4\sqrt{5}+5\sqrt{5}}{10}}{\dfrac{10-10}{10}} = \dfrac{\dfrac{9\sqrt{5}}{10}}{\dfrac{0}{10}}$; undefined

(e) $\sin(2\alpha) = 2\sin\alpha\cos\alpha = 2\cdot\left(-\dfrac{2}{3}\right)\cdot\left(-\dfrac{\sqrt{5}}{3}\right) = \dfrac{4\sqrt{5}}{9}$

(f) $\cos(2\beta) = \cos^2\beta - \sin^2\beta = \left(-\dfrac{2}{3}\right)^2 - \left(-\dfrac{\sqrt{5}}{3}\right)^2 = \dfrac{4}{9} - \dfrac{5}{9} = -\dfrac{1}{9}$

(g) $\sin\dfrac{\beta}{2} = \sqrt{\dfrac{1-\cos\beta}{2}} = \sqrt{\dfrac{1-\left(-\dfrac{2}{3}\right)}{2}} = \sqrt{\dfrac{\dfrac{5}{3}}{2}} = \sqrt{\dfrac{5}{6}} = \dfrac{\sqrt{30}}{6}$

(h) $\cos\dfrac{\alpha}{2} = -\sqrt{\dfrac{1+\cos\alpha}{2}} = -\sqrt{\dfrac{1+\left(-\dfrac{\sqrt{5}}{3}\right)}{2}} = -\sqrt{\dfrac{\dfrac{3-\sqrt{5}}{3}}{2}} = -\sqrt{\dfrac{3-\sqrt{5}}{6}}$

$= -\dfrac{\sqrt{6\left(3-\sqrt{5}\right)}}{6} = -\dfrac{\sqrt{6}\sqrt{3-\sqrt{5}}}{6}$

71. $\cos\left(\sin^{-1}\dfrac{3}{5} - \cos^{-1}\dfrac{1}{2}\right)$

Let $\alpha = \sin^{-1}\dfrac{3}{5}$ and $\beta = \cos^{-1}\dfrac{1}{2}$. α is in quadrant I; β is in quadrant I.

Then $\sin\alpha = \dfrac{3}{5}$, $0 \le \alpha \le \dfrac{\pi}{2}$, and $\cos\beta = \dfrac{1}{2}$, $0 \le \beta \le \dfrac{\pi}{2}$.

$\cos\alpha = \sqrt{1 - \sin^2\alpha} = \sqrt{1 - \left(\dfrac{3}{5}\right)^2} = \sqrt{1 - \dfrac{9}{25}} = \sqrt{\dfrac{16}{25}} = \dfrac{4}{5}$

$\sin\beta = \sqrt{1 - \cos^2\beta} = \sqrt{1 - \left(\dfrac{1}{2}\right)^2} = \sqrt{1 - \dfrac{1}{4}} = \sqrt{\dfrac{3}{4}} = \dfrac{\sqrt{3}}{2}$

$\cos\left(\sin^{-1}\dfrac{3}{5} - \cos^{-1}\dfrac{1}{2}\right) = \cos(\alpha - \beta) = \cos\alpha\cos\beta + \sin\alpha\sin\beta = \left(\dfrac{4}{5}\right)\cdot\left(\dfrac{1}{2}\right) + \left(\dfrac{3}{5}\right)\cdot\left(\dfrac{\sqrt{3}}{2}\right) = \dfrac{4 + 3\sqrt{3}}{10}$

73. $\tan\left[\sin^{-1}\left(-\dfrac{1}{2}\right)-\tan^{-1}\dfrac{3}{4}\right]$

Let $\alpha=\sin^{-1}\left(-\dfrac{1}{2}\right)$ and $\beta=\tan^{-1}\dfrac{3}{4}$. α is in quadrant IV; β is in quadrant I.

Then $\sin\alpha=-\dfrac{1}{2}$, $0\le\alpha\le\dfrac{\pi}{2}$, and $\tan\beta=\dfrac{3}{4}$, $0<\beta<\dfrac{\pi}{2}$.

$\cos\alpha=\sqrt{1-\sin^2\alpha}=\sqrt{1-\left(-\dfrac{1}{2}\right)^2}=\sqrt{1-\dfrac{1}{4}}=\sqrt{\dfrac{3}{4}}=\dfrac{\sqrt{3}}{2}$; $\tan\alpha=-\dfrac{1}{\sqrt{3}}=-\dfrac{\sqrt{3}}{3}$

$\tan\left[\sin^{-1}\left(-\dfrac{1}{2}\right)-\tan^{-1}\dfrac{3}{4}\right]=\tan(\alpha-\beta)=\dfrac{\tan\alpha-\tan\beta}{1+\tan\alpha\tan\beta}=\dfrac{-\dfrac{\sqrt{3}}{3}-\dfrac{3}{4}}{1+\left(-\dfrac{\sqrt{3}}{3}\right)\cdot\left(\dfrac{3}{4}\right)}$

$=\dfrac{\dfrac{-4\sqrt{3}-9}{12}}{1-\dfrac{3\sqrt{3}}{12}}=\left(\dfrac{-9-4\sqrt{3}}{12-3\sqrt{3}}\right)\cdot\left(\dfrac{12+3\sqrt{3}}{12+3\sqrt{3}}\right)=\dfrac{-144-75\sqrt{3}}{117}=\dfrac{-48-25\sqrt{3}}{39}=-\dfrac{48+25\sqrt{3}}{39}$

75. $\sin\left[2\cos^{-1}\left(-\dfrac{3}{5}\right)\right]$

Let $\alpha=\cos^{-1}\left(-\dfrac{3}{5}\right)$. α is in quadrant II.

Then $\cos\alpha=-\dfrac{3}{5}$, $\dfrac{\pi}{2}\le\alpha\le\pi$.

$\sin\alpha=\sqrt{1-\cos^2\alpha}=\sqrt{1-\left(-\dfrac{3}{5}\right)^2}=\sqrt{1-\dfrac{9}{25}}=\sqrt{\dfrac{16}{25}}=\dfrac{4}{5}$

$\sin\left[2\cos^{-1}\left(-\dfrac{3}{5}\right)\right]=\sin2\alpha=2\sin\alpha\cos\alpha=2\cdot\left(\dfrac{4}{5}\right)\cdot\left(-\dfrac{3}{5}\right)=-\dfrac{24}{25}$

77. $\cos\theta=\dfrac{1}{2}$

$\theta=\dfrac{\pi}{3}+2k\pi$ or $\theta=\dfrac{5\pi}{3}+2k\pi$, k is any integer

The solution set is $\left\{\dfrac{\pi}{3},\ \dfrac{5\pi}{3}\right\}$.

79. $2\cos\theta+\sqrt{2}=0$

$2\cos\theta=-\sqrt{2}\Rightarrow\cos\theta=-\dfrac{\sqrt{2}}{2}$

$\theta=\dfrac{3\pi}{4}+2k\pi$ or $\theta=\dfrac{5\pi}{4}+2k\pi$, k is any integer

The solution set is $\left\{\dfrac{3\pi}{4},\ \dfrac{5\pi}{4}\right\}$.

81. $\sin(2\theta) + 1 = 0$

$\sin(2\theta) = -1$

$2\theta = \dfrac{3\pi}{2} + 2k\pi \Rightarrow \quad \theta = \dfrac{3\pi}{4} + k\pi$, k is any integer

The solution set is $\left\{\dfrac{3\pi}{4}, \dfrac{7\pi}{4}\right\}$.

83. $\tan(2\theta) = 0$

$2\theta = 0 + k\pi \Rightarrow \theta = \dfrac{k\pi}{2}$, k is any integer

The solution set is $\left\{0, \dfrac{\pi}{2}, \pi, \dfrac{3\pi}{2}\right\}$.

85. $\sec^2\theta = 4$

$\sec\theta = \pm 2 \Rightarrow \cos\theta = \pm\dfrac{1}{2}$

$\theta = \dfrac{\pi}{3} + k\pi$, k is any integer

$\theta = \dfrac{2\pi}{3} + k\pi$, k is any integer

The solution set is $\left\{\dfrac{\pi}{3}, \dfrac{2\pi}{3}, \dfrac{4\pi}{3}, \dfrac{5\pi}{3}\right\}$.

87. $\sin\theta = \tan\theta$

$\sin\theta = \dfrac{\sin\theta}{\cos\theta}$

$\sin\theta\cos\theta = \sin\theta$

$\sin\theta\cos\theta - \sin\theta = 0$

$\sin\theta(\cos\theta - 1) = 0$

$\cos\theta - 1 = 0$

$\cos\theta = 1 \Rightarrow \theta = 0$

or $\sin\theta = 0 \Rightarrow \theta = 0, \pi$

The solution set is $\left\{0, \pi\right\}$.

89. $\sin\theta + \sin(2\theta) = 0$

$\sin\theta + 2\sin\theta\cos\theta = 0$

$\sin\theta(1 + 2\cos\theta) = 0$

$1 + 2\cos\theta = 0$

$\cos\theta = -\dfrac{1}{2} \Rightarrow \theta = \dfrac{2\pi}{3}, \dfrac{4\pi}{3}$

or $\sin\theta = 0 \Rightarrow \theta = 0, \pi$

The solution set is $\left\{0, \dfrac{2\pi}{3}, \pi, \dfrac{4\pi}{3}\right\}$.

91.
$$\sin(2\theta) - \cos\theta - 2\sin\theta + 1 = 0$$
$$2\sin\theta\cos\theta - \cos\theta - 2\sin\theta + 1 = 0$$
$$\cos\theta(2\sin\theta - 1) - 1(2\sin\theta - 1) = 0$$
$$(2\sin\theta - 1)(\cos\theta - 1) = 0$$
$$2\sin\theta - 1 = 0$$
$$\sin\theta = \frac{1}{2} \Rightarrow \theta = \frac{\pi}{6}, \frac{5\pi}{6}$$
or $\cos\theta - 1 = 0$
$$\cos\theta = 1 \Rightarrow \theta = 0$$

The solution set is $\left\{0, \dfrac{\pi}{6}, \dfrac{5\pi}{6}\right\}$.

93.
$$2\sin^2\theta - 3\sin\theta + 1 = 0$$
$$(2\sin\theta - 1)(\sin\theta - 1) = 0$$
$$2\sin\theta - 1 = 0$$
$$\sin\theta = \frac{1}{2} \Rightarrow \theta = \frac{\pi}{6}, \frac{5\pi}{6}$$
or $\sin\theta - 1 = 0$
$$\sin\theta = 1 \Rightarrow \theta = \frac{\pi}{2}$$

The solution set is $\left\{\dfrac{\pi}{6}, \dfrac{\pi}{2}, \dfrac{5\pi}{6}\right\}$.

95.
$$4\sin^2\theta = 1 + 4\cos\theta$$
$$4\left(1 - \cos^2\theta\right) = 1 + 4\cos\theta$$
$$4 - 4\cos^2\theta = 1 + 4\cos\theta$$
$$4\cos^2\theta + 4\cos\theta - 3 = 0$$
$$(2\cos\theta - 1)(2\cos\theta + 3) = 0$$
$$2\cos\theta - 1 = 0$$
$$\cos\theta = \frac{1}{2} \Rightarrow \theta = \frac{\pi}{3}, \frac{5\pi}{3}$$
or $2\cos\theta + 3 = 0$
$$\cos\theta = -\frac{3}{2}, \text{ which is impossible}$$

The solution set is $\left\{\dfrac{\pi}{3}, \dfrac{5\pi}{3}\right\}$.

97.
$$\sin(2\theta) = \sqrt{2}\cos\theta$$
$$2\sin\theta\cos\theta = \sqrt{2}\cos\theta$$
$$2\sin\theta\cos\theta - \sqrt{2}\cos\theta = 0$$
$$\cos\theta\left(2\sin\theta - \sqrt{2}\right) = 0$$
$$\cos\theta = 0 \Rightarrow \theta = \frac{\pi}{2}, \frac{3\pi}{2}$$
or $2\sin\theta - \sqrt{2} = 0$
$$\sin\theta = \frac{\sqrt{2}}{2} \Rightarrow \theta = \frac{\pi}{4}, \frac{3\pi}{4}$$

The solution set is $\left\{\dfrac{\pi}{4}, \dfrac{\pi}{2}, \dfrac{3\pi}{4}, \dfrac{3\pi}{2}\right\}$.

99.
$$\sin\theta - \cos\theta = 1$$
Divide each side by $\sqrt{2}$:
$$\frac{1}{\sqrt{2}}\sin\theta - \frac{1}{\sqrt{2}}\cos\theta = \frac{1}{\sqrt{2}}$$
Rewrite using the difference of two angles formula where
$\phi = \dfrac{\pi}{4}$, so $\cos\phi = \dfrac{1}{\sqrt{2}}$ and $\sin\phi = \dfrac{1}{\sqrt{2}}$.
$$\sin\theta\cos\phi - \cos\theta\sin\phi = \frac{1}{\sqrt{2}}$$
$$\sin(\theta - \phi) = \frac{\sqrt{2}}{2}$$
$$\theta - \phi = \frac{\pi}{4} \quad \text{or} \quad \theta - \phi = \frac{3\pi}{4}$$
$$\theta - \frac{\pi}{4} = \frac{\pi}{4} \quad \text{or} \quad \theta - \frac{\pi}{4} = \frac{3\pi}{4}$$
$$\theta = \frac{\pi}{2} \quad \text{or} \quad \theta = \pi$$

The solution set is $\left\{\dfrac{\pi}{2}, \pi\right\}$.

101. $\sin^{-1}0.7 \approx 0.78$ **103.** $\tan^{-1}(-2) \approx -1.11$

105. $\sec^{-1}3 = \cos^{-1}\dfrac{1}{3} \approx 1.23$

107. $2x = 5\cos x$
Find the intersection of
$y_1 = 2x$ and $y_2 = 5\cos x$:

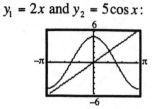

The solution set is $\{1.11\}$.

109. $2\sin x + 3\cos x = 4x$
Find the intersection of
$y_1 = 2\sin x + 3\cos x$ and $y_2 = 4x$:

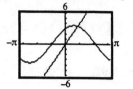

The solution set is $\{0.87\}$.

111. $\sin x = \ln x$
Find the intersection of
$y_1 = \sin x$ and $y_2 = \ln x$:

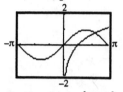

The solution set is $\{2.22\}$.

113. Using a half-angle formula:

$$\sin 15° = \sin\left(\frac{30°}{2}\right) = \sqrt{\frac{1-\cos 30°}{2}} = \sqrt{\frac{1-\frac{\sqrt{3}}{2}}{2}} = \sqrt{\frac{2-\sqrt{3}}{4}} = \frac{\sqrt{2-\sqrt{3}}}{2}$$

Note: since 15° lies in quadrant I, we have $\sin 15° > 0$.
Using a difference formula:
$$\sin 15° = \sin\left(45° - 30°\right) = \sin 45°\cdot\cos 30° - \cos 45°\cdot\sin 30°$$

$$= \frac{\sqrt{2}}{2}\cdot\frac{\sqrt{3}}{2} - \frac{\sqrt{2}}{2}\cdot\frac{1}{2} = \frac{1}{4}\left(\sqrt{6} - \sqrt{2}\right)$$

$$= \frac{\sqrt{2}\sqrt{3} - \sqrt{2}}{4} = \frac{\sqrt{2}\left(\sqrt{3} - 1\right)}{4} = \sqrt{\left(\frac{\sqrt{2}\left(\sqrt{3} - 1\right)}{4}\right)^2}$$

$$= \sqrt{\frac{2\left(\sqrt{3} - 1\right)^2}{16}} = \sqrt{\frac{2\left(3 - 2\sqrt{3} + 1\right)}{16}} = \sqrt{\frac{2\left(4 - 2\sqrt{3}\right)}{16}}$$

$$= \sqrt{\frac{4\left(2 - \sqrt{3}\right)}{16}} = \sqrt{\frac{2 - \sqrt{3}}{4}}$$

$$= \frac{\sqrt{2-\sqrt{3}}}{2}$$

Chapter 3

Analytic Trigonometry

3.CR   Cumulative Review

1. $3x^2 + x - 1 = 0$

$$x = \frac{-b \pm \sqrt{b^2 - 4ac}}{2a} = \frac{-1 \pm \sqrt{1^2 - 4(3)(-1)}}{2(3)}$$

$$= \frac{-1 \pm \sqrt{1 + 12}}{6} = \frac{-1 \pm \sqrt{13}}{6}$$

The solution set is $\left\{ \dfrac{-1 - \sqrt{13}}{6}, \dfrac{-1 + \sqrt{13}}{6} \right\}$.

3. $3x + y^2 = 9$

x-intercept: $3x + 0^2 = 9 \Rightarrow 3x = 9 \Rightarrow x = 3;\ (3,0)$

y-intercepts: $3(0) + y^2 = 9 \Rightarrow y^2 = 9 \Rightarrow y = \pm 3;\ (0,-3),(0,3)$

Test for symmetry:

   x-axis :   Replace y by $-y$: $3x + (-y)^2 = 9 \Rightarrow 3x + y^2 = 9$

   which is equivalent to $3x + y^2 = 9$.

   y-axis :   Replace x by $-x$: $3(-x) + y^2 = 9 \Rightarrow -3x + y^2 = 9$,

   which is not equivalent to $3x + y^2 = 9$.

   Origin :   Replace x by $-x$ and y by $-y$: $3(-x) + (-y)^2 = 9 \Rightarrow -3x + y^2 = 9$,

   which is not equivalent to $3x + y^2 = 9$.

Therefore, the graph is symmetric with respect to the *x*-axis.

5. $y = 3\sqrt{x} - 2$

Using the graph of $y = \sqrt{x}$, stretch vertically by a factor of 3, and vertically shift down 2 units.

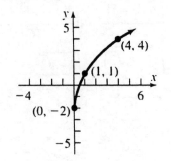

7. (a) $y = x^3$

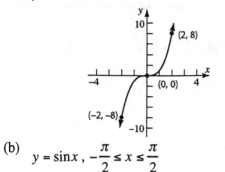

Inverse function: $y = \sqrt[3]{x}$

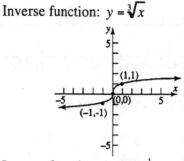

(b) $y = \sin x$, $-\dfrac{\pi}{2} \le x \le \dfrac{\pi}{2}$

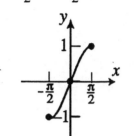

Inverse function: $y = \sin^{-1} x$

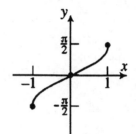

(c) $y = \cos x$, $0 \le x \le \pi$

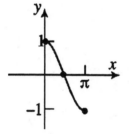

Inverse function: $y = \cos^{-1} x$

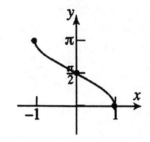

9. $\cos\!\left(\tan^{-1} 2\right)$

Find the angle θ, $-\dfrac{\pi}{2} < \theta < \dfrac{\pi}{2}$, whose tangent equals 2.

$\tan\theta = 2$, $-\dfrac{\pi}{2} < \theta < \dfrac{\pi}{2} \Rightarrow \theta$ is in Quadrant I

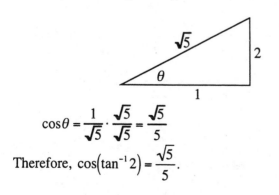

$\cos\theta = \dfrac{1}{\sqrt{5}} \cdot \dfrac{\sqrt{5}}{\sqrt{5}} = \dfrac{\sqrt{5}}{5}$

Therefore, $\cos\!\left(\tan^{-1} 2\right) = \dfrac{\sqrt{5}}{5}$.

Applications of Trigonometric Functions

4.1 Right Triangle Trigonometry; Applications

1. $a = \sqrt{5^2 - 3^2} = \sqrt{25 - 9} = \sqrt{16} = 4$

3. False

5. angle of elevation

7. True

9. opposite = 5; adjacent = 12
   Find the hypotenuse:
   $5^2 + 12^2 = (\text{hypotenuse})^2 \Rightarrow (\text{hypotenuse})^2 = 25 + 144 = 169 \Rightarrow \text{hypotenuse} = 13$

   $\sin\theta = \dfrac{\text{opp}}{\text{hyp}} = \dfrac{5}{13}$ $\qquad \cos\theta = \dfrac{\text{adj}}{\text{hyp}} = \dfrac{12}{13}$ $\qquad \tan\theta = \dfrac{\text{opp}}{\text{adj}} = \dfrac{5}{12}$

   $\csc\theta = \dfrac{\text{hyp}}{\text{opp}} = \dfrac{13}{5}$ $\qquad \sec\theta = \dfrac{\text{hyp}}{\text{adj}} = \dfrac{13}{12}$ $\qquad \cot\theta = \dfrac{\text{adj}}{\text{opp}} = \dfrac{12}{5}$

11. opposite = 2; adjacent = 3
    Find the hypotenuse:
    $2^2 + 3^2 = (\text{hypotenuse})^2 \Rightarrow (\text{hypotenuse})^2 = 4 + 9 = 13 \Rightarrow \text{hypotenuse} = \sqrt{13}$

    $\sin\theta = \dfrac{\text{opp}}{\text{hyp}} = \dfrac{2}{\sqrt{13}} \dfrac{\sqrt{13}}{\sqrt{13}} = \dfrac{2\sqrt{13}}{13}$ $\qquad \cos\theta = \dfrac{\text{adj}}{\text{hyp}} = \dfrac{3}{\sqrt{13}} \dfrac{\sqrt{13}}{\sqrt{13}} = \dfrac{3\sqrt{13}}{13}$ $\qquad \tan\theta = \dfrac{\text{opp}}{\text{adj}} = \dfrac{2}{3}$

    $\csc\theta = \dfrac{\text{hyp}}{\text{opp}} = \dfrac{\sqrt{13}}{2}$ $\qquad \sec\theta = \dfrac{\text{hyp}}{\text{adj}} = \dfrac{\sqrt{13}}{3}$ $\qquad \cot\theta = \dfrac{\text{adj}}{\text{opp}} = \dfrac{3}{2}$

13. adjacent = 2; hypotenuse = 4
    Find the opposite side:
    $(\text{opposite})^2 + 2^2 = 4^2 \Rightarrow (\text{opposite})^2 = 16 - 4 = 12 \Rightarrow \text{opposite} = \sqrt{12} = 2\sqrt{3}$

    $\sin\theta = \dfrac{\text{opp}}{\text{hyp}} = \dfrac{2\sqrt{3}}{4} = \dfrac{\sqrt{3}}{2}$ $\qquad \cos\theta = \dfrac{\text{adj}}{\text{hyp}} = \dfrac{2}{4} = \dfrac{1}{2}$ $\qquad \tan\theta = \dfrac{\text{opp}}{\text{adj}} = \dfrac{2\sqrt{3}}{2} = \sqrt{3}$

    $\csc\theta = \dfrac{\text{hyp}}{\text{opp}} = \dfrac{4}{2\sqrt{3}} \dfrac{\sqrt{3}}{\sqrt{3}} = \dfrac{2\sqrt{3}}{3}$ $\quad \sec\theta = \dfrac{\text{hyp}}{\text{adj}} = \dfrac{4}{2} = 2$ $\quad \cot\theta = \dfrac{\text{adj}}{\text{opp}} = \dfrac{2}{2\sqrt{3}} \dfrac{\sqrt{3}}{\sqrt{3}} = \dfrac{\sqrt{3}}{3}$

15. opposite $= \sqrt{2}$; adjacent $= 1$
Find the hypotenuse:

$$\left(\sqrt{2}\right)^2 + 1^2 = (\text{hypotenuse})^2 \Rightarrow (\text{hypotenuse})^2 = 2 + 1 = 3 \Rightarrow \text{hypotenuse} = \sqrt{3}$$

$$\sin\theta = \frac{\text{opp}}{\text{hyp}} = \frac{\sqrt{2}}{\sqrt{3}}\frac{\sqrt{3}}{\sqrt{3}} = \frac{\sqrt{6}}{3} \qquad \cos\theta = \frac{\text{adj}}{\text{hyp}} = \frac{1}{\sqrt{3}}\frac{\sqrt{3}}{\sqrt{3}} = \frac{\sqrt{3}}{3} \qquad \tan\theta = \frac{\text{opp}}{\text{adj}} = \frac{\sqrt{2}}{1} = \sqrt{2}$$

$$\csc\theta = \frac{\text{hyp}}{\text{opp}} = \frac{\sqrt{3}}{\sqrt{2}}\frac{\sqrt{2}}{\sqrt{2}} = \frac{\sqrt{6}}{2} \qquad \sec\theta = \frac{\text{hyp}}{\text{adj}} = \frac{\sqrt{3}}{1} = \sqrt{3} \qquad \cot\theta = \frac{\text{adj}}{\text{opp}} = \frac{1}{\sqrt{2}}\frac{\sqrt{2}}{\sqrt{2}} = \frac{\sqrt{2}}{2}$$

17. opposite $= 1$; hypotenuse $= \sqrt{5}$
Find the adjacent side:

$$1^2 + (\text{adjacent})^2 = \left(\sqrt{5}\right)^2 \Rightarrow (\text{adjacent})^2 = 5 - 1 = 4 \Rightarrow \text{adjacent} = 2$$

$$\sin\theta = \frac{\text{opp}}{\text{hyp}} = \frac{1}{\sqrt{5}}\frac{\sqrt{5}}{\sqrt{5}} = \frac{\sqrt{5}}{5} \qquad \cos\theta = \frac{\text{adj}}{\text{hyp}} = \frac{2}{\sqrt{5}}\frac{\sqrt{5}}{\sqrt{5}} = \frac{2\sqrt{5}}{5} \qquad \tan\theta = \frac{\text{opp}}{\text{adj}} = \frac{1}{2}$$

$$\csc\theta = \frac{\text{hyp}}{\text{opp}} = \frac{\sqrt{5}}{1} = \sqrt{5} \qquad \sec\theta = \frac{\text{hyp}}{\text{adj}} = \frac{\sqrt{5}}{2} \qquad \cot\theta = \frac{\text{adj}}{\text{opp}} = \frac{2}{1} = 2$$

19. $\sin 38° - \cos 52° = \sin 38° - \sin(90° - 52°) = \sin 38° - \sin 38° = 0$

21. $\dfrac{\cos 10°}{\sin 80°} = \dfrac{\sin(90° - 10°)}{\sin 80°} = \dfrac{\sin 80°}{\sin 80°} = 1$

23. $1 - \cos^2 20° - \cos^2 70° = \sin^2 20° - \sin^2(90° - 70°) = \sin^2 20° - \sin^2 20° = 0$

25. $\tan 20° - \dfrac{\cos 70°}{\cos 20°} = \tan 20° - \dfrac{\sin(90° - 70°)}{\cos 20°} = \tan 20° - \dfrac{\sin 20°}{\cos 20°} = \tan 20° - \tan 20° = 0$

27. $\cos 35° \cdot \sin 55° + \cos 55° \cdot \sin 35° = \cos 35° \cdot \cos 35° + \sin 35° \cdot \sin 35° = \cos^2 35° + \sin^2 35° = 1$

29. $b = 5$, $\beta = 20°$

$$\sin\beta = \frac{b}{c} \Rightarrow \sin 20° = \frac{5}{c} \Rightarrow c = \frac{5}{\sin 20°} \approx 14.62$$

$$\tan\beta = \frac{b}{a} \Rightarrow \tan 20° = \frac{5}{a} \Rightarrow a = \frac{5}{\tan 20°} \approx 13.74$$

$$\alpha = 90° - \beta = 90° - 20° = 70°$$

31. $a = 6$, $\beta = 40°$

$$\cos\beta = \frac{a}{c} \Rightarrow \cos 40° = \frac{6}{c} \Rightarrow c = \frac{6}{\cos 40°} \approx 7.83$$

$$\tan\beta = \frac{b}{a} \Rightarrow \tan 40° = \frac{b}{6} \Rightarrow b = 6\tan 40° \approx 5.03$$

$$\alpha = 90° - \beta = 90° - 40° = 50°$$

33. $b = 4$, $\alpha = 10°$

$$\tan\alpha = \frac{a}{b} \Rightarrow \tan 10° = \frac{a}{4} \Rightarrow a = 4\tan 10° \approx 0.71$$

$$\cos\alpha = \frac{b}{c} \Rightarrow \cos 10° = \frac{4}{c} \Rightarrow c = \frac{4}{\cos 10°} \approx 4.06$$

$$\beta = 90° - \alpha = 90° - 10° = 80°$$

35. $a = 5$, $\alpha = 25°$

$$\tan\alpha = \frac{a}{b} \Rightarrow \tan 25° = \frac{5}{b} \Rightarrow b = \frac{5}{\tan 25°} \approx 10.72$$

$$\sin\alpha = \frac{a}{c} \Rightarrow \sin 25° = \frac{5}{c} \Rightarrow c = \frac{5}{\sin 25°} \approx 11.83$$

$$\beta = 90° - \alpha = 90° - 25° = 65°$$

37. $c = 9, \ \beta = 20°$

$$\sin\beta = \frac{b}{c} \Rightarrow \sin 20° = \frac{b}{9} \Rightarrow b = 9\sin 20° \approx 3.08$$

$$\cos\beta = \frac{a}{c} \Rightarrow \cos 20° = \frac{a}{9} \Rightarrow a = 9\cos 20° \approx 8.46$$

$$\beta = 90° - \alpha = 90° - 20° = 70°$$

39. $a = 5, \ b = 3$

$$c^2 = a^2 + b^2 = 5^2 + 3^2 = 25 + 9 = 34$$

$$c = \sqrt{34} \approx 5.83$$

$$\tan\alpha = \frac{a}{b} = \frac{5}{3} \Rightarrow \alpha \approx 59.0°$$

$$\beta = 90° - \alpha = 90° - 59.0° = 31.0°$$

41. $a = 2, \ c = 5$

$$c^2 = a^2 + b^2 \ \Rightarrow \ b^2 = c^2 - a^2 = 5^2 - 2^2 = 25 - 4 = 21 \ \Rightarrow \ b = \sqrt{21} \approx 4.58$$

$$\sin\alpha = \frac{a}{c} = \frac{2}{5} \Rightarrow \alpha \approx 23.6°$$

$$\beta = 90° - \alpha = 90° - 23.6° = 66.4°$$

43. $c = 8, \ \alpha = 35°$

$$\sin 35° = \frac{a}{8} \ \Rightarrow \ a = 8\sin 35° \approx 4.59 \text{ in.}$$

$$\cos 35° = \frac{b}{8} \ \Rightarrow \ b = 8\cos 35° \approx 6.55 \text{ in.}$$

45. $\alpha = 25°, \ a = 5$

$$\sin 25° = \frac{5}{c} \ \Rightarrow \ c = \frac{5}{\sin 25°} \approx 11.83 \text{ in.}$$

$\alpha = 25°, \ b = 5$

$$\cos 25° = \frac{5}{c} \ \Rightarrow \ c = \frac{5}{\cos 25°} \approx 5.52 \text{ in.}$$

47. $c = 5, \ a = 2$

$$\sin\alpha = \frac{2}{5} = 0.4000 \ \Rightarrow \ \alpha \approx 23.6 \ \Rightarrow \ \beta = 90° - \alpha = 90° - 23.6° \approx 66.4°$$

49. $$\tan 35° = \frac{b}{100} \ \Rightarrow \ b = 100\tan 35° \approx 70.02 \text{ feet}$$

51. $$\tan 85.361° = \frac{a}{80} \ \Rightarrow \ a = 80\tan 85.361° \approx 985.91 \text{ feet}$$

53.

$$\tan 20° = \frac{50}{x} \Rightarrow x = \frac{50}{\tan 20°} \approx 137.37 \text{ meters}$$

55.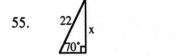

$$\sin 70° = \frac{x}{22} \quad \Rightarrow \quad x = 22\sin 70° \approx 20.67 \text{ feet}$$

57.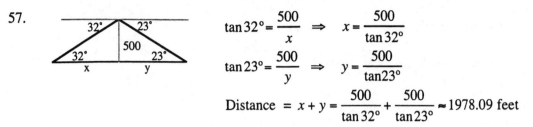

$$\tan 32° = \frac{500}{x} \quad \Rightarrow \quad x = \frac{500}{\tan 32°}$$

$$\tan 23° = \frac{500}{y} \quad \Rightarrow \quad y = \frac{500}{\tan 23°}$$

$$\text{Distance} = x + y = \frac{500}{\tan 32°} + \frac{500}{\tan 23°} \approx 1978.09 \text{ feet}$$

59. Let h represent the height of Lincoln's face.

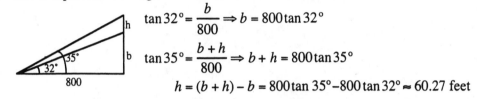

$$\tan 32° = \frac{b}{800} \Rightarrow b = 800\tan 32°$$

$$\tan 35° = \frac{b+h}{800} \Rightarrow b + h = 800\tan 35°$$

$$h = (b + h) - b = 800\tan 35° - 800\tan 32° \approx 60.27 \text{ feet}$$

61.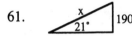

$$\sin 21° = \frac{190}{x} \Rightarrow x = \frac{190}{\sin 21°} \approx 530.18 \text{ ft}$$

63.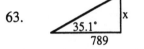

$$\tan 35.1° = \frac{x}{789} \Rightarrow x = 789\tan 35.1° \approx 554.52 \text{ ft}$$

65. (a)
$$\tan 15° = \frac{30}{x} \Rightarrow x = \frac{30}{\tan 15°} \approx 111.96 \text{ feet}$$
The truck is traveling at 111.96 ft/sec.
$$\frac{111.96 \text{ ft}}{\text{sec}} \cdot \frac{1 \text{ mile}}{5280 \text{ ft}} \cdot \frac{3600 \text{ sec}}{\text{hr}} \approx 76.3 \text{ mph}$$

(b)
$$\tan 20° = \frac{30}{x} \Rightarrow x = \frac{30}{\tan 20°} \approx 82.42 \text{ feet}$$
The truck is traveling at 82.42 ft/sec.
$$\frac{82.42 \text{ ft}}{\text{sec}} \cdot \frac{1 \text{ mile}}{5280 \text{ ft}} \cdot \frac{3600 \text{ sec}}{\text{hr}} \approx 56.20 \text{ mph}$$

(c) A ticket is issued for traveling at a speed of 60 mi/hr or more.
$$\frac{60 \text{ mi}}{\text{hr}} \cdot \frac{5280 \text{ ft}}{\text{mi}} \cdot \frac{1\text{hr}}{3600 \text{ sec}} = 88 \text{ ft / sec.}$$
If $\tan\theta \le \frac{30}{88}$, the trooper should issue a ticket.
$$\tan\theta \le \frac{30}{88} \Rightarrow \theta \le \tan^{-1}\left(\frac{30}{88}\right) \approx 18.8°$$
A ticket is issued if $\theta \le 18.8°$.

67. Find angle θ: (see the figure)

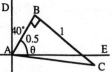

$$\tan\theta = \frac{1}{0.5} = 2 \Rightarrow \theta = \tan^{-1}2 \approx 63.4°$$

$$\angle DAC = 40° + 63.4° = 103.4°$$

$$\angle EAC = 103.4° - 90° = 13.4°$$

The bearing the control tower should use is S76.6°E.

69. The height of the beam above the wall is $46 - 20 = 26$ feet.

$$\tan\theta = \frac{26}{10} = 2.6 \Rightarrow \theta = \tan^{-1}2.6 \approx 69.0°$$

71. The length of the highway $= x + y + z$

$$\sin 40° = \frac{1}{x} \Rightarrow x = \frac{1}{\sin 40°}$$

$$\sin 50° = \frac{1}{z} \Rightarrow z = \frac{1}{\sin 50°}$$

$$\tan 40° = \frac{1}{a} \Rightarrow a = \frac{1}{\tan 40°}$$

$$\tan 50° = \frac{1}{b} \Rightarrow b = \frac{1}{\tan 50°}$$

$$a + y + b = 3 \Rightarrow y = 3 - a - b$$

The length of the highway is: $\dfrac{1}{\sin 40°} + \dfrac{1}{\sin 50°} + 3 - \dfrac{1}{\tan 40°} - \dfrac{1}{\tan 50°} \approx$ miles.

73. With the camera 10 feet from George, the amount that will be seen by the lens above or below the 4-foot level is a, where $\tan 20° = \dfrac{a}{10}$. Thus, $a = 10\tan 20° \approx 3.64$ feet.

So George's head will be seen by the lens, but his feet will not.
In order to see George's head and feet, the camera must be x feet from George.

Solve: $\tan 20° = \dfrac{4}{x} \Rightarrow x = \dfrac{4}{\tan 20°} \approx 10.99$ feet

The camera will need to be moved back 1 foot to see George's feet and head.

75. Let θ = the central angle formed by the top of the lighthouse, the center of the Earth and the point P on the Earth's surface where the line of sight from the top of the lighthouse is tangent to the Earth. Note also that 362 feet $= \dfrac{362}{5280}$ miles.

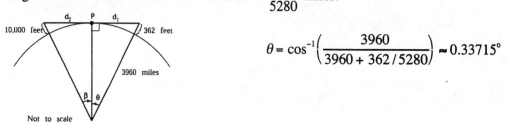

$$\theta = \cos^{-1}\left(\frac{3960}{3960 + 362/5280}\right) \approx 0.33715°$$

<u>Verify the airplane information:</u>

Let β = the central angle formed by the plane, the center of the Earth and the point P.

$$\beta = \cos^{-1}\left(\frac{3960}{3960+10,000/5280}\right) \approx 1.77169°$$

Note that $\tan\theta = \dfrac{d_1}{3690} \Rightarrow d_1 = 3960\tan\theta$ and $\tan\beta = \dfrac{d_2}{3690} \Rightarrow d_2 = 3960\tan\beta$

So

$$d_1 + d_2 = 3960\tan\theta + 3960\tan\beta \approx 3960\tan\left(0.33715°\right) + 3960\tan\left(1.77169°\right) \approx 146 \text{ miles}$$

To express this distance in nautical miles, we express the total angle $\theta + \beta$ in minutes. That is, $\theta + \beta \approx \left(0.33715° + 1.77169°\right)\cdot 60 \approx 126.5$ nautical miles. Therefore, a plane flying at an altitude of 10,000 feet can see the lighthouse 120 miles away.

<u>Verify the ship information:</u>

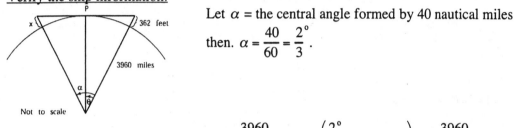

Let α = the central angle formed by 40 nautical miles

then. $\alpha = \dfrac{40}{60} = \dfrac{2°}{3}$.

$$\cos(\alpha - \theta) = \frac{3960}{3960+x} \Rightarrow \cos\left(\frac{2°}{3} - 0.33715°\right) = \frac{3960}{3960+x}$$

$$(3960+x)\cos\left(\frac{2°}{3} - 0.33715°\right) = 3960 \Rightarrow 3960 + x = \frac{3960}{\cos\left(\frac{2°}{3} - 0.33715°\right)}$$

$$x = \frac{3960}{\cos\left(\frac{2°}{3} - 0.33715°\right)} - 3960$$

$$\approx 0.06549 \text{ mile} \approx (0.06549 \text{ mi})\left(5280\frac{\text{ft}}{\text{mi}}\right) \approx 346 \text{ feet}$$

Therefore, a ship that is 346 feet above sea level can see the lighthouse from a distance of 40 nautical miles.

77. Answers will vary.

Chapter 4

Applications of Trigonometric Functions

4.2 The Law of Sines

1. $\sin\alpha\cos\beta - \cos\alpha\sin\beta$

3. $\sin\theta = 2$
   There is no angle θ with $\sin\theta > 1$. Therefore, the equation has no solution.

5. $\dfrac{\sin\alpha}{a} = \dfrac{\sin\beta}{b} = \dfrac{\sin\gamma}{c}$

7. True

9. $c = 5, \ \beta = 45°, \ \gamma = 95°$
   $\alpha = 180° - \beta - \gamma = 180° - 45° - 95° = 40°$

   $\dfrac{\sin\alpha}{a} = \dfrac{\sin\gamma}{c} \Rightarrow \dfrac{\sin 40°}{a} = \dfrac{\sin 95°}{5} \Rightarrow a = \dfrac{5\sin 40°}{\sin 95°} \approx 3.23$

   $\dfrac{\sin\beta}{b} = \dfrac{\sin\gamma}{c} \Rightarrow \dfrac{\sin 45°}{b} = \dfrac{\sin 95°}{5} \Rightarrow b = \dfrac{5\sin 45°}{\sin 95°} \approx 3.55$

11. $b = 3, \ \alpha = 50°, \ \gamma = 85°$
    $\beta = 180° - \alpha - \gamma = 180° - 50° - 85° = 45°$

    $\dfrac{\sin\alpha}{a} = \dfrac{\sin\beta}{b} \Rightarrow \dfrac{\sin 50°}{a} = \dfrac{\sin 45°}{3} \Rightarrow a = \dfrac{3\sin 50°}{\sin 45°} \approx 3.25$

    $\dfrac{\sin\gamma}{c} = \dfrac{\sin\beta}{b} \Rightarrow \dfrac{\sin 85°}{c} = \dfrac{\sin 45°}{3} \Rightarrow c = \dfrac{3\sin 85°}{\sin 45°} \approx 4.23$

13. $b = 7, \ \alpha = 40°, \ \beta = 45°$
    $\gamma = 180° - \alpha - \beta = 180° - 40° - 45° = 95°$

    $\dfrac{\sin\alpha}{a} = \dfrac{\sin\beta}{b} \Rightarrow \dfrac{\sin 40°}{a} = \dfrac{\sin 45°}{7} \Rightarrow a = \dfrac{7\sin 40°}{\sin 45°} \approx 6.36$

    $\dfrac{\sin\gamma}{c} = \dfrac{\sin\beta}{b} \Rightarrow \dfrac{\sin 95°}{c} = \dfrac{\sin 45°}{7} \Rightarrow c = \dfrac{7\sin 95°}{\sin 45°} \approx 9.86$

15. $b = 2, \ \beta = 40°, \ \gamma = 100°$
    $\alpha = 180° - \beta - \gamma = 180° - 40° - 100° = 40°$

    $\dfrac{\sin\alpha}{a} = \dfrac{\sin\beta}{b} \Rightarrow \dfrac{\sin 40°}{a} = \dfrac{\sin 40°}{2} \Rightarrow a = \dfrac{2\sin 40°}{\sin 40°} = 2$

    $\dfrac{\sin\gamma}{c} = \dfrac{\sin\beta}{b} \Rightarrow \dfrac{\sin 100°}{c} = \dfrac{\sin 40°}{2} \Rightarrow c = \dfrac{2\sin 100°}{\sin 40°} \approx 3.06$

17. $\alpha = 40°$, $\beta = 20°$, $a = 2$
$\gamma = 180° - \alpha - \beta = 180° - 40° - 20° = 120°$

$$\frac{\sin\alpha}{a} = \frac{\sin\beta}{b} \Rightarrow \frac{\sin 40°}{2} = \frac{\sin 20°}{b} \Rightarrow b = \frac{2\sin 20°}{\sin 40°} \approx 1.06$$

$$\frac{\sin\gamma}{c} = \frac{\sin\alpha}{a} \Rightarrow \frac{\sin 120°}{c} = \frac{\sin 40°}{2} \Rightarrow c = \frac{2\sin 120°}{\sin 40°} \approx 2.69$$

19. $\beta = 70°$, $\gamma = 10°$, $b = 5$
$\alpha = 180° - \beta - \gamma = 180° - 70° - 10° = 100°$

$$\frac{\sin\alpha}{a} = \frac{\sin\beta}{b} \Rightarrow \frac{\sin 100°}{a} = \frac{\sin 70°}{5} \Rightarrow a = \frac{5\sin 100°}{\sin 70°} \approx 5.24$$

$$\frac{\sin\gamma}{c} = \frac{\sin\beta}{b} \Rightarrow \frac{\sin 10°}{c} = \frac{\sin 70°}{5} \Rightarrow c = \frac{5\sin 10°}{\sin 70°} \approx 0.92$$

21. $\alpha = 110°$, $\gamma = 30°$, $c = 3$
$\beta = 180° - \alpha - \gamma = 180° - 110° - 30° = 40°$

$$\frac{\sin\alpha}{a} = \frac{\sin\gamma}{c} \Rightarrow \frac{\sin 110°}{a} = \frac{\sin 30°}{3} \Rightarrow a = \frac{3\sin 110°}{\sin 30°} \approx 5.64$$

$$\frac{\sin\gamma}{c} = \frac{\sin\beta}{b} \Rightarrow \frac{\sin 30°}{3} = \frac{\sin 40°}{b} \Rightarrow b = \frac{3\sin 40°}{\sin 30°} \approx 3.86$$

23. $\alpha = 40°$, $\beta = 40°$, $c = 2$
$\gamma = 180° - \alpha - \beta = 180° - 40° - 40° = 100°$

$$\frac{\sin\alpha}{a} = \frac{\sin\gamma}{c} \Rightarrow \frac{\sin 40°}{a} = \frac{\sin 100°}{2} \Rightarrow a = \frac{2\sin 40°}{\sin 100°} \approx 1.31$$

$$\frac{\sin\beta}{b} = \frac{\sin\gamma}{c} \Rightarrow \frac{\sin 40°}{b} = \frac{\sin 100°}{2} \Rightarrow b = \frac{2\sin 40°}{\sin 100°} \approx 1.31$$

25. $a = 3$, $b = 2$, $\alpha = 50°$

$$\frac{\sin\beta}{b} = \frac{\sin\alpha}{a} \Rightarrow \frac{\sin\beta}{2} = \frac{\sin(50°)}{3} \Rightarrow \sin\beta = \frac{2\sin(50°)}{3} \approx 0.5107$$

$\beta = \sin^{-1}(0.5107)$

$\beta = 30.7°$ or $\beta = 149.3°$
The second value is discarded because $\alpha + \beta > 180°$.
$\gamma = 180° - \alpha - \beta = 180° - 50° - 30.7° = 99.3°$

$$\frac{\sin\gamma}{c} = \frac{\sin\alpha}{a} \Rightarrow \frac{\sin 99.3°}{c} = \frac{\sin 50°}{3} \Rightarrow c = \frac{3\sin 99.3°}{\sin 50°} \approx 3.86$$

One triangle: $\beta \approx 30.7°$, $\gamma \approx 99.3°$, $c \approx 3.86$

27. $b = 5, \ c = 3, \ \beta = 100°$

$$\frac{\sin\beta}{b} = \frac{\sin\gamma}{c} \Rightarrow \frac{\sin 100°}{5} = \frac{\sin\gamma}{3} \Rightarrow \sin\gamma = \frac{3\sin 100°}{5} \approx 0.5909$$

$\gamma = \sin^{-1}(0.5909)$

$\gamma = 36.2°$ or $\gamma = 143.8°$

The second value is discarded because $\beta + \gamma > 180°$.

$\alpha = 180° - \beta - \gamma = 180° - 100° - 36.2° = 43.8°$

$$\frac{\sin\beta}{b} = \frac{\sin\alpha}{a} \Rightarrow \frac{\sin 100°}{5} = \frac{\sin 43.8°}{a} \Rightarrow a = \frac{5\sin 43.8°}{\sin 100°} \approx 3.51$$

One triangle: $\alpha \approx 43.8°, \ \gamma \approx 36.2°, \ a \approx 3.51$

29. $a = 4, \ b = 5, \ \alpha = 60°$

$$\frac{\sin\beta}{b} = \frac{\sin\alpha}{a} \Rightarrow \frac{\sin\beta}{5} = \frac{\sin 60°}{4} \Rightarrow \sin\beta = \frac{5\sin 60°}{4} \approx 1.0825$$

There is no angle β for which $\sin\beta > 1$. Therefore, there is no triangle with the given measurements.

31. $b = 4, \ c = 6, \ \beta = 20°$

$$\frac{\sin\beta}{b} = \frac{\sin\gamma}{c} \Rightarrow \frac{\sin 20°}{4} = \frac{\sin\gamma}{6} \Rightarrow \sin\gamma = \frac{6\sin 20°}{4} \approx 0.5130$$

$\gamma = \sin^{-1}(0.5130)$

$\gamma_1 = 30.9°$ or $\gamma_2 = 149.1°$

For both values, $\beta + \gamma < 180°$. Therefore, there are two triangles.

$\alpha_1 = 180° - \beta - \gamma_1 = 180° - 20° - 30.9° = 129.1°$

$$\frac{\sin\beta}{b} = \frac{\sin\alpha_1}{a_1} \Rightarrow \frac{\sin 20°}{4} = \frac{\sin 129.1°}{a_1} \Rightarrow a_1 = \frac{4\sin 129.1°}{\sin 20°} \approx 9.08$$

$\alpha_2 = 180° - \beta - \gamma_2 = 180° - 20° - 149.1° = 10.9°$

$$\frac{\sin\beta}{b} = \frac{\sin\alpha_2}{a_2} \Rightarrow \frac{\sin 20°}{4} = \frac{\sin 10.9°}{a_2} \Rightarrow a_2 = \frac{4\sin 10.9°}{\sin 20°} \approx 2.21$$

Two triangles: $\alpha_1 \approx 129.1°, \ \gamma_1 \approx 30.9°, \ a_1 \approx 9.08$
    or $\alpha_2 \approx 10.9°, \ \gamma_2 \approx 149.1°, \ a_2 \approx 2.21$

33. $a = 2, \ c = 1, \ \gamma = 100°$

$$\frac{\sin\gamma}{c} = \frac{\sin\alpha}{a} \Rightarrow \frac{\sin 100°}{1} = \frac{\sin\alpha}{2} \Rightarrow \sin\alpha = \frac{2\sin 100°}{1} \approx 1.9696$$

There is no angle α for which $\sin\alpha > 1$. Therefore, there is no triangle with the given measurements.

35. $a = 2, \ c = 1, \ \gamma = 25°$

$$\frac{\sin\alpha}{a} = \frac{\sin\gamma}{c} \Rightarrow \frac{\sin\alpha}{2} = \frac{\sin 25°}{1} \Rightarrow \sin\alpha = \frac{2\sin 25°}{1} \approx 0.8452$$

$\alpha = \sin^{-1}(0.8452)$

$\alpha_1 = 57.7°$ or $\alpha_2 = 122.3°$

For both values, $\alpha + \gamma < 180°$. Therefore, there are two triangles.

$\beta_1 = 180° - \alpha_1 - \gamma = 180° - 57.7° - 25° = 97.3°$

$\dfrac{\sin\beta_1}{b_1} = \dfrac{\sin\gamma}{c} \Rightarrow \dfrac{\sin 97.3°}{b_1} = \dfrac{\sin 25°}{1} \Rightarrow b_1 = \dfrac{1\sin 97.3°}{\sin 25°} \approx 2.35$

$\beta_2 = 180° - \alpha_2 - \gamma = 180° - 122.3° - 25° = 32.7°$

$\dfrac{\sin\beta_2}{b_2} = \dfrac{\sin\gamma}{c} \Rightarrow \dfrac{\sin 32.7°}{b_2} = \dfrac{\sin 25°}{1} \Rightarrow b_2 = \dfrac{1\sin 32.7°}{\sin 25°} \approx 1.28$

Two triangles: $\alpha_1 \approx 57.7°$, $\beta_1 \approx 97.3°$, $b_1 \approx 2.35$

or $\alpha_2 \approx 122.3°$, $\beta_2 \approx 32.7°$, $b_2 \approx 1.28$

37. (a) Find γ ; then use the Law of Sines:

$\gamma = 180° - 60° - 55° = 65°$

$\dfrac{\sin 55°}{a} = \dfrac{\sin 65°}{150} \Rightarrow a = \dfrac{150\sin 55°}{\sin 65°} \approx 135.58$ miles

$\dfrac{\sin 60°}{b} = \dfrac{\sin 65°}{150} \Rightarrow b = \dfrac{150\sin 60°}{\sin 65°} \approx 143.33$ miles

   (b) $t = \dfrac{a}{r} = \dfrac{135.6}{200} \approx 0.68$ hours or ≈ 41 minutes

39. $\angle CAB = 180° - 25° = 155°$ $\angle ABC = 180° - 155° - 15° = 10°$

Let c represent the distance from A to B.

$\dfrac{\sin 15°}{c} = \dfrac{\sin 10°}{1000} \Rightarrow c = \dfrac{1000\sin 15°}{\sin 10°} \approx 1490.48$

The length of the proposed ski lift is approximately 1490 feet.

41. Find the distance from B to the plane:

$\gamma = 180° - 40° - 35° = 105°$ $(\gamma = \angle APB)$

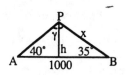

$\dfrac{\sin 40°}{x} = \dfrac{\sin 105°}{1000} \Rightarrow x = \dfrac{1000\sin 40°}{\sin 105°} \approx 665.46$ feet

Find the height:

$\sin 35° = \dfrac{h}{x} = \dfrac{h}{665.46} \Rightarrow h = (665.46)\sin 35° \approx 381.69$ feet

The plane is about 381.69 feet high.

43. (a) $\angle ABC = 180° - 40° = 140°$

Find the angle at city C:

$\dfrac{\sin C}{150} = \dfrac{\sin(140°)}{300} \Rightarrow \sin C = \dfrac{150\sin(140°)}{300} \approx 0.3214$

$C = \sin^{-1}(0.3214) \approx 18.7°$

Let y be the distance from city A to city C.

Find the angle at city A:
$$A = 180° - 140° - 18.7° = 21.3°$$

$$\frac{\sin 21.3°}{y} = \frac{\sin 140°}{300} \Rightarrow y = \frac{300 \sin 21.3°}{\sin 140°} \approx 169.54 \text{ miles}$$

The distance from city B to city C is approximately 169.54 miles.

(b) To find the angle to turn, subtract angle C from 180°:
$$180° - 18.7° = 161.3°$$

The pilot needs to turn through an angle of 161.3° to return to city A.

45. Find angle β ($\angle ACB$):

$$\frac{\sin \beta}{123} = \frac{\sin 60°}{184.5} \Rightarrow \sin \beta = \frac{123 \sin 60°}{184.5} \approx 0.5774$$

$$\beta = \sin^{-1}(0.5774) \approx 35.3°$$

$$\angle CAB = 180° - 60° - 35.3° \approx 84.7°$$

Find the perpendicular distance:

$$\sin 84.7° = \frac{h}{184.5} \Rightarrow h = 184.5 \sin 84.7° = 183.71 \text{ feet}$$

47. $\alpha = 180° - 140° = 40°$ $\beta = 180° - 135° = 45°$
$\gamma = 180° - 40° - 45° = 95°$

$$\frac{\sin 40°}{a} = \frac{\sin 95°}{2} \Rightarrow a = \frac{2 \sin 40°}{\sin 95°} \approx 1.290 \text{ mi}$$

$$\frac{\sin 45°}{b} = \frac{\sin 95°}{2} \Rightarrow b = \frac{2 \sin 45°}{\sin 95°} \approx 1.420 \text{ mi}$$

$$\overline{BE} = 1.290 - 0.125 = 1.165 \text{ mi}$$

$$\overline{AD} = 1.420 - 0.125 = 1.295 \text{ mi}$$

For the isosceles triangle,

$$\angle CDE = \angle CED = \frac{180° - 95°}{2} = 42.5°$$

$$\frac{\sin 95°}{DE} = \frac{\sin 42.5°}{0.125} \Rightarrow DE = \frac{0.125 \sin 95°}{\sin 42.5°} \approx 0.184 \text{ miles}$$

The approximate length of the highway is $1.165 + 1.295 + 0.184 = 2.64$ miles.

49. Using the Law of Sines:
$$\frac{\sin 105°}{88} = \frac{\sin 25°}{L}$$

$$L = \frac{88 \sin 25°}{\sin 105°} \approx 38.50 \text{ inches}$$

51.

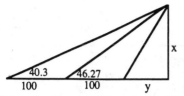

Using the Law of Sines twice yields two equations relating x and y.
Equation 1:

$$\frac{\sin 46.27°}{x} = \frac{\sin(90° - 46.27°)}{y + 100}$$

$$(y + 100)\sin 46.27° = x\sin 43.73°$$

$$y\sin 46.27° + 100\sin 46.27° = x\sin 43.73°$$

$$y = \frac{x\sin 43.73° - 100\sin 46.27°}{\sin 46.27°}$$

Equation 2:

$$\frac{\sin 40.3°}{x} = \frac{\sin(90° - 40.3°)}{y + 200}$$

$$(y + 200)\sin 40.3° = x\sin 49.7°$$

$$y\sin 40.3° + 200\sin 40.3° = x\sin 49.7°$$

$$y = \frac{x\sin 49.7° - 200\sin 40.3°}{\sin 40.3°}$$

Set the two equations equal to each other and solve for x.

$$\frac{x\sin 43.73° - 100\sin 46.27°}{\sin 46.27°} = \frac{x\sin 49.7° - 200\sin 40.3°}{\sin 40.3°}$$

$$x\sin 43.73°·\sin 40.3° - 100\sin 46.27°·\sin 40.3° = x\sin 49.7°·\sin 46.27° - 200\sin 40.3°·\sin 46.27°$$

$$x\sin 43.73°·\sin 40.3° - x\sin 49.7°·\sin 46.27° = 100\sin 46.27°·\sin 40.3° - 200\sin 40.3°·\sin 46.27°$$

$$x = \frac{100\sin 46.27°·\sin 40.3° - 200\sin 40.3°·\sin 46.27°}{\sin 43.73°·\sin 40.3° - \sin 49.7°·\sin 46.27°}$$

$$\approx 449.36 \text{ feet}$$

The current height of the pyramid is about 449.36 feet.

53. Using the Law of Sines:

$$\frac{\sin 15°}{57,910,000} = \frac{\sin \beta}{149,600,000} \Rightarrow \sin \beta = \frac{149,600,000 \cdot \sin 15°}{57,910,000} = \frac{14,960 \cdot \sin 15°}{5791}$$

$$\beta = \sin^{-1}\left(\frac{14,960 \cdot \sin 15°}{5791}\right) \approx 41.96° \text{ or } \beta \approx 138.04°$$

$$\gamma \approx 180° - 41.96° - 15° = 123.04° \text{ or } \gamma \approx 180° - 138.04° - 15° = 26.96°$$

$$\frac{\sin15°}{57,910,000} = \frac{\sin\gamma}{x} \Rightarrow x = \frac{57,910,000 \cdot \sin\gamma}{\sin15°}$$

$$x = \frac{57,910,000 \cdot \sin123.04°}{\sin15°} \approx 187,564,951.5 \text{ km}$$

$$\text{or} \quad x = \frac{57,910,000 \cdot \sin26.96°}{\sin15°} \approx 101,439,834.5 \text{ km}$$

So the approximate possible distances between Earth and Mercury are 101,439,834.5 km and 187,564,951.5 km.

55.

Using the Law of Sines twice yields two equations relating x and h.

Equation 1:

$$\frac{\sin30°}{h} = \frac{\sin60°}{x}$$

$$x = \frac{h\sin60°}{\sin30°}$$

Equation 2:

$$\frac{\sin20°}{h} = \frac{\sin70°}{x+40}$$

$$x = \frac{h\sin70°}{\sin20°} - 40$$

Set the two equations equal to each other and solve for h.

$$\frac{h\sin60°}{\sin30°} = \frac{h\sin70°}{\sin20°} - 40$$

$$h\left(\frac{\sin60°}{\sin30°} - \frac{\sin70°}{\sin20°}\right) = -40$$

$$h = \frac{-40}{\dfrac{\sin60°}{\sin30°} - \dfrac{\sin70°}{\sin20°}}$$

$$\approx 39.39 \text{ feet}$$

The height of the tree is about 39.39 feet.

57. Find the distance from B to the helicopter:

$$\gamma = 180° - 40° - 25° = 115° \qquad (\gamma = \angle APB)$$

$$\frac{\sin40°}{x} = \frac{\sin115°}{100} \Rightarrow x = \frac{100\sin40°}{\sin115°} \approx 70.9 \text{ feet}$$

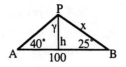

Find the height:

$$\sin25° = \frac{h}{x} \approx \frac{h}{70.9} \Rightarrow h \approx (70.9)\sin25° \approx 29.96 \text{ feet}$$

The helicopter is about 30 feet high.

59. $\dfrac{a-b}{c} = \dfrac{a}{c} - \dfrac{b}{c} = \dfrac{\sin\alpha}{\sin\gamma} - \dfrac{\sin\beta}{\sin\gamma} = \dfrac{\sin\alpha - \sin\beta}{\sin\gamma} = \dfrac{2\sin\left(\dfrac{\alpha-\beta}{2}\right)\cos\left(\dfrac{\alpha+\beta}{2}\right)}{\sin\left(2\cdot\dfrac{\gamma}{2}\right)}$

$= \dfrac{2\sin\left(\dfrac{\alpha-\beta}{2}\right)\cos\left(\dfrac{\alpha+\beta}{2}\right)}{2\sin\left(\dfrac{\gamma}{2}\right)\cos\left(\dfrac{\gamma}{2}\right)} = \dfrac{\sin\left(\dfrac{\alpha-\beta}{2}\right)\cos\left(\dfrac{\pi}{2}-\dfrac{\gamma}{2}\right)}{\sin\left(\dfrac{\gamma}{2}\right)\cos\left(\dfrac{\gamma}{2}\right)} = \dfrac{\sin\left(\dfrac{\alpha-\beta}{2}\right)\sin\left(\dfrac{\gamma}{2}\right)}{\sin\left(\dfrac{\gamma}{2}\right)\cos\left(\dfrac{\gamma}{2}\right)}$

$= \dfrac{\sin\left(\dfrac{\alpha-\beta}{2}\right)}{\cos\left(\dfrac{\gamma}{2}\right)}$

$= \dfrac{\sin\left[\dfrac{1}{2}(\alpha-\beta)\right]}{\cos\left(\dfrac{1}{2}\gamma\right)}$

61. Derive the Law of Tangents:

$\dfrac{a-b}{a+b} = \dfrac{\dfrac{a-b}{c}}{\dfrac{a+b}{c}} = \dfrac{\dfrac{\sin\left(\dfrac{1}{2}(\alpha-\beta)\right)}{\cos\left(\dfrac{1}{2}\gamma\right)}}{\dfrac{\cos\left(\dfrac{1}{2}(\alpha-\beta)\right)}{\sin\left(\dfrac{1}{2}\gamma\right)}} = \dfrac{\sin\left(\dfrac{1}{2}(\alpha-\beta)\right)}{\cos\left(\dfrac{1}{2}\gamma\right)} \cdot \dfrac{\sin\left(\dfrac{1}{2}\gamma\right)}{\cos\left(\dfrac{1}{2}(\alpha-\beta)\right)}$

$= \tan\left(\dfrac{1}{2}(\alpha-\beta)\right)\tan\left(\dfrac{1}{2}\gamma\right) = \tan\left(\dfrac{1}{2}(\alpha-\beta)\right)\tan\left(\dfrac{1}{2}(\pi-(\alpha+\beta))\right)$

$= \tan\left(\dfrac{1}{2}(\alpha-\beta)\right)\tan\left(\dfrac{\pi}{2}-\left(\dfrac{\alpha+\beta}{2}\right)\right) = \tan\left(\dfrac{1}{2}(\alpha-\beta)\right)\cot\left(\dfrac{\alpha+\beta}{2}\right)$

$= \dfrac{\tan\left(\dfrac{1}{2}(\alpha-\beta)\right)}{\tan\left(\dfrac{1}{2}(\alpha+\beta)\right)}$

63–65.   Answers will vary.

Applications of Trigonometric Functions

4.3 The Law of Cosines

1. $d = \sqrt{\left(x_2 - x_1\right)^2 + \left(y_2 - y_1\right)^2}$

3. Cosines

5. Cosines

7. False

9. $a = 2,\ c = 4,\ \beta = 45°\qquad b^2 = a^2 + c^2 - 2ac\cos\beta$

$b^2 = 2^2 + 4^2 - 2\cdot 2\cdot 4\cos 45° = 20 - 16\cdot\dfrac{\sqrt{2}}{2} = 20 - 8\sqrt{2}$

$b \approx 2.95$

$a^2 = b^2 + c^2 - 2bc\cos\alpha \Rightarrow 2bc\cos\alpha = b^2 + c^2 - a^2 \Rightarrow \cos\alpha = \dfrac{b^2 + c^2 - a^2}{2bc}$

$\cos\alpha = \dfrac{2.95^2 + 4^2 - 2^2}{2(2.95)(4)} = \dfrac{20.7025}{23.6} \Rightarrow \alpha \approx 28.7°$

$\gamma = 180° - \alpha - \beta \approx 180° - 28.7° - 45° \approx 106.3°$

11. $a = 2,\ b = 3,\ \gamma = 95°\qquad c^2 = a^2 + b^2 - 2ab\cos\gamma$

$c^2 = 2^2 + 3^2 - 2\cdot 2\cdot 3\cos 95° = 13 - 12\cos 95°$

$c \approx 3.75$

$a^2 = b^2 + c^2 - 2bc\cos\alpha \Rightarrow \cos\alpha = \dfrac{b^2 + c^2 - a^2}{2bc} = \dfrac{3^2 + 3.75^2 - 2^2}{2(3)(3.75)} = \dfrac{19.0625}{22.5} \Rightarrow \alpha \approx 32.1°$

$\beta = 180° - \alpha - \gamma \approx 180° - 32.1° - 95° = 52.9°$

13. $a = 6,\ b = 5,\ c = 8$

$a^2 = b^2 + c^2 - 2bc\cos\alpha \Rightarrow \cos\alpha = \dfrac{b^2 + c^2 - a^2}{2bc} = \dfrac{5^2 + 8^2 - 6^2}{2(5)(8)} = \dfrac{53}{80} \Rightarrow \alpha \approx 48.5°$

$b^2 = a^2 + c^2 - 2ac\cos\beta \Rightarrow \cos\beta = \dfrac{a^2 + c^2 - b^2}{2ac} = \dfrac{6^2 + 8^2 - 5^2}{2(6)(8)} = \dfrac{75}{96} \Rightarrow \beta \approx 38.6°$

$\gamma = 180° - \alpha - \beta \approx 180° - 48.5° - 38.6° \approx 92.9°$

15. $a = 9,\ b = 6,\ c = 4$

$a^2 = b^2 + c^2 - 2bc\cos\alpha \Rightarrow \cos\alpha = \dfrac{b^2 + c^2 - a^2}{2bc} = \dfrac{6^2 + 4^2 - 9^2}{2(6)(4)} = -\dfrac{29}{48} \Rightarrow \alpha \approx 127.2°$

$b^2 = a^2 + c^2 - 2ac\cos\beta \Rightarrow \cos\beta = \dfrac{a^2 + c^2 - b^2}{2ac} = \dfrac{9^2 + 4^2 - 6^2}{2(9)(4)} = \dfrac{61}{72} \Rightarrow \beta \approx 32.1°$

$\gamma = 180° - \alpha - \beta \approx 180° - 127.2° - 32.1° = 20.7°$

17. $a = 3,\ b = 4,\ \gamma = 40°$

$c^2 = a^2 + b^2 - 2ab\cos\gamma$

$c^2 = 3^2 + 4^2 - 2\cdot3\cdot4\cos40° = 25 - 24\cos40°$

$c \approx 2.57$

$a^2 = b^2 + c^2 - 2bc\cos\alpha \Rightarrow \cos\alpha = \dfrac{b^2 + c^2 - a^2}{2bc} = \dfrac{4^2 + 2.57^2 - 3^2}{2(4)(2.57)} = \dfrac{13.6049}{20.56} \Rightarrow \alpha \approx 48.6°$

$\beta = 180° - \alpha - \gamma \approx 180° - 48.6° - 40° = 91.4°$

19. $b = 1,\ c = 3,\ \alpha = 80°$

$a^2 = b^2 + c^2 - 2bc\cos\alpha$

$a^2 = 1^2 + 3^2 - 2\cdot1\cdot3\cos80° = 10 - 6\cos80°$

$a \approx 2.99$

$b^2 = a^2 + c^2 - 2ac\cos\beta \Rightarrow \cos\beta = \dfrac{a^2 + c^2 - b^2}{2ac} = \dfrac{2.99^2 + 3^2 - 1^2}{2(2.99)(3)} = \dfrac{16.9401}{17.94} \Rightarrow \beta \approx 19.2°$

$\gamma = 180° - \alpha - \beta \approx 180° - 80° - 19.2° = 80.8°$

21. $a = 3,\ c = 2,\ \beta = 110°$

$b^2 = a^2 + c^2 - 2ac\cos\beta$

$b^2 = 3^2 + 2^2 - 2\cdot3\cdot2\cos110° = 13 - 12\cos110°$

$b \approx 4.14$

$c^2 = a^2 + b^2 - 2ab\cos\gamma \Rightarrow \cos\gamma = \dfrac{a^2 + b^2 - c^2}{2ab} = \dfrac{3^2 + 4.14^2 - 2^2}{2(3)(4.14)} = \dfrac{22.1396}{24.84} \Rightarrow \gamma \approx 27.0°$

$\alpha = 180° - \beta - \gamma \approx 180° - 110° - 27.0° = 43.0°$

23. $a = 2,\ b = 2,\ \gamma = 50°$

$c^2 = a^2 + b^2 - 2ab\cos\gamma$

$c^2 = 2^2 + 2^2 - 2\cdot2\cdot2\cos50° = 8 - 8\cos50°$

$c \approx 1.69$

$a^2 = b^2 + c^2 - 2bc\cos\alpha \Rightarrow \cos\alpha = \dfrac{b^2 + c^2 - a^2}{2bc} = \dfrac{2^2 + 1.69^2 - 2^2}{2(2)(1.69)} = \dfrac{2.8561}{6.76} \Rightarrow \alpha \approx 65.0°$

$\beta = 180° - \alpha - \gamma \approx 180° - 65.0° - 50° = 65.0°$

25. $a = 12, \ b = 13, \ c = 5$

$$a^2 = b^2 + c^2 - 2bc\cos\alpha \Rightarrow \cos\alpha = \frac{b^2 + c^2 - a^2}{2bc} = \frac{13^2 + 5^2 - 12^2}{2(13)(5)} = \frac{50}{130} \Rightarrow \alpha \approx 67.4°$$

$$b^2 = a^2 + c^2 - 2ac\cos\beta \Rightarrow \cos\beta = \frac{a^2 + c^2 - b^2}{2ac} = \frac{12^2 + 5^2 - 13^2}{2(12)(5)} = 0 \Rightarrow \beta = 90°$$

$$\gamma = 180° - \alpha - \beta \approx 180° - 67.4° - 90° = 22.6°$$

27. $a = 2, \ b = 2, \ c = 2$

$$a^2 = b^2 + c^2 - 2bc\cos\alpha \Rightarrow \cos\alpha = \frac{b^2 + c^2 - a^2}{2bc} = \frac{2^2 + 2^2 - 2^2}{2(2)(2)} = 0.5 \Rightarrow \alpha = 60°$$

$$b^2 = a^2 + c^2 - 2ac\cos\beta \Rightarrow \cos\beta = \frac{a^2 + c^2 - b^2}{2ac} = \frac{2^2 + 2^2 - 2^2}{2(2)(2)} = 0.5 \Rightarrow \beta = 60°$$

$$\gamma = 180° - \alpha - \beta \approx 180° - 60° - 60° = 60°$$

29. $a = 5, \ b = 8, \ c = 9$

$$a^2 = b^2 + c^2 - 2bc\cos\alpha \Rightarrow \cos\alpha = \frac{b^2 + c^2 - a^2}{2bc} = \frac{8^2 + 9^2 - 5^2}{2(8)(9)} = \frac{120}{144} \Rightarrow \alpha \approx 33.6°$$

$$b^2 = a^2 + c^2 - 2ac\cos\beta \Rightarrow \cos\beta = \frac{a^2 + c^2 - b^2}{2ac} = \frac{5^2 + 9^2 - 8^2}{2(5)(9)} = \frac{42}{90} \Rightarrow \beta \approx 62.2°$$

$$\gamma = 180° - \alpha - \beta \approx 180° - 33.6° - 62.2° = 84.2°$$

31. $a = 10, \ b = 8, \ c = 5$

$$a^2 = b^2 + c^2 - 2bc\cos\alpha \Rightarrow \cos\alpha = \frac{b^2 + c^2 - a^2}{2bc} = \frac{8^2 + 5^2 - 10^2}{2(8)(5)} \approx -\frac{11}{80} \Rightarrow \alpha \approx 97.9°$$

$$b^2 = a^2 + c^2 - 2ac\cos\beta \Rightarrow \cos\beta = \frac{a^2 + c^2 - b^2}{2ac} = \frac{10^2 + 5^2 - 8^2}{2(10)(5)} = \frac{61}{100} \Rightarrow \beta \approx 52.4°$$

$$\gamma = 180° - \alpha - \beta \approx 180° - 97.9° - 52.4° = 29.7°$$

33. Find the third side of the triangle using the Law of Cosines:
$a = 50, \ b = 70, \ \gamma = 70°$
$$c^2 = a^2 + b^2 - 2ab\cos\gamma = 50^2 + 70^2 - 2 \cdot 50 \cdot 70\cos70° = 7400 - 7000\cos70° \Rightarrow c \approx 70.75$$
The houses are approximately 70.75 feet apart.

35. After 10 hours the ship will have traveled 150 nautical miles along its altered course.
Use the Law of Cosines to find the distance from Barbados on the new course.
$a = 600, \ b = 150, \ \gamma = 20°$
$$c^2 = a^2 + b^2 - 2ab\cos\gamma = 600^2 + 150^2 - 2 \cdot 600 \cdot 150\cos20° = 382,500 - 180,000\cos20°$$
$$c \approx 461.9 \text{ nautical miles}$$

(a)   Use the Law of Cosines to find the angle opposite the side of 600:

$$\cos \alpha = \frac{b^2 + c^2 - a^2}{2bc}$$

$$\cos \alpha = \frac{150^2 + 461.9^2 - 600^2}{2(150)(461.9)} = -\frac{124,148.39}{138,570} \Rightarrow \alpha \approx 153.6°$$

The captain needs to turn the ship through an angle of $180° - 153.6° = 26.4°$.

(b) $t = \dfrac{461.9}{15} \approx 30.8$ hours are required for the second leg of the trip. The total time for the trip will be 40.8 hours.

37.   (a)   Find x in the figure:

$$x^2 = 60.5^2 + 90^2 - 2(60.5)90 \cos 45°$$

$x \approx 63.7$ feet
It is about 63.7 feet from the pitching rubber to first base.

(b)   Use the Pythagorean Theorem to find y in the figure:

$$90^2 + 90^2 = (60.5 + y)^2 \Rightarrow 8100 + 8100 = (60.5 + y)^2$$

$$16,200 = (60.5 + y)^2 \Rightarrow 60.5 + y \approx 127.3 \Rightarrow y \approx 66.8 \text{ feet}$$

It is about 66.8 feet from the pitching rubber to second base.

(c)   Find β in the figure by using the Law of Cosines:

$$\cos \beta = \frac{60.5^2 + 63.7^2 - 90^2}{2(60.5)(63.7)} = -\frac{382.06}{7707.7} \Rightarrow \beta \approx 92.8°$$

The pitcher needs to turn through an angle of 92.8° to face first base.

39.   (a)   Find x by using the Law of Cosines:

$$x^2 = 500^2 + 100^2 - 2(500)100 \cos 80°$$

$$= 260,000 - 100,000 \cos 80°$$

$x \approx 492.6$ feet
The guy wire needs to be about 492.6 feet long.

(b)   Use the Pythagorean Theorem to find the value of y:

$$y^2 = 100^2 + 250^2 = 72,500$$

$y = 269.3$ feet
The guy wire needs to be about 269.3 feet long.

41.   Find x by using the Law of Cosines:

$$x^2 = 400^2 + 90^2 - 2(400)90 \cos(45°)$$

$$= 168,100 - 36,000\sqrt{2}$$

$x \approx 342.33$ feet
It is approximately 342.33 feet from dead center to third base.

43. Use the Law of Cosines:

$$L^2 = x^2 + r^2 - 2xr\cos\theta$$

$$x^2 - 2xr\cos\theta + r^2 - L^2 = 0$$

$$x = \frac{2r\cos\theta + \sqrt{(2r\cos\theta)^2 - 4(1)(r^2 - L^2)}}{2(1)}$$

$$x = \frac{2r\cos\theta + \sqrt{4r^2\cos^2\theta - 4(r^2 - L^2)}}{2}$$

$$x = r\cos\theta + \sqrt{r^2\cos^2\theta + L^2 - r^2}$$

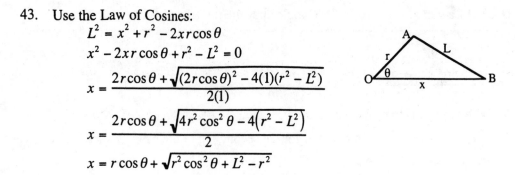

45.

$$\cos\frac{\gamma}{2} = \sqrt{\frac{1 + \cos\gamma}{2}} = \sqrt{\frac{1 + \dfrac{a^2 + b^2 - c^2}{2ab}}{2}} = \sqrt{\frac{2ab + a^2 + b^2 - c^2}{4ab}} = \sqrt{\frac{(a+b)^2 - c^2}{4ab}}$$

$$= \sqrt{\frac{(a+b+c)(a+b-c)}{4ab}} = \sqrt{\frac{2s(2s - c - c)}{4ab}} = \sqrt{\frac{4s(s-c)}{4ab}} = \sqrt{\frac{s(s-c)}{ab}}$$

47.

$$\frac{\cos\alpha}{a} + \frac{\cos\beta}{b} + \frac{\cos\gamma}{c} = \frac{b^2 + c^2 - a^2}{2bca} + \frac{a^2 + c^2 - b^2}{2acb} + \frac{a^2 + b^2 - c^2}{2abc}$$

$$= \frac{b^2 + c^2 - a^2 + a^2 + c^2 - b^2 + a^2 + b^2 - c^2}{2abc} = \frac{a^2 + b^2 + c^2}{2abc}$$

49–51.   Answers will vary.

Applications of Trigonometric Functions

4.4 The Area of a Triangle

1. $\dfrac{1}{2}bh$ 3.   False

5. $a = 2,\ c = 4,\ \beta = 45°$

   $A = \dfrac{1}{2}ac\sin\beta = \dfrac{1}{2}(2)(4)\sin 45° \approx 2.83$

7. $a = 2,\ b = 3,\ \gamma = 95°$

   $A = \dfrac{1}{2}ab\sin\gamma = \dfrac{1}{2}(2)(3)\sin 95° \approx 2.99$

9. $a = 6,\ b = 5,\ c = 8$

   $s = \dfrac{1}{2}(a+b+c) = \dfrac{1}{2}(6+5+8) = \dfrac{19}{2}$

   $A = \sqrt{s(s-a)(s-b)(s-c)} = \sqrt{\left(\dfrac{19}{2}\right)\left(\dfrac{7}{2}\right)\left(\dfrac{9}{2}\right)\left(\dfrac{3}{2}\right)} = \sqrt{\dfrac{3591}{16}} \approx 14.98$

11. $a = 9,\ b = 6,\ c = 4$

    $s = \dfrac{1}{2}(a+b+c) = \dfrac{1}{2}(9+6+4) = \dfrac{19}{2}$

    $A = \sqrt{s(s-a)(s-b)(s-c)} = \sqrt{\left(\dfrac{19}{2}\right)\left(\dfrac{1}{2}\right)\left(\dfrac{7}{2}\right)\left(\dfrac{11}{2}\right)} = \sqrt{\dfrac{1463}{16}} \approx 9.56$

13. $a = 3,\ b = 4,\ \gamma = 40°$

    $A = \dfrac{1}{2}ab\sin\gamma = \dfrac{1}{2}(3)(4)\sin 40° \approx 3.86$

15. $b = 1,\ c = 3,\ \alpha = 80°$

    $A = \dfrac{1}{2}bc\sin\alpha = \dfrac{1}{2}(1)(3)\sin 80° \approx 1.48$

17. $a = 3,\ c = 2,\ \beta = 110°$

    $A = \dfrac{1}{2}ac\sin\beta = \dfrac{1}{2}(3)(2)\sin 110° \approx 2.82$

19. $a = 12,\ b = 13,\ c = 5$

$$s = \frac{1}{2}(a+b+c) = \frac{1}{2}(12+13+5) = 15$$

$$A = \sqrt{s(s-a)(s-b)(s-c)} = \sqrt{(15)(3)(2)(10)} = \sqrt{900} = 30$$

21. $a = 2,\ b = 2,\ c = 2$

$$s = \frac{1}{2}(a+b+c) = \frac{1}{2}(2+2+2) = 3$$

$$A = \sqrt{s(s-a)(s-b)(s-c)} = \sqrt{(3)(1)(1)(1)} = \sqrt{3} \approx 1.73$$

23. $a = 5,\ b = 8,\ c = 9$

$$s = \frac{1}{2}(a+b+c) = \frac{1}{2}(5+8+9) = 11$$

$$A = \sqrt{s(s-a)(s-b)(s-c)} = \sqrt{(11)(6)(3)(2)} = \sqrt{396} \approx 19.90$$

25. Use the Law of Sines in the area of the triangle formula:

$$A = \frac{1}{2}ab\sin\gamma = \frac{1}{2}a\sin\gamma\left(\frac{a\sin\beta}{\sin\alpha}\right) = \frac{a^2\sin\beta\sin\gamma}{2\sin\alpha}$$

27. $\alpha = 40^\circ,\ \beta = 20^\circ,\ a = 2 \qquad \gamma = 180^\circ - \alpha - \beta = 180^\circ - 40^\circ - 20^\circ = 120^\circ$

$$A = \frac{a^2\sin\beta\sin\gamma}{2\sin\alpha} = \frac{2^2\sin20^\circ\cdot\sin120^\circ}{2\sin40^\circ} \approx 0.92$$

29. $\beta = 70^\circ,\ \gamma = 10^\circ,\ b = 5 \qquad \alpha = 180^\circ - \beta - \gamma = 180^\circ - 70^\circ - 10^\circ = 100^\circ$

$$A = \frac{b^2\sin\alpha\sin\gamma}{2\sin\beta} = \frac{5^2\sin100^\circ\cdot\sin10^\circ}{2\sin70^\circ} \approx 2.27$$

31. $\alpha = 110^\circ,\ \gamma = 30^\circ,\ c = 3 \qquad \beta = 180^\circ - \alpha - \gamma = 180^\circ - 110^\circ - 30^\circ = 40^\circ$

$$A = \frac{c^2\sin\alpha\sin\beta}{2\sin\gamma} = \frac{3^2\sin110^\circ\cdot\sin40^\circ}{2\sin30^\circ} \approx 5.44$$

33. Area of a sector $= \frac{1}{2}r^2\theta$ where θ is in radians.

$$\theta = 70\cdot\frac{\pi}{180} = \frac{7\pi}{18}$$

Area of the sector $= \frac{1}{2}\cdot8^2\cdot\frac{7\pi}{18} = \frac{112\pi}{9}$ square feet

Area of the triangle $= \frac{1}{2}\cdot8\cdot8\sin70^\circ = 32\sin70^\circ$ square feet

Area of the segment $= \frac{112\pi}{9} - 32\sin70^\circ \approx 9.03$ square feet

35. Find the area of the lot using Heron's Formula:
     $a = 100, \ b = 50, \ c = 75$

$$s = \frac{1}{2}(a+b+c) = \frac{1}{2}(100+50+75) = \frac{225}{2}$$

$$A = \sqrt{s(s-a)(s-b)(s-c)} = \sqrt{\left(\frac{225}{2}\right)\left(\frac{25}{2}\right)\left(\frac{125}{2}\right)\left(\frac{75}{2}\right)} = \sqrt{\frac{52,734,375}{16}} \approx 1815.46$$

Cost $= (\$3)(1815.46) = \$5446.38$

37. The area of the shaded region = the area of the semicircle – the area of the triangle.

Area of the semicircle $= \frac{1}{2}\pi r^2 = \frac{1}{2}\pi(4)^2 = 8\pi$ square centimeters

The triangle is a right triangle. Find the other leg:
$6^2 + b^2 = 8^2 \Rightarrow b^2 = 64 - 36 = 28 \Rightarrow b = \sqrt{28} = 2\sqrt{7}$

Area of the triangle $= \frac{1}{2}\cdot 6 \cdot 2\sqrt{7} = 6\sqrt{7}$ square centimeters

Area of the shaded region $= 8\pi - 6\sqrt{7} \approx 9.26$ square centimeters

39. The area is the sum of the area of a triangle and a sector.

Area of the triangle $= \frac{1}{2}r\cdot r\sin(\pi - \theta) = \frac{1}{2}r^2\sin(\pi - \theta)$

Area of the sector $= \frac{1}{2}r^2\theta$

$$A = \frac{1}{2}r^2\sin(\pi - \theta) + \frac{1}{2}r^2\theta = \frac{1}{2}r^2(\sin(\pi - \theta) + \theta)$$

$$= \frac{1}{2}r^2(\sin\pi\cos\theta - \cos\pi\sin\theta + \theta)$$

$$= \frac{1}{2}r^2(0 + \sin\theta + \theta)$$

$$= \frac{1}{2}r^2(\theta + \sin\theta)$$

41. $\sin\theta = \frac{y}{1} = y; \qquad \cos\theta = \frac{x}{1} = x$

(a) $A = 2xy = 2\cos\theta\sin\theta$

(b) $2\cos\theta\sin\theta = 2\sin\theta\cos\theta = \sin(2\theta)$

(c) The largest value of the sine function is 1. Solve:
     $\sin(2\theta) = 1$

$$2\theta = \frac{\pi}{2} \Rightarrow \theta = \frac{\pi}{4} = 45°$$

(d) $x = \cos\dfrac{\pi}{4} = \dfrac{\sqrt{2}}{2}; \qquad y = \sin\dfrac{\pi}{4} = \dfrac{\sqrt{2}}{2}$

The dimensions are $\dfrac{\sqrt{2}}{2}$ by $\sqrt{2}$.

43. (a) Area $\Delta OAC = \frac{1}{2}|OC|\cdot|AC| = \frac{1}{2}\cdot\frac{|OC|}{1}\cdot\frac{|AC|}{1} = \frac{1}{2}\cos\alpha\sin\alpha = \frac{1}{2}\sin\alpha\cos\alpha$

     (b) Area $\Delta OCB = \frac{1}{2}|OC|\cdot|BC| = \frac{1}{2}\cdot|OB|^2\cdot\frac{|OC|}{|OB|}\cdot\frac{|BC|}{|OB|} = \frac{1}{2}|OB|^2\cos\beta\sin\beta$

$$= \frac{1}{2}|OB|^2\sin\beta\cos\beta$$

     (c) Area $\Delta OAB = \frac{1}{2}|BD|\cdot|OA| = \frac{1}{2}|BD|\cdot 1 = \frac{1}{2}\cdot|OB|\cdot\frac{|BD|}{|OB|} = \frac{1}{2}|OB|\sin(\alpha+\beta)$

     (d) $\dfrac{\cos\alpha}{\cos\beta} = \dfrac{\dfrac{|OC|}{|OA|}}{\dfrac{|OC|}{|OB|}} = \dfrac{|OC|}{1}\cdot\dfrac{|OB|}{|OC|} = |OB|$

     (e) Area $\Delta OAB =$ Area $\Delta OAC +$ Area ΔOCB

$$\frac{1}{2}|OB|\sin(\alpha+\beta) = \frac{1}{2}\sin\alpha\cos\alpha + \frac{1}{2}|OB|^2\sin\beta\cos\beta$$

$$\frac{\cos\alpha}{\cos\beta}\sin(\alpha+\beta) = \sin\alpha\cos\alpha + \frac{\cos^2\alpha}{\cos^2\beta}\sin\beta\cos\beta$$

$$\sin(\alpha+\beta) = \frac{\cos\beta}{\cos\alpha}\sin\alpha\cos\alpha + \frac{\cos\alpha}{\cos\beta}\sin\beta\cos\beta$$

$$\sin(\alpha+\beta) = \sin\alpha\cos\beta + \cos\alpha\sin\beta$$

45. The grazing area must be considered in sections. A_1 represents $\frac{3}{4}$ of a circle:

$A_1 = \frac{3}{4}\pi(100)^2 = 7500\pi \approx 23{,}562$ square feet

Angles are needed to find A_2 and A_3: (see the figure)

In $\Delta ABC, \angle CBA = 45°, AB = 10, AC = 90$

Find $\angle BCA$:

$$\frac{\sin\angle CBA}{90} = \frac{\sin\angle BCA}{10} \Rightarrow \frac{\sin 45°}{90} = \frac{\sin\angle BCA}{10}$$

$\sin\angle BCA = \dfrac{10\sin 45°}{90} \approx 0.0786$

$\angle BCA \approx 4.5°$

$m\angle BAC = 180° - 45° - 4.5° = 130.5°$

$m\angle DAC = 130.5° - 90° = 40.5°$

Area of $A_3 = \frac{1}{2}(10)(90)\sin 40.5° \approx 292$ square feet.

The angle for sector A_2 is $90° - 40.5° = 49.5°$.

Area of sector $A_2 = \frac{1}{2}(90)^2\left((49.5)\cdot\frac{\pi}{180}\right) \approx 3499$ square feet.

Since the cow can go in either direction around the barn, A_2 must be doubled. Total grazing area is: $23,562 + 2(3499) + 292 = 30,852$ square feet.

47. $K = \dfrac{1}{2}h_1 a$, so $h_1 = \dfrac{2K}{a}$, similarly $h_2 = \dfrac{2K}{b}$ and $h_3 = \dfrac{2K}{c}$.

$$\dfrac{1}{h_1} + \dfrac{1}{h_2} + \dfrac{1}{h_3} = \dfrac{a}{2K} + \dfrac{b}{2K} + \dfrac{c}{2K} = \dfrac{a+b+c}{2K} = \dfrac{2s}{2K} = \dfrac{s}{K}$$

49. $h = \dfrac{a\sin\beta\sin\gamma}{\sin\alpha}$ where h is the altitude to side a.

In $\triangle OAB$, c is opposite angle AOB. The two adjacent angles are $\dfrac{\alpha}{2}$ and $\dfrac{\beta}{2}$.

Then $r = \dfrac{c\sin\dfrac{\alpha}{2}\sin\dfrac{\beta}{2}}{\sin(\angle AOB)}$.

$$\angle AOB = \pi - \left(\dfrac{\alpha}{2} + \dfrac{\beta}{2}\right)$$

$$\sin(\angle AOB) = \sin\left(\pi - \left(\dfrac{\alpha}{2} + \dfrac{\beta}{2}\right)\right) = \sin\left(\dfrac{\alpha}{2} + \dfrac{\beta}{2}\right) = \sin\left(\dfrac{\alpha+\beta}{2}\right) = \cos\left(\dfrac{\pi}{2} - \left(\dfrac{\alpha+\beta}{2}\right)\right)$$

$$= \cos\left(\dfrac{\pi - (\alpha+\beta)}{2}\right) = \cos\dfrac{\gamma}{2}$$

Thus, $r = \dfrac{c\sin\dfrac{\alpha}{2}\sin\dfrac{\beta}{2}}{\cos\dfrac{\gamma}{2}}$.

51. Use the result of Problem 50:

$$\cot\dfrac{\alpha}{2} + \cot\dfrac{\beta}{2} + \cot\dfrac{\gamma}{2} = \dfrac{s-a}{r} + \dfrac{s-b}{r} + \dfrac{s-c}{r} = \dfrac{s-a+s-b+s-c}{r}$$

$$= \dfrac{3s - (a+b+c)}{r} = \dfrac{3s - 2s}{r} = \dfrac{s}{r}$$

53. Answers will vary.

Applications of Trigonometric Functions

4.5 Simple Harmonic Motion; Damped Motion; Combining Waves

1. $|5| = 5$; $\dfrac{2\pi}{4} = \dfrac{\pi}{2}$

3. simple harmonic motion; damped motion

5. $d = -5\cos(\pi t)$

7. $d = -6\cos(2t)$

9. $d = -5\sin(\pi t)$

11. $d = -6\sin(2t)$

13. $d = 5\sin(3t)$
    (a) Simple harmonic
    (b) 5 meters
    (c) $\dfrac{2\pi}{3}$ seconds
    (d) $\dfrac{3}{2\pi}$ oscillation/second

15. $d = 6\cos(\pi t)$
    (a) Simple harmonic
    (b) 6 meters
    (c) 2 seconds
    (d) $\dfrac{1}{2}$ oscillation/second

17. $d = -3\sin\left(\dfrac{1}{2}t\right)$
    (a) Simple harmonic
    (b) 3 meters
    (c) 4π seconds
    (d) $\dfrac{1}{4\pi}$ oscillation/second

19. $d = 6 + 2\cos(2\pi t)$
    (a) Simple harmonic
    (b) 2 meters
    (c) 1 second
    (d) 1 oscillation/second

21. $d(t) = e^{-t/\pi}\cos(2t)$, $\qquad 0 \le t \le 2\pi$

23. $d(t) = e^{-t/2\pi}\cos(t)$, $\qquad 0 \le t \le 2\pi$

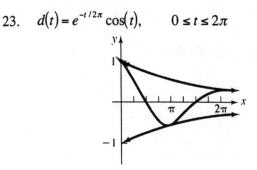

25. $f(x) = x + \cos x$

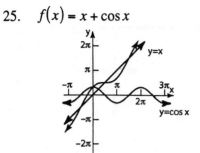

27. $f(x) = x - \sin x$

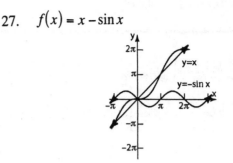

29. $f(x) = \sin x + \cos x$

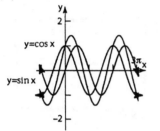

31. $f(x) = \sin x + \sin(2x)$

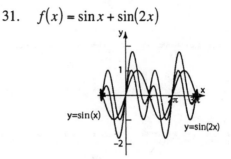

33. (a) Graph:

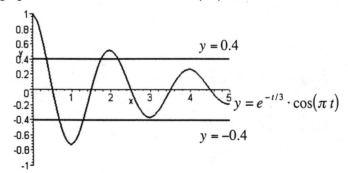

(b) The graph of V touches the graph of $y = e^{-t/3}$
when $t = 0, 2$.
The graph of V touches the graph of
$y = -e^{-t/3}$ when $t = 1, 3$.

(c) To solve the inequality $-0.4 < e^{-t/3} \cdot \cos(\pi t) < 0.4$ on the interval $0 \le t \le 3$,
we consider the graphs of $y = -0.4; \quad y = e^{-t/3} \cdot \cos(\pi t); \quad$ and $\quad y = 0.4$.

On the interval $0 \le t \le 3$, we can use the INTERSECT feature on a calculator to
determine that $y = e^{-t/3} \cdot \cos(\pi t)$ intersects $y = 0.4$ when $t \approx 0.35$, $t \approx 1.75$,
and $t \approx 2.19$, $y = e^{-t/3} \cdot \cos(\pi t)$ intersects $y = -0.4$ when $t \approx 0.67$ and $t \approx 1.29$
and the graph shows that $-0.4 < e^{-t/3} \cdot \cos(\pi t) < 0.4$ when $t = 3$.
Therefore, the voltage V is between -0.4 and 0.4 on the intervals
$0.35 < t < 0.67$, $1.29 < t < 1.75$ and $2.19 < t \le 3$.

213

35. $y = \sin(2\pi(852)t) + \sin(2\pi(1209)t)$

37.   Graph $f(x) = \dfrac{\sin x}{x}$:

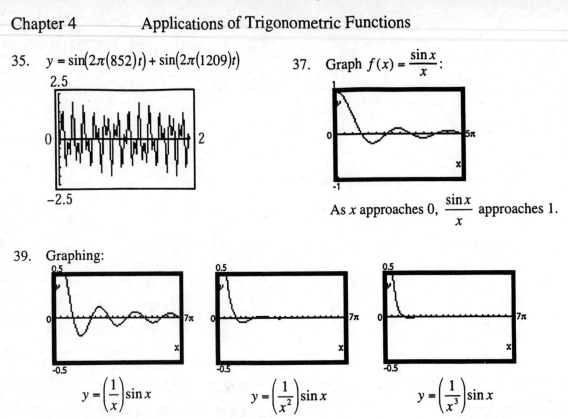

As x approaches 0, $\dfrac{\sin x}{x}$ approaches 1.

39.   Graphing:

$$y = \left(\frac{1}{x}\right)\sin x$$

$$y = \left(\frac{1}{x^2}\right)\sin x$$

$$y = \left(\frac{1}{x^3}\right)\sin x$$

As x gets larger, the graph of $y = \left(\dfrac{1}{x^n}\right)\sin x$ gets closer to $y = 0$.

41.   Answers will vary.

Chapter 4

Applications of Trigonometric Functions

4.R   Chapter Review

1. opposite = 4; adjacent = 3
    Find the hypotenuse:
    $$4^2 + 3^2 = (\text{hypotenuse})^2 \Rightarrow (\text{hypotenuse})^2 = 16 + 9 = 25 \Rightarrow \text{hypotenuse} = 5$$
    $$\sin\theta = \frac{\text{opp}}{\text{hyp}} = \frac{4}{5} \qquad \cos\theta = \frac{\text{adj}}{\text{hyp}} = \frac{3}{5} \qquad \tan\theta = \frac{\text{opp}}{\text{adj}} = \frac{4}{3}$$
    $$\csc\theta = \frac{\text{hyp}}{\text{opp}} = \frac{5}{4} \qquad \sec\theta = \frac{\text{hyp}}{\text{adj}} = \frac{5}{3} \qquad \cot\theta = \frac{\text{adj}}{\text{opp}} = \frac{3}{4}$$

3. adjacent = 2; hypotenuse = 4
    Find the opposite side:
    $$(\text{opposite})^2 + 2^2 = 4^2 \Rightarrow (\text{opposite})^2 = 16 - 4 = 12 \Rightarrow \text{opposite} = \sqrt{12} = 2\sqrt{3}$$
    $$\sin\theta = \frac{\text{opp}}{\text{hyp}} = \frac{2\sqrt{3}}{4} = \frac{\sqrt{3}}{2} \qquad \cos\theta = \frac{\text{adj}}{\text{hyp}} = \frac{2}{4} = \frac{1}{2} \qquad \tan\theta = \frac{\text{opp}}{\text{adj}} = \frac{2\sqrt{3}}{2} = \sqrt{3}$$
    $$\csc\theta = \frac{\text{hyp}}{\text{opp}} = \frac{4}{2\sqrt{3}}\frac{\sqrt{3}}{\sqrt{3}} = \frac{2\sqrt{3}}{3} \qquad \sec\theta = \frac{\text{hyp}}{\text{adj}} = \frac{4}{2} = 2 \qquad \cot\theta = \frac{\text{adj}}{\text{opp}} = \frac{2}{2\sqrt{3}}\frac{\sqrt{3}}{\sqrt{3}} = \frac{\sqrt{3}}{3}$$

5. $\cos 62° - \sin 28° = \cos(90° - 28°) - \sin 28° = \sin 28° - \sin 28° = 0$

7. $\dfrac{\sec 55°}{\csc 35°} = \dfrac{\sec 55°}{\csc(90° - 55°)} = \dfrac{\sec 55°}{\sec 55°} = 1$

9. $\cos^2 40° + \cos^2 50° = \cos^2 40° + \cos^2(90° - 40°) = \cos^2 40° + \sin^2 40° = 1$

11. $c = 10, \ \beta = 20°$
    $$\sin\beta = \frac{b}{c} \Rightarrow \sin 20° = \frac{b}{10} \Rightarrow b = 10\sin 20° \approx 3.42$$
    $$\cos\beta = \frac{a}{c} \Rightarrow \cos 20° = \frac{a}{10} \Rightarrow a = 10\cos 20° \approx 9.40$$
    $$\alpha = 90° - \beta = 90° - 20° = 70°$$

13. $b = 2, \; c = 5$

$$c^2 = a^2 + b^2 \Rightarrow a^2 = c^2 - b^2 = 5^2 - 2^2 = 25 - 4 = 21 \Rightarrow a = \sqrt{21} \approx 4.58$$

$$\sin\beta = \frac{b}{c} = \frac{2}{5} \Rightarrow \beta \approx 23.6°$$

$$\alpha = 90° - \beta \approx 90° - 23.6° = 66.4°$$

15. $\alpha = 50°, \; \beta = 30°, \; a = 1$

$$\gamma = 180° - \alpha - \beta = 180° - 50° - 30° = 100°$$

$$\frac{\sin\alpha}{a} = \frac{\sin\beta}{b} \Rightarrow \frac{\sin 50°}{1} = \frac{\sin 30°}{b} \Rightarrow b = \frac{1\sin 30°}{\sin 50°} \approx 0.65$$

$$\frac{\sin\gamma}{c} = \frac{\sin\alpha}{a} \Rightarrow \frac{\sin 100°}{c} = \frac{\sin 50°}{1} \Rightarrow c = \frac{1\sin 100°}{\sin 50°} \approx 1.29$$

17. $\alpha = 100°, \; c = 2, \; a = 5$

$$\frac{\sin\gamma}{c} = \frac{\sin\alpha}{a} \Rightarrow \frac{\sin\gamma}{2} = \frac{\sin 100°}{5} \Rightarrow \sin\gamma = \frac{2\sin 100°}{5} \approx 0.3939$$

$$\gamma \approx 23.2° \text{ or } \gamma \approx 156.8°$$

The second value is discarded because $\alpha + \gamma > 180°$.

$$\beta = 180° - \alpha - \gamma \approx 180° - 100° - 23.2° = 56.8°$$

$$\frac{\sin\beta}{b} = \frac{\sin\alpha}{a} \Rightarrow \frac{\sin 56.8°}{b} = \frac{\sin 100°}{5} \Rightarrow b = \frac{5\sin 56.8°}{\sin 100°} \approx 4.25$$

19. $a = 3, \; c = 1, \; \gamma = 110°$

$$\frac{\sin\gamma}{c} = \frac{\sin\alpha}{a} \Rightarrow \frac{\sin 110°}{1} = \frac{\sin\alpha}{3} \Rightarrow \sin\alpha = \frac{3\sin 110°}{1} \approx 2.8191$$

There is no angle α for which $\sin\alpha > 1$. Therefore, there is no triangle with the given measurements.

21. $a = 3, \; c = 1, \; \beta = 100°$

$$b^2 = a^2 + c^2 - 2ac\cos\beta = 3^2 + 1^2 - 2 \cdot 3 \cdot 1\cos 100° = 10 - 6\cos 100° \Rightarrow b \approx 3.32$$

$$a^2 = b^2 + c^2 - 2bc\cos\alpha \Rightarrow \cos\alpha = \frac{b^2 + c^2 - a^2}{2bc} = \frac{3.32^2 + 1^2 - 3^2}{2(3.32)(1)} = \frac{3.0224}{6.64} \Rightarrow \alpha \approx 62.9°$$

$$\gamma = 180° - \alpha - \beta \approx 180° - 62.9° - 100° = 17.1°$$

23. $a = 2, \; b = 3, \; c = 1$

$$a^2 = b^2 + c^2 - 2bc\cos\alpha \Rightarrow \cos\alpha = \frac{b^2 + c^2 - a^2}{2bc} = \frac{3^2 + 1^2 - 2^2}{2(3)(1)} = 1 \Rightarrow \alpha \approx 0°$$

No triangle exists with an angle of $0°$.

25. $a = 1,\ b = 3,\ \gamma = 40°$

$c^2 = a^2 + b^2 - 2ab\cos\gamma$

$c^2 = 1^2 + 3^2 - 2 \cdot 1 \cdot 3\cos 40° = 10 - 6\cos 40° \Rightarrow c \approx 2.32$

$a^2 = b^2 + c^2 - 2bc\cos\alpha \Rightarrow \cos\alpha = \dfrac{b^2 + c^2 - a^2}{2bc} = \dfrac{3^2 + 2.32^2 - 1^2}{2(3)(2.32)} = \dfrac{13.3824}{13.92} \Rightarrow \alpha \approx 16.0°$

$\beta = 180° - \alpha - \gamma \approx 180° - 16.0° - 40° = 124.0°$

27. $a = 5,\ b = 3,\ \alpha = 80°$

$\dfrac{\sin\beta}{b} = \dfrac{\sin\alpha}{a} \Rightarrow \dfrac{\sin\beta}{3} = \dfrac{\sin 80°}{5} \Rightarrow \sin\beta = \dfrac{3\sin 80°}{5} \approx 0.5909$

$\beta \approx 36.2°$ or $\beta \approx 143.8°$

The second value is discarded because $\alpha + \beta > 180°$.

$\gamma = 180° - \alpha - \beta \approx 180° - 80° - 36.2° = 63.8°$

$\dfrac{\sin\gamma}{c} = \dfrac{\sin\alpha}{a} \Rightarrow \dfrac{\sin 63.8°}{c} = \dfrac{\sin 80°}{5} \Rightarrow c = \dfrac{5\sin 63.8°}{\sin 80°} \approx 4.56$

29. $a = 1,\ b = \dfrac{1}{2},\ c = \dfrac{4}{3}$

$a^2 = b^2 + c^2 - 2bc\cos\alpha \Rightarrow \cos\alpha = \dfrac{b^2 + c^2 - a^2}{2bc} = \dfrac{(1/2)^2 + (4/3)^2 - 1^2}{2(1/2)(4/3)} = \dfrac{\tfrac{36}{37}}{\tfrac{4}{3}} \Rightarrow \alpha \approx 39.6°$

$b^2 = a^2 + c^2 - 2ac\cos\beta \Rightarrow \cos\beta = \dfrac{a^2 + c^2 - b^2}{2ac} = \dfrac{1^2 + (4/3)^2 - (1/2)^2}{2(1)(4/3)} = \dfrac{\tfrac{91}{36}}{\tfrac{8}{3}} \Rightarrow \beta \approx 18.6°$

$\gamma = 180° - \alpha - \beta \approx 180° - 39.6° - 18.6° \approx 121.8°$

31. $a = 3,\ \alpha = 10°,\ b = 4$

$\dfrac{\sin\beta}{b} = \dfrac{\sin\alpha}{a} \Rightarrow \dfrac{\sin\beta}{4} = \dfrac{\sin 10°}{3} \Rightarrow \sin\beta = \dfrac{4\sin 10°}{3} \approx 0.2315$

$\beta_1 \approx 13.4°$ or $\beta_2 \approx 166.6°$

For both values, $\alpha + \beta < 180°$. Therefore, there are two triangles.

$\gamma_1 = 180° - \alpha - \beta_1 \approx 180° - 10° - 13.4° \approx 156.6°$

$\dfrac{\sin\alpha}{a} = \dfrac{\sin\gamma_1}{c_1} \Rightarrow \dfrac{\sin 10°}{3} = \dfrac{\sin 156.6°}{c_1} \Rightarrow c_1 = \dfrac{3\sin 156.6°}{\sin 10°} \approx 6.86$

$\gamma_2 = 180° - \alpha - \beta_2 \approx 180° - 10° - 166.6° \approx 3.4°$

$\dfrac{\sin\alpha}{a} = \dfrac{\sin\gamma_2}{c_2} \Rightarrow \dfrac{\sin 10°}{3} = \dfrac{\sin 3.4°}{c_2} \Rightarrow c_2 = \dfrac{3\sin 3.4°}{\sin 10°} \approx 1.02$

Two triangles: $\beta_1 \approx 13.4°,\ \gamma_1 \approx 156.6°,\ c_1 \approx 6.86$

or $\beta_2 \approx 166.6°,\ \gamma_2 \approx 3.4°,\ c_2 \approx 1.02$

33. $c = 5,\ b = 4,\ \alpha = 70°$

$a^2 = b^2 + c^2 - 2bc\cos\alpha$

$a^2 = 4^2 + 5^2 - 2\cdot 4\cdot 5\cos 70° = 41 - 40\cos 70° \Rightarrow a \approx 5.23$

$c^2 = a^2 + b^2 - 2ab\cos\gamma \Rightarrow \cos\gamma = \dfrac{a^2 + b^2 - c^2}{2ab} = \dfrac{5.23^2 + 4^2 - 5^2}{2(5.23)(4)} = \dfrac{18.3529}{41.48} \Rightarrow \gamma \approx 64.0°$

$\beta = 180° - \alpha - \gamma \approx 180° - 70° - 64.0° \approx 46.0°$

35. $a = 2,\ b = 3,\ \gamma = 40°$

$A = \dfrac{1}{2}ab\sin\gamma = \dfrac{1}{2}(2)(3)\sin 40° \approx 1.93$

37. $b = 4,\ c = 10,\ \alpha = 70°$

$A = \dfrac{1}{2}bc\sin\alpha = \dfrac{1}{2}(4)(10)\sin 70° \approx 18.79$

39. $a = 4,\ b = 3,\ c = 5$

$s = \dfrac{1}{2}(a + b + c) = \dfrac{1}{2}(4 + 3 + 5) = 6$

$A = \sqrt{s(s-a)(s-b)(s-c)} = \sqrt{(6)(2)(3)(1)} = \sqrt{36} = 6$

41. $a = 4,\ b = 2,\ c = 5$

$s = \dfrac{1}{2}(a + b + c) = \dfrac{1}{2}(4 + 2 + 5) = \dfrac{11}{2}$

$A = \sqrt{s(s-a)(s-b)(s-c)} = \sqrt{(11/2)(3/2)(7/2)(1/2)} = \sqrt{231/16} \approx 3.80$

43. $\alpha = 50°,\ \beta = 30°,\ a = 1 \qquad \gamma = 180° - \alpha - \beta = 180° - 50° - 30° = 100°$

$A = \dfrac{a^2 \sin\beta \sin\gamma}{2\sin\alpha} = \dfrac{1^2 \sin 30°\cdot \sin 100°}{2\sin 50°} \approx 0.32$

45. Use right triangle methods:

$\tan 65° = \dfrac{500}{b} \Rightarrow b = \dfrac{500}{\tan 65°} \approx 233.15$

$\tan 25° = \dfrac{500}{a + b} \Rightarrow a + b = \dfrac{500}{\tan 25°} \approx 1072.25$

$a \approx 1072.25 - 233.15 = 839.1$ feet

The lake is approximately 839 feet long.

47. $\tan 25° = \dfrac{b}{50} \Rightarrow b = 50\tan 25° \approx 23.32$ feet

49. 1454 ft ≈ 0.2754 mile

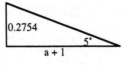

$\tan 5° \approx \dfrac{0.2754}{a + 1}$

$a + 1 = \dfrac{0.2754}{\tan 5°} \approx 3.15 \Rightarrow a \approx 2.15$ miles

The boat is about 2.15 miles offshore.

51. $\angle ABC = 180° - 20° = 160°$

Find the angle at city C: $\dfrac{\sin C}{100} = \dfrac{\sin 160°}{300} \Rightarrow \sin C = \dfrac{100\sin 160°}{300} \Rightarrow C \approx 6.55°$

Find the angle at city A: $A \approx 180° - 160° - 6.55° = 13.45°$

$\dfrac{\sin 13.45°}{y} = \dfrac{\sin 160°}{300} \Rightarrow y = \dfrac{300\sin 13.45°}{\sin 160°} \approx 204.07$ miles

The distance from city B to city C is approximately 204 miles.

53. Draw a line perpendicular to the shore:

(a) $\angle ACB = 12° + 30° = 42°$

$\angle ABC = 90° - 30° = 60°$

$\angle CAB = 90° - 12° = 78°$

$\dfrac{\sin 60°}{b} = \dfrac{\sin 42°}{2} \Rightarrow b = \dfrac{2\sin 60°}{\sin 42°} \approx 2.59$ miles

(b) $\dfrac{\sin 78°}{a} = \dfrac{\sin 42°}{2} \Rightarrow a = \dfrac{2\sin 78°}{\sin 42°} \approx 2.92$ miles

(c) $\cos 12° = \dfrac{x}{2.59} \Rightarrow x = 2.59\cos 12° \approx 2.53$ miles

55. (a) After 4 hours, the sailboat would have sailed $18(4) = 72$ miles.

Find the third side of the triangle to determine the distance from the island:

$a = 72,\ b = 200,\ \gamma = 15°$

$c^2 = a^2 + b^2 - 2ab\cos\gamma$

$c^2 = 72^2 + 200^2 - 2 \cdot 72 \cdot 200\cos 15°$

$\quad = 45,184 - 28,800\cos 15° \Rightarrow c \approx 131.8$ miles

The sailboat is about 131.8 miles from the island.

(b) Find the measure of the angle opposite the 200 side:

$\cos\beta = \dfrac{a^2 + c^2 - b^2}{2ac} \Rightarrow \cos\beta = \dfrac{72^2 + 131.8^2 - 200^2}{2(72)(131.8)} = -\dfrac{17,444.76}{18,979.2} \Rightarrow \beta \approx 156.8°$

The sailboat should turn through an angle of $180° - 156.8° = 23.2°$ to correct its course.

(c) The original trip would have taken: $t = \dfrac{200}{18} \approx 11.1$ hours.

The actual trip takes: $t = 4 + \dfrac{131.8}{18} \approx 11.3$ hours.

The trip takes about 0.2 hour, that is, 12 minutes longer.

57. Find the lengths of the two unknown sides of the middle triangle:

$x^2 = 100^2 + 125^2 - 2(100)(125)\cos 50° \Rightarrow x \approx 97.75$ feet

$y^2 = 70^2 + 50^2 - 2(70)(50)\cos 100° \Rightarrow y \approx 92.82$ feet

Find the areas of the three triangles:

$$A_1 = \frac{1}{2}(100)(125)\sin 50° \approx 4787.78 \qquad A_2 = \frac{1}{2}(50)(70)\sin 100° \approx 1723.41$$

$$s = \frac{1}{2}(50 + 97.75 + 92.82) = 120.285$$

$$A_3 = \sqrt{(120.285)(70.285)(22.535)(27.465)} \approx 2287.47$$

The approximate area of the lake is $4787.78 + 1723.41 + 2287.47 = 8798.67$ sq. ft.

59.   Area of the segment = area of the sector–area of the triangle.

$$\text{Area of sector} = \frac{1}{2}r^2\theta = \frac{1}{2}\cdot 6^2\left(50\cdot\frac{\pi}{180}\right) \approx 15.708 \text{ in}^2$$

$$\text{Area of triangle} = \frac{1}{2}ab\sin\theta = \frac{1}{2}\cdot 6\cdot 6\sin 50° \approx 13.789 \text{ in}^2$$

$$\text{Area of segment} = 15.708 - 13.789 \approx 1.92 \text{ in}^2$$

61.   Extend the tangent line until it meets a line extended through the centers of the pulleys. Label these extensions x and y. The distance between the points of tangency is z. Two similar triangles are formed.

Therefore:

$$\frac{24+y}{y} = \frac{6.5}{2.5}$$

where $24 + y$ is the hypotenuse of the larger triangle and y is the hypotenuse of the smaller triangle .

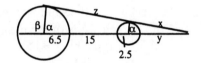

Solve for y:

$$6.5y = 2.5(24 + y) \Rightarrow 6.5y = 60 + 2.5y \Rightarrow 4y = 60 \Rightarrow y = 15$$

Use the Pythagorean Theorem to find x:

$$x^2 + 2.5^2 = 15^2 \Rightarrow x^2 = 225 - 6.25 = 218.75 \Rightarrow x \approx 14.79$$

Use the Pythagorean Theorem to find z:

$$(z + 14.79)^2 + 6.5^2 = (24 + 15)^2 \Rightarrow (z + 14.79)^2 = 1521 - 42.25 = 1478.75$$

$$z + 14.79 \approx 38.45 \Rightarrow z \approx 23.66$$

Find α:

$$\cos\alpha = \frac{2.5}{15} \approx 0.1667 \Rightarrow \alpha \approx 1.4033 \text{ radians}$$

$$\beta \approx \pi - 1.4033 \approx 1.7383 \text{ radians}$$

The arc length on the top of the larger pulley is about: $6.5(1.7383) = 11.30$ inches.
The arc length on the top of the smaller pulley is about: $2.5(1.4033) = 3.51$ inches.
The distance between the points of tangency is about 23.66 inches.
The length of the belt is about: $2(11.30 + 3.51 + 23.66) = 76.94$ inches.

63. $d = -3\cos\left(\frac{\pi}{2}t\right)$

65. $d = 6\sin(2t)$
  (a) Simple harmonic
  (b) 6 feet
  (c) π seconds
  (d) $\dfrac{1}{\pi}$ oscillation/second

67. $d = -2\cos(\pi t)$
  (a) Simple harmonic
  (b) 2 feet
  (c) 2 seconds
  (d) $\dfrac{1}{2}$ oscillation/second

69. $y = e^{-x/2\pi}\sin(2x), \quad 0 \le x \le 2\pi$

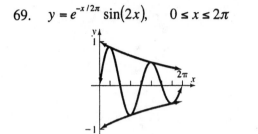

71. $y = x\cos x, \quad 0 \le x \le 2\pi$

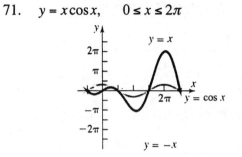

73. $y = 2\sin x + \cos(2x), \quad 0 \le x \le 2\pi$

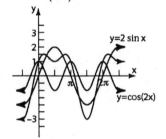

Applications of Trigonometric Functions

4.CR Cumulative Review

1.
$$3x^2 + 1 = 4x$$
$$3x^2 - 4x + 1 = 0$$
$$(3x - 1)(x - 1) = 0$$
$$x = \frac{1}{3} \text{ or } x = 1$$

The solution set is $\left\{\frac{1}{3}, 1\right\}$.

3. $f(x) = \sqrt{x^2 - 3x - 4}$

f will be defined provided $g(x) = x^2 - 3x - 4 \geq 0$.

$$x^2 - 3x - 4 \geq 0$$
$$(x - 4)(x + 1) \geq 0$$

$x = 4, x = -1$ are the zeros.

Interval	Test Number	$g(x)$	Positive/Negative
$-\infty < x < -1$	-2	6	Positive
$-1 < x < 4$	0	-4	Negative
$4 < x < \infty$	5	6	Positive

The domain of $f(x) = \sqrt{x^2 - 3x - 4}$ is $\left\{ x \mid -\infty < x \leq -1 \text{ or } 4 \leq x < \infty \right\}$.

5. $y = -2\cos(2x - \pi) = -2\cos\left(2\left(x - \frac{\pi}{2}\right)\right)$

Amplitude: $|A| = |-2| = 2$

Period: $T = \frac{2\pi}{2} = \pi$

Phase Shift: $\dfrac{\phi}{\omega} = \dfrac{\pi}{2}$

7. (a) $y = e^x$, $0 \leq x \leq 4$

(b) $y = \sin x$, $0 \leq x \leq 4$

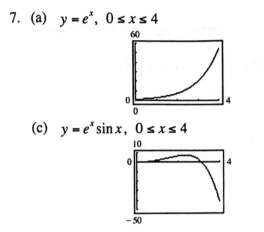

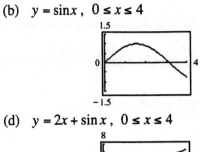

(c) $y = e^x \sin x$, $0 \leq x \leq 4$

(d) $y = 2x + \sin x$, $0 \leq x \leq 4$

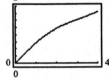

9. $a = 20$, $c = 15$, $\gamma = 40°$

$$\frac{\sin \gamma}{c} = \frac{\sin \alpha}{a} \Rightarrow \frac{\sin 40°}{15} = \frac{\sin \alpha}{20} \Rightarrow \sin \alpha = \frac{20 \sin 40°}{15}$$

$\alpha \approx 59.0°$ or $\alpha \approx 121.0°$

Case 1: $\alpha \approx 58.99° \Rightarrow \beta \approx 180° - (40° + 59.0°) = 81.0°$

$$\frac{\sin \gamma}{c} = \frac{\sin \beta}{b} \Rightarrow \frac{\sin 40°}{15} = \frac{\sin 81.0°}{b}$$

$$b \approx \frac{15 \sin 81.0°}{\sin 40°} \approx 23.05$$

Therefore, $\alpha \approx 59.0°$, $\beta \approx 81.0°$, $b \approx 23.05$.

Case 2: $\alpha \approx 121.0° \Rightarrow \beta \approx 180° - (40° + 121.0°) = 19.0°$

$$\frac{\sin \gamma}{c} = \frac{\sin \beta}{b} \Rightarrow \frac{\sin 40°}{15} = \frac{\sin 19.0°}{b}$$

$$b \approx \frac{15 \sin 19.0°}{\sin 40°} \approx 7.60$$

Therefore, $\alpha \approx 121.0°$, $\beta \approx 19.0°$, $b \approx 7.60$.

11. $r = 3$, $\theta = 60° \Rightarrow \theta = 60 \cdot \frac{\pi}{180} = \frac{\pi}{3}$

$s = r\theta = 3 \cdot \frac{\pi}{3} = \pi$ units

Chapter 5

Polar Coordinates; Vectors

5.1 Polar Coordinates

1.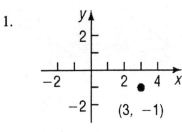

3. $\dfrac{b}{\sqrt{a^2+b^2}}$

5. pole, polar axis

7. $-\sqrt{3}, -1$

9. True

11. *A*   13. *C*

15. *B*   17. *A*

19. $(3, 90°)$

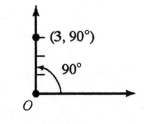

21. $(-2, 0)$
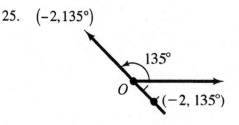

23. $\left(6, \dfrac{\pi}{6}\right)$

25. $(-2, 135°)$

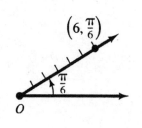

27. $\left(-1, -\dfrac{\pi}{3}\right)$

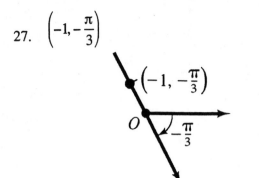

29. $(-2, -\pi)$

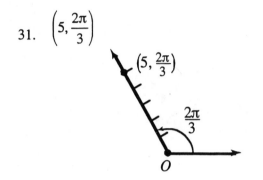

31. $\left(5, \dfrac{2\pi}{3}\right)$

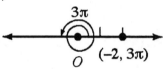

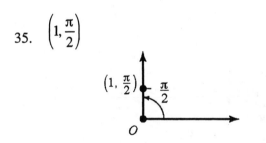

(a) $r > 0, \ -2\pi \le \theta < 0$ $\left(5, -\dfrac{4\pi}{3}\right)$

(b) $r < 0, \ 0 \le \theta < 2\pi$ $\left(-5, \dfrac{5\pi}{3}\right)$

(c) $r > 0, \ 2\pi \le \theta < 4\pi$ $\left(5, \dfrac{8\pi}{3}\right)$

33. $(-2, 3\pi)$

(a) $r > 0, \ -2\pi \le \theta < 0$ $(2, -2\pi)$

(b) $r < 0, \ 0 \le \theta < 2\pi$ $(-2, \pi)$

(c) $r > 0, \ 2\pi \le \theta < 4\pi$ $(2, 2\pi)$

35. $\left(1, \dfrac{\pi}{2}\right)$

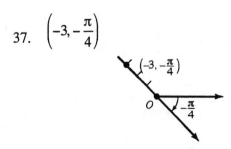

(a) $r > 0, \ -2\pi \le \theta < 0$ $\left(1, -\dfrac{3\pi}{2}\right)$

(b) $r < 0, \ 0 \le \theta < 2\pi$ $\left(-1, \dfrac{3\pi}{2}\right)$

(c) $r > 0, \ 2\pi \le \theta < 4\pi$ $\left(1, \dfrac{5\pi}{2}\right)$

37. $\left(-3, -\dfrac{\pi}{4}\right)$

(a) $r > 0, \ -2\pi \le \theta < 0$ $\left(3, -\dfrac{5\pi}{4}\right)$

(b) $r < 0, \ 0 \le \theta < 2\pi$ $\left(-3, \dfrac{7\pi}{4}\right)$

(c) $r > 0, \ 2\pi \le \theta < 4\pi$ $\left(3, \dfrac{11\pi}{4}\right)$

39.　$x = r\cos\theta = 3\cos\dfrac{\pi}{2} = 3\cdot 0 = 0$

　　$y = r\sin\theta = 3\sin\dfrac{\pi}{2} = 3\cdot 1 = 3$

　　The rectangular coordinates of the point $\left(3, \dfrac{\pi}{2}\right)$ are $(0, 3)$.

41.　$x = r\cos\theta = -2\cos 0 = -2\cdot 1 = -2$
　　$y = r\sin\theta = -2\sin 0 = -2\cdot 0 = 0$
　　The rectangular coordinates of the point $(-2, 0)$ are $(-2, 0)$.

43.　$x = r\cos\theta = 6\cos 150° = 6\left(-\dfrac{\sqrt{3}}{2}\right) = -3\sqrt{3}$

　　$y = r\sin\theta = 6\sin 150° = 6\cdot\dfrac{1}{2} = 3$

　　The rectangular coordinates of the point $(6, 150°)$ are $\left(-3\sqrt{3}, 3\right)$.

45.　$x = r\cos\theta = -2\cos\dfrac{3\pi}{4} = -2\left(-\dfrac{\sqrt{2}}{2}\right) = \sqrt{2}$

　　$y = r\sin\theta = -2\sin\dfrac{3\pi}{4} = -2\cdot\dfrac{\sqrt{2}}{2} = -\sqrt{2}$

　　The rectangular coordinates of the point $\left(-2, \dfrac{3\pi}{4}\right)$ are $\left(\sqrt{2}, -\sqrt{2}\right)$.

47.　$x = r\cos\theta = -1\cos\left(-\dfrac{\pi}{3}\right) = -1\cdot\dfrac{1}{2} = -\dfrac{1}{2}$

　　$y = r\sin\theta = -1\sin\left(-\dfrac{\pi}{3}\right) = -1\left(-\dfrac{\sqrt{3}}{2}\right) = \dfrac{\sqrt{3}}{2}$

　　The rectangular coordinates of the point $\left(-1, -\dfrac{\pi}{3}\right)$ are $\left(-\dfrac{1}{2}, \dfrac{\sqrt{3}}{2}\right)$.

49.　$x = r\cos\theta = -2\cos(-180°) = -2(-1) = 2$
　　$y = r\sin\theta = -2\sin(-180°) = -2\cdot 0 = 0$
　　The rectangular coordinates of the point $(-2, -180°)$ are $(2, 0)$.

51.　$x = r\cos\theta = 7.5\cos 110° \approx 7.5(-0.3420) \approx -2.57$
　　$y = r\sin\theta = 7.5\sin 110° \approx 7.5(0.9397) \approx 7.05$
　　The rectangular coordinates of the point $(7.5, 110°)$ are $(-2.57, 7.05)$.

53. $x = r\cos\theta = 6.3\cos(3.8) \approx 6.3(-0.7910) \approx -4.98$
$y = r\sin\theta = 6.3\sin(3.8) \approx 6.3(-0.6119) \approx -3.85$
The rectangular coordinates of the point $(6.3, 3.8)$ are $(-4.98, -3.85)$.

55. $r = \sqrt{x^2 + y^2} = \sqrt{3^2 + 0^2} = \sqrt{9} = 3 \qquad \theta = \tan^{-1}\left(\dfrac{y}{x}\right) = \tan^{-1}\left(\dfrac{0}{3}\right) = \tan^{-1}0 = 0$
Polar coordinates of the point $(3, 0)$ are $(3, 0)$.

57. $r = \sqrt{x^2 + y^2} = \sqrt{(-1)^2 + 0^2} = \sqrt{1} = 1 \qquad \theta = \tan^{-1}\left(\dfrac{y}{x}\right) = \tan^{-1}\left(\dfrac{0}{-1}\right) = \tan^{-1}0 = 0$
The point lies on the negative x-axis thus $\theta = \pi$.
Polar coordinates of the point $(-1, 0)$ are $(1, \pi)$.

59. The point $(1, -1)$ lies in quadrant IV.
$r = \sqrt{x^2 + y^2} = \sqrt{1^2 + (-1)^2} = \sqrt{2} \qquad \theta = \tan^{-1}\left(\dfrac{y}{x}\right) = \tan^{-1}\left(\dfrac{-1}{1}\right) = \tan^{-1}(-1) = -\dfrac{\pi}{4}$
Polar coordinates of the point $(1, -1)$ are $\left(\sqrt{2}, -\dfrac{\pi}{4}\right)$.

61. The point $\left(\sqrt{3}, 1\right)$ lies in quadrant I.
$r = \sqrt{x^2 + y^2} = \sqrt{\left(\sqrt{3}\right)^2 + 1^2} = \sqrt{4} = 2 \qquad \theta = \tan^{-1}\left(\dfrac{y}{x}\right) = \tan^{-1}\dfrac{1}{\sqrt{3}} = \dfrac{\pi}{6}$
Polar coordinates of the point $\left(\sqrt{3}, 1\right)$ are $\left(2, \dfrac{\pi}{6}\right)$.

63. The point $(1.3, -2.1)$ lies in quadrant IV.
$r = \sqrt{x^2 + y^2} = \sqrt{1.3^2 + (-2.1)^2} = \sqrt{6.1} \approx 2.47$
$\theta = \tan^{-1}\left(\dfrac{y}{x}\right) = \tan^{-1}\left(\dfrac{-2.1}{1.3}\right) \approx \tan^{-1}(-1.6154) \approx -1.02$
Polar coordinates of the point $(1.3, -2.1)$ are $(2.47, -1.02)$.

65. The point $(8.3, 4.2)$ lies in quadrant I.
$r = \sqrt{x^2 + y^2} = \sqrt{8.3^2 + 4.2^2} = \sqrt{86.53} \approx 9.30$
$\theta = \tan^{-1}\left(\dfrac{y}{x}\right) = \tan^{-1}\left(\dfrac{4.2}{8.3}\right) \approx \tan^{-1}(0.5060) \approx 0.47$
Polar coordinates of the point $(8.3, 4.2)$ are $(9.30, 0.47)$.

67. $2x^2 + 2y^2 = 3$

$2(x^2 + y^2) = 3$

$2r^2 = 3$

$r^2 = \dfrac{3}{2}$

69. $x^2 = 4y$

$(r\cos\theta)^2 = 4r\sin\theta$

$r^2\cos^2\theta - 4r\sin\theta = 0$

71. $2xy = 1$

$2(r\cos\theta)(r\sin\theta) = 1$

$2r^2\sin\theta\cos\theta = 1$

$r^2\sin 2\theta = 1$

73. $x = 4$

$r\cos\theta = 4$

75. $r = \cos\theta$

$r^2 = r\cos\theta$

$x^2 + y^2 = x$

$x^2 - x + y^2 = 0$

77. $r^2 = \cos\theta$

$r^3 = r\cos\theta$

$(x^2 + y^2)^{3/2} = x$

$(x^2 + y^2)^{3/2} - x = 0$

79. $r = 2$

$\sqrt{x^2 + y^2} = 2$

$x^2 + y^2 = 4$

81. $r = \dfrac{4}{1 - \cos\theta}$

$r(1 - \cos\theta) = 4$

$r - r\cos\theta = 4$

$\sqrt{x^2 + y^2} - x = 4$

$\sqrt{x^2 + y^2} = x + 4$

$x^2 + y^2 = x^2 + 8x + 16$

$y^2 = 8(x + 2)$

83. Rewrite the polar coordinates in rectangular form:

$P_1 = (r_1, \theta_1) \Rightarrow P_1 = (r_1\cos\theta_1, r_1\sin\theta_1)$

$P_2 = (r_2, \theta_2) \Rightarrow P_2 = (r_2\cos\theta_2, r_2\sin\theta_2)$

$d = \sqrt{(r_2\cos\theta_2 - r_1\cos\theta_1)^2 + (r_2\sin\theta_2 - r_1\sin\theta_1)^2}$

$= \sqrt{r_2^2\cos^2\theta_2 - 2r_1r_2\cos\theta_2\cos\theta_1 + r_1^2\cos^2\theta_1 + r_2^2\sin^2\theta_2 - 2r_1r_2\sin\theta_2\sin\theta_1 + r_1^2\sin^2\theta_1}$

$= \sqrt{r_2^2(\cos^2\theta_2 + \sin^2\theta_2) + r_1^2(\cos^2\theta_1 + \sin^2\theta_1) - 2r_1r_2(\cos\theta_2\cos\theta_1 + \sin\theta_2\sin\theta_1)}$

$= \sqrt{r_2^2 + r_1^2 - 2r_1r_2\cos(\theta_2 - \theta_1)}$

85. Answers will vary.

Chapter 5

Polar Coordinates; Vectors

5.2   Polar Equations and Graphs

1. $(-4,6)$

3. $\left(x-(-2)\right)^2+(y-5)^2=3^2 \Rightarrow (x+2)^2+(y-5)^2=9$

5. $-\dfrac{\sqrt{2}}{2}$

7.   polar equation

9. $-r$

11.   False

13. $r=4$
The equation is of the form $r=a,\ \ a>0$.
It is a circle, center at the pole and radius 4.
Transform to rectangular form:
$$r=4$$
$$r^2=16$$
$$x^2+y^2=16$$

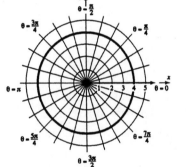

15. $\theta=\dfrac{\pi}{3}$
The equation is of the form $\theta=\alpha$. It is a line, passing through the pole at an angle of $\dfrac{\pi}{3}$.
Transform to rectangular form:
$$\theta=\frac{\pi}{3} \Rightarrow \tan\theta=\tan\frac{\pi}{3}$$
$$\frac{y}{x}=\sqrt{3}$$
$$y=\sqrt{3}x$$

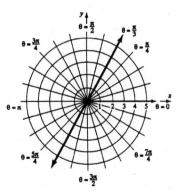

17. $r \sin \theta = 4$

The equation is of the form $r \sin \theta = b$. It is
a horizontal line, 4 units above the pole.
Transform to rectangular form:
$$r \sin \theta = 4$$
$$y = 4$$

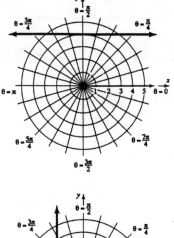

19. $r \cos \theta = -2$

The equation is of the form $r \cos \theta = a$. It is
a vertical line, 2 units to the left of the pole.
Transform to rectangular form:
$$r \cos \theta = -2$$
$$x = -2$$

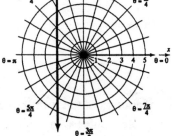

21. $r = 2 \cos \theta$

The equation is of the form
$r = \pm 2a \cos \theta$, $a > 0$. It is a circle, passing
through the pole, and center on the polar
axis.
Transform to rectangular form:
$$r = 2 \cos \theta$$
$$r^2 = 2r \cos \theta$$
$$x^2 + y^2 = 2x$$
$$x^2 - 2x + y^2 = 0$$
$$(x-1)^2 + y^2 = 1$$
center $(1,0)$; radius 1

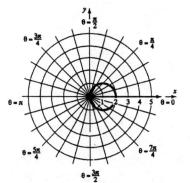

23. $r = -4\sin\theta$

The equation is of the form
$r = \pm 2a\sin\theta, \ a > 0$. It is a circle, passing through the pole, and center on the line
$\theta = \dfrac{\pi}{2}$.

Transform to rectangular form:
$$r = -4\sin\theta$$
$$r^2 = -4r\sin\theta$$
$$x^2 + y^2 = -4y$$
$$x^2 + y^2 + 4y = 0$$
$$x^2 + (y+2)^2 = 4$$
center $(0,-2)$; radius 2

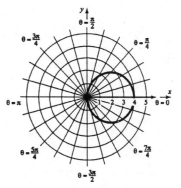

25. $r\sec\theta = 4$

The equation is a circle, passing through the pole, center on the polar axis and radius 2.
Transform to rectangular form:
$$r\sec\theta = 4$$
$$r \cdot \dfrac{1}{\cos\theta} = 4$$
$$r = 4\cos\theta$$
$$r^2 = 4r\cos\theta$$
$$x^2 + y^2 = 4x$$
$$x^2 - 4x + y^2 = 0$$
$$(x-2)^2 + y^2 = 4$$
center $(2,0)$; radius 2

27. $r\csc\theta = -2$

The equation is a circle, passing through the pole, center on the line $\theta = \dfrac{\pi}{2}$ and radius 1.
Transform to rectangular form:
$$r\csc\theta = -2$$
$$r \cdot \dfrac{1}{\sin\theta} = -2$$
$$r = -2\sin\theta$$
$$r^2 = -2r\sin\theta$$
$$x^2 + y^2 = -2y$$
$$x^2 + y^2 + 2y = 0$$
$$x^2 + (y+1)^2 = 1$$
center $(0,-1)$; radius 1

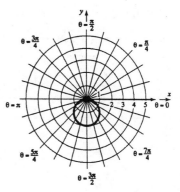

29. E   31. F   33. H   35. D

37. $r = 2 + 2\cos\theta$ The graph will be a cardioid. Check for symmetry:
Polar axis: Replace θ by $-\theta$. The result is $r = 2 + 2\cos(-\theta) = 2 + 2\cos\theta$.
          The graph is symmetric with respect to the polar axis.

The line $\theta = \dfrac{\pi}{2}$: Replace θ by $\pi - \theta$.

$$r = 2 + 2\cos(\pi - \theta) = 2 + 2\big(\cos(\pi)\cos\theta + \sin(\pi)\sin\theta\big)$$

$$= 2 + 2(-\cos\theta + 0) = 2 - 2\cos\theta$$

          The test fails.
The pole: Replace r by $-r$. $-r = 2 + 2\cos\theta$. The test fails.
Due to symmetry with respect to the polar axis, assign values to θ from 0 to π.

θ	0	$\dfrac{\pi}{6}$	$\dfrac{\pi}{3}$	$\dfrac{\pi}{2}$	$\dfrac{2\pi}{3}$	$\dfrac{5\pi}{6}$	π
$r = 2 + 2\cos\theta$	4	$2 + \sqrt{3} \approx 3.7$	3	2	1	$2 - \sqrt{3} \approx 0.3$	0

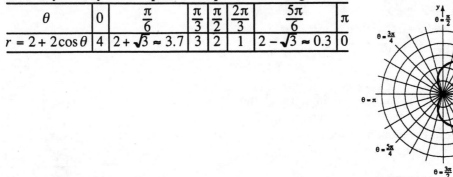

39. $r = 3 - 3\sin\theta$ The graph will be a cardioid. Check for symmetry:
Polar axis: Replace θ by $-\theta$. The result is $r = 3 - 3\sin(-\theta) = 3 + 3\sin\theta$. The test fails.

The line $\theta = \dfrac{\pi}{2}$: Replace θ by $\pi - \theta$.

$$r = 3 - 3\sin(\pi - \theta) = 3 - 3\big(\sin(\pi)\cos\theta - \cos(\pi)\sin\theta\big)$$

$$= 3 - 3(0 + \sin\theta) = 3 - 3\sin\theta$$

          The graph is symmetric with respect to the line $\theta = \dfrac{\pi}{2}$.

The pole: Replace r by $-r$. $-r = 3 - 3\sin\theta$. The test fails.

Due to symmetry with respect to the line $\theta = \dfrac{\pi}{2}$, assign values to θ from $-\dfrac{\pi}{2}$ to $\dfrac{\pi}{2}$.

θ	$-\dfrac{\pi}{2}$	$-\dfrac{\pi}{3}$	$-\dfrac{\pi}{6}$	0	$\dfrac{\pi}{6}$	$\dfrac{\pi}{3}$	$\dfrac{\pi}{2}$
$r = 3 - 3\sin\theta$	6	$3 + \dfrac{3\sqrt{3}}{2} \approx 5.6$	$\dfrac{9}{2}$	3	$\dfrac{3}{2}$	$3 - \dfrac{3\sqrt{3}}{2} \approx 0.4$	0

41. $r = 2 + \sin\theta$ The graph will be a limacon without an inner loop.
Check for symmetry:
Polar axis: Replace θ by $-\theta$. The result is $r = 2 + \sin(-\theta) = 2 - \sin\theta$. The test fails.

The line $\theta = \frac{\pi}{2}$: Replace θ by $\pi - \theta$.

$$r = 2 + \sin(\pi - \theta) = 2 + (\sin(\pi)\cos\theta - \cos(\pi)\sin\theta)$$

$$= 2 + (0 + \sin\theta) = 2 + \sin\theta$$

The graph is symmetric with respect to the line $\theta = \frac{\pi}{2}$.

The pole: Replace r by $-r$. $-r = 2 + \sin\theta$. The test fails.

Due to symmetry with respect to the line $\theta = \frac{\pi}{2}$, assign values to θ from $-\frac{\pi}{2}$ to $\frac{\pi}{2}$.

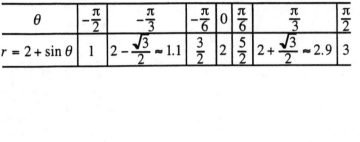

θ	$-\frac{\pi}{2}$	$-\frac{\pi}{3}$	$-\frac{\pi}{6}$	0	$\frac{\pi}{6}$	$\frac{\pi}{3}$	$\frac{\pi}{2}$
$r = 2 + \sin\theta$	1	$2 - \frac{\sqrt{3}}{2} \approx 1.1$	$\frac{3}{2}$	2	$\frac{5}{2}$	$2 + \frac{\sqrt{3}}{2} \approx 2.9$	3

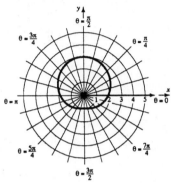

43. $r = 4 - 2\cos\theta$ The graph will be a limacon without an inner loop.
Check for symmetry:
Polar axis: Replace θ by $-\theta$. The result is $r = 4 - 2\cos(-\theta) = 4 - 2\cos\theta$.
The graph is symmetric with respect to the polar axis.

The line $\theta = \frac{\pi}{2}$: Replace θ by $\pi - \theta$.

$$r = 4 - 2\cos(\pi - \theta) = 4 - 2(\cos(\pi)\cos\theta + \sin(\pi)\sin\theta)$$

$$= 4 - 2(-\cos\theta + 0) = 4 + 2\cos\theta$$

The test fails.

The pole: Replace r by $-r$. $-r = 4 - 2\cos\theta$. The test fails.

Due to symmetry with respect to the polar axis, assign values to θ from 0 to π.

θ	0	$\frac{\pi}{6}$	$\frac{\pi}{3}$	$\frac{\pi}{2}$	$\frac{2\pi}{3}$	$\frac{5\pi}{6}$	π
$r = 4 - 2\cos\theta$	2	$4 - \sqrt{3} \approx 2.3$	3	4	5	$4 + \sqrt{3} \approx 5.7$	6

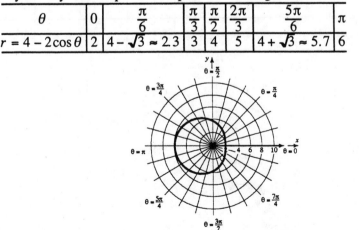

233

45. $r = 1 + 2\sin\theta$ The graph will be a limacon with an inner loop.

Check for symmetry:

Polar axis: Replace θ by $-\theta$. The result is $r = 1 + 2\sin(-\theta) = 1 - 2\sin\theta$. The test fails.

The line $\theta = \dfrac{\pi}{2}$: Replace θ by $\pi - \theta$.

$$r = 1 + 2\sin(\pi - \theta) = 1 + 2(\sin(\pi)\cos\theta - \cos(\pi)\sin\theta)$$

$$= 1 + 2(0 + \sin\theta) = 1 + 2\sin\theta$$

The graph is symmetric with respect to the line $\theta = \dfrac{\pi}{2}$.

The pole: Replace r by $-r$. $-r = 1 + 2\sin\theta$. The test fails.

Due to symmetry with respect to the line $\theta = \dfrac{\pi}{2}$, assign values to θ from $-\dfrac{\pi}{2}$ to $\dfrac{\pi}{2}$.

θ	$-\dfrac{\pi}{2}$	$-\dfrac{\pi}{3}$	$-\dfrac{\pi}{6}$	0	$\dfrac{\pi}{6}$	$\dfrac{\pi}{3}$	$\dfrac{\pi}{2}$
$r = 1 + 2\sin\theta$	-1	$1 - \sqrt{3} \approx -0.7$	0	1	2	$1 + \sqrt{3} \approx 2.7$	3

47. $r = 2 - 3\cos\theta$ The graph will be a limacon with an inner loop.

Check for symmetry:

Polar axis: Replace θ by $-\theta$. The result is $r = 2 - 3\cos(-\theta) = 2 - 3\cos\theta$.

The graph is symmetric with respect to the polar axis.

The line $\theta = \dfrac{\pi}{2}$: Replace θ by $\pi - \theta$.

$$r = 2 - 3\cos(\pi - \theta) = 2 - 3(\cos(\pi)\cos\theta + \sin(\pi)\sin\theta)$$

$$= 2 - 3(-\cos\theta + 0) = 2 + 3\cos\theta$$

The test fails.

The pole: Replace r by $-r$. $-r = 2 - 3\cos\theta$. The test fails.

Due to symmetry with respect to the polar axis, assign values to θ from 0 to π.

θ	0	$\dfrac{\pi}{6}$	$\dfrac{\pi}{3}$	$\dfrac{\pi}{2}$	$\dfrac{2\pi}{3}$	$\dfrac{5\pi}{6}$	π
$r = 2 - 3\cos\theta$	-1	$2 - \dfrac{3\sqrt{3}}{2} \approx -0.6$	$\dfrac{1}{2}$	2	$\dfrac{7}{2}$	$2 + \dfrac{3\sqrt{3}}{2} \approx 4.6$	5

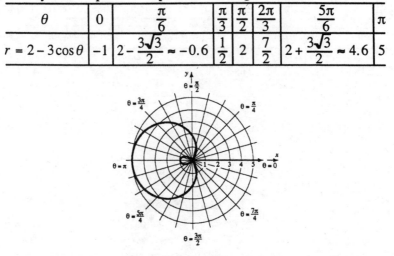

49. $r = 3\cos(2\theta)$ The graph will be a rose with four petals. Check for symmetry:
Polar axis: Replace θ by $-\theta$. $r = 3\cos(2(-\theta)) = 3\cos(-2\theta) = 3\cos(2\theta)$.

The graph is symmetric with respect to the polar axis.

The line $\theta = \dfrac{\pi}{2}$: Replace θ by $\pi - \theta$.

$$r = 3\cos(2(\pi - \theta)) = 3\cos(2\pi - 2\theta)$$
$$= 3(\cos(2\pi)\cos(2\theta) + \sin(2\pi)\sin(2\theta)) = 3(\cos 2\theta + 0) = 3\cos(2\theta)$$

The graph is symmetric with respect to the line $\theta = \dfrac{\pi}{2}$.

The pole: Since the graph is symmetric with respect to both the polar axis and the
line $\theta = \dfrac{\pi}{2}$, it is also symmetric with respect to the pole.

Due to symmetry, assign values to θ from 0 to $\dfrac{\pi}{2}$.

θ	0	$\dfrac{\pi}{6}$	$\dfrac{\pi}{4}$	$\dfrac{\pi}{3}$	$\dfrac{\pi}{2}$
$r = 3\cos(2\theta)$	3	$\dfrac{3}{2}$	0	$-\dfrac{3}{2}$	-3

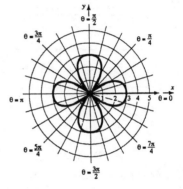

51. $r = 4\sin(5\theta)$ The graph will be a rose with five petals. Check for symmetry:
Polar axis: Replace θ by $-\theta$. $r = 4\sin(5(-\theta)) = 4\sin(-5\theta) = -4\sin(5\theta)$. The test fails.

The line $\theta = \dfrac{\pi}{2}$: Replace θ by $\pi - \theta$.

$$r = 4\sin(5(\pi - \theta)) = 4\sin(5\pi - 5\theta)$$
$$= 4(\sin(5\pi)\cos(5\theta) - \cos(5\pi)\sin(5\theta)) = 4(0 + \sin(5\theta)) = 4\sin(5\theta)$$

The graph is symmetric with respect to the line $\theta = \dfrac{\pi}{2}$.

The pole: Replace r by $-r$. $-r = 4\sin(5\theta)$. The test fails.

Due to symmetry with respect to the line $\theta = \dfrac{\pi}{2}$, assign values to θ from $-\dfrac{\pi}{2}$ to $\dfrac{\pi}{2}$.

θ	$-\dfrac{\pi}{2}$	$-\dfrac{\pi}{3}$	$-\dfrac{\pi}{4}$	$-\dfrac{\pi}{6}$	0	$\dfrac{\pi}{6}$	$\dfrac{\pi}{4}$	$\dfrac{\pi}{3}$	$\dfrac{\pi}{2}$
$r = 4\sin(5\theta)$	-4	$2\sqrt{3} \approx 3.5$	$2\sqrt{2} \approx 2.8$	-2	0	2	$-2\sqrt{2} \approx -2.8$	$-2\sqrt{3} \approx -3.5$	4

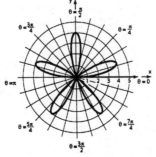

53. $r^2 = 9\cos(2\theta)$ The graph will be a lemniscate. Check for symmetry:

Polar axis: Replace θ by $-\theta$. $r^2 = 9\cos(2(-\theta)) = 9\cos(-2\theta) = 9\cos(2\theta)$.

   The graph is symmetric with respect to the polar axis.

The line $\theta = \dfrac{\pi}{2}$: Replace θ by $\pi - \theta$.

$$r^2 = 9\cos(2(\pi - \theta)) = 9\cos(2\pi - 2\theta)$$
$$= 9(\cos(2\pi)\cos 2\theta + \sin(2\pi)\sin 2\theta) = 9(\cos 2\theta + 0) = 9\cos(2\theta)$$

   The graph is symmetric with respect to the line $\theta = \dfrac{\pi}{2}$.

The pole: Since the graph is symmetric with respect to both the polar axis and the line $\theta = \dfrac{\pi}{2}$, it is also symmetric with respect to the pole.

Due to symmetry, assign values to θ from 0 to $\dfrac{\pi}{2}$.

θ	0	$\dfrac{\pi}{6}$	$\dfrac{\pi}{4}$	$\dfrac{\pi}{3}$	$\dfrac{\pi}{2}$
$r = \pm\sqrt{9\cos(2\theta)}$	± 3	$\pm\dfrac{3\sqrt{2}}{2} \approx \pm 2.1$	0	not defined	not defined

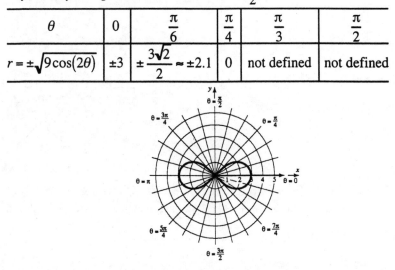

55. $r = 2^{\theta}$ The graph will be a spiral. Check for symmetry:

Polar axis: Replace θ by $-\theta$. $r = 2^{-\theta}$. The test fails.

The line $\theta = \dfrac{\pi}{2}$: Replace θ by $\pi - \theta$. $r = 2^{\pi-\theta}$. The test fails.

The pole: Replace r by $-r$. $-r = 2^{\theta}$. The test fails.

θ	$-\pi$	$-\dfrac{\pi}{2}$	$-\dfrac{\pi}{4}$	0	$\dfrac{\pi}{4}$	$\dfrac{\pi}{2}$	π	$\dfrac{3\pi}{2}$	2π
$r = 2^{\theta}$	0.1	0.3	0.6	1	1.7	3.0	8.8	26.2	77.9

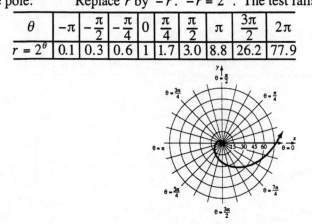

57. $r = 1 - \cos\theta$ The graph will be a cardioid. Check for symmetry:
Polar axis: Replace θ by $-\theta$. The result is $r = 1 - \cos(-\theta) = 1 - \cos\theta$.
   The graph is symmetric with respect to the polar axis.

The line $\theta = \dfrac{\pi}{2}$: Replace θ by $\pi - \theta$.

$$r = 1 - \cos(\pi - \theta) = 1 - (\cos(\pi)\cos\theta + \sin(\pi)\sin\theta)$$

$$= 1 - (-\cos\theta + 0) = 1 + \cos\theta. \quad \text{The test fails}$$

The pole: Replace r by $-r$. $-r = 1 - \cos\theta$. The test fails.
Due to symmetry, assign values to θ from 0 to π.

θ	0	$\dfrac{\pi}{6}$	$\dfrac{\pi}{3}$	$\dfrac{\pi}{2}$	$\dfrac{2\pi}{3}$	$\dfrac{5\pi}{6}$	π
$r = 1 - \cos\theta$	0	$1 - \dfrac{\sqrt{3}}{2} \approx 0.1$	$\dfrac{1}{2}$	1	$\dfrac{3}{2}$	$1 + \dfrac{\sqrt{3}}{2} \approx 1.9$	2

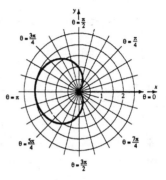

59. $r = 1 - 3\cos\theta$ The graph will be a limacon with an inner loop.
Check for symmetry:
Polar axis: Replace θ by $-\theta$. The result is $r = 1 - 3\cos(-\theta) = 1 - 3\cos\theta$.
   The graph is symmetric with respect to the polar axis.

The line $\theta = \dfrac{\pi}{2}$: Replace θ by $\pi - \theta$.

$$r = 1 - 3\cos(\pi - \theta) = 1 - 3(\cos(\pi)\cos\theta + \sin(\pi)\sin\theta)$$

$$= 1 - 3(-\cos\theta + 0) = 1 + 3\cos\theta$$

   The test fails.

The pole: Replace r by $-r$. $-r = 1 - 3\cos\theta$. The test fails.
Due to symmetry, assign values to θ from 0 to π.

θ	0	$\dfrac{\pi}{6}$	$\dfrac{\pi}{3}$	$\dfrac{\pi}{2}$	$\dfrac{2\pi}{3}$	$\dfrac{5\pi}{6}$	π
$r = 1 - 3\cos\theta$	-2	$1 - \dfrac{3\sqrt{3}}{2} \approx -1.6$	$-\dfrac{1}{2}$	1	$\dfrac{5}{2}$	$1 + \dfrac{3\sqrt{3}}{2} \approx 3.6$	4

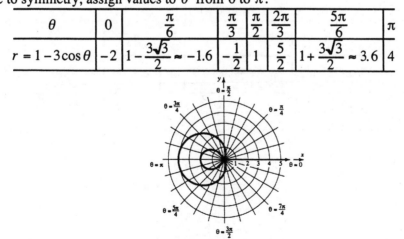

61. The graph is a cardioid whose equation is of the form $r = a + b\cos\theta$.
     The graph contains the point $(6,0)$, so we have $6 = a + b\cos0 \Rightarrow 6 = a + b(1) \Rightarrow 6 = a + b$.

     The graph contains the point $\left(3, \dfrac{\pi}{2}\right)$, so we have $3 = a + b\cos\dfrac{\pi}{2} \Rightarrow 3 = a + b(0) \Rightarrow 3 = a$.

     Substituting $a = 3$ into the first equation yields: $6 = a + b \Rightarrow 6 = 3 + b \Rightarrow 3 = b$.
     Therefore, the graph has equation $r = 3 + 3\cos\theta$.

63. The graph is a limacon without inner loop whose equation is of the form $r = a + b\sin\theta$,
     where $0 < b < a$.
     The graph contains the point $(4,0)$, so we have $4 = a + b\sin0 \Rightarrow 4 = a + b(0) \Rightarrow 4 = a$.

     The graph contains the point $\left(5, \dfrac{\pi}{2}\right)$, so we have $5 = a + b\sin\dfrac{\pi}{2} \Rightarrow 5 = a + b(1) \Rightarrow 5 = a + b$.

     Substituting $a = 4$ into the second equation yields: $5 = a + b \Rightarrow 5 = 4 + b \Rightarrow 1 = b$.
     Therefore, the graph has equation $r = 4 + \sin\theta$.

65. $r = \dfrac{2}{1 - \cos\theta}$ Check for symmetry:

     Polar axis: Replace θ by $-\theta$. The result is $r = \dfrac{2}{1 - \cos(-\theta)} = \dfrac{2}{1 - \cos\theta}$.

          The graph is symmetric with respect to the polar axis.

     The line $\theta = \dfrac{\pi}{2}$: Replace θ by $\pi - \theta$.

     $$r = \frac{2}{1 - \cos(\pi - \theta)} = \frac{2}{1 - (\cos\pi\cos\theta + \sin\pi\sin\theta)}$$

     $$= \frac{2}{1 - (-\cos\theta + 0)} = \frac{2}{1 + \cos\theta}$$

     The test fails.

     The pole: Replace r by $-r$. $-r = \dfrac{2}{1 - \cos\theta}$. The test fails.

     Due to symmetry, assign values to θ from 0 to π.

θ	0	$\dfrac{\pi}{6}$	$\dfrac{\pi}{3}$	$\dfrac{\pi}{2}$	$\dfrac{2\pi}{3}$	$\dfrac{5\pi}{6}$	π
$r = \dfrac{2}{1 - \cos\theta}$	undefined	$\dfrac{2}{1 - \sqrt{3}/2} \approx 14.9$	4	2	$\dfrac{4}{3}$	$\dfrac{2}{1 + \sqrt{3}/2} \approx 1.1$	1

67. $r = \dfrac{1}{3 - 2\cos\theta}$ Check for symmetry:

Polar axis: Replace θ by $-\theta$. The result is $r = \dfrac{1}{3 - 2\cos(-\theta)} = \dfrac{1}{3 - 2\cos\theta}$.

The graph is symmetric with respect to the polar axis.

The line $\theta = \dfrac{\pi}{2}$: Replace θ by $\pi - \theta$.

$$r = \frac{1}{3 - 2\cos(\pi - \theta)} = \frac{1}{3 - 2(\cos\pi\cos\theta + \sin\pi\sin\theta)}$$

$$= \frac{1}{3 - 2(-\cos\theta + 0)} = \frac{1}{3 + 2\cos\theta}$$

The test fails.

The pole: Replace r by $-r$. $-r = \dfrac{1}{3 - 2\cos\theta}$. The test fails.

Due to symmetry, assign values to θ from 0 to π.

θ	0	$\dfrac{\pi}{6}$	$\dfrac{\pi}{3}$	$\dfrac{\pi}{2}$	$\dfrac{2\pi}{3}$	$\dfrac{5\pi}{6}$	π
$r = \dfrac{1}{3 - 2\cos\theta}$	1	$\dfrac{1}{3 - \sqrt{3}} \approx 0.8$	$\dfrac{1}{2}$	$\dfrac{1}{3}$	$\dfrac{1}{4}$	$\dfrac{1}{3 + \sqrt{3}} \approx 0.2$	$\dfrac{1}{5}$

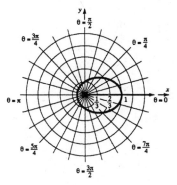

69. $r = \theta, \ \theta \geq 0$ Check for symmetry:

Polar axis: Replace θ by $-\theta$. $r = -\theta$. The test fails.

The line $\theta = \dfrac{\pi}{2}$: Replace θ by $\pi - \theta$. $r = \pi - \theta$. The test fails.

The pole: Replace r by $-r$. $-r = \theta$. The test fails.

θ	0	$\dfrac{\pi}{6}$	$\dfrac{\pi}{3}$	$\dfrac{\pi}{2}$	π	$\dfrac{3\pi}{2}$	2π
$r = \theta$	0	$\dfrac{\pi}{6} \approx 0.5$	$\dfrac{\pi}{3} \approx 1.0$	$\dfrac{\pi}{2} \approx 1.6$	$\pi \approx 3.1$	$\dfrac{3\pi}{2} \approx 4.7$	$2\pi \approx 6.3$

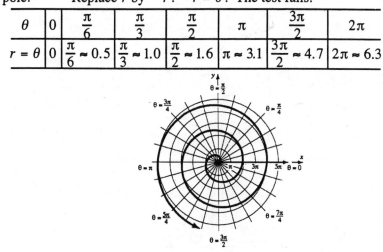

71. $r = \csc\theta - 2 = \dfrac{1}{\sin\theta} - 2,\ \ 0 < \theta < \pi$ Check for symmetry:

Polar axis: Replace θ by $-\theta$. $r = \csc(-\theta) - 2 = -\csc\theta - 2$. The test fails.

The line $\theta = \dfrac{\pi}{2}$: Replace θ by $\pi - \theta$.

$$r = \csc(\pi - \theta) - 2 = \frac{1}{\sin(\pi - \theta)} - 2 = \frac{1}{\sin\pi\cos\theta - \cos\pi\sin\theta} - 2 = \frac{1}{\sin\theta} - 2 = \csc\theta - 2$$

The graph is symmetric with respect to the line $\theta = \dfrac{\pi}{2}$.

The pole: Replace r by $-r$. $-r = \csc\theta - 2$. The test fails.

Due to symmetry, assign values to θ from 0 to $\dfrac{\pi}{2}$.

θ	0	$\dfrac{\pi}{6}$	$\dfrac{\pi}{4}$	$\dfrac{\pi}{3}$	$\dfrac{\pi}{2}$
$r = \csc\theta - 2$	not defined	0	$\sqrt{2} - 2 \approx -0.6$	$\dfrac{2\sqrt{3}}{3} - 2 \approx -0.8$	-1

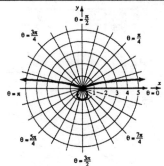

73. $r = \tan\theta,\ \ -\dfrac{\pi}{2} < \theta < \dfrac{\pi}{2}$ Check for symmetry:

Polar axis: Replace θ by $-\theta$. $r = \tan(-\theta) = -\tan\theta$. The test fails.

The line $\theta = \dfrac{\pi}{2}$: Replace θ by $\pi - \theta$.

$$r = \tan(\pi - \theta) = \frac{\tan(\pi) - \tan\theta}{1 + \tan(\pi)\tan\theta} = \frac{-\tan\theta}{1} = -\tan\theta$$

The test fails.

The pole: Replace r by $-r$. $-r = \tan\theta$. The test fails.

θ	$-\dfrac{\pi}{3}$	$-\dfrac{\pi}{4}$	$-\dfrac{\pi}{6}$	0	$\dfrac{\pi}{6}$	$\dfrac{\pi}{4}$	$\dfrac{\pi}{3}$
$r = \tan\theta$	$-\sqrt{3} \approx -1.7$	-1	$-\dfrac{\sqrt{3}}{3} \approx -0.6$	0	$\dfrac{\sqrt{3}}{3} \approx 0.6$	1	$\sqrt{3} \approx 1.7$

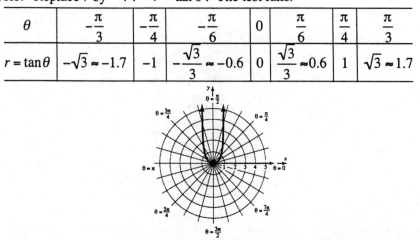

75. Convert the equation to rectangular form:
$$r \sin \theta = a \Rightarrow y = a$$
The graph of $r \sin \theta = a$ is a horizontal line a units above the pole if $a > 0$, and $|a|$ units below the pole if $a < 0$.

77. Convert the equation to rectangular form:
$$r = 2a \sin \theta, \, a > 0$$
$$r^2 = 2ar \sin \theta$$
$$x^2 + y^2 = 2ay \Rightarrow x^2 + y^2 - 2ay = 0 \Rightarrow x^2 + (y - a)^2 = a^2$$
Circle: radius a, center at rectangular coordinates $(0, a)$.

79. Convert the equation to rectangular form:
$$r = 2a \cos \theta, \, a > 0$$
$$r^2 = 2ar \cos \theta$$
$$x^2 + y^2 = 2ax \Rightarrow x^2 - 2ax + y^2 = 0 \Rightarrow (x - a)^2 + y^2 = a^2$$
Circle: radius a, center at rectangular coordinates $(a, 0)$.

81. (a) $r^2 = \cos \theta$: $r^2 = \cos(\pi - \theta) \Rightarrow r^2 = -\cos \theta$ Test fails.
$$(-r)^2 = \cos(-\theta) \Rightarrow r^2 = \cos \theta \quad \text{New test works.}$$
(b) $r^2 = \sin \theta$: $r^2 = \sin(\pi - \theta) \Rightarrow r^2 = \sin \theta$ Test works.
$$(-r)^2 = \sin(-\theta) \Rightarrow r^2 = -\sin \theta \quad \text{New test fails.}$$

83. Answers will vary.

Chapter 5

Polar Coordinates; Vectors

5.3 The Complex Plane; De Moivre's Theorem

1. $-4 + 3i$

3. $\cos\alpha\cos\beta - \sin\alpha\sin\beta$

5. magnitude, modulus, argument

7. three

9. False

11. $r = \sqrt{x^2 + y^2} = \sqrt{1^2 + 1^2} = \sqrt{2}$

$\tan\theta = \dfrac{y}{x} = 1 \ \Rightarrow \ \theta = 45°$

The polar form of $z = 1 + i$ is

$z = r(\cos\theta + i\sin\theta)$

$\quad = \sqrt{2}(\cos 45° + i\sin 45°)$

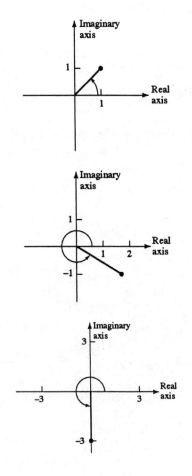

13. $r = \sqrt{x^2 + y^2} = \sqrt{\left(\sqrt{3}\right)^2 + (-1)^2} = \sqrt{4} = 2$

$\tan\theta = \dfrac{y}{x} = \dfrac{-1}{\sqrt{3}} = -\dfrac{\sqrt{3}}{3} \ \Rightarrow \ \theta = 330°$

The polar form of $z = \sqrt{3} - i$ is

$z = r(\cos\theta + i\sin\theta)$

$\quad = 2(\cos 330° + i\sin 330°)$

15. $r = \sqrt{x^2 + y^2} = \sqrt{0^2 + (-3)^2} = \sqrt{9} = 3$

$\tan\theta = \dfrac{y}{x} = \dfrac{-3}{0} \Rightarrow \theta = 270°$

The polar form of $z = -3i$ is

$z = r(\cos\theta + i\sin\theta)$

$\quad = 3(\cos 270° + i\sin 270°)$

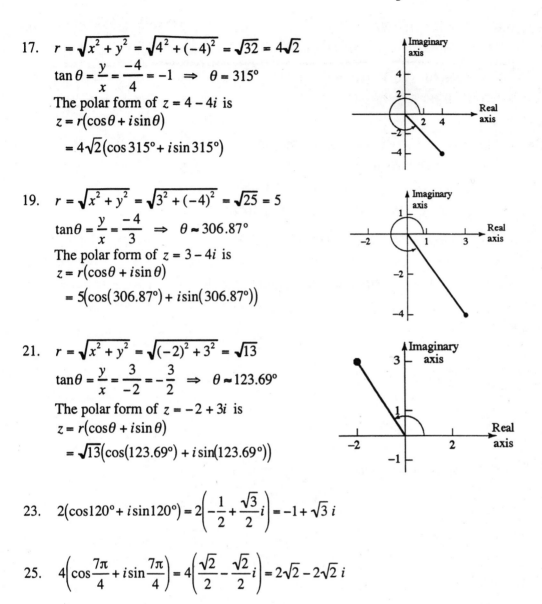

17. $r = \sqrt{x^2 + y^2} = \sqrt{4^2 + (-4)^2} = \sqrt{32} = 4\sqrt{2}$

$\tan\theta = \dfrac{y}{x} = \dfrac{-4}{4} = -1 \implies \theta = 315°$

The polar form of $z = 4 - 4i$ is

$z = r(\cos\theta + i\sin\theta)$

$= 4\sqrt{2}(\cos 315° + i\sin 315°)$

19. $r = \sqrt{x^2 + y^2} = \sqrt{3^2 + (-4)^2} = \sqrt{25} = 5$

$\tan\theta = \dfrac{y}{x} = \dfrac{-4}{3} \implies \theta \approx 306.87°$

The polar form of $z = 3 - 4i$ is

$z = r(\cos\theta + i\sin\theta)$

$= 5(\cos(306.87°) + i\sin(306.87°))$

21. $r = \sqrt{x^2 + y^2} = \sqrt{(-2)^2 + 3^2} = \sqrt{13}$

$\tan\theta = \dfrac{y}{x} = \dfrac{3}{-2} = -\dfrac{3}{2} \implies \theta \approx 123.69°$

The polar form of $z = -2 + 3i$ is

$z = r(\cos\theta + i\sin\theta)$

$= \sqrt{13}(\cos(123.69°) + i\sin(123.69°))$

23. $2(\cos 120° + i\sin 120°) = 2\left(-\dfrac{1}{2} + \dfrac{\sqrt{3}}{2}i\right) = -1 + \sqrt{3}\,i$

25. $4\left(\cos\dfrac{7\pi}{4} + i\sin\dfrac{7\pi}{4}\right) = 4\left(\dfrac{\sqrt{2}}{2} - \dfrac{\sqrt{2}}{2}i\right) = 2\sqrt{2} - 2\sqrt{2}\,i$

27. $3\left(\cos\dfrac{3\pi}{2} + i\sin\dfrac{3\pi}{2}\right) = 3(0 - 1i) = -3i$

29. $0.2(\cos 100° + i\sin 100°) \approx 0.2(-0.1736 + 0.9848i) \approx -0.0347 + 0.1970\,i$

31. $2\left(\cos\dfrac{\pi}{18} + i\sin\dfrac{\pi}{18}\right) \approx 2(0.9848 + 0.1736i) = 1.9696 + 0.3472i$

33. $z \cdot w = 2(\cos 40° + i \sin 40°) \cdot 4(\cos 20° + i \sin 20°)$

$\quad\quad = 2 \cdot 4(\cos(40° + 20°) + i \sin(40° + 20°)) = 8(\cos 60° + i \sin 60°)$

$\dfrac{z}{w} = \dfrac{2(\cos 40° + i \sin 40°)}{4(\cos 20° + i \sin 20°)} = \dfrac{2}{4}(\cos(40° - 20°) + i \sin(40° - 20°))$

$\quad\quad = \dfrac{1}{2}(\cos 20° + i \sin 20°)$

35. $z \cdot w = 3(\cos 130° + i \sin 130°) \cdot 4(\cos 270° + i \sin 270°)$

$\quad\quad = 3 \cdot 4(\cos(130° + 270°) + i \sin(130° + 270°)) = 12(\cos 400° + i \sin 400°)$

$\quad\quad = 12(\cos(400° - 360°) + i \sin(400° - 360°)) = 12(\cos 40° + i \sin 40°)$

$\dfrac{z}{w} = \dfrac{3(\cos 130° + i \sin 130°)}{4(\cos 270° + i \sin 270°)} = \dfrac{3}{4}(\cos(130° - 270°) + i \sin(130° - 270°))$

$\quad\quad = \dfrac{3}{4}(\cos(-140°) + i \sin(-140°)) = \dfrac{3}{4}(\cos(360° - 140°) + i \sin(360° - 140°))$

$\quad\quad = \dfrac{3}{4}(\cos 220° + i \sin 220°)$

37. $z \cdot w = 2\left(\cos \dfrac{\pi}{8} + i \sin \dfrac{\pi}{8}\right) \cdot 2\left(\cos \dfrac{\pi}{10} + i \sin \dfrac{\pi}{10}\right) = 2 \cdot 2\left(\cos\left(\dfrac{\pi}{8} + \dfrac{\pi}{10}\right) + i \sin\left(\dfrac{\pi}{8} + \dfrac{\pi}{10}\right)\right)$

$\quad\quad = 4\left(\cos \dfrac{9\pi}{40} + i \sin \dfrac{9\pi}{40}\right)$

$\dfrac{z}{w} = \dfrac{2\left(\cos \dfrac{\pi}{8} + i \sin \dfrac{\pi}{8}\right)}{2\left(\cos \dfrac{\pi}{10} + i \sin \dfrac{\pi}{10}\right)} = \dfrac{2}{2}\left(\cos\left(\dfrac{\pi}{8} - \dfrac{\pi}{10}\right) + i \sin\left(\dfrac{\pi}{8} - \dfrac{\pi}{10}\right)\right) = \cos \dfrac{\pi}{40} + i \sin \dfrac{\pi}{40}$

39. $z = 2 + 2i \quad r = \sqrt{2^2 + 2^2} = \sqrt{8} = 2\sqrt{2} \quad \tan \theta = \dfrac{2}{2} = 1 \Rightarrow \theta = 45°$

$z = 2\sqrt{2}(\cos 45° + i \sin 45°)$

$w = \sqrt{3} - i \quad r = \sqrt{\left(\sqrt{3}\right)^2 + (-1)^2} = \sqrt{4} = 2 \quad \tan \theta = \dfrac{-1}{\sqrt{3}} = -\dfrac{\sqrt{3}}{3} \Rightarrow \theta = 330°$

$w = 2(\cos 330° + i \sin 330°)$

$z \cdot w = 2\sqrt{2}(\cos 45° + i \sin 45°) \cdot 2(\cos 330° + i \sin 330°)$

$\quad\quad = 2\sqrt{2} \cdot 2(\cos(45° + 330°) + i \sin(45° + 330°)) = 4\sqrt{2}(\cos 375° + i \sin 375°)$

$\quad\quad = 4\sqrt{2}(\cos(375° - 360°) + i \sin(375° - 360°)) = 4\sqrt{2}(\cos 15° + i \sin 15°)$

$\dfrac{z}{w} = \dfrac{2\sqrt{2}(\cos 45° + i \sin 45°)}{2(\cos 330° + i \sin 330°)} = \dfrac{2\sqrt{2}}{2}(\cos(45° - 330°) + i \sin(45° - 330°))$

$\quad\quad = \sqrt{2}(\cos(-285°) + i \sin(-285°)) = \sqrt{2}(\cos(360° - 285°) + i \sin(360° - 285°))$

$\quad\quad = \sqrt{2}(\cos 75° + i \sin 75°)$

41. $\left[4(\cos 40° + i\sin 40°)\right]^3 = 4^3\left(\cos(3 \cdot 40°) + i\sin(3 \cdot 40°)\right) = 64(\cos 120° + i\sin 120°)$

$$= 64\left(-\frac{1}{2} + \frac{\sqrt{3}}{2}i\right) = -32 + 32\sqrt{3}\,i$$

43. $\left[2\left(\cos\frac{\pi}{10} + i\sin\frac{\pi}{10}\right)\right]^5 = 2^5\left(\cos\left(5 \cdot \frac{\pi}{10}\right) + i\sin\left(5 \cdot \frac{\pi}{10}\right)\right) = 32\left(\cos\frac{\pi}{2} + i\sin\frac{\pi}{2}\right)$

$$= 32(0 + 1i) = 0 + 32\,i$$

45. $\left[\sqrt{3}(\cos 10° + i\sin 10°)\right]^6 = \left(\sqrt{3}\right)^6\left(\cos(6 \cdot 10°) + i\sin(6 \cdot 10°)\right) = 27(\cos 60° + i\sin 60°)$

$$= 27\left(\frac{1}{2} + \frac{\sqrt{3}}{2}i\right) = \frac{27}{2} + \frac{27\sqrt{3}}{2}i$$

47. $\left[\sqrt{5}\left(\cos\frac{3\pi}{16} + i\sin\frac{3\pi}{16}\right)\right]^4 = \left(\sqrt{5}\right)^4\left(\cos\left(4 \cdot \frac{3\pi}{16}\right) + i\sin\left(4 \cdot \frac{3\pi}{16}\right)\right)$

$$= 25\left(\cos\frac{3\pi}{4} + i\sin\frac{3\pi}{4}\right) = 25\left(-\frac{\sqrt{2}}{2} + \frac{\sqrt{2}}{2}i\right) = -\frac{25\sqrt{2}}{2} + \frac{25\sqrt{2}}{2}i$$

49. $1 - i$ $r = \sqrt{1^2 + (-1)^2} = \sqrt{2}$ $\tan\theta = \frac{-1}{1} = -1 \Rightarrow \theta = \frac{7\pi}{4}$

$$1 - i = \sqrt{2}\left(\cos\frac{7\pi}{4} + i\sin\frac{7\pi}{4}\right)$$

$$(1-i)^5 = \left[\sqrt{2}\left(\cos\frac{7\pi}{4} + i\sin\frac{7\pi}{4}\right)\right]^5 = \left(\sqrt{2}\right)^5\left(\cos\left(5 \cdot \frac{7\pi}{4}\right) + i\sin\left(5 \cdot \frac{7\pi}{4}\right)\right)$$

$$= 4\sqrt{2}\left(\cos\frac{35\pi}{4} + i\sin\frac{35\pi}{4}\right) = 4\sqrt{2}\left(-\frac{\sqrt{2}}{2} + \frac{\sqrt{2}}{2}i\right) = -4 + 4\,i$$

51. $\sqrt{2} - i$ $r = \sqrt{\left(\sqrt{2}\right)^2 + (-1)^2} = \sqrt{3}$ $\tan\theta = \frac{-1}{\sqrt{2}} = -\frac{\sqrt{2}}{2} \Rightarrow \theta \approx 324.7°$

$$\sqrt{2} - i \approx \sqrt{3}\left(\cos(324.7°) + i\sin(324.7°)\right)$$

$$\left(\sqrt{2} - i\right)^6 \approx \left[\sqrt{3}\left(\cos(324.7°) + i\sin(324.7°)\right)\right]^6 = \left(\sqrt{3}\right)^6\left(\cos(6 \cdot 324.7°) + i\sin(6 \cdot 324.7°)\right)$$

$$= 27\left(\cos(1948.2°) + i\sin(1948.2°)\right) \approx 27(-0.8499 + 0.5270\,i)$$

$$= -22.9473 + 14.229\,i$$

53. $1+i$ $r = \sqrt{1^2 + 1^2} = \sqrt{2}$ $\tan\theta = \dfrac{1}{1} = 1 \Rightarrow \theta = 45°$

$1 + i = \sqrt{2}\left(\cos 45° + i\sin 45°\right)$

The three complex cube roots of $1 + i = \sqrt{2}\left(\cos 45° + i\sin 45°\right)$ are:

$$z_k = \sqrt[3]{\sqrt{2}}\left[\cos\left(\frac{45°}{3} + \frac{360°k}{3}\right) + i\sin\left(\frac{45°}{3} + \frac{360°k}{3}\right)\right]$$

$$= \sqrt[6]{2}\left[\cos(15° + 120°k) + i\sin(15° + 120°k)\right]$$

$z_0 = \sqrt[6]{2}\left[\cos(15° + 120°\cdot 0) + i\sin(15° + 120°\cdot 0)\right] = \sqrt[6]{2}\left(\cos 15° + i\sin 15°\right)$

$z_1 = \sqrt[6]{2}\left[\cos(15° + 120°\cdot 1) + i\sin(15° + 120°\cdot 1)\right] = \sqrt[6]{2}\left(\cos 135° + i\sin 135°\right)$

$z_2 = \sqrt[6]{2}\left[\cos(15° + 120°\cdot 2) + i\sin(15° + 120°\cdot 2)\right] = \sqrt[6]{2}\left(\cos 255° + i\sin 255°\right)$

55. $4 - 4\sqrt{3}\,i$ $r = \sqrt{4^2 + \left(-4\sqrt{3}\right)^2} = \sqrt{64} = 8$ $\tan\theta = \dfrac{-4\sqrt{3}}{4} = -\sqrt{3} \Rightarrow \theta = 300°$

$4 - 4\sqrt{3}\,i = 8\left(\cos 300° + i\sin 300°\right)$

The four complex fourth roots of $4 - 4\sqrt{3}\,i = 8\left(\cos 300° + i\sin 300°\right)$ are:

$$z_k = \sqrt[4]{8}\left[\cos\left(\frac{300°}{4} + \frac{360°k}{4}\right) + i\sin\left(\frac{300°}{4} + \frac{360°k}{4}\right)\right]$$

$$= \sqrt[4]{8}\left[\cos(75° + 90°k) + i\sin(75° + 90°k)\right]$$

$z_0 = \sqrt[4]{8}\left[\cos(75° + 90°\cdot 0) + i\sin(75° + 90°\cdot 0)\right] = \sqrt[4]{8}\left(\cos 75° + i\sin 75°\right)$

$z_1 = \sqrt[4]{8}\left[\cos(75° + 90°\cdot 1) + i\sin(75° + 90°\cdot 1)\right] = \sqrt[4]{8}\left(\cos 165° + i\sin 165°\right)$

$z_2 = \sqrt[4]{8}\left[\cos(75° + 90°\cdot 2) + i\sin(75° + 90°\cdot 2)\right] = \sqrt[4]{8}\left(\cos 255° + i\sin 255°\right)$

$z_3 = \sqrt[4]{8}\left[\cos(75° + 90°\cdot 3) + i\sin(75° + 90°\cdot 3)\right] = \sqrt[4]{8}\left(\cos 345° + i\sin 345°\right)$

57. $-16i$ $r = \sqrt{0^2 + \left(-16\right)^2} = \sqrt{256} = 16$ $\tan\theta = \dfrac{-16}{0} \Rightarrow \theta = 270°$

$-16i = 16\left(\cos 270° + i\sin 270°\right)$

The four complex fourth roots of $-16i = 16\left(\cos 270° + i\sin 270°\right)$ are:

$$z_k = \sqrt[4]{16}\left[\cos\left(\frac{270°}{4} + \frac{360°k}{4}\right) + i\sin\left(\frac{270°}{4} + \frac{360°k}{4}\right)\right]$$

$$= 2\left[\cos(67.5° + 90°k) + i\sin(67.5° + 90°k)\right]$$

$z_0 = 2\left[\cos(67.5° + 90°\cdot 0) + i\sin(67.5° + 90°\cdot 0)\right] = 2\left(\cos(67.5°) + i\sin(67.5°)\right)$

$z_1 = 2\left[\cos(67.5° + 90°\cdot 1) + i\sin(67.5° + 90°\cdot 1)\right] = 2\left(\cos(157.5°) + i\sin(157.5°)\right)$

$z_2 = 2\left[\cos(67.5° + 90°\cdot 2) + i\sin(67.5° + 90°\cdot 2)\right] = 2\left(\cos(247.5°) + i\sin(247.5°)\right)$

$z_3 = 2\left[\cos(67.5° + 90°\cdot 3) + i\sin(67.5° + 90°\cdot 3)\right] = 2\left(\cos(337.5°) + i\sin(337.5°)\right)$

59. i $r = \sqrt{0^2 + 1^2} = \sqrt{1} = 1$ $\tan\theta = \dfrac{1}{0} \Rightarrow \theta = 90°$

$i = 1(\cos 90° + i\sin 90°)$

The five complex fifth roots of $i = 1(\cos 90° + i\sin 90°)$ are:

$$z_k = \sqrt[5]{1}\left[\cos\left(\frac{90°}{5} + \frac{360°k}{5}\right) + i\sin\left(\frac{90°}{5} + \frac{360°k}{5}\right)\right]$$

$$= 1\left[\cos(18° + 72°k) + i\sin(18° + 72°k)\right]$$

$z_0 = 1\left[\cos(18° + 72°\cdot 0) + i\sin(18° + 72°\cdot 0)\right] = \cos 18° + i\sin 18°$

$z_1 = 1\left[\cos(18° + 72°\cdot 1) + i\sin(18° + 72°\cdot 1)\right] = \cos 90° + i\sin 90°$

$z_2 = 1\left[\cos(18° + 72°\cdot 2) + i\sin(18° + 72°\cdot 2)\right] = \cos 162° + i\sin 162°$

$z_3 = 1\left[\cos(18° + 72°\cdot 3) + i\sin(18° + 72°\cdot 3)\right] = \cos 234° + i\sin 234°$

$z_4 = 1\left[\cos(18° + 72°\cdot 4) + i\sin(18° + 72°\cdot 4)\right] = \cos 306° + i\sin 306°$

61. $1 = 1 + 0i$ $r = \sqrt{1^2 + 0^2} = \sqrt{1} = 1$ $\tan\theta = \dfrac{0}{1} = 0 \Rightarrow \theta = 0°$

$1 + 0i = 1(\cos 0° + i\sin 0°)$

The four complex fourth roots of unity are:

$$z_k = \sqrt[4]{1}\left[\cos\left(\frac{0°}{4} + \frac{360°k}{4}\right) + i\sin\left(\frac{0°}{4} + \frac{360°k}{4}\right)\right]$$

$$= 1\left[\cos(90°k) + i\sin(90°k)\right]$$

$z_0 = \cos(90°\cdot 0) + i\sin(90°\cdot 0) = \cos 0° + i\sin 0° = 1 + 0i = 1$

$z_1 = \cos(90°\cdot 1) + i\sin(90°\cdot 1) = \cos 90° + i\sin 90° = 0 + 1i = i$

$z_2 = \cos(90°\cdot 2) + i\sin(90°\cdot 2) = \cos 180° + i\sin 180° = -1 + 0i = -1$

$z_3 = \cos(90°\cdot 3) + i\sin(90°\cdot 3) = \cos 270° + i\sin 270° = 0 - 1i = -i$

The complex fourth roots of unity are: $1, i, -1, -i$.

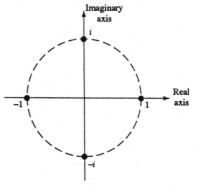

63. Let $w = r(\cos\theta + i\sin\theta)$ be a complex number. If $w \neq 0$, there are n distinct nth roots of w, given by the formula:

$$z_k = \sqrt[n]{r}\left(\cos\left(\frac{\theta}{n} + \frac{2k\pi}{n}\right) + i\sin\left(\frac{\theta}{n} + \frac{2k\pi}{n}\right)\right), \text{ where } k = 0, 1, 2, ..., n-1$$

$|z_k| = \sqrt[n]{r}$ for all k

65. Examining the formula for the distinct complex nth roots of the complex number $w = r(\cos\theta + i\sin\theta)$,

$$z_k = \sqrt[n]{r}\left(\cos\left(\frac{\theta}{n} + \frac{2k\pi}{n}\right) + i\sin\left(\frac{\theta}{n} + \frac{2k\pi}{n}\right)\right), \text{where } k = 0, 1, 2, ..., n-1$$

we see that the z_k are spaced apart by an angle of $\dfrac{2\pi}{n}$.

Polar Coordinates; Vectors

5.4   Vectors

1.   unit

3.   horizontal, vertical

5.   True

7.   **v + w**

9.   **3v**

11.   **v − w**

13.   **3v + u − 2w**

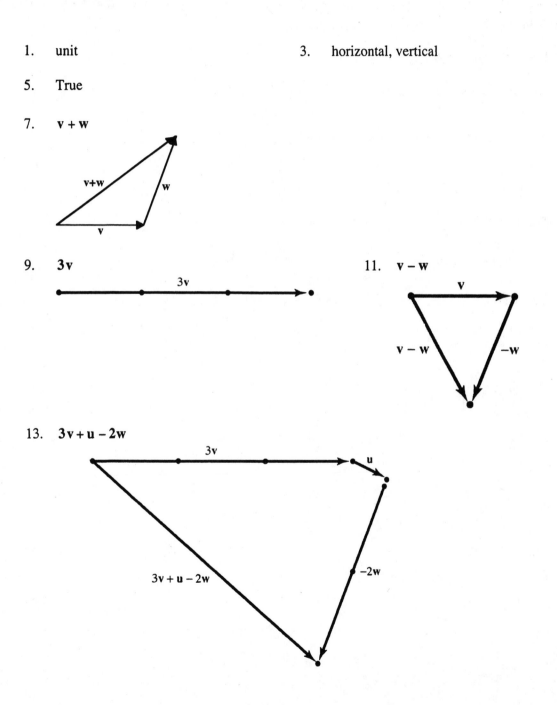

15.   True

17.   False $C = -F + E - D$

19.   False $D - E = H + G$

21.   True

23.   If $\|\mathbf{v}\| = 4$, then $\|3\mathbf{v}\| = |3| \|\mathbf{v}\| = 3(4) = 12$.

25. $P = (0, 0)$, $Q = (3, 4)$ $\mathbf{v} = (3 - 0)\mathbf{i} + (4 - 0)\mathbf{j} = 3\mathbf{i} + 4\mathbf{j}$

27. $P = (3, 2)$, $Q = (5, 6)$ $\mathbf{v} = (5 - 3)\mathbf{i} + (6 - 2)\mathbf{j} = 2\mathbf{i} + 4\mathbf{j}$

29. $P = (-2, -1)$, $Q = (6, -2)$ $\mathbf{v} = (6 - (-2))\mathbf{i} + (-2 - (-1))\mathbf{j} = 8\mathbf{i} - \mathbf{j}$

31. $P = (1, 0)$, $Q = (0, 1)$ $\mathbf{v} = (0 - 1)\mathbf{i} + (1 - 0)\mathbf{j} = -\mathbf{i} + \mathbf{j}$

33.   For $\mathbf{v} = 3\mathbf{i} - 4\mathbf{j}$, $\|\mathbf{v}\| = \sqrt{3^2 + (-4)^2} = \sqrt{25} = 5$

35.   For $\mathbf{v} = \mathbf{i} - \mathbf{j}$, $\|\mathbf{v}\| = \sqrt{1^2 + (-1)^2} = \sqrt{2}$

37.   For $\mathbf{v} = -2\mathbf{i} + 3\mathbf{j}$, $\|\mathbf{v}\| = \sqrt{(-2)^2 + 3^2} = \sqrt{13}$

39. $2\mathbf{v} + 3\mathbf{w} = 2(3\mathbf{i} - 5\mathbf{j}) + 3(-2\mathbf{i} + 3\mathbf{j}) = 6\mathbf{i} - 10\mathbf{j} - 6\mathbf{i} + 9\mathbf{j} = -\mathbf{j}$

41. $\|\mathbf{v} - \mathbf{w}\| = \|(3\mathbf{i} - 5\mathbf{j}) - (-2\mathbf{i} + 3\mathbf{j})\| = \|5\mathbf{i} - 8\mathbf{j}\| = \sqrt{5^2 + (-8)^2} = \sqrt{89}$

43. $\|\mathbf{v}\| - \|\mathbf{w}\| = \|3\mathbf{i} - 5\mathbf{j}\| - \|-2\mathbf{i} + 3\mathbf{j}\| = \sqrt{3^2 + (-5)^2} - \sqrt{(-2)^2 + 3^2} = \sqrt{34} - \sqrt{13}$

45. $\mathbf{u} = \dfrac{\mathbf{v}}{\|\mathbf{v}\|} = \dfrac{5\mathbf{i}}{\|5\mathbf{i}\|} = \dfrac{5\mathbf{i}}{\sqrt{25 + 0}} = \dfrac{5\mathbf{i}}{5} = \mathbf{i}$

47. $\mathbf{u} = \dfrac{\mathbf{v}}{\|\mathbf{v}\|} = \dfrac{3\mathbf{i} - 4\mathbf{j}}{\|3\mathbf{i} - 4\mathbf{j}\|} = \dfrac{3\mathbf{i} - 4\mathbf{j}}{\sqrt{3^2 + (-4)^2}} = \dfrac{3\mathbf{i} - 4\mathbf{j}}{\sqrt{25}} = \dfrac{3\mathbf{i} - 4\mathbf{j}}{5} = \dfrac{3}{5}\mathbf{i} - \dfrac{4}{5}\mathbf{j}$

49. $\mathbf{u} = \dfrac{\mathbf{v}}{\|\mathbf{v}\|} = \dfrac{\mathbf{i} - \mathbf{j}}{\|\mathbf{i} - \mathbf{j}\|} = \dfrac{\mathbf{i} - \mathbf{j}}{\sqrt{1^2 + (-1)^2}} = \dfrac{\mathbf{i} - \mathbf{j}}{\sqrt{2}} = \dfrac{1}{\sqrt{2}}\mathbf{i} - \dfrac{1}{\sqrt{2}}\mathbf{j} = \dfrac{\sqrt{2}}{2}\mathbf{i} - \dfrac{\sqrt{2}}{2}\mathbf{j}$

51. Let $\mathbf{v} = a\mathbf{i} + b\mathbf{j}$. We want $\|\mathbf{v}\| = 4$ and $a = 2b$.

$\|\mathbf{v}\| = \sqrt{a^2 + b^2} = \sqrt{(2b)^2 + b^2} = \sqrt{5b^2}$

$\sqrt{5b^2} = 4 \;\Rightarrow\; 5b^2 = 16 \;\Rightarrow\; b^2 = \dfrac{16}{5} \;\Rightarrow\; b = \pm\sqrt{\dfrac{16}{5}} = \pm\dfrac{4}{\sqrt{5}} = \pm\dfrac{4\sqrt{5}}{5}$

$a = 2b = \pm\dfrac{8\sqrt{5}}{5}$

$\mathbf{v} = \dfrac{8\sqrt{5}}{5}\mathbf{i} + \dfrac{4\sqrt{5}}{5}\mathbf{j}$ or $\mathbf{v} = -\dfrac{8\sqrt{5}}{5}\mathbf{i} - \dfrac{4\sqrt{5}}{5}\mathbf{j}$

53. $\mathbf{v} = 2\mathbf{i} - \mathbf{j},\; \mathbf{w} = x\mathbf{i} + 3\mathbf{j}\quad \|\mathbf{v} + \mathbf{w}\| = 5$

$\|\mathbf{v} + \mathbf{w}\| = \|2\mathbf{i} - \mathbf{j} + x\mathbf{i} + 3\mathbf{j}\| = \|(2 + x)\mathbf{i} + 2\mathbf{j}\| = \sqrt{(2 + x)^2 + 2^2}$

$\qquad = \sqrt{x^2 + 4x + 4 + 4} = \sqrt{x^2 + 4x + 8}$

Solve for x:

$\sqrt{x^2 + 4x + 8} = 5 \Rightarrow x^2 + 4x + 8 = 25 \Rightarrow x^2 + 4x - 17 = 0$

$x = \dfrac{-4 \pm \sqrt{16 - 4(1)(-17)}}{2(1)} = \dfrac{-4 \pm \sqrt{84}}{2} = \dfrac{-4 \pm 2\sqrt{21}}{2} = -2 \pm \sqrt{21}$

$x = -2 + \sqrt{21} \approx 2.58$ or $x = -2 - \sqrt{21} \approx -6.58$

55. $\|\mathbf{v}\| = 5,\;\; \alpha = 60°$

$\mathbf{v} = \|\mathbf{v}\|(\cos\alpha\,\mathbf{i} + \sin\alpha\,\mathbf{j}) = 5(\cos(60°)\mathbf{i} + \sin(60°)\mathbf{j}) = 5\left(\dfrac{1}{2}\mathbf{i} + \dfrac{\sqrt{3}}{2}\mathbf{j}\right) = \dfrac{5}{2}\mathbf{i} + \dfrac{5\sqrt{3}}{2}\mathbf{j}$

57. $\|\mathbf{v}\| = 14,\;\; \alpha = 120°$

$\mathbf{v} = \|\mathbf{v}\|(\cos\alpha\,\mathbf{i} + \sin\alpha\,\mathbf{j}) = 14(\cos(120°)\mathbf{i} + \sin(120°)\mathbf{j}) = 14\left(-\dfrac{1}{2}\mathbf{i} + \dfrac{\sqrt{3}}{2}\mathbf{j}\right) = -7\mathbf{i} + 7\sqrt{3}\mathbf{j}$

59. $\|\mathbf{v}\| = 25,\;\; \alpha = 330°$

$\mathbf{v} = \|\mathbf{v}\|(\cos\alpha\,\mathbf{i} + \sin\alpha\,\mathbf{j}) = 25(\cos(330°)\mathbf{i} + \sin(330°)\mathbf{j}) = 25\left(\dfrac{\sqrt{3}}{2}\mathbf{i} - \dfrac{1}{2}\mathbf{j}\right) = \dfrac{25\sqrt{3}}{2}\mathbf{i} - \dfrac{25}{2}\mathbf{j}$

61. $\mathbf{F} = 40(\cos(30°)\mathbf{i} + \sin(30°)\mathbf{j}) = 40\left(\dfrac{\sqrt{3}}{2}\mathbf{i} + \dfrac{1}{2}\mathbf{j}\right) = 20\sqrt{3}\,\mathbf{i} + 20\mathbf{j} = 20\left(\sqrt{3}\,\mathbf{i} + \mathbf{j}\right)$

63. $\mathbf{F}_1 = 40(\cos(30°)\mathbf{i} + \sin(30°)\mathbf{j}) = 40\left(\dfrac{\sqrt{3}}{2}\mathbf{i} + \dfrac{1}{2}\mathbf{j}\right) = 20\sqrt{3}\mathbf{i} + 20\mathbf{j}$

$\mathbf{F}_2 = 60(\cos(-45°)\mathbf{i} + \sin(-45°)\mathbf{j}) = 60\left(\dfrac{\sqrt{2}}{2}\mathbf{i} - \dfrac{\sqrt{2}}{2}\mathbf{j}\right) = 30\sqrt{2}\,\mathbf{i} - 30\sqrt{2}\mathbf{j}$

$\mathbf{F}_1 + \mathbf{F}_2 = 20\sqrt{3}\mathbf{i} + 20\mathbf{j} + 30\sqrt{2}\,\mathbf{i} - 30\sqrt{2}\mathbf{j} = \left(20\sqrt{3} + 30\sqrt{2}\right)\mathbf{i} + \left(20 - 30\sqrt{2}\right)\mathbf{j}$

magnitude of $\mathbf{F}_1 + \mathbf{F}_2 = \sqrt{\left(20\sqrt{3} + 30\sqrt{2}\right)^2 + \left(20 - 30\sqrt{2}\right)^2} \approx 80.26$ newtons

direction of $\mathbf{F}_1 + \mathbf{F}_2 = \tan^{-1}\left(\dfrac{20 - 30\sqrt{2}}{20\sqrt{3} + 30\sqrt{2}}\right) \approx -16.22°$

65. Let $\mathbf{F}_1$ be the tension on the left cable and $\mathbf{F}_2$ be the tension on the right cable.
Let $\mathbf{F}_3$ represent the force of the weight of the box.

$\mathbf{F}_1 = \|\mathbf{F}_1\|\left(\cos(155°)\mathbf{i} + \sin(155°)\mathbf{j}\right) \approx \|\mathbf{F}_1\|\left(-0.9063\mathbf{i} + 0.4226\mathbf{j}\right)$

$\mathbf{F}_2 = \|\mathbf{F}_2\|\left(\cos(40°)\mathbf{i} + \sin(40°)\mathbf{j}\right) \approx \|\mathbf{F}_2\|\left(0.7660\mathbf{i} + 0.6428\mathbf{j}\right)$

$\mathbf{F}_3 = -1000\mathbf{j}$

For equilibrium, the sum of the force vectors must be zero.

$\mathbf{F}_1 + \mathbf{F}_2 + \mathbf{F}_3 = -0.9063\|\mathbf{F}_1\|\mathbf{i} + 0.4226\|\mathbf{F}_1\|\mathbf{j} + 0.7660\|\mathbf{F}_2\|\mathbf{i} + 0.6428\|\mathbf{F}_2\|\mathbf{j} - 1000\mathbf{j}$

$\qquad = \left(-0.9063\|\mathbf{F}_1\| + 0.7660\|\mathbf{F}_2\|\right)\mathbf{i} + \left(0.4226\|\mathbf{F}_1\| + 0.6428\|\mathbf{F}_2\| - 1000\right)\mathbf{j} = 0$

Set the $\mathbf{i}$ and $\mathbf{j}$ components equal to zero and solve:

$\begin{cases} -0.9063\|\mathbf{F}_1\| + 0.7660\|\mathbf{F}_2\| = 0 \;\Rightarrow\; \|\mathbf{F}_2\| = \dfrac{0.9063}{0.7660}\|\mathbf{F}_1\| = 1.1832\|\mathbf{F}_1\| \\[2mm] 0.4226\|\mathbf{F}_1\| + 0.6428\|\mathbf{F}_2\| - 1000 = 0 \end{cases}$

$0.4226\|\mathbf{F}_1\| + 0.6428\left(1.1832\|\mathbf{F}_1\|\right) - 1000 = 0 \Rightarrow 1.1832\|\mathbf{F}_1\| = 1000$

$\|\mathbf{F}_1\| = 845.17$ pounds

$\|\mathbf{F}_2\| = 1.1832(845.17) = 1000$ pounds

The tension in the left cable is about 845.17 pounds and the tension in the right cable is about 1000 pounds.

67. Let $\mathbf{F}_1$ be the tension on the left end of the rope and $\mathbf{F}_2$ be the tension on the right end of the rope. Let $\mathbf{F}_3$ represent the force of the weight of the tightrope walker.

$\mathbf{F}_1 = \|\mathbf{F}_1\|\left(\cos(175.8°)\mathbf{i} + \sin(175.8°)\mathbf{j}\right) \approx \|\mathbf{F}_1\|\left(-0.9973\mathbf{i} + 0.0732\mathbf{j}\right)$

$\mathbf{F}_2 = \|\mathbf{F}_2\|\left(\cos(3.7°)\mathbf{i} + \sin(3.7°)\mathbf{j}\right) \approx \|\mathbf{F}_2\|\left(0.9979\mathbf{i} + 0.0645\mathbf{j}\right)$

$\mathbf{F}_3 = -150\mathbf{j}$

For equilibrium, the sum of the force vectors must be zero.

$\mathbf{F}_1 + \mathbf{F}_2 + \mathbf{F}_3 = -0.9973\|\mathbf{F}_1\|\mathbf{i} + 0.0732\|\mathbf{F}_1\|\mathbf{j} + 0.9979\|\mathbf{F}_2\|\mathbf{i} + 0.0645\|\mathbf{F}_2\|\mathbf{j} - 150\mathbf{j}$

$\qquad = \left(-0.9973\|\mathbf{F}_1\| + 0.9979\|\mathbf{F}_2\|\right)\mathbf{i} + \left(0.0732\|\mathbf{F}_1\| + 0.0645\|\mathbf{F}_2\| - 150\right)\mathbf{j} = 0$

Set the **i** and **j** components equal to zero and solve:

$$\begin{cases} -0.9973\|\mathbf{F}_1\| + 0.9979\|\mathbf{F}_2\| = 0 \;\Rightarrow\; \|\mathbf{F}_2\| = \dfrac{0.9973}{0.9979}\|\mathbf{F}_1\| = 0.9994\|\mathbf{F}_1\| \\[2mm] 0.0732\|\mathbf{F}_1\| + 0.0645\|\mathbf{F}_2\| - 150 = 0 \end{cases}$$

$$0.0732\|\mathbf{F}_1\| + 0.0645\big(0.9994\|\mathbf{F}_1\|\big) - 150 = 0 \Rightarrow 0.1377\|\mathbf{F}_1\| = 150$$

$$\|\mathbf{F}_1\| = 1089.3 \text{ pounds}; \quad \|\mathbf{F}_2\| = 0.9994(1089.3) = 1088.6 \text{ pounds}$$

The tension in the left end of the rope is about 1089.3 pounds and the tension in the right end of the rope is about 1088.6 pounds.

69. The given forces are: $\mathbf{F}_1 = -3\mathbf{i}; \quad \mathbf{F}_2 = -\mathbf{i} + 4\mathbf{j}; \quad \mathbf{F}_3 = 4\mathbf{i} - 2\mathbf{j}; \quad \mathbf{F}_4 = -4\mathbf{j}$

A vector $\mathbf{v} = a\mathbf{i} + b\mathbf{j}$ needs to be added for equilibrium. Find vector $\mathbf{v} = a\mathbf{i} + b\mathbf{j}$:

$$\mathbf{F}_1 + \mathbf{F}_2 + \mathbf{F}_3 + \mathbf{F}_4 + \mathbf{v} = 0$$

$$-3\mathbf{i} + (-\mathbf{i} + 4\mathbf{j}) + (4\mathbf{i} - 2\mathbf{j}) + (-4\mathbf{j}) + (a\mathbf{i} + b\mathbf{j}) = 0$$

$$0\mathbf{i} - 2\mathbf{j} + (a\mathbf{i} + b\mathbf{j}) = 0$$

$$a\mathbf{i} + (-2 + b)\mathbf{j} = 0$$

$$a = 0$$

$$-2 + b = 0 \;\Rightarrow\; b = 2$$

Therefore, $\mathbf{v} = 2\mathbf{j}$.

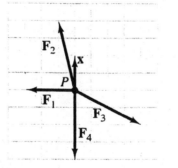

71. Answers will vary.

Polar Coordinates; Vectors

5.5   The Dot Product

1. $c^2 = a^2 + b^2 - 2ab\cos\gamma$ 3.   parallel

5.   True

7. $\mathbf{v} = \mathbf{i} - \mathbf{j},\quad \mathbf{w} = \mathbf{i} + \mathbf{j}$
   (a) $\mathbf{v} \cdot \mathbf{w} = 1(1) + (-1)(1) = 1 - 1 = 0$
   (b) $\cos\theta = \dfrac{\mathbf{v} \cdot \mathbf{w}}{\|\mathbf{v}\|\|\mathbf{w}\|} = \dfrac{0}{\sqrt{1^2 + (-1)^2}\sqrt{1^2 + 1^2}} = \dfrac{0}{\sqrt{2}\sqrt{2}} = \dfrac{0}{2} = 0 \Rightarrow \theta = 90°$
   (c)   The vectors are orthogonal.

9. $\mathbf{v} = 2\mathbf{i} + \mathbf{j},\quad \mathbf{w} = \mathbf{i} + 2\mathbf{j}$
   (a) $\mathbf{v} \cdot \mathbf{w} = 2(1) + 1(2) = 2 + 2 = 4$
   (b) $\cos\theta = \dfrac{\mathbf{v} \cdot \mathbf{w}}{\|\mathbf{v}\|\|\mathbf{w}\|} = \dfrac{4}{\sqrt{2^2 + 1^2}\sqrt{1^2 + 2^2}} = \dfrac{4}{\sqrt{5}\sqrt{5}} = \dfrac{4}{5} = 0.80 \Rightarrow \theta \approx 36.87°$
   (c)   The vectors are neither parallel nor orthogonal.

11. $\mathbf{v} = \sqrt{3}\,\mathbf{i} - \mathbf{j},\quad \mathbf{w} = \mathbf{i} + \mathbf{j}$
   (a) $\mathbf{v} \cdot \mathbf{w} = \sqrt{3}(1) + (-1)(1) = \sqrt{3} - 1$
   (b) $\cos\theta = \dfrac{\mathbf{v} \cdot \mathbf{w}}{\|\mathbf{v}\|\|\mathbf{w}\|} = \dfrac{\sqrt{3} - 1}{\sqrt{\left(\sqrt{3}\right)^2 + (-1)^2}\sqrt{1^2 + 1^2}} = \dfrac{\sqrt{3} - 1}{\sqrt{4}\sqrt{2}} = \dfrac{\sqrt{3} - 1}{2\sqrt{2}} = \dfrac{\sqrt{6} - \sqrt{2}}{4} \Rightarrow \theta = 75°$
   (c)   The vectors are neither parallel nor orthogonal.

13. $\mathbf{v} = 3\mathbf{i} + 4\mathbf{j},\quad \mathbf{w} = 4\mathbf{i} + 3\mathbf{j}$
   (a) $\mathbf{v} \cdot \mathbf{w} = 3(4) + 4(3) = 12 + 12 = 24$
   (b) $\cos\theta = \dfrac{\mathbf{v} \cdot \mathbf{w}}{\|\mathbf{v}\|\|\mathbf{w}\|} = \dfrac{24}{\sqrt{3^2 + 4^2}\sqrt{4^2 + 3^2}} = \dfrac{24}{\sqrt{25}\sqrt{25}} = \dfrac{24}{25} = 0.96 \Rightarrow \theta \approx 16.26°$
   (c)   The vectors are neither parallel nor orthogonal.

15. $\mathbf{v} = 4\mathbf{i},\quad \mathbf{w} = \mathbf{j}$
   (a) $\mathbf{v} \cdot \mathbf{w} = 4(0) + 0(1) = 0 + 0 = 0$
   (b) $\cos\theta = \dfrac{\mathbf{v} \cdot \mathbf{w}}{\|\mathbf{v}\|\|\mathbf{w}\|} = \dfrac{0}{\sqrt{4^2 + 0^2}\sqrt{0^2 + 1^2}} = \dfrac{0}{4 \cdot 1} = \dfrac{0}{4} = 0 \Rightarrow \theta = 90°$
   (c)   The vectors are orthogonal.

17. $v = i - aj$, $w = 2i + 3j$

Two vectors are orthogonal if the dot product is zero. Solve for a:

$$v \cdot w = 1(2) + (-a)(3) = 2 - 3a$$

$$2 - 3a = 0 \Rightarrow 3a = 2 \Rightarrow a = \frac{2}{3}$$

19. $v = 2i - 3j$, $w = i - j$

$$v_1 = \frac{v \cdot w}{(\|w\|)^2} w = \frac{2(1) + (-3)(-1)}{\left(\sqrt{1^2 + (-1)^2}\right)^2}(i - j) = \frac{5}{2}(i - j) = \frac{5}{2}i - \frac{5}{2}j$$

$$v_2 = v - v_1 = (2i - 3j) - \left(\frac{5}{2}i - \frac{5}{2}j\right) = -\frac{1}{2}i - \frac{1}{2}j$$

21. $v = i - j$, $w = i + 2j$

$$v_1 = \frac{v \cdot w}{(\|w\|)^2} w = \frac{1(1) + (-1)(2)}{\left(\sqrt{1^2 + 2^2}\right)^2}(i + 2j) = -\frac{1}{5}(i + 2j) = -\frac{1}{5}i - \frac{2}{5}j$$

$$v_2 = v - v_1 = (i - j) - \left(-\frac{1}{5}i - \frac{2}{5}j\right) = \frac{6}{5}i - \frac{3}{5}j$$

23. $v = 3i + j$, $w = -2i - j$

$$v_1 = \frac{v \cdot w}{(\|w\|)^2} w = \frac{3(-2) + 1(-1)}{\left(\sqrt{(-2)^2 + (-1)^2}\right)^2}(-2i - j) = -\frac{7}{5}(-2i - j) = \frac{14}{5}i + \frac{7}{5}j$$

$$v_2 = v - v_1 = (3i + j) - \left(\frac{14}{5}i + \frac{7}{5}j\right) = \frac{1}{5}i - \frac{2}{5}j$$

25. Let v_a = the velocity of the plane in still air.

v_w = the velocity of the wind.

v_g = the velocity of the plane relative to the ground.

$v_g = v_a + v_w$

$$v_a = 550\left(\cos(225°)i + \sin(225°)j\right) = 550\left(-\frac{\sqrt{2}}{2}i - \frac{\sqrt{2}}{2}j\right) = -275\sqrt{2}\,i - 275\sqrt{2}\,j$$

$v_w = 80i$

$$v_g = v_a + v_w = -275\sqrt{2}\,i - 275\sqrt{2}\,j + 80i = \left(80 - 275\sqrt{2}\right)i - 275\sqrt{2}\,j$$

The speed of the plane relative to the ground is:

$$\|v_g\| = \sqrt{\left(80 - 275\sqrt{2}\right)^2 + \left(-275\sqrt{2}\right)^2} = \sqrt{6400 - 44,000\sqrt{2} + 151,250 + 151,250}$$

$$\approx \sqrt{246,674.6} \approx 496.66 \text{ miles per hour}$$

To find the direction, find the angle between $\mathbf{v_g}$ and a convenient vector such as due south, $-\mathbf{j}$.

$$\cos\theta = \frac{\mathbf{v_g}\cdot(-\mathbf{j})}{\|\mathbf{v_g}\|\|-\mathbf{j}\|} = \frac{\left(80-275\sqrt{2}\right)(0)+\left(-275\sqrt{2}\right)(-1)}{496.66\sqrt{0^2+(-1)^2}} = \frac{275\sqrt{2}}{496.66} \approx 0.7830$$

$$\theta \approx 38.46°$$

The plane is traveling with a ground speed of about 496.66 miles per hour in an approximate direction of 38.46 degrees west of south.

27. Let the positive x-axis point downstream, so that the velocity of the current is $\mathbf{v_c} = 3\mathbf{i}$.
Let $\mathbf{v_w}$ = the velocity of the boat in the water.
Let $\mathbf{v_g}$ = the velocity of the boat relative to the land.
Then $\mathbf{v_g} = \mathbf{v_w} + \mathbf{v_c}$ and $\mathbf{v_g} = k_j$ since the boat is going directly across the river.
The speed of the boat is $|\mathbf{v_w}| = 20$; we need to find the direction.

   Let $\mathbf{v_w} = a\mathbf{i} + b\mathbf{j}$ so $\|\mathbf{v_w}\| = \sqrt{a^2+b^2} = 20 \Rightarrow a^2+b^2 = 400$.
Since $\mathbf{v_g} = \mathbf{v_w} + \mathbf{v_c}$, $k\mathbf{j} = a\mathbf{i} + b\mathbf{j} + 3\mathbf{i} \Rightarrow k\mathbf{j} = (a+3)\mathbf{i} + b\mathbf{j}$
   $a+3 = 0$ and $k = b \Rightarrow a = -3$
   $a^2+b^2 = 400 \Rightarrow 9+b^2 = 400 \Rightarrow b^2 = 391 \Rightarrow k = b \approx 19.77$
   $\mathbf{v_w} = -3\mathbf{i} + 19.77\mathbf{j}$ and $\mathbf{v_g} = 19.77\mathbf{j}$
Find the angle between $\mathbf{v_w}$ and $\mathbf{j}$:

$$\cos\theta = \frac{\mathbf{v_w}\cdot\mathbf{j}}{\|\mathbf{v_w}\|\|\mathbf{j}\|} = \frac{-3(0)+19.77(1)}{20\sqrt{0^2+1^2}} = \frac{19.77}{20} = 0.9885$$

$$\theta \approx 8.70°$$

The heading of the boat needs to be about 8.70 degrees upstream.
The velocity of the boat directly across the river is about 19.77 kilometers per hour. The time to cross the river is: $t = \dfrac{0.5}{19.77} \approx 0.025$ hours, that is, $t = \dfrac{0.5}{19.77} \approx 1.5$ minutes.

29. Split the force into the components going down the hill and perpendicular to the hill.
   $\mathbf{F_d} = \mathbf{F}\sin 8° = 5300\sin 8°$
   ≈ 737.62 pounds
   $\mathbf{F_p} = \mathbf{F}\cos 8° = 5300\cos 8°$
   ≈ 5248.42 pounds

The force required to keep the car from rolling down the hill is about 737.62 pounds.
The force perpendicular to the hill is approximately 5248.42 pounds.

31. Let $\mathbf{v_a}$ = the velocity of the plane in still air.
   $\mathbf{v_w}$ = the velocity of the wind.
   $\mathbf{v_g}$ = the velocity of the plane relative to the ground.
   $\mathbf{v_g} = \mathbf{v_a} + \mathbf{v_w}$

$$\mathbf{v_a} = 500\big(\cos(45°)\mathbf{i} + \sin(45°)\mathbf{j}\big) = 500\left(\frac{\sqrt{2}}{2}\mathbf{i} + \frac{\sqrt{2}}{2}\mathbf{j}\right) = 250\sqrt{2}\,\mathbf{i} + 250\sqrt{2}\,\mathbf{j}$$

$$\mathbf{v_w} = 60\big(\cos(120°)\mathbf{i} + \sin(120°)\mathbf{j}\big) = 60\left(-\frac{1}{2}\mathbf{i} + \frac{\sqrt{3}}{2}\mathbf{j}\right) = -30\mathbf{i} + 30\sqrt{3}\,\mathbf{j}$$

$$\mathbf{v_g} = \mathbf{v_a} + \mathbf{v_w} = 250\sqrt{2}\,\mathbf{i} + 250\sqrt{2}\,\mathbf{j} - 30\mathbf{i} + 30\sqrt{3}\,\mathbf{j}$$

$$= \big(-30 + 250\sqrt{2}\big)\mathbf{i} + \big(250\sqrt{2} + 30\sqrt{3}\big)\mathbf{j}$$

The speed of the plane relative to the ground is:

$$\|\mathbf{v_g}\| = \sqrt{\big(-30 + 250\sqrt{2}\big)^2 + \big(250\sqrt{2} + 30\sqrt{3}\big)^2}$$

$$\approx \sqrt{269{,}129.1} \approx 518.8 \text{ kilometers per hour}$$

To find the direction, find the angle between $\mathbf{v_g}$ and a convenient vector such as due north, $\mathbf{j}$.

$$\cos\theta = \frac{\mathbf{v_g} \cdot \mathbf{j}}{\|\mathbf{v_g}\|\,\|\mathbf{j}\|} = \frac{\big(-30 + 250\sqrt{2}\big)(0) + \big(250\sqrt{2} + 30\sqrt{3}\big)(1)}{518.8\sqrt{0^2 + 1^2}} = \frac{250\sqrt{2} + 30\sqrt{3}}{518.8}$$

$$\approx \frac{405.5}{518.8} \approx 0.7816 \Rightarrow \theta \approx 38.59°$$

The plane is traveling with a ground speed of about 518.78 kilometers per hour in a direction of 38.59 degrees east of north.

33. Let the positive x-axis point downstream, so that the velocity of the current is $\mathbf{v_c} = 3\mathbf{i}$.

Let $\mathbf{v_w}$ = the velocity of the boat in the water.

Let $\mathbf{v_g}$ = the velocity of the boat relative to the land.

Then $\mathbf{v_g} = \mathbf{v_w} + \mathbf{v_c}$

The speed of the boat is $\|\mathbf{v_w}\| = 20$; its heading is directly across the river, so $\mathbf{v_w} = 20\mathbf{j}$.

Then $\mathbf{v_g} = \mathbf{v_w} + \mathbf{v_c} = 20\mathbf{j} + 3\mathbf{i} = 3\mathbf{i} + 20\mathbf{j}$

$$\|\mathbf{v_g}\| = \sqrt{3^2 + 20^2} = \sqrt{409} \approx 20.22 \text{ miles per hour}$$

Find the angle between $\mathbf{v_g}$ and $\mathbf{j}$:

$$\cos\theta = \frac{\mathbf{v_g} \cdot \mathbf{j}}{\|\mathbf{v_g}\|\,\|\mathbf{j}\|} = \frac{3(0) + 20(1)}{20.2\sqrt{0^2 + 1^2}} = \frac{20}{20.22} \approx 0.9891 \Rightarrow \theta \approx 8.47°$$

The approximate direction of the boat will be 8.47 degrees downstream.

35. $$\mathbf{F} = 3\big(\cos(60°)\mathbf{i} + \sin(60°)\mathbf{j}\big) = 3\left(\frac{1}{2}\mathbf{i} + \frac{\sqrt{3}}{2}\mathbf{j}\right) = \frac{3}{2}\mathbf{i} + \frac{3\sqrt{3}}{2}\mathbf{j}$$

$$W = \mathbf{F} \cdot \overrightarrow{AB} = \left(\frac{3}{2}\mathbf{i} + \frac{3\sqrt{3}}{2}\mathbf{j}\right) \cdot 2\mathbf{i} = \frac{3}{2}(2) + \frac{3\sqrt{3}}{2}(0) = 3 \text{ foot-pounds}$$

37. $\mathbf{F} = 20\left(\cos(30°)\mathbf{i} + \sin(30°)\mathbf{j}\right) = 20\left(\dfrac{\sqrt{3}}{2}\mathbf{i} + \dfrac{1}{2}\mathbf{j}\right) = 10\sqrt{3}\mathbf{i} + 10\mathbf{j}$

$W = \mathbf{F} \cdot \overrightarrow{AB} = \left(10\sqrt{3}\mathbf{i} + 10\mathbf{j}\right) \cdot 100\mathbf{i} = 10\sqrt{3}(100) + 10(0) \approx 1732$ foot-pounds

39. Let $\mathbf{u} = a_1\mathbf{i} + b_1\mathbf{j}$, $\mathbf{v} = a_2\mathbf{i} + b_2\mathbf{j}$, $\mathbf{w} = a_3\mathbf{i} + b_3\mathbf{j}$

$\mathbf{u} \cdot (\mathbf{v} + \mathbf{w}) = \left(a_1\mathbf{i} + b_1\mathbf{j}\right) \cdot \left(a_2\mathbf{i} + b_2\mathbf{j} + a_3\mathbf{i} + b_3\mathbf{j}\right) = \left(a_1\mathbf{i} + b_1\mathbf{j}\right) \cdot \left(a_2\mathbf{i} + a_3\mathbf{i} + b_2\mathbf{j} + b_3\mathbf{j}\right)$

$= \left(a_1\mathbf{i} + b_1\mathbf{j}\right) \cdot \left((a_2 + a_3)\mathbf{i} + (b_2 + b_3)\mathbf{j}\right) = a_1(a_2 + a_3) + b_1(b_2 + b_3)$

$= a_1 a_2 + a_1 a_3 + b_1 b_2 + b_1 b_3 = a_1 a_2 + b_1 b_2 + a_1 a_3 + b_1 b_3$

$= \left(a_1\mathbf{i} + b_1\mathbf{j}\right) \cdot \left(a_2\mathbf{i} + b_2\mathbf{j}\right) + \left(a_1\mathbf{i} + b_1\mathbf{j}\right) \cdot \left(a_3\mathbf{i} + b_3\mathbf{j}\right) = \mathbf{u} \cdot \mathbf{v} + \mathbf{u} \cdot \mathbf{w}$

41. Let $\mathbf{v} = a\,\mathbf{i} + b\,\mathbf{j}$.

Since $\mathbf{v}$ is a unit vector, $\|\mathbf{v}\| = \sqrt{a^2 + b^2} = 1$ or $a^2 + b^2 = 1$

If α is the angle between $\mathbf{v}$ and $\mathbf{i}$, then $\cos\alpha = \dfrac{\mathbf{v} \cdot \mathbf{i}}{\|\mathbf{v}\|\|\mathbf{i}\|} \Rightarrow \cos\alpha = \dfrac{(a\mathbf{i} + b\mathbf{j}) \cdot \mathbf{i}}{1 \cdot 1} = a.$

$a^2 + b^2 = 1 \Rightarrow \cos^2\alpha + b^2 = 1 \Rightarrow b^2 = 1 - \cos^2\alpha \Rightarrow b^2 = \sin^2\alpha \Rightarrow b = \sin\alpha$

Thus, $\mathbf{v} = \cos\alpha\,\mathbf{i} + \sin\alpha\,\mathbf{j}$.

43. Let $\mathbf{v} = a\,\mathbf{i} + b\,\mathbf{j}$.

$\mathbf{v}_1 = $ The projection of $\mathbf{v}$ onto $\mathbf{i} = \dfrac{\mathbf{v} \cdot \mathbf{i}}{\left(\|\mathbf{i}\|\right)^2}\mathbf{i} = \dfrac{(a\mathbf{i} + b\mathbf{j}) \cdot \mathbf{i}}{\left(\sqrt{1^2 + 0^2}\right)^2}\mathbf{i} = \dfrac{a(1) + b(0)}{1^2}\mathbf{i} = a\mathbf{i}.$

$\mathbf{v}_2 = \mathbf{v} - \mathbf{v}_1 = a\mathbf{i} + b\mathbf{j} - a\mathbf{i} = b\mathbf{j}$

Since $\mathbf{v} \cdot \mathbf{i} = (a\mathbf{i} + b\mathbf{j}) \cdot \mathbf{i} = (a)(1) + (b)(0) = a$ and $\mathbf{v} \cdot \mathbf{j} = (a\mathbf{i} + b\mathbf{j}) \cdot \mathbf{j} = (a)(0) + (b)(1) = b$,

$\mathbf{v} = \mathbf{v}_1 + \mathbf{v}_2 = (\mathbf{v} \cdot \mathbf{i})\mathbf{i} + (\mathbf{v} \cdot \mathbf{j})\mathbf{j}.$

45. $(\mathbf{v} - \alpha\mathbf{w}) \cdot \mathbf{w} = \mathbf{v} \cdot \mathbf{w} - \alpha\mathbf{w} \cdot \mathbf{w} = \mathbf{v} \cdot \mathbf{w} - \alpha\left(\|\mathbf{w}\|\right)^2 = \mathbf{v} \cdot \mathbf{w} - \dfrac{\mathbf{v} \cdot \mathbf{w}}{\left(\|\mathbf{w}\|\right)^2}\left(\|\mathbf{w}\|\right)^2 = 0$

Therefore the vectors are orthogonal.

47. If $\mathbf{F}$ is orthogonal to $\overrightarrow{AB}$, then $\mathbf{F} \cdot \overrightarrow{AB} = 0$. So $W = \mathbf{F} \cdot \overrightarrow{AB} = 0$.

49. Answers will vary.

Chapter 5

Polar Coordinates; Vectors

5.6 Vectors in Space

1. $\sqrt{(x_2 - x_1)^2 + (y_2 - y_1)^2}$

3. components

5. False

7. $y = 0$ is the set of all points in the xz-plane, that is, all points of the form $(x, 0, z)$.

9. $z = 2$ is the set of all points of the form $(x, y, 2)$, that is, the plane two units above the xy-plane.

11. $x = -4$ is the set of all points of the form $(-4, y, z)$, that is, the plane four units to the right of the yz-plane.

13. $x = 1$ and $y = 2$ is the set of all points of the form $(1, 2, z)$, that is, a line parallel to the z-axis.

15. $d = \sqrt{(4-0)^2 + (1-0)^2 + (2-0)^2} = \sqrt{16+1+4} = \sqrt{21}$

17. $d = \sqrt{(0-(-1))^2 + (-2-2)^2 + (1-(-3))^2} = \sqrt{1+16+16} = \sqrt{33}$

19. $d = \sqrt{(3-4)^2 + (2-(-2))^2 + (1-(-2))^2} = \sqrt{1+16+9} = \sqrt{26}$

21. The bottom of the box is formed by the vertices $(0, 0, 0)$, $(2, 0, 0)$, $(0, 1, 0)$, and $(2, 1, 0)$. The top of the box is formed by the vertices $(0, 0, 3)$, $(2, 0, 3)$, $(0, 1, 3)$, and $(2, 1, 3)$.

23. The bottom of the box is formed by the vertices $(1, 2, 3)$, $(3, 2, 3)$, $(3, 4, 3)$, and $(1, 4, 3)$. The top of the box is formed by the vertices $(3, 4, 5)$, $(1, 2, 5)$, $(3, 2, 5)$, and $(1, 4, 5)$.

25. The bottom of the box is formed by the vertices $(-1, 0, 2)$, $(4, 0, 2)$, $(-1, 2, 2)$, and $(4, 2, 2)$. The top of the box is formed by the vertices $(4, 2, 5)$, $(-1, 0, 5)$, $(4, 0, 5)$, and $(-1, 2, 5)$.

27. $\mathbf{v} = (3-0)\mathbf{i} + (4-0)\mathbf{j} + (-1-0)\mathbf{k} = 3\mathbf{i} + 4\mathbf{j} - \mathbf{k}$

29. $\mathbf{v} = (5-3)\mathbf{i} + (6-2)\mathbf{j} + (0-(-1))\mathbf{k} = 2\mathbf{i} + 4\mathbf{j} + \mathbf{k}$

31. $\mathbf{v} = (6-(-2))\mathbf{i} + (-2-(-1))\mathbf{j} + (4-4)\mathbf{k} = 8\mathbf{i} - \mathbf{j}$

33. $\|\mathbf{v}\| = \sqrt{3^2 + (-6)^2 + (-2)^2} = \sqrt{9 + 36 + 4} = \sqrt{49} = 7$

35. $\|\mathbf{v}\| = \sqrt{1^2 + (-1)^2 + 1^2} = \sqrt{1 + 1 + 1} = \sqrt{3}$

37. $\|\mathbf{v}\| = \sqrt{(-2)^2 + 3^2 + (-3)^2} = \sqrt{4 + 9 + 9} = \sqrt{22}$

39. $2\mathbf{v} + 3\mathbf{w} = 2(3\mathbf{i} - 5\mathbf{j} + 2\mathbf{k}) + 3(-2\mathbf{i} + 3\mathbf{j} - 2\mathbf{k}) = 6\mathbf{i} - 10\mathbf{j} + 4\mathbf{k} - 6\mathbf{i} + 9\mathbf{j} - 6\mathbf{k}$
$= 0\mathbf{i} - 1\mathbf{j} - 2\mathbf{k} = -\mathbf{j} - 2\mathbf{k}$

41. $\|\mathbf{v} - \mathbf{w}\| = \|(3\mathbf{i} - 5\mathbf{j} + 2\mathbf{k}) - (-2\mathbf{i} + 3\mathbf{j} - 2\mathbf{k})\| = \|3\mathbf{i} - 5\mathbf{j} + 2\mathbf{k} + 2\mathbf{i} - 3\mathbf{j} + 2\mathbf{k}\|$
$= \|5\mathbf{i} - 8\mathbf{j} + 4\mathbf{k}\| = \sqrt{5^2 + (-8)^2 + 4^2} = \sqrt{25 + 64 + 16} = \sqrt{105}$

43. $\|\mathbf{v}\| - \|\mathbf{w}\| = \|3\mathbf{i} - 5\mathbf{j} + 2\mathbf{k}\| - \|-2\mathbf{i} + 3\mathbf{j} - 2\mathbf{k}\|$
$= \sqrt{3^2 + (-5)^2 + 2^2} - \sqrt{(-2)^2 + 3^2 + (-2)^2} = \sqrt{38} - \sqrt{17}$

45. $\mathbf{u} = \dfrac{\mathbf{v}}{\|\mathbf{v}\|} = \dfrac{5\mathbf{i}}{\sqrt{5^2 + 0^2 + 0^2}} = \dfrac{5\mathbf{i}}{5} = \mathbf{i}$

47. $\mathbf{u} = \dfrac{\mathbf{v}}{\|\mathbf{v}\|} = \dfrac{3\mathbf{i} - 6\mathbf{j} - 2\mathbf{k}}{\sqrt{3^2 + (-6)^2 + (-2)^2}} = \dfrac{3\mathbf{i} - 6\mathbf{j} - 2\mathbf{k}}{7} = \dfrac{3}{7}\mathbf{i} - \dfrac{6}{7}\mathbf{j} - \dfrac{2}{7}\mathbf{k}$

49. $\mathbf{u} = \dfrac{\mathbf{v}}{\|\mathbf{v}\|} = \dfrac{\mathbf{i} + \mathbf{j} + \mathbf{k}}{\sqrt{1^2 + 1^2 + 1^2}} = \dfrac{\mathbf{i} + \mathbf{j} + \mathbf{k}}{\sqrt{3}} = \dfrac{1}{\sqrt{3}}\mathbf{i} + \dfrac{1}{\sqrt{3}}\mathbf{j} + \dfrac{1}{\sqrt{3}}\mathbf{k} = \dfrac{\sqrt{3}}{3}\mathbf{i} + \dfrac{\sqrt{3}}{3}\mathbf{j} + \dfrac{\sqrt{3}}{3}\mathbf{k}$

51. $\mathbf{v} \cdot \mathbf{w} = (\mathbf{i} - \mathbf{j}) \cdot (\mathbf{i} + \mathbf{j} + \mathbf{k}) = 1 \cdot 1 + (-1)(1) + 0 \cdot 1 = 1 - 1 + 0 = 0$
$\cos\theta = \dfrac{\mathbf{v} \cdot \mathbf{w}}{\|\mathbf{v}\|\|\mathbf{w}\|} = \dfrac{0}{\sqrt{1^2 + (-1)^2 + 0^2}\sqrt{1^2 + 1^2 + 1^2}} = \dfrac{0}{\sqrt{2}\sqrt{3}} = \dfrac{0}{\sqrt{6}} = 0$
$\theta = \dfrac{\pi}{2}$ radians $= 90°$

53. $\mathbf{v} \cdot \mathbf{w} = (2\mathbf{i} + \mathbf{j} - 3\mathbf{k}) \cdot (\mathbf{i} + 2\mathbf{j} + 2\mathbf{k}) = 2 \cdot 1 + 1(2) + (-3)(2) = 2 + 2 - 6 = -2$
$\cos\theta = \dfrac{\mathbf{v} \cdot \mathbf{w}}{\|\mathbf{v}\|\|\mathbf{w}\|} = \dfrac{-2}{\sqrt{2^2 + 1^2 + (-3)^2}\sqrt{1^2 + 2^2 + 2^2}} = \dfrac{-2}{\sqrt{14}\sqrt{9}} = \dfrac{-2}{3\sqrt{14}}$
$\theta \approx 1.75$ radians $\approx 100.3°$

55. $\mathbf{v} \cdot \mathbf{w} = (3\mathbf{i} - \mathbf{j} + 2\mathbf{k}) \cdot (\mathbf{i} + \mathbf{j} - \mathbf{k}) = 3 \cdot 1 + (-1)(1) + 2(-1) = 3 - 1 - 2 = 0$
$\cos\theta = \dfrac{\mathbf{v} \cdot \mathbf{w}}{\|\mathbf{v}\|\|\mathbf{w}\|} = \dfrac{0}{\sqrt{3^2 + (-1)^2 + 2^2}\sqrt{1^2 + 1^2 + (-1)^2}} = \dfrac{0}{\sqrt{14}\sqrt{3}} = 0$
$\theta = \dfrac{\pi}{2}$ radians $= 90°$

57. $\mathbf{v} \cdot \mathbf{w} = (3\mathbf{i} + 4\mathbf{j} + \mathbf{k}) \cdot (6\mathbf{i} + 8\mathbf{j} + 2\mathbf{k}) = 3 \cdot 6 + 4 \cdot 8 + 1 \cdot 2 = 18 + 32 + 2 = 52$

$$\cos\theta = \frac{\mathbf{v} \cdot \mathbf{w}}{\|\mathbf{v}\| \|\mathbf{w}\|} = \frac{52}{\sqrt{3^2 + 4^2 + 1^2}\sqrt{6^2 + 8^2 + 2^2}} = \frac{52}{\sqrt{26}\sqrt{104}} = \frac{52}{52} = 1$$

$\theta = 0$ radians $= 0°$

59. $\cos\alpha = \dfrac{a}{\|\mathbf{v}\|} = \dfrac{3}{\sqrt{3^2 + (-6)^2 + (-2)^2}} = \dfrac{3}{\sqrt{49}} = \dfrac{3}{7} \Rightarrow \alpha \approx 64.6°$

$\cos\beta = \dfrac{b}{\|\mathbf{v}\|} = \dfrac{-6}{\sqrt{3^2 + (-6)^2 + (-2)^2}} = \dfrac{-6}{\sqrt{49}} = -\dfrac{6}{7} \Rightarrow \beta \approx 149.0°$

$\cos\gamma = \dfrac{c}{\|\mathbf{v}\|} = \dfrac{-2}{\sqrt{3^2 + (-6)^2 + (-2)^2}} = \dfrac{-2}{\sqrt{49}} = -\dfrac{2}{7} \Rightarrow \gamma \approx 106.6°$

$\mathbf{v} = 7\big(\cos(64.6°)\mathbf{i} + \cos(149.0°)\mathbf{j} + \cos(106.6°)\mathbf{k}\big)$

61. $\cos\alpha = \dfrac{a}{\|\mathbf{v}\|} = \dfrac{1}{\sqrt{1^2 + 1^2 + 1^2}} = \dfrac{1}{\sqrt{3}} = \dfrac{\sqrt{3}}{3} \Rightarrow \alpha \approx 54.7°$

$\cos\beta = \dfrac{b}{\|\mathbf{v}\|} = \dfrac{1}{\sqrt{1^2 + 1^2 + 1^2}} = \dfrac{1}{\sqrt{3}} = \dfrac{\sqrt{3}}{3} \Rightarrow \beta \approx 54.7°$

$\cos\gamma = \dfrac{c}{\|\mathbf{v}\|} = \dfrac{1}{\sqrt{1^2 + 1^2 + 1^2}} = \dfrac{1}{\sqrt{3}} = \dfrac{\sqrt{3}}{3} \Rightarrow \gamma \approx 54.7°$

$\mathbf{v} = \sqrt{3}\big(\cos(54.7°)\mathbf{i} + \cos(54.7°)\mathbf{j} + \cos(54.7°)\mathbf{k}\big)$

63. $\cos\alpha = \dfrac{a}{\|\mathbf{v}\|} = \dfrac{1}{\sqrt{1^2 + 1^2 + 0^2}} = \dfrac{1}{\sqrt{2}} = \dfrac{\sqrt{2}}{2} \Rightarrow \alpha = 45°$

$\cos\beta = \dfrac{b}{\|\mathbf{v}\|} = \dfrac{1}{\sqrt{1^2 + 1^2 + 0^2}} = \dfrac{1}{\sqrt{2}} = \dfrac{\sqrt{2}}{2} \Rightarrow \beta = 45°$

$\cos\gamma = \dfrac{c}{\|\mathbf{v}\|} = \dfrac{0}{\sqrt{1^2 + 1^2 + 0^2}} = \dfrac{0}{\sqrt{2}} = 0 \Rightarrow \gamma = 90°$

$\mathbf{v} = \sqrt{2}\big(\cos(45°)\mathbf{i} + \cos(45°)\mathbf{j} + \cos(90°)\mathbf{k}\big)$

65. $\cos\alpha = \dfrac{a}{\|\mathbf{v}\|} = \dfrac{3}{\sqrt{3^2 + (-5)^2 + 2^2}} = \dfrac{3}{\sqrt{38}} \Rightarrow \alpha \approx 60.9°$

$\cos\beta = \dfrac{b}{\|\mathbf{v}\|} = \dfrac{-5}{\sqrt{3^2 + (-5)^2 + 2^2}} = -\dfrac{5}{\sqrt{38}} \Rightarrow \beta \approx 144.2°$

$\cos\gamma = \dfrac{c}{\|\mathbf{v}\|} = \dfrac{2}{\sqrt{3^2 + (-5)^2 + 2^2}} = \dfrac{2}{\sqrt{38}} \Rightarrow \gamma \approx 71.1°$

$\mathbf{v} = \sqrt{38}\big(\cos(60.9°)\mathbf{i} + \cos(144.2°)\mathbf{j} + \cos(71.1°)\mathbf{k}\big)$

67. $d(P_0, P) = \sqrt{(x - x_0)^2 + (y - y_0)^2 + (z - z_0)^2} = r$ 69. $(x - 1)^2 + (y - 2)^2 + (z - 2)^2 = 4$

$\Rightarrow (x - x_0)^2 + (y - y_0)^2 + (z - z_0)^2 = r^2$

71. $x^2 + y^2 + z^2 + 2x - 2y = 2$

$x^2 + 2x + y^2 - 2y + z^2 = 2$

$x^2 + 2x + 1 + y^2 - 2y + 1 + z^2 = 2 + 1 + 1$

$(x + 1)^2 + (y - 1)^2 + (z - 0)^2 = 4$

$(x + 1)^2 + (y - 1)^2 + (z - 0)^2 = 2^2$

Center: $(-1, 1, 0)$; Radius: 2

73. $x^2 + y^2 + z^2 - 4x + 4y + 2z = 0$

$x^2 - 4x + y^2 + 4y + z^2 + 2z = 0$

$x^2 - 4x + 4 + y^2 + 4y + 4 + z^2 + 2z + 1 = 4 + 4 + 1$

$(x - 2)^2 + (y + 2)^2 + (z + 1)^2 = 9$

$(x - 2)^2 + (y + 2)^2 + (z + 1)^2 = 3^2$

Center: $(2, -2, -1)$; Radius: 3

75. $2x^2 + 2y^2 + 2z^2 - 8x + 4z = -1$

$x^2 - 4x + y^2 + z^2 + 2z = -\dfrac{1}{2}$

$x^2 - 4x + 4 + y^2 + z^2 + 2z + 1 = -\dfrac{1}{2} + 4 + 1$

$(x - 2)^2 + (y - 0)^2 + (z + 1)^2 = \dfrac{9}{2}$

$(x - 2)^2 + (y - 0)^2 + (z + 1)^2 = \left(\dfrac{3}{\sqrt{2}}\right)^2$

Center: $(2, 0, -1)$; Radius: $\dfrac{3\sqrt{2}}{2}$

77. Write the force as a vector:

$\cos\alpha = \dfrac{2}{\sqrt{2^2 + 1^2 + 2^2}} = \dfrac{2}{\sqrt{9}} = \dfrac{2}{3}$; $\cos\beta = \dfrac{1}{3}$; $\cos\gamma = \dfrac{2}{3}$

$\mathbf{F} = 3\left(\dfrac{2}{3}\mathbf{i} + \dfrac{1}{3}\mathbf{j} + \dfrac{2}{3}\mathbf{k}\right)$

$W = 3\left(\dfrac{2}{3}\mathbf{i} + \dfrac{1}{3}\mathbf{j} + \dfrac{2}{3}\mathbf{k}\right) \cdot 2\mathbf{j} = 3\left(\dfrac{1}{3} \cdot 2\right) = 2$ joules

79. $W = \mathbf{F} \cdot \mathbf{u} = (2\mathbf{i} - \mathbf{j} - \mathbf{k}) \cdot (3\mathbf{i} + 2\mathbf{j} - 5\mathbf{k}) = 2 \cdot 3 + (-1)(2) + (-1)(-5) = 9$ joules

Chapter 5

Polar Coordinates; Vectors

5.7   The Cross Product

1.   True

3.   True

5.   False

7. $\begin{vmatrix} 3 & 4 \\ 1 & 2 \end{vmatrix} = 3 \cdot 2 - 1 \cdot 4 = 6 - 4 = 2$

9. $\begin{vmatrix} 6 & 5 \\ -2 & -1 \end{vmatrix} = 6(-1) - (-2)(5) = -6 + 10 = 4$

11. $\begin{vmatrix} A & B & C \\ 2 & 1 & 4 \\ 1 & 3 & 1 \end{vmatrix} = \begin{vmatrix} 1 & 4 \\ 3 & 1 \end{vmatrix} A - \begin{vmatrix} 2 & 4 \\ 1 & 1 \end{vmatrix} B + \begin{vmatrix} 2 & 1 \\ 1 & 3 \end{vmatrix} C = (1 - 12)A - (2 - 4)B + (6 - 1)C$

$\qquad = -11A + 2B + 5C$

13. $\begin{vmatrix} A & B & C \\ -1 & 3 & 5 \\ 5 & 0 & -2 \end{vmatrix} = \begin{vmatrix} 3 & 5 \\ 0 & -2 \end{vmatrix} A - \begin{vmatrix} -1 & 5 \\ 5 & -2 \end{vmatrix} B + \begin{vmatrix} -1 & 3 \\ 5 & 0 \end{vmatrix} C = (-6 - 0)A - (2 - 25)B + (0 - 15)C$

$\qquad = -6A + 23B - 15C$

15.   (a) $\mathbf{v} \times \mathbf{w} = \begin{vmatrix} \mathbf{i} & \mathbf{j} & \mathbf{k} \\ 2 & -3 & 1 \\ 3 & -2 & -1 \end{vmatrix} = \begin{vmatrix} -3 & 1 \\ -2 & -1 \end{vmatrix} \mathbf{i} - \begin{vmatrix} 2 & 1 \\ 3 & -1 \end{vmatrix} \mathbf{j} + \begin{vmatrix} 2 & -3 \\ 3 & -2 \end{vmatrix} \mathbf{k} = 5\mathbf{i} + 5\mathbf{j} + 5\mathbf{k}$

(b) $\mathbf{w} \times \mathbf{v} = \begin{vmatrix} \mathbf{i} & \mathbf{j} & \mathbf{k} \\ 3 & -2 & -1 \\ 2 & -3 & 1 \end{vmatrix} = \begin{vmatrix} -2 & -1 \\ -3 & 1 \end{vmatrix} \mathbf{i} - \begin{vmatrix} 3 & -1 \\ 2 & 1 \end{vmatrix} \mathbf{j} + \begin{vmatrix} 3 & -2 \\ 2 & -3 \end{vmatrix} \mathbf{k} = -5\mathbf{i} - 5\mathbf{j} - 5\mathbf{k}$

(c) $\mathbf{w} \times \mathbf{w} = \begin{vmatrix} \mathbf{i} & \mathbf{j} & \mathbf{k} \\ 3 & -2 & -1 \\ 3 & -2 & -1 \end{vmatrix} = \begin{vmatrix} -2 & -1 \\ -2 & -1 \end{vmatrix} \mathbf{i} - \begin{vmatrix} 3 & -1 \\ 3 & -1 \end{vmatrix} \mathbf{j} + \begin{vmatrix} 3 & -2 \\ 3 & -2 \end{vmatrix} \mathbf{k} = 0\mathbf{i} + 0\mathbf{j} + 0\mathbf{k} = \mathbf{0}$

(d) $\mathbf{v} \times \mathbf{v} = \begin{vmatrix} \mathbf{i} & \mathbf{j} & \mathbf{k} \\ 2 & -3 & 1 \\ 2 & -3 & 1 \end{vmatrix} = \begin{vmatrix} -3 & 1 \\ -3 & 1 \end{vmatrix} \mathbf{i} - \begin{vmatrix} 2 & 1 \\ 2 & 1 \end{vmatrix} \mathbf{j} + \begin{vmatrix} 2 & -3 \\ 2 & -3 \end{vmatrix} \mathbf{k} = 0\mathbf{i} + 0\mathbf{j} + 0\mathbf{k} = \mathbf{0}$

17. (a) $\mathbf{v} \times \mathbf{w} = \begin{vmatrix} \mathbf{i} & \mathbf{j} & \mathbf{k} \\ 1 & 1 & 0 \\ 2 & 1 & 1 \end{vmatrix} = \begin{vmatrix} 1 & 0 \\ 1 & 1 \end{vmatrix} \mathbf{i} - \begin{vmatrix} 1 & 0 \\ 2 & 1 \end{vmatrix} \mathbf{j} + \begin{vmatrix} 1 & 1 \\ 2 & 1 \end{vmatrix} \mathbf{k} = \mathbf{i} - \mathbf{j} - \mathbf{k}$

(b) $\mathbf{w} \times \mathbf{v} = \begin{vmatrix} \mathbf{i} & \mathbf{j} & \mathbf{k} \\ 2 & 1 & 1 \\ 1 & 1 & 0 \end{vmatrix} = \begin{vmatrix} 1 & 1 \\ 1 & 0 \end{vmatrix} \mathbf{i} - \begin{vmatrix} 2 & 1 \\ 1 & 0 \end{vmatrix} \mathbf{j} + \begin{vmatrix} 2 & 1 \\ 1 & 1 \end{vmatrix} \mathbf{k} = -\mathbf{i} + \mathbf{j} + \mathbf{k}$

(c) $\mathbf{w} \times \mathbf{w} = \begin{vmatrix} \mathbf{i} & \mathbf{j} & \mathbf{k} \\ 2 & 1 & 1 \\ 2 & 1 & 1 \end{vmatrix} = \begin{vmatrix} 1 & 1 \\ 1 & 1 \end{vmatrix} \mathbf{i} - \begin{vmatrix} 2 & 1 \\ 2 & 1 \end{vmatrix} \mathbf{j} + \begin{vmatrix} 2 & 1 \\ 2 & 1 \end{vmatrix} \mathbf{k} = 0\mathbf{i} + 0\mathbf{j} + 0\mathbf{k} = \mathbf{0}$

(d) $\mathbf{v} \times \mathbf{v} = \begin{vmatrix} \mathbf{i} & \mathbf{j} & \mathbf{k} \\ 1 & 1 & 0 \\ 1 & 1 & 0 \end{vmatrix} = \begin{vmatrix} 1 & 0 \\ 1 & 0 \end{vmatrix} \mathbf{i} - \begin{vmatrix} 1 & 0 \\ 1 & 0 \end{vmatrix} \mathbf{j} + \begin{vmatrix} 1 & 1 \\ 1 & 1 \end{vmatrix} \mathbf{k} = 0\mathbf{i} + 0\mathbf{j} + 0\mathbf{k} = \mathbf{0}$

19. (a) $\mathbf{v} \times \mathbf{w} = \begin{vmatrix} \mathbf{i} & \mathbf{j} & \mathbf{k} \\ 2 & -1 & 2 \\ 0 & 1 & -1 \end{vmatrix} = \begin{vmatrix} -1 & 2 \\ 1 & -1 \end{vmatrix} \mathbf{i} - \begin{vmatrix} 2 & 2 \\ 0 & -1 \end{vmatrix} \mathbf{j} + \begin{vmatrix} 2 & -1 \\ 0 & 1 \end{vmatrix} \mathbf{k} = -\mathbf{i} + 2\mathbf{j} + 2\mathbf{k}$

(b) $\mathbf{w} \times \mathbf{v} = \begin{vmatrix} \mathbf{i} & \mathbf{j} & \mathbf{k} \\ 0 & 1 & -1 \\ 2 & -1 & 2 \end{vmatrix} = \begin{vmatrix} 1 & -1 \\ -1 & 2 \end{vmatrix} \mathbf{i} - \begin{vmatrix} 0 & -1 \\ 2 & 2 \end{vmatrix} \mathbf{j} + \begin{vmatrix} 0 & 1 \\ 2 & -1 \end{vmatrix} \mathbf{k} = \mathbf{i} - 2\mathbf{j} - 2\mathbf{k}$

(c) $\mathbf{w} \times \mathbf{w} = \begin{vmatrix} \mathbf{i} & \mathbf{j} & \mathbf{k} \\ 0 & 1 & -1 \\ 0 & 1 & -1 \end{vmatrix} = \begin{vmatrix} 1 & -1 \\ 1 & -1 \end{vmatrix} \mathbf{i} - \begin{vmatrix} 0 & -1 \\ 0 & -1 \end{vmatrix} \mathbf{j} + \begin{vmatrix} 0 & 1 \\ 0 & 1 \end{vmatrix} \mathbf{k} = 0\mathbf{i} + 0\mathbf{j} + 0\mathbf{k} = \mathbf{0}$

(d) $\mathbf{v} \times \mathbf{v} = \begin{vmatrix} \mathbf{i} & \mathbf{j} & \mathbf{k} \\ 2 & -1 & 2 \\ 2 & -1 & 2 \end{vmatrix} = \begin{vmatrix} -1 & 2 \\ -1 & 2 \end{vmatrix} \mathbf{i} - \begin{vmatrix} 2 & 2 \\ 2 & 2 \end{vmatrix} \mathbf{j} + \begin{vmatrix} 2 & -1 \\ 2 & -1 \end{vmatrix} \mathbf{k} = 0\mathbf{i} + 0\mathbf{j} + 0\mathbf{k} = \mathbf{0}$

21. (a) $\mathbf{v} \times \mathbf{w} = \begin{vmatrix} \mathbf{i} & \mathbf{j} & \mathbf{k} \\ 1 & -1 & -1 \\ 4 & 0 & -3 \end{vmatrix} = \begin{vmatrix} -1 & -1 \\ 0 & -3 \end{vmatrix} \mathbf{i} - \begin{vmatrix} 1 & -1 \\ 4 & -3 \end{vmatrix} \mathbf{j} + \begin{vmatrix} 1 & -1 \\ 4 & 0 \end{vmatrix} \mathbf{k} = 3\mathbf{i} - \mathbf{j} + 4\mathbf{k}$

(b) $\mathbf{w} \times \mathbf{v} = \begin{vmatrix} \mathbf{i} & \mathbf{j} & \mathbf{k} \\ 4 & 0 & -3 \\ 1 & -1 & -1 \end{vmatrix} = \begin{vmatrix} 0 & -3 \\ -1 & -1 \end{vmatrix} \mathbf{i} - \begin{vmatrix} 4 & -3 \\ 1 & -1 \end{vmatrix} \mathbf{j} + \begin{vmatrix} 4 & 0 \\ 1 & -1 \end{vmatrix} \mathbf{k} = -3\mathbf{i} + \mathbf{j} - 4\mathbf{k}$

(c) $\mathbf{w} \times \mathbf{w} = \begin{vmatrix} \mathbf{i} & \mathbf{j} & \mathbf{k} \\ 4 & 0 & -3 \\ 4 & 0 & -3 \end{vmatrix} = \begin{vmatrix} 0 & -3 \\ 0 & -3 \end{vmatrix} \mathbf{i} - \begin{vmatrix} 4 & -3 \\ 4 & -3 \end{vmatrix} \mathbf{j} + \begin{vmatrix} 4 & 0 \\ 4 & 0 \end{vmatrix} \mathbf{k} = 0\mathbf{i} + 0\mathbf{j} + 0\mathbf{k} = \mathbf{0}$

(d) $\mathbf{v} \times \mathbf{v} = \begin{vmatrix} \mathbf{i} & \mathbf{j} & \mathbf{k} \\ 1 & -1 & -1 \\ 1 & -1 & -1 \end{vmatrix} = \begin{vmatrix} -1 & -1 \\ -1 & -1 \end{vmatrix} \mathbf{i} - \begin{vmatrix} 1 & -1 \\ 1 & -1 \end{vmatrix} \mathbf{j} + \begin{vmatrix} 1 & -1 \\ 1 & -1 \end{vmatrix} \mathbf{k} = 0\mathbf{i} + 0\mathbf{j} + 0\mathbf{k} = \mathbf{0}$

23. $\mathbf{u} \times \mathbf{v} = \begin{vmatrix} \mathbf{i} & \mathbf{j} & \mathbf{k} \\ 2 & -3 & 1 \\ -3 & 3 & 2 \end{vmatrix} = \begin{vmatrix} -3 & 1 \\ 3 & 2 \end{vmatrix} \mathbf{i} - \begin{vmatrix} 2 & 1 \\ -3 & 2 \end{vmatrix} \mathbf{j} + \begin{vmatrix} 2 & -3 \\ -3 & 3 \end{vmatrix} \mathbf{k} = -9\mathbf{i} - 7\mathbf{j} - 3\mathbf{k}$

25. $\mathbf{v} \times \mathbf{u} = \begin{vmatrix} \mathbf{i} & \mathbf{j} & \mathbf{k} \\ -3 & 3 & 2 \\ 2 & -3 & 1 \end{vmatrix} = \begin{vmatrix} 3 & 2 \\ -3 & 1 \end{vmatrix} \mathbf{i} - \begin{vmatrix} -3 & 2 \\ 2 & 1 \end{vmatrix} \mathbf{j} + \begin{vmatrix} -3 & 3 \\ 2 & -3 \end{vmatrix} \mathbf{k} = 9\mathbf{i} + 7\mathbf{j} + 3\mathbf{k}$

27. $\mathbf{v} \times \mathbf{v} = \begin{vmatrix} \mathbf{i} & \mathbf{j} & \mathbf{k} \\ -3 & 3 & 2 \\ -3 & 3 & 2 \end{vmatrix} = \begin{vmatrix} 3 & 2 \\ 3 & 2 \end{vmatrix} \mathbf{i} - \begin{vmatrix} -3 & 2 \\ -3 & 2 \end{vmatrix} \mathbf{j} + \begin{vmatrix} -3 & 3 \\ -3 & 3 \end{vmatrix} \mathbf{k} = 0\mathbf{i} + 0\mathbf{j} + 0\mathbf{k} = \mathbf{0}$

29. $(3\mathbf{u}) \times \mathbf{v} = \begin{vmatrix} \mathbf{i} & \mathbf{j} & \mathbf{k} \\ 6 & -9 & 3 \\ -3 & 3 & 2 \end{vmatrix} = \begin{vmatrix} -9 & 3 \\ 3 & 2 \end{vmatrix} \mathbf{i} - \begin{vmatrix} 6 & 3 \\ -3 & 2 \end{vmatrix} \mathbf{j} + \begin{vmatrix} 6 & -9 \\ -3 & 3 \end{vmatrix} \mathbf{k} = -27\mathbf{i} - 21\mathbf{j} - 9\mathbf{k}$

31. $\mathbf{u} \times (2\mathbf{v}) = \begin{vmatrix} \mathbf{i} & \mathbf{j} & \mathbf{k} \\ 2 & -3 & 1 \\ -6 & 6 & 4 \end{vmatrix} = \begin{vmatrix} -3 & 1 \\ 6 & 4 \end{vmatrix} \mathbf{i} - \begin{vmatrix} 2 & 1 \\ -6 & 4 \end{vmatrix} \mathbf{j} + \begin{vmatrix} 2 & -3 \\ -6 & 6 \end{vmatrix} \mathbf{k} = -18\mathbf{i} - 14\mathbf{j} - 6\mathbf{k}$

33. $\mathbf{u} \bullet (\mathbf{u} \times \mathbf{v}) = \mathbf{u} \bullet \begin{vmatrix} \mathbf{i} & \mathbf{j} & \mathbf{k} \\ 2 & -3 & 1 \\ -3 & 3 & 2 \end{vmatrix} = \mathbf{u} \bullet \left(\begin{vmatrix} -3 & 1 \\ 3 & 2 \end{vmatrix} \mathbf{i} - \begin{vmatrix} 2 & 1 \\ -3 & 2 \end{vmatrix} \mathbf{j} + \begin{vmatrix} 2 & -3 \\ -3 & 3 \end{vmatrix} \mathbf{k} \right)$

$= (2\mathbf{i} - 3\mathbf{j} + \mathbf{k}) \bullet (-9\mathbf{i} - 7\mathbf{j} - 3\mathbf{k}) = 2(-9) + (-3)(-7) + 1(-3) = -18 + 21 - 3 = 0$

35. $\mathbf{u} \bullet (\mathbf{v} \times \mathbf{w}) = \mathbf{u} \bullet \begin{vmatrix} \mathbf{i} & \mathbf{j} & \mathbf{k} \\ -3 & 3 & 2 \\ 1 & 1 & 3 \end{vmatrix} = \mathbf{u} \bullet \left(\begin{vmatrix} 3 & 2 \\ 1 & 3 \end{vmatrix} \mathbf{i} - \begin{vmatrix} -3 & 2 \\ 1 & 3 \end{vmatrix} \mathbf{j} + \begin{vmatrix} -3 & 3 \\ 1 & 1 \end{vmatrix} \mathbf{k} \right)$

$= (2\mathbf{i} - 3\mathbf{j} + \mathbf{k}) \bullet (7\mathbf{i} + 11\mathbf{j} - 6\mathbf{k}) = 2 \cdot 7 + (-3)(11) + 1(-6) = 14 - 33 - 6 = -25$

37. $\mathbf{v} \bullet (\mathbf{u} \times \mathbf{w}) = \mathbf{v} \bullet \begin{vmatrix} \mathbf{i} & \mathbf{j} & \mathbf{k} \\ 2 & -3 & 1 \\ 1 & 1 & 3 \end{vmatrix} = \mathbf{v} \bullet \left(\begin{vmatrix} -3 & 1 \\ 1 & 3 \end{vmatrix} \mathbf{i} - \begin{vmatrix} 2 & 1 \\ 1 & 3 \end{vmatrix} \mathbf{j} + \begin{vmatrix} 2 & -3 \\ 1 & 1 \end{vmatrix} \mathbf{k} \right)$

$= (-3\mathbf{i} + 3\mathbf{j} + 2\mathbf{k}) \bullet (-10\mathbf{i} - 5\mathbf{j} + 5\mathbf{k}) = -3(-10) + 3(-5) + 2 \cdot 5 = 30 - 15 + 10 = 25$

39. $\mathbf{u} \times (\mathbf{v} \times \mathbf{v}) = \mathbf{u} \times \begin{vmatrix} \mathbf{i} & \mathbf{j} & \mathbf{k} \\ -3 & 3 & 2 \\ -3 & 3 & 2 \end{vmatrix} = \mathbf{u} \times \left(\begin{vmatrix} 3 & 2 \\ 3 & 2 \end{vmatrix} \mathbf{i} - \begin{vmatrix} -3 & 2 \\ -3 & 2 \end{vmatrix} \mathbf{j} + \begin{vmatrix} -3 & 3 \\ -3 & 3 \end{vmatrix} \mathbf{k} \right)$

$= (2\mathbf{i} - 3\mathbf{j} + \mathbf{k}) \times (0\mathbf{i} + 0\mathbf{j} + 0\mathbf{k}) = \begin{vmatrix} \mathbf{i} & \mathbf{j} & \mathbf{k} \\ 2 & -3 & 1 \\ 0 & 0 & 0 \end{vmatrix}$

$= \begin{vmatrix} -3 & 1 \\ 0 & 0 \end{vmatrix} \mathbf{i} - \begin{vmatrix} 2 & 1 \\ 0 & 0 \end{vmatrix} \mathbf{j} + \begin{vmatrix} 2 & -3 \\ 0 & 0 \end{vmatrix} \mathbf{k} = 0\mathbf{i} + 0\mathbf{j} + 0\mathbf{k} = \mathbf{0}$

41. $\mathbf{u} \times \mathbf{v} = \begin{vmatrix} \mathbf{i} & \mathbf{j} & \mathbf{k} \\ 2 & -3 & 1 \\ -3 & 3 & 2 \end{vmatrix} = \begin{vmatrix} -3 & 1 \\ 3 & 2 \end{vmatrix} \mathbf{i} - \begin{vmatrix} 2 & 1 \\ -3 & 2 \end{vmatrix} \mathbf{j} + \begin{vmatrix} 2 & -3 \\ -3 & 3 \end{vmatrix} \mathbf{k} = -9\mathbf{i} - 7\mathbf{j} - 3\mathbf{k}$ is orthogonal to

both $\mathbf{u}$ and $\mathbf{v}$, so choose any vector of the form $c(-9\mathbf{i} - 7\mathbf{j} - 3\mathbf{k})$, where c is a nonzero scalar.

43. A vector that is orthogonal to both $\mathbf{u}$ and $\mathbf{i} + \mathbf{j}$ is $\mathbf{u} \times (\mathbf{i} + \mathbf{j})$.

$\mathbf{u} \times (\mathbf{i} + \mathbf{j}) = \begin{vmatrix} \mathbf{i} & \mathbf{j} & \mathbf{k} \\ 2 & -3 & 1 \\ 1 & 1 & 0 \end{vmatrix} = \begin{vmatrix} -3 & 1 \\ 1 & 0 \end{vmatrix} \mathbf{i} - \begin{vmatrix} 2 & 1 \\ 1 & 0 \end{vmatrix} \mathbf{j} + \begin{vmatrix} 2 & -3 \\ 1 & 1 \end{vmatrix} \mathbf{k} = -\mathbf{i} + \mathbf{j} + 5\mathbf{k}$, so choose any vector

of the form $c(-1\mathbf{i} + 1\mathbf{j} + 5\mathbf{k})$, where c is a nonzero scalar.

45. $\mathbf{u} = \overrightarrow{P_1P_2} = \mathbf{i} + 2\mathbf{j} + 3\mathbf{k}$ $\mathbf{v} = \overrightarrow{P_1P_3} = -2\mathbf{i} + 3\mathbf{j} + 0\mathbf{k}$

$\mathbf{u} \times \mathbf{v} = \begin{vmatrix} \mathbf{i} & \mathbf{j} & \mathbf{k} \\ 1 & 2 & 3 \\ -2 & 3 & 0 \end{vmatrix} = \begin{vmatrix} 2 & 3 \\ 3 & 0 \end{vmatrix} \mathbf{i} - \begin{vmatrix} 1 & 3 \\ -2 & 0 \end{vmatrix} \mathbf{j} + \begin{vmatrix} 1 & 2 \\ -2 & 3 \end{vmatrix} \mathbf{k} = -9\mathbf{i} - 6\mathbf{j} + 7\mathbf{k}$

Area $= \| \mathbf{u} \times \mathbf{v} \| = \sqrt{(-9)^2 + (-6)^2 + 7^2} = \sqrt{166}$

47. $\mathbf{u} = \overrightarrow{P_1P_2} = -3\mathbf{i} + \mathbf{j} + 4\mathbf{k}$ $\mathbf{v} = \overrightarrow{P_1P_3} = -\mathbf{i} - 4\mathbf{j} + 3\mathbf{k}$

$\mathbf{u} \times \mathbf{v} = \begin{vmatrix} \mathbf{i} & \mathbf{j} & \mathbf{k} \\ -3 & 1 & 4 \\ -1 & -4 & 3 \end{vmatrix} = \begin{vmatrix} 1 & 4 \\ -4 & 3 \end{vmatrix} \mathbf{i} - \begin{vmatrix} -3 & 4 \\ -1 & 3 \end{vmatrix} \mathbf{j} + \begin{vmatrix} -3 & 1 \\ -1 & -4 \end{vmatrix} \mathbf{k} = 19\mathbf{i} + 5\mathbf{j} + 13\mathbf{k}$

Area $= \| \mathbf{u} \times \mathbf{v} \| = \sqrt{19^2 + 5^2 + 13^2} = \sqrt{555}$

49. $\mathbf{u} = \overrightarrow{P_1P_2} = 0\mathbf{i} + \mathbf{j} + 1\mathbf{k}$ $\mathbf{v} = \overrightarrow{P_1P_3} = -3\mathbf{i} + 2\mathbf{j} - 2\mathbf{k}$

$\mathbf{u} \times \mathbf{v} = \begin{vmatrix} \mathbf{i} & \mathbf{j} & \mathbf{k} \\ 0 & 1 & 1 \\ -3 & 2 & -2 \end{vmatrix} = \begin{vmatrix} 1 & 1 \\ 2 & -2 \end{vmatrix} \mathbf{i} - \begin{vmatrix} 0 & 1 \\ -3 & -2 \end{vmatrix} \mathbf{j} + \begin{vmatrix} 0 & 1 \\ -3 & 2 \end{vmatrix} \mathbf{k} = -4\mathbf{i} - 3\mathbf{j} + 3\mathbf{k}$

Area $= \| \mathbf{u} \times \mathbf{v} \| = \sqrt{(-4)^2 + (-3)^2 + 3^2} = \sqrt{34}$

51. $\mathbf{u} = \overrightarrow{P_1P_2} = 3\mathbf{i} + 0\mathbf{j} - 2\mathbf{k}$ $\mathbf{v} = \overrightarrow{P_1P_3} = 5\mathbf{i} - 7\mathbf{j} + 3\mathbf{k}$

$\mathbf{u} \times \mathbf{v} = \begin{vmatrix} \mathbf{i} & \mathbf{j} & \mathbf{k} \\ 3 & 0 & -2 \\ 5 & -7 & 3 \end{vmatrix} = \begin{vmatrix} 0 & -2 \\ -7 & 3 \end{vmatrix} \mathbf{i} - \begin{vmatrix} 3 & -2 \\ 5 & 3 \end{vmatrix} \mathbf{j} + \begin{vmatrix} 3 & 0 \\ 5 & -7 \end{vmatrix} \mathbf{k} = -14\mathbf{i} - 19\mathbf{j} - 21\mathbf{k}$

Area $= \| \mathbf{u} \times \mathbf{v} \| = \sqrt{(-14)^2 + (-19)^2 + (-21)^2} = \sqrt{998}$

53. $\mathbf{v} \times \mathbf{w} = \begin{vmatrix} \mathbf{i} & \mathbf{j} & \mathbf{k} \\ 1 & 3 & -2 \\ -2 & 1 & 3 \end{vmatrix} = \begin{vmatrix} 3 & -2 \\ 1 & 3 \end{vmatrix} \mathbf{i} - \begin{vmatrix} 1 & -2 \\ -2 & 3 \end{vmatrix} \mathbf{j} + \begin{vmatrix} 1 & 3 \\ -2 & 1 \end{vmatrix} \mathbf{k} = 11\mathbf{i} + \mathbf{j} + 7\mathbf{k}$

$\|\mathbf{v} \times \mathbf{w}\| = \sqrt{11^2 + 1^2 + 7^2} = \sqrt{171} = 3\sqrt{19}$

$\mathbf{u} = \pm \dfrac{\mathbf{v} \times \mathbf{w}}{\|\mathbf{v} \times \mathbf{w}\|} = \pm \dfrac{11\mathbf{i} + \mathbf{j} + 7\mathbf{k}}{3\sqrt{19}} = \pm \left(\dfrac{11}{3\sqrt{19}} \mathbf{i} + \dfrac{1}{3\sqrt{19}} \mathbf{j} + \dfrac{7}{3\sqrt{19}} \mathbf{k} \right)$

$= \pm \left(\dfrac{11\sqrt{19}}{57} \mathbf{i} + \dfrac{\sqrt{19}}{57} \mathbf{j} + \dfrac{7\sqrt{19}}{57} \mathbf{k} \right)$

55.   Prove: $\mathbf{u} \times \mathbf{v} = -(\mathbf{v} \times \mathbf{u})$

     Let $\mathbf{u} = a_1 \mathbf{i} + b_1 \mathbf{j} + c_1 \mathbf{k}$ and $\mathbf{v} = a_2 \mathbf{i} + b_2 \mathbf{j} + c_2 \mathbf{k}$

$\mathbf{u} \times \mathbf{v} = \begin{vmatrix} \mathbf{i} & \mathbf{j} & \mathbf{k} \\ a_1 & b_1 & c_1 \\ a_2 & b_2 & c_2 \end{vmatrix} = \begin{vmatrix} b_1 & c_1 \\ b_2 & c_2 \end{vmatrix} \mathbf{i} - \begin{vmatrix} a_1 & c_1 \\ a_2 & c_2 \end{vmatrix} \mathbf{j} + \begin{vmatrix} a_1 & b_1 \\ a_2 & b_2 \end{vmatrix} \mathbf{k}$

$= (b_1 c_2 - b_2 c_1) \mathbf{i} - (a_1 c_2 - a_2 c_1) \mathbf{j} + (a_1 b_2 - a_2 b_1) \mathbf{k}$

$= -(b_2 c_1 - b_1 c_2) \mathbf{i} + (a_2 c_1 - a_1 c_2) \mathbf{j} - (a_2 b_1 - a_1 b_2) \mathbf{k}$

$= -\big((b_2 c_1 - b_1 c_2) \mathbf{i} - (a_2 c_1 - a_1 c_2) \mathbf{j} + (a_2 b_1 - a_1 b_2) \mathbf{k} \big)$

$= -\left(\begin{vmatrix} b_2 & c_2 \\ b_1 & c_1 \end{vmatrix} \mathbf{i} - \begin{vmatrix} a_2 & c_2 \\ a_1 & c_1 \end{vmatrix} \mathbf{j} + \begin{vmatrix} a_2 & b_2 \\ a_1 & b_1 \end{vmatrix} \mathbf{k} \right) = - \begin{vmatrix} \mathbf{i} & \mathbf{j} & \mathbf{k} \\ a_2 & b_2 & c_2 \\ a_1 & b_1 & c_1 \end{vmatrix} = -(\mathbf{v} \times \mathbf{u})$

57.   Prove: $\|\mathbf{u} \times \mathbf{v}\|^2 = \|\mathbf{u}\|^2 \|\mathbf{v}\|^2 - (\mathbf{u} \bullet \mathbf{v})^2$

     Let $\mathbf{u} = a_1 \mathbf{i} + b_1 \mathbf{j} + c_1 \mathbf{k}$ and $\mathbf{v} = a_2 \mathbf{i} + b_2 \mathbf{j} + c_2 \mathbf{k}$

$\mathbf{u} \times \mathbf{v} = \begin{vmatrix} \mathbf{i} & \mathbf{j} & \mathbf{k} \\ a_1 & b_1 & c_1 \\ a_2 & b_2 & c_2 \end{vmatrix} = \begin{vmatrix} b_1 & c_1 \\ b_2 & c_2 \end{vmatrix} \mathbf{i} - \begin{vmatrix} a_1 & c_1 \\ a_2 & c_2 \end{vmatrix} \mathbf{j} + \begin{vmatrix} a_1 & b_1 \\ a_2 & b_2 \end{vmatrix} \mathbf{k}$

$= (b_1 c_2 - b_2 c_1) \mathbf{i} - (a_1 c_2 - a_2 c_1) \mathbf{j} + (a_1 b_2 - a_2 b_1) \mathbf{k}$

$\|\mathbf{u} \times \mathbf{v}\|^2 = (b_1 c_2 - b_2 c_1)^2 + (a_1 c_2 - a_2 c_1)^2 + (a_1 b_2 - a_2 b_1)^2$

$= b_1^2 c_2^2 - 2 b_1 b_2 c_1 c_2 + b_2^2 c_1^2 + a_1^2 c_2^2 - 2 a_1 a_2 c_1 c_2 + a_2^2 c_1^2$

$\qquad\qquad + a_1^2 b_2^2 - 2 a_1 a_2 b_1 b_2 + a_2^2 b_1^2$

$= a_1^2 b_2^2 + a_1^2 c_2^2 + a_2^2 b_1^2 + a_2^2 c_1^2 + b_1^2 c_2^2 + b_2^2 c_1^2 - 2 a_1 a_2 b_1 b_2$

$\qquad\qquad\qquad\qquad - 2 a_1 a_2 c_1 c_2 - 2 b_1 b_2 c_1 c_2$

$$\|\mathbf{u}\|^2 = a_1^2 + b_1^2 + c_1^2; \qquad \|\mathbf{v}\|^2 = a_2^2 + b_2^2 + c_2^2; \qquad (\mathbf{u} \bullet \mathbf{v})^2 = (a_1a_2 + b_1b_2 + c_1c_2)^2$$

$$\|\mathbf{u}\|^2\|\mathbf{v}\|^2 - (\mathbf{u} \bullet \mathbf{v})^2$$

$$= (a_1^2 + b_1^2 + c_1^2)(a_2^2 + b_2^2 + c_2^2) - (a_1a_2 + b_1b_2 + c_1c_2)^2$$

$$= a_1^2a_2^2 + a_1^2b_2^2 + a_1^2c_2^2 + b_1^2a_2^2 + b_1^2b_2^2 + b_1^2c_2^2 + c_1^2a_2^2 + c_1^2b_2^2 + c_1^2c_2^2$$
$$- a_1^2a_2^2 + a_1a_2b_1b_2 + a_1a_2c_1c_2 + a_1a_2b_1b_2 + b_1^2b_2^2$$
$$+ b_1b_2c_1c_2 + a_1a_2c_1c_2 + b_1b_2c_1c_2 + c_1^2c_2^2$$

$$= a_1^2b_2^2 + a_1^2c_2^2 + a_2^2b_1^2 + a_2^2c_1^2 + b_1^2c_2^2 + b_2^2c_1^2 - 2a_1a_2b_1b_2$$
$$- 2a_1a_2c_1c_2 - 2b_1b_2c_1c_2$$

$$= \|\mathbf{u} \times \mathbf{v}\|^2$$

59.   If $\mathbf{u}$ and $\mathbf{v}$ are orthogonal, then $\mathbf{u} \bullet \mathbf{v} = 0$. From problem 57, then:

$$\|\mathbf{u} \times \mathbf{v}\|^2 = \|\mathbf{u}\|^2\|\mathbf{v}\|^2 - (\mathbf{u} \bullet \mathbf{v})^2 = \|\mathbf{u}\|^2\|\mathbf{v}\|^2 - (0)^2 = \|\mathbf{u}\|^2\|\mathbf{v}\|^2$$

$$\|\mathbf{u} \times \mathbf{v}\| = \|\mathbf{u}\|\|\mathbf{v}\|$$

61. $\mathbf{u} \bullet \mathbf{v} = 0 \implies \mathbf{u}$ and $\mathbf{v}$ are orthogonal.

$\mathbf{u} \times \mathbf{v} = \mathbf{0} \implies \mathbf{u}$ and $\mathbf{v}$ are parallel.

Therefore, if $\mathbf{u} \bullet \mathbf{v} = 0$ and $\mathbf{u} \times \mathbf{v} = \mathbf{0}$, then either $\mathbf{u} = \mathbf{0}$ or $\mathbf{v} = \mathbf{0}$.

Chapter 5

Polar Coordinates; Vectors

5.R Chapter Review

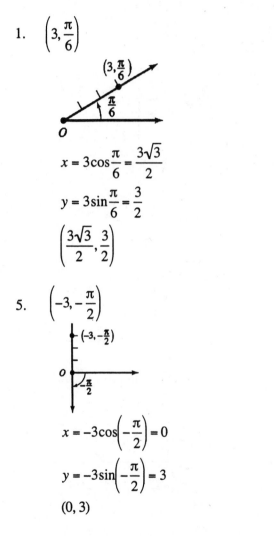

1. $\left(3, \dfrac{\pi}{6}\right)$

$x = 3\cos\dfrac{\pi}{6} = \dfrac{3\sqrt{3}}{2}$

$y = 3\sin\dfrac{\pi}{6} = \dfrac{3}{2}$

$\left(\dfrac{3\sqrt{3}}{2}, \dfrac{3}{2}\right)$

3. $\left(-2, \dfrac{4\pi}{3}\right)$

$x = -2\cos\dfrac{4\pi}{3} = 1$

$y = -2\sin\dfrac{4\pi}{3} = \sqrt{3}$

$\left(1, \sqrt{3}\right)$

5. $\left(-3, -\dfrac{\pi}{2}\right)$

$x = -3\cos\left(-\dfrac{\pi}{2}\right) = 0$

$y = -3\sin\left(-\dfrac{\pi}{2}\right) = 3$

$(0, 3)$

7. The point $(-3, 3)$ lies in quadrant II.

$r = \sqrt{x^2 + y^2} = \sqrt{(-3)^2 + 3^2} = 3\sqrt{2}$ $\qquad \theta = \tan^{-1}\left(\dfrac{y}{x}\right) = \tan^{-1}\left(\dfrac{3}{-3}\right) = \tan^{-1}(-1) = -\dfrac{\pi}{4}$

Polar coordinates of the point $(-3, 3)$ are $\left(-3\sqrt{2}, -\dfrac{\pi}{4}\right)$ or $\left(3\sqrt{2}, \dfrac{3\pi}{4}\right)$.

9.   The point $(0, -2)$ lies on the negative y-axis.

$r = \sqrt{x^2 + y^2} = \sqrt{0^2 + (-2)^2} = 2$ $\theta = \tan^{-1}\left(\dfrac{y}{x}\right) = \tan^{-1}\left(\dfrac{-2}{0}\right)$, $\dfrac{-2}{0}$ is undefined $\Rightarrow \theta = -\dfrac{\pi}{2}$

Polar coordinates of the point $(0, -2)$ are $\left(2, -\dfrac{\pi}{2}\right)$ or $\left(-2, \dfrac{\pi}{2}\right)$.

11.   The point $(3, 4)$ lies in quadrant I.

$r = \sqrt{x^2 + y^2} = \sqrt{3^2 + 4^2} = 5$ $\theta = \tan^{-1}\left(\dfrac{y}{x}\right) = \tan^{-1}\dfrac{4}{3} \approx 0.93$

Polar coordinates of the point $(3, 4)$ are $(5, 0.93)$ or $(-5, 4.07)$.

13.
$$r = 2\sin\theta$$
$$r^2 = 2r\sin\theta$$
$$x^2 + y^2 = 2y$$
$$x^2 + y^2 - 2y = 0$$
$$x^2 + y^2 - 2y + 1 = 1$$
$$x^2 + (y-1)^2 = 1^2$$
circle with center $(0,1)$, radius 1.

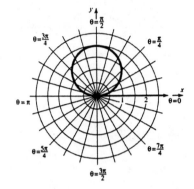

15.
$$r = 5$$
$$r^2 = 25$$
$$x^2 + y^2 = 5^2$$
circle with center $(0,0)$, radius 5.

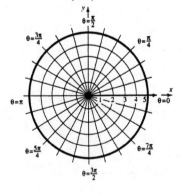

17.
$$r\cos\theta + 3r\sin\theta = 6$$
$$x + 3y = 6$$
$$3y = -x + 6$$
$$y = -\dfrac{1}{3}x + 2$$

line through $(0,2)$ and $(6,2)$, slope $-\dfrac{1}{3}$

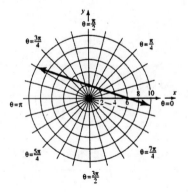

19. $r = 4\cos\theta$ The graph will be a circle, radius 2, center (2,0). Check for symmetry:
Polar axis: Replace θ by $-\theta$. The result is $r = 4\cos(-\theta) = 4\cos\theta$.

The graph is symmetric with respect to the polar axis.

The line $\theta = \dfrac{\pi}{2}$: Replace θ by $\pi - \theta$.

$$r = 4\cos(\pi - \theta) = 4(\cos(\pi)\cos\theta + \sin(\pi)\sin\theta)$$

$$= 4(-\cos\theta + 0) = -4\cos\theta$$

The test fails.

The pole: Replace r by $-r$. $-r = 4\cos\theta$. The test fails.

Due to symmetry with respect to the polar axis, assign values to θ from 0 to π.

θ	0	$\dfrac{\pi}{6}$	$\dfrac{\pi}{3}$	$\dfrac{\pi}{2}$	$\dfrac{2\pi}{3}$	$\dfrac{5\pi}{6}$	π
$r = 4\cos\theta$	4	$2\sqrt{3} \approx 3.5$	2	0	-2	$-2\sqrt{3} \approx -3.5$	-4

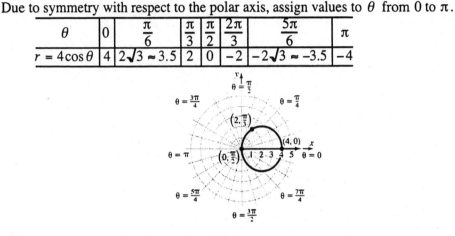

21. $r = 3 - 3\sin\theta$ The graph will be a cardioid. Check for symmetry:
Polar axis: Replace θ by $-\theta$. The result is $r = 3 - 3\sin(-\theta) = 3 + 3\sin\theta$. The test fails.

The line $\theta = \dfrac{\pi}{2}$: Replace θ by $\pi - \theta$.

$$r = 3 - 3\sin(\pi - \theta) = 3 - 3(\sin(\pi)\cos\theta - \cos(\pi)\sin\theta)$$

$$= 3 - 3(0 + \sin\theta) = 3 - 3\sin\theta$$

The graph is symmetric with respect to the line $\theta = \dfrac{\pi}{2}$.

The pole: Replace r by $-r$. $-r = 3 - 3\sin\theta$. The test fails.

Due to symmetry with respect to the line $\theta = \dfrac{\pi}{2}$, assign values to θ from $-\dfrac{\pi}{2}$ to $\dfrac{\pi}{2}$.

θ	$-\dfrac{\pi}{2}$	$-\dfrac{\pi}{3}$	$-\dfrac{\pi}{6}$	0	$\dfrac{\pi}{6}$	$\dfrac{\pi}{3}$	$\dfrac{\pi}{2}$
$r = 3 - 3\sin\theta$	6	$3 + \dfrac{3\sqrt{3}}{2} \approx 5.6$	$\dfrac{9}{2}$	3	$\dfrac{3}{2}$	$3 - \dfrac{3\sqrt{3}}{2} \approx 0.4$	0

23. $r = 4 - \cos\theta$ The graph will be a limacon without inner loop.

Check for symmetry:

Polar axis: Replace θ by $-\theta$. The result is $r = 4 - \cos(-\theta) = 4 - \cos\theta$.

The graph is symmetric with respect to the polar axis.

The line $\theta = \dfrac{\pi}{2}$: Replace θ by $\pi - \theta$.

$$r = 4 - \cos(\pi - \theta) = 4 - (\cos(\pi)\cos\theta + \sin(\pi)\sin\theta)$$

$$= 4 - (-\cos\theta + 0) = 4 + \cos\theta$$

The test fails.

The pole: Replace r by $-r$. $-r = 4 - \cos\theta$. The test fails.

Due to symmetry with respect to the polar axis, assign values to θ from 0 to π.

θ	0	$\dfrac{\pi}{6}$	$\dfrac{\pi}{3}$	$\dfrac{\pi}{2}$	$\dfrac{2\pi}{3}$	$\dfrac{5\pi}{6}$	π
$r = 4 - \cos\theta$	3	$4 - \dfrac{\sqrt{3}}{2} \approx 3.1$	$\dfrac{7}{2}$	4	$\dfrac{9}{2}$	$4 + \dfrac{\sqrt{3}}{2} \approx 4.9$	5

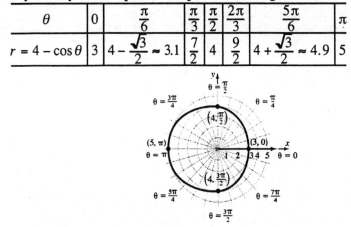

25. $r = \sqrt{x^2 + y^2} = \sqrt{(-1)^2 + (-1)^2} = \sqrt{2}$

$\tan\theta = \dfrac{y}{x} = \dfrac{-1}{-1} = 1 \Rightarrow \theta = 225°$

The polar form of $z = -1 - i$ is $z = r(\cos\theta + i\sin\theta) = \sqrt{2}(\cos 225° + i\sin 225°)$.

27. $r = \sqrt{x^2 + y^2} = \sqrt{4^2 + (-3)^2} = \sqrt{25} = 5$

$\tan\theta = \dfrac{y}{x} = -\dfrac{3}{4} \Rightarrow \theta \approx 323.1°$

The polar form of $z = 4 - 3i$ is $z = r(\cos\theta + i\sin\theta) = 5(\cos(323.1°) + i\sin(323.1°))$.

29. $2(\cos 150° + i\sin 150°) = 2\left(-\dfrac{\sqrt{3}}{2} + \dfrac{1}{2}i\right) = -\sqrt{3} + i$

31. $\quad 3\left(\cos\dfrac{2\pi}{3} + i\sin\dfrac{2\pi}{3}\right) = 3\left(-\dfrac{1}{2} + \dfrac{\sqrt{3}}{2}i\right) = -\dfrac{3}{2} + \dfrac{3\sqrt{3}}{2}i$

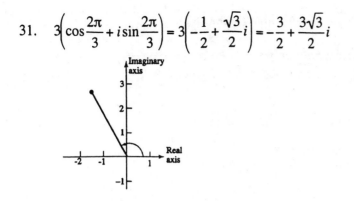

33. $\quad 0.1\left(\cos 350° + i\sin 350°\right) \approx 0.1\left(0.9848 - 0.1736i\right) = 0.0985 - 0.0174i$

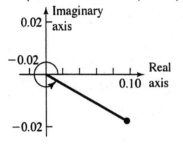

35. $\quad z\cdot w = \left(\cos 80° + i\sin 80°\right)\cdot\left(\cos 50° + i\sin 50°\right)$

$\qquad = 1\cdot 1\left(\cos(80° + 50°) + i\sin(80° + 50°)\right) = \cos 130° + i\sin 130°$

$\quad \dfrac{z}{w} = \dfrac{\cos 80° + i\sin 80°}{\cos 50° + i\sin 50°} = \dfrac{1}{1}\left(\cos(80° - 50°) + i\sin(80° - 50°)\right)$

$\qquad = \cos 30° + i\sin 30°$

37. $\quad z\cdot w = 3\left(\cos\dfrac{9\pi}{5} + i\sin\dfrac{9\pi}{5}\right)\cdot 2\left(\cos\dfrac{\pi}{5} + i\sin\dfrac{\pi}{5}\right) = 3\cdot 2\left(\cos\left(\dfrac{9\pi}{5} + \dfrac{\pi}{5}\right) + i\sin\left(\dfrac{9\pi}{5} + \dfrac{\pi}{5}\right)\right)$

$\qquad = 6\cdot\left(\cos 2\pi + i\sin 2\pi\right) = 6\left(\cos 0 + i\sin 0\right) = 6$

$\quad \dfrac{z}{w} = \dfrac{3\cdot\left(\cos\dfrac{9\pi}{5} + i\sin\dfrac{9\pi}{5}\right)}{2\cdot\left(\cos\dfrac{\pi}{5} + i\sin\dfrac{\pi}{5}\right)} = \dfrac{3}{2}\left(\cos\left(\dfrac{9\pi}{5} - \dfrac{\pi}{5}\right) + i\sin\left(\dfrac{9\pi}{5} - \dfrac{\pi}{5}\right)\right) = \dfrac{3}{2}\left(\cos\dfrac{8\pi}{5} + i\sin\dfrac{8\pi}{5}\right)$

39. $\quad z\cdot w = 5\left(\cos 10° + i\sin 10°\right)\cdot\left(\cos 355° + i\sin 355°\right)$

$\qquad = 5\cdot 1\left(\cos(10° + 355°) + i\sin(10° + 355°)\right) = 5\cdot\left(\cos 365° + i\sin 365°\right)$

$\qquad = 5\cdot\left(\cos 5° + i\sin 5°\right)$

$\quad \dfrac{z}{w} = \dfrac{5\left(\cos 10° + i\sin 10°\right)}{\cos 355° + i\sin 355°} = \dfrac{5}{1}\left(\cos(10° - 355°) + i\sin(10° - 355°)\right)$

$\qquad = 5\cdot\left(\cos(-345°) + i\sin(-345°)\right) = 5\cdot\left(\cos 15° + i\sin 15°\right)$

41. $\left[3(\cos 20° + i\sin 20°)\right]^3 = 3^3(\cos(3\cdot 20°) + i\sin(3\cdot 20°)) = 27(\cos 60° + i\sin 60°)$

$$= 27\left(\frac{1}{2} + \frac{\sqrt{3}}{2}i\right) = \frac{27}{2} + \frac{27\sqrt{3}}{2}i$$

43. $\left[\sqrt{2}\left(\cos\frac{5\pi}{8} + i\sin\frac{5\pi}{8}\right)\right]^4 = \left(\sqrt{2}\right)^4\left(\cos\left(4\cdot\frac{5\pi}{8}\right) + i\sin\left(4\cdot\frac{5\pi}{8}\right)\right)$

$$= 4\cdot\left(\cos\frac{5\pi}{2} + i\sin\frac{5\pi}{2}\right) = 4(0 + 1i) = 4i$$

45. $1 - \sqrt{3}i \quad r = \sqrt{1^2 + \left(-\sqrt{3}\right)^2} = 2 \quad \tan\theta = \frac{-\sqrt{3}}{1} = -\sqrt{3} \Rightarrow \theta = 300°$

$1 - \sqrt{3}i = 2(\cos 300° + i\sin 300°)$

$\left(1 - \sqrt{3}i\right)^6 = \left[2(\cos 300° + i\sin 300°)\right]^6 = 2^6\cdot(\cos(6\cdot 300°) + i\sin(6\cdot 300°))$

$$= 64\cdot(\cos 1800° + i\sin 1800°) = 64\cdot(\cos 0° + i\sin 0°) = 64 + 0i = 64$$

47. $3 + 4i \quad r = \sqrt{3^2 + 4^2} = 5 \quad \tan\theta = \frac{4}{3} \Rightarrow \theta \approx 53.1°$

$3 + 4i = 5\cdot(\cos(53.1°) + i\sin(53.1°))$

$(3 + 4i)^4 = \left[5^4\cdot(\cos(4\cdot 53.1°) + i\sin(4\cdot 53.1°))\right]^4 = 625\cdot(\cos(212.4°) + i\sin(212.4°))$

$$\approx 625\cdot(-0.8443 + i(-0.5358)) = -527.7 - 334.9i$$

49. $27 + 0i \quad r = \sqrt{27^2 + 0^2} = 27 \quad \tan\theta = \frac{0}{27} = 0 \Rightarrow \theta = 0°$

$27 + 0i = 27(\cos 0° + i\sin 0°)$

The three complex cube roots of $27 + 0i = 27(\cos 0° + i\sin 0°)$ are:

$$z_k = \sqrt[3]{27}\cdot\left[\cos\left(\frac{0°}{3} + \frac{360°\cdot k}{3}\right) + i\sin\left(\frac{0°}{3} + \frac{360°\cdot k}{3}\right)\right]$$

$= 3\left[\cos(120°\,k) + i\sin(120°\cdot k)\right]$

$z_0 = 3\left[\cos(120°\cdot 0) + i\sin(120°\cdot 0)\right] = 3\cdot(\cos 0° + i\sin 0°) = 3$

$z_1 = 3\left[\cos(120°\cdot 1) + i\sin(120°\cdot 1)\right] = 3\cdot(\cos 120° + i\sin 120°) = -\frac{3}{2} + \frac{3\sqrt{3}}{2}i$

$z_2 = 3\left[\cos(120°\cdot 2) + i\sin(120°\cdot 2)\right] = 3\cdot(\cos 240° + i\sin 240°) = -\frac{3}{2} - \frac{3\sqrt{3}}{2}i$

51.

53.

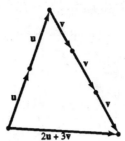

55. $P = (1, -2)$, $Q = (3, -6)$ $\mathbf{v} = (3-1)\mathbf{i} + (-6-(-2))\mathbf{j} = 2\mathbf{i} - 4\mathbf{j}$
$$\|\mathbf{v}\| = \sqrt{2^2 + (-4)^2} = \sqrt{20} = 2\sqrt{5}$$

57. $P = (0, -2)$, $Q = (-1, 1)$ $\mathbf{v} = (-1-0)\mathbf{i} + (1-(-2))\mathbf{j} = -1\mathbf{i} + 3\mathbf{j}$
$$\|\mathbf{v}\| = \sqrt{(-1)^2 + 3^2} = \sqrt{10}$$

59. $\mathbf{v} + \mathbf{w} = \left(-2\mathbf{i} + \mathbf{j}\right) + \left(4\mathbf{i} - 3\mathbf{j}\right) = 2\mathbf{i} - 2\mathbf{j}$

61. $4\mathbf{v} - 3\mathbf{w} = 4\left(-2\mathbf{i} + \mathbf{j}\right) - 3\left(4\mathbf{i} - 3\mathbf{j}\right) = -8\mathbf{i} + 4\mathbf{j} - 12\mathbf{i} + 9\mathbf{j} = -20\mathbf{i} + 13\mathbf{j}$

63. $\|\mathbf{v}\| = \|-2\mathbf{i} + \mathbf{j}\| = \sqrt{(-2)^2 + 1^2} = \sqrt{5}$

65. $\|\mathbf{v}\| + \|\mathbf{w}\| = \|-2\mathbf{i} + \mathbf{j}\| + \|4\mathbf{i} - 3\mathbf{j}\| = \sqrt{(-2)^2 + 1^2} + \sqrt{4^2 + (-3)^2} = \sqrt{5} + 5 \approx 7.24$

67. $\mathbf{u} = \dfrac{\mathbf{v}}{\|\mathbf{v}\|} = \dfrac{-2\mathbf{i} + \mathbf{j}}{\|-2\mathbf{i} + \mathbf{j}\|} = \dfrac{-2\mathbf{i} + \mathbf{j}}{\sqrt{(-2)^2 + 1^2}} = \dfrac{-2\mathbf{i} + \mathbf{j}}{\sqrt{5}} = -\dfrac{2\sqrt{5}}{5}\mathbf{i} + \dfrac{\sqrt{5}}{5}\mathbf{j}$

69. Let $\mathbf{v} = x \cdot \mathbf{i} + y \cdot \mathbf{j}$, $\|\mathbf{v}\| = 3$, with the angle between $\mathbf{v}$ and $\mathbf{i}$ equal to $60°$.
$\|\mathbf{v}\| = 3 \Rightarrow \sqrt{x^2 + y^2} = 3 \Rightarrow x^2 + y^2 = 9$

The angle between $\mathbf{v}$ and $\mathbf{i}$ equals $60°$. Thus, $\cos 60° = \dfrac{\mathbf{v} \cdot \mathbf{i}}{\|\mathbf{v}\| \|\mathbf{i}\|} = \dfrac{x}{3(1)} = \dfrac{x}{3}$.

We also conclude that $\mathbf{v}$ lies in Quadrant I.

$\cos 60° = \dfrac{x}{3}$

$\dfrac{1}{2} = \dfrac{x}{3} \Rightarrow x = \dfrac{3}{2}$

$x^2 + y^2 = 9 \Rightarrow \left(\dfrac{3}{2}\right)^2 + y^2 = 9$

$y^2 = 9 - \left(\dfrac{3}{2}\right)^2 \Rightarrow y = \pm\sqrt{9 - \left(\dfrac{3}{2}\right)^2} = \pm\sqrt{9 - \dfrac{9}{4}} = \pm\sqrt{\dfrac{36-9}{4}} = \pm\sqrt{\dfrac{27}{4}} = \pm\dfrac{3\sqrt{3}}{2}$

Since **v** lies in Quadrant I, $y = \dfrac{3\sqrt{3}}{2}$.

So $\mathbf{v} = x \cdot \mathbf{i} + y \cdot \mathbf{j} = \dfrac{3}{2} \cdot \mathbf{i} + \dfrac{3\sqrt{3}}{2} \cdot \mathbf{j}$.

71. $d(P_1, P_2) = \sqrt{(4-1)^2 + (-2-3)^2 + (1-(-2))^2} = \sqrt{9 + 25 + 9} = \sqrt{43} \approx 6.56$

73. $\mathbf{v} = (4-1)\mathbf{i} + (-2-3)\mathbf{j} + (1-(-2))\mathbf{k} = 3\mathbf{i} - 5\mathbf{j} + 3\mathbf{k}$

75. $4\mathbf{v} - 3\mathbf{w} = 4(3\mathbf{i} + \mathbf{j} - 2\mathbf{k}) - 3(-3\mathbf{i} + 2\mathbf{j} - \mathbf{k}) = 12\mathbf{i} + 4\mathbf{j} - 8\mathbf{k} + 9\mathbf{i} - 6\mathbf{j} + 3\mathbf{k}$
$= 21\mathbf{i} - 2\mathbf{j} - 5\mathbf{k}$

77. $\|\mathbf{v} - \mathbf{w}\| = \|(3\mathbf{i} + \mathbf{j} - 2\mathbf{k}) - (-3\mathbf{i} + 2\mathbf{j} - \mathbf{k})\| = \|3\mathbf{i} + \mathbf{j} - 2\mathbf{k} + 3\mathbf{i} - 2\mathbf{j} + \mathbf{k}\|$
$= \|6\mathbf{i} - \mathbf{j} - \mathbf{k}\| = \sqrt{6^2 + (-1)^2 + (-1)^2} = \sqrt{36 + 1 + 1} = \sqrt{38}$

79. $\|\mathbf{v}\| - \|\mathbf{w}\| = \|3\mathbf{i} + \mathbf{j} - 2\mathbf{k}\| - \|-3\mathbf{i} + 2\mathbf{j} - \mathbf{k}\|$
$= \sqrt{3^2 + 1^2 + (-2)^2} - \sqrt{(-3)^2 + 2^2 + (-1)^2} = \sqrt{14} - \sqrt{14} = 0$

81. $\mathbf{v} \times \mathbf{w} = \begin{vmatrix} \mathbf{i} & \mathbf{j} & \mathbf{k} \\ 3 & 1 & -2 \\ -3 & 2 & -1 \end{vmatrix} = \begin{vmatrix} 1 & -2 \\ 2 & -1 \end{vmatrix}\mathbf{i} - \begin{vmatrix} 3 & -2 \\ -3 & -1 \end{vmatrix}\mathbf{j} + \begin{vmatrix} 3 & 1 \\ -3 & 2 \end{vmatrix}\mathbf{k} = 3\mathbf{i} + 9\mathbf{j} + 9\mathbf{k}$

83. Same direction:
$\dfrac{\mathbf{v}}{\|\mathbf{v}\|} = \dfrac{3\mathbf{i} + \mathbf{j} - 2\mathbf{k}}{\sqrt{3^2 + 1^2 + (-2)^2}} = \dfrac{3\mathbf{i} + \mathbf{j} - 2\mathbf{k}}{\sqrt{14}} = \dfrac{3\sqrt{14}}{14}\mathbf{i} + \dfrac{\sqrt{14}}{14}\mathbf{j} - \dfrac{\sqrt{14}}{7}\mathbf{k}$
Opposite direction:
$\dfrac{-\mathbf{v}}{\|\mathbf{v}\|} = -\dfrac{3\sqrt{14}}{14}\mathbf{i} - \dfrac{\sqrt{14}}{14}\mathbf{j} + \dfrac{\sqrt{14}}{7}\mathbf{k}$

85. $\mathbf{v} = -2\mathbf{i} + \mathbf{j}, \quad \mathbf{w} = 4\mathbf{i} - 3\mathbf{j}$
$\mathbf{v} \cdot \mathbf{w} = -2(4) + 1(-3) = -8 - 3 = -11$
$\cos\theta = \dfrac{\mathbf{v} \cdot \mathbf{w}}{\|\mathbf{v}\|\|\mathbf{w}\|} = \dfrac{-11}{\sqrt{(-2)^2 + 1^2}\sqrt{4^2 + (-3)^2}} = \dfrac{-11}{\sqrt{5} \cdot 5} = \dfrac{-11}{5\sqrt{5}} \approx -0.9839 \Rightarrow \theta \approx 169.7°$

87. $\mathbf{v} = \mathbf{i} - 3\mathbf{j}, \quad \mathbf{w} = -\mathbf{i} + \mathbf{j}$
$\mathbf{v} \cdot \mathbf{w} = 1(-1) + (-3)(1) = -1 - 3 = -4$
$\cos\theta = \dfrac{\mathbf{v} \cdot \mathbf{w}}{\|\mathbf{v}\|\|\mathbf{w}\|} = \dfrac{-4}{\sqrt{1^2 + (-3)^2}\sqrt{(-1)^2 + 1^2}} = \dfrac{-4}{\sqrt{10}\sqrt{2}} = \dfrac{-2}{\sqrt{5}} \approx -0.8944 \Rightarrow \theta \approx 153.4°$

89. $\mathbf{v} \cdot \mathbf{w} = (\mathbf{i} + \mathbf{j} + \mathbf{k}) \cdot (\mathbf{i} - \mathbf{j} + \mathbf{k}) = (1)(1) + 1(-1) + (1)(1) = 1 - 1 + 1 = 1$

$$\cos\theta = \frac{\mathbf{v} \cdot \mathbf{w}}{\|\mathbf{v}\| \|\mathbf{w}\|} = \frac{1}{\sqrt{1^2 + 1^2 + 1^2} \sqrt{1^2 + (-1)^2 + 1^2}} = \frac{1}{\sqrt{3}\sqrt{3}} = \frac{1}{3} \Rightarrow \theta \approx 70.5°$$

91. $\mathbf{v} \cdot \mathbf{w} = (4\mathbf{i} - \mathbf{j} + 2\mathbf{k}) \cdot (\mathbf{i} - 2\mathbf{j} - 3\mathbf{k}) = (4)(1) + (-1)(-2) + (2)(-3) = 4 + 2 - 6 = 0$

$$\cos\theta = \frac{\mathbf{v} \cdot \mathbf{w}}{\|\mathbf{v}\| \|\mathbf{w}\|} = \frac{0}{\sqrt{4^2 + (-1)^2 + 2^2} \sqrt{1^2 + (-2)^2 + (-3)^2}} = 0 \Rightarrow \theta = 90°$$

93. $\mathbf{v} = 2\mathbf{i} + 3\mathbf{j}, \quad \mathbf{w} = -4\mathbf{i} - 6\mathbf{j}$

$\mathbf{v} \cdot \mathbf{w} = (2)(-4) + (3)(-6) = -8 - 18 = -26$

$$\cos\theta = \frac{\mathbf{v} \cdot \mathbf{w}}{\|\mathbf{v}\| \|\mathbf{w}\|} = \frac{-26}{\sqrt{2^2 + 3^2} \sqrt{(-4)^2 + (-6)^2}} = \frac{-5}{\sqrt{13}\sqrt{52}} = \frac{-26}{\sqrt{676}} = -1$$

$\theta = \cos^{-1}(-1) = 180°$ Therefore, the vectors are parallel.

95. $\mathbf{v} = 3\mathbf{i} - 4\mathbf{j}, \quad \mathbf{w} = -3\mathbf{i} + 4\mathbf{j}$

$\mathbf{v} \cdot \mathbf{w} = (3)(-3) + (-4)(4) = -9 - 16 = -25$

$$\cos\theta = \frac{\mathbf{v} \cdot \mathbf{w}}{\|\mathbf{v}\| \|\mathbf{w}\|} = \frac{-25}{\sqrt{3^2 + (-4)^2} \sqrt{(-3)^2 + 4^2}} = \frac{-25}{\sqrt{25}\sqrt{25}} = \frac{-25}{25} = -1$$

$\theta = \cos^{-1}(-1) = 180°$ Therefore, the vectors are parallel.

97. $\mathbf{v} = 3\mathbf{i} - 2\mathbf{j}, \quad \mathbf{w} = 4\mathbf{i} + 6\mathbf{j}$

$\mathbf{v} \cdot \mathbf{w} = (3)(4) + (-2)(6) = 12 - 12 = 0$

Therefore, the vectors are orthogonal.

99. $\mathbf{v} = 2\mathbf{i} + \mathbf{j}, \quad \mathbf{w} = -4\mathbf{i} + 3\mathbf{j}$

The decomposition of $\mathbf{v}$ into 2 vectors $\mathbf{v}_1$ and $\mathbf{v}_2$ so that $\mathbf{v}_1$ is parallel to $\mathbf{w}$ and $\mathbf{v}_2$ is perpendicular to $\mathbf{w}$ is given by:

$$\mathbf{v}_1 = \frac{\mathbf{v} \cdot \mathbf{w}}{\|\mathbf{w}\|^2} \mathbf{w} \text{ and } \mathbf{v}_2 = \mathbf{v} - \mathbf{v}_1$$

$$\mathbf{v}_1 = \frac{\mathbf{v} \cdot \mathbf{w}}{\|\mathbf{w}\|^2} = \frac{(2\mathbf{i} + \mathbf{j}) \cdot (-4\mathbf{i} + 3\mathbf{j})}{\left(\sqrt{(-4)^2 + 3^2}\right)^2} (-4\mathbf{i} + 3\mathbf{j}) = \frac{(2)(-4) + (1)(3)}{25}(-4\mathbf{i} + 3\mathbf{j})$$

$$= \left(-\frac{1}{5}\right)(-4\mathbf{i} + 3\mathbf{j}) = \frac{4}{5}\mathbf{i} - \frac{3}{5}\mathbf{j}$$

$$\mathbf{v}_2 = \mathbf{v} - \mathbf{v}_1 = 2\mathbf{i} + \mathbf{j} - \left(\frac{4}{5}\mathbf{i} - \frac{3}{5}\mathbf{j}\right) = \frac{6}{5}\mathbf{i} + \frac{8}{5}\mathbf{j}$$

101. $\mathbf{v} = 2\mathbf{i} + 3\mathbf{j}, \quad \mathbf{w} = 3\mathbf{i} + \mathbf{j}$

The projection of $\mathbf{v}$ onto $\mathbf{w}$ is given by:

$$\frac{\mathbf{v} \cdot \mathbf{w}}{\|\mathbf{w}\|^2} \mathbf{w} = \frac{(2\mathbf{i} + 3\mathbf{j}) \cdot (3\mathbf{i} + \mathbf{j})}{\left(\sqrt{3^2 + 1^2}\right)^2} (3\mathbf{i} + \mathbf{j}) = \frac{(2)(3) + (3)(1)}{10}(3\mathbf{i} + \mathbf{j}) = \left(\frac{9}{10}\right)(3\mathbf{i} + \mathbf{j}) = \frac{27}{10}\mathbf{i} + \frac{9}{10}\mathbf{j}$$

103. $\cos\alpha = \dfrac{a}{\|\mathbf{v}\|} = \dfrac{3}{\sqrt{3^2 + (-4)^2 + 2^2}} = \dfrac{3}{\sqrt{29}} \implies \alpha \approx 56.1°$

$\cos\beta = \dfrac{b}{\|\mathbf{v}\|} = \dfrac{-4}{\sqrt{3^2 + (-4)^2 + 2^2}} = -\dfrac{4}{\sqrt{29}} \implies \beta \approx 138.0°$

$\cos\gamma = \dfrac{c}{\|\mathbf{v}\|} = \dfrac{2}{\sqrt{3^2 + (-4)^2 + 2^2}} = \dfrac{2}{\sqrt{29}} \implies \gamma \approx 68.2°$

105. $\mathbf{u} = \overrightarrow{P_1 P_2} = \mathbf{i} + 2\mathbf{j} + 3\mathbf{k} \qquad \mathbf{v} = \overrightarrow{P_1 P_3} = 5\mathbf{i} + 4\mathbf{j} + \mathbf{k}$

$$\mathbf{u} \times \mathbf{v} = \begin{vmatrix} \mathbf{i} & \mathbf{j} & \mathbf{k} \\ 1 & 2 & 3 \\ 5 & 4 & 1 \end{vmatrix} = \begin{vmatrix} 2 & 3 \\ 4 & 1 \end{vmatrix}\mathbf{i} - \begin{vmatrix} 1 & 3 \\ 5 & 1 \end{vmatrix}\mathbf{j} + \begin{vmatrix} 1 & 2 \\ 5 & 4 \end{vmatrix}\mathbf{k} = -10\mathbf{i} + 14\mathbf{j} - 6\mathbf{k}$$

Area $= \|\mathbf{u} \times \mathbf{v}\| = \sqrt{(-10)^2 + 14^2 + (-6)^2} = \sqrt{332} = 2\sqrt{83} \approx 18.2$ sq. units

107. $\mathbf{v} \times \mathbf{u} = -(\mathbf{u} \times \mathbf{v}) = -(2\mathbf{i} - 3\mathbf{j} + \mathbf{k}) = -2\mathbf{i} + 3\mathbf{j} - \mathbf{k}$

109. Let the positive x-axis point downstream, so that the velocity of the current is $\mathbf{v}_c = 2\mathbf{i}$.

Let $\mathbf{v}_w$ = the velocity of the swimmer in the water.

Let $\mathbf{v}_g$ = the velocity of the swimmer relative to the land.

Then $\mathbf{v}_g = \mathbf{v}_w + \mathbf{v}_c$

The speed of the swimmer is $\|\mathbf{v}_w\| = 5$; the heading is directly across the river, so $\mathbf{v}_w = 5\mathbf{j}$.

Then $\mathbf{v}_g = \mathbf{v}_w + \mathbf{v}_c = 5\mathbf{j} + 2\mathbf{i} = 2\mathbf{i} + 5\mathbf{j}$

$\implies \|\mathbf{v}_g\| = \sqrt{2^2 + 5^2} = \sqrt{29} \approx 5.39$ miles per hour

Since the river is 1 mile wide, it takes the swimmer about 0.2 hour to cross the river. The swimmer will end up $(0.2)(2) = 0.4$ mile downstream.

111. Let $\mathbf{F}_1$ be the tension on the left cable and $\mathbf{F}_2$ be the tension on the right cable.

Let $\mathbf{F}_3$ represent the force of the weight of the box.

$\mathbf{F}_1 = \|\mathbf{F}_1\|\left(\cos(140°)\mathbf{i} + \sin(140°)\mathbf{j}\right) \approx \|\mathbf{F}_1\|(-0.7660\mathbf{i} + 0.6428\mathbf{j})$

$\mathbf{F}_2 = \|\mathbf{F}_2\|\left(\cos(30°)\mathbf{i} + \sin(30°)\mathbf{j}\right) \approx \|\mathbf{F}_2\|(0.8660\mathbf{i} + 0.5000\mathbf{j})$

$\mathbf{F}_3 = -2000\mathbf{j}$

For equilibrium, the sum of the force vectors must be zero.

$\mathbf{F}_1 + \mathbf{F}_2 + \mathbf{F}_3 = -0.7660\|\mathbf{F}_1\|\mathbf{i} + 0.6428\|\mathbf{F}_1\|\mathbf{j} + 0.8660\|\mathbf{F}_2\|\mathbf{i} + 0.5000\|\mathbf{F}_2\|\mathbf{j} - 2000\mathbf{j}$

$= \left(-0.7660\|\mathbf{F}_1\| + 0.8660\|\mathbf{F}_2\|\right)\mathbf{i} + \left(0.6428\|\mathbf{F}_1\| + 0.5000\|\mathbf{F}_2\| - 2000\right)\mathbf{j}$

$= \mathbf{0}$

Set the $\mathbf{i}$ and $\mathbf{j}$ components equal to zero and solve:

$$\begin{cases} -0.7660\|\mathbf{F}_1\| + 0.8660\|\mathbf{F}_2\| = 0 \implies \|\mathbf{F}_2\| = \dfrac{0.7660}{0.8660}\|\mathbf{F}_1\| = 0.8845\|\mathbf{F}_1\| \\ 0.6428\|\mathbf{F}_1\| + 0.5000\|\mathbf{F}_2\| - 2000 = 0 \end{cases}$$

$0.6428\|\mathbf{F_1}\| + 0.5000(0.8845\|\mathbf{F_1}\|) - 2000 = 0$

$1.0851\|\mathbf{F_1}\| = 2000 \Rightarrow \|\mathbf{F_1}\| \approx 1843$ pounds; $\|\mathbf{F_2}\| = 0.8845(1843) = 1630$ pounds

The tension in the left cable is about 1843 pounds and the tension in the right cable is about 1630 pounds.

113. $\mathbf{F} = 5\left(\cos(60°)\mathbf{i} + \sin(60°)\mathbf{j}\right) = 5\left(\dfrac{1}{2}\mathbf{i} + \dfrac{\sqrt{3}}{2}\mathbf{j}\right) = \dfrac{5}{2}\mathbf{i} + \dfrac{5\sqrt{3}}{2}\mathbf{j}$

$\overrightarrow{AB} = 20\mathbf{i}$

$W = \mathbf{F} \cdot \overrightarrow{AB} = \left(\dfrac{5}{2}\mathbf{i} + \dfrac{5\sqrt{3}}{2}\mathbf{j}\right) \cdot 20\mathbf{i} = \left(\dfrac{5}{2}\right)(20) + \left(\dfrac{5\sqrt{3}}{2}\right)(0) = 50$ foot-pounds

Polar Coordinates; Vectors

5.CR Cumulative Review

1. $\sin(2\theta) = 1$

$2\theta = \dfrac{\pi}{2} + 2k\pi$, k is any integer

$\theta = \dfrac{\pi}{4} + k\pi$, k is any integer

The solution set on the interval $0 \le \theta < 2\pi$

is $\left\{ \dfrac{\pi}{4}, \dfrac{5\pi}{4} \right\}$.

3. The circle with center point (0,1) and radius has equation:

$(x - h)^2 + (y - k)^2 = r^2$

$(x - 0)^2 + (y - 1)^2 = 3^2$

$x^2 + (y - 1)^2 = 9$

$x^2 + y^2 - 2y + 1 = 9$

$x^2 + y^2 - 2y - 8 = 0$

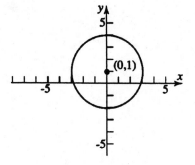

5. $x^2 + y^3 = 2x^4$

Test for symmetry:

x - axis : Replace y by $-y$: $x^2 + (-y)^3 = 2x^4 \Rightarrow x^2 - y^3 = 2x^4$

which is not equivalent to $x^2 + y^3 = 2x^4$.

y - axis : Replace x by $-x$: $(-x)^2 + y^3 = 2(-x)^4 \Rightarrow x^2 + y^3 = 2x^4$,

which is equivalent to $x^2 + y^3 = 2x^4$.

Origin : Replace x by $-x$ and y by $-y$: $(-x)^2 + (-y)^3 = 2(-x)^4 \Rightarrow x^2 - y^3 = 2x^4$,

which is not equivalent to $x^2 + y^3 = 2x^4$.

Therefore, the graph is symmetric with respect to the y-axis.

7. $y = |\sin x| = \begin{cases} \sin x, & \text{when } \sin x \geq 0 \\ -\sin x, & \text{when } \sin x < 0 \end{cases}$

$\qquad = \begin{cases} \sin x, & \text{when } 0 \leq x \leq \pi \\ -\sin x, & \text{when } \pi < x < 2\pi \end{cases}$

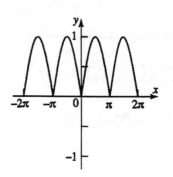

9. $\sin^{-1}\left(-\dfrac{1}{2}\right)$

We are finding the angle θ, $-\dfrac{\pi}{2} \leq \theta \leq \dfrac{\pi}{2}$, whose sine equals $-\dfrac{1}{2}$.

$\sin\theta = -\dfrac{1}{2} \qquad -\dfrac{\pi}{2} \leq \theta \leq \dfrac{\pi}{2}$

$\theta = -\dfrac{\pi}{6} \Rightarrow \sin^{-1}\left(-\dfrac{1}{2}\right) = -\dfrac{\pi}{6}$

11.   Graphing $r = 2$ and $\theta = \dfrac{\pi}{3}$ using polar coordinates:

$r = 2$ yields a circle, centered at $(0,0)$, with radius $= 2$.

$\theta = \dfrac{\pi}{3}$ yields a line passing through the point $(0,0)$, forming an angle of $\theta = \dfrac{\pi}{3}$ with the positive x-axis.

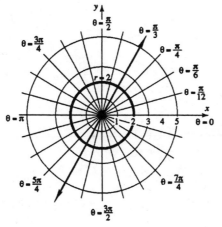

Chapter 6

Analytic Geometry

6.2   The Parabola

1.
$$\sqrt{(x_2 - x_1)^2 + (y_2 - y_1)^2}$$

3.
$$(x+4)^2 = 9$$
$$x + 4 = \pm 3$$
$$x + 4 = 3 \Rightarrow x = -1$$
or $x + 4 = -3 \Rightarrow x = -7$
The solution set is $\{-7, -1\}$

5.   3, up

7.   paraboloid of revolution

9.   True

11. *B*   **13.** *E*   **15.** *H*   **17.** *C*

19.   The focus is $(4, 0)$ and the vertex is $(0, 0)$. Both lie on the horizontal line $y = 0$. $a = 4$ and since $(4, 0)$ is to the right of $(0, 0)$, the parabola opens to the right. The equation of the parabola is:
$$y^2 = 4ax$$
$$y^2 = 4 \cdot 4 \cdot x$$
$$y^2 = 16x$$
Letting $x = 4$, we find $y^2 = 64$ or $y = \pm 8$.
The points $(4, 8)$ and $(4, -8)$ define the latus rectum.

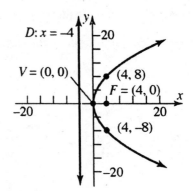

21.   The focus is $(0, -3)$ and the vertex is $(0, 0)$. Both lie on the vertical line $x = 0$. $a = 3$ and since $(0, -3)$ is below $(0, 0)$, the parabola opens down. The equation of the parabola is:
$$x^2 = -4ay$$
$$x^2 = -4 \cdot 3 \cdot y$$
$$x^2 = -12y$$
Letting $y = -3$, we find $x^2 = 36$ or $x = \pm 6$.
The points $(6, 3)$ and $(6, -3)$ define the latus rectum.

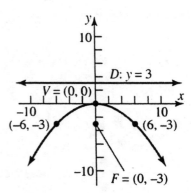

23. The focus is $(-2, 0)$ and the directrix is $x = 2$. The
vertex is $(0, 0)$. $a = 2$ and since $(-2, 0)$ is to the left
of $(0, 0)$, the parabola opens to the left. The
equation of the parabola is:

$$y^2 = -4ax$$
$$y^2 = -4 \cdot 2 \cdot x$$
$$y^2 = -8x$$

Letting $x = -2$, we find $y^2 = 16$ or $y = \pm 4$. The
points $(-2, 4)$ and $(-2, -4)$ define the latus rectum.

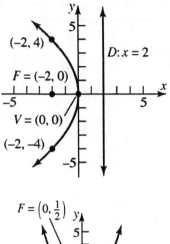

25. The directrix is $y = -\dfrac{1}{2}$ and the vertex is $(0, 0)$. The

focus is $\left(0, \dfrac{1}{2}\right)$. $a = \dfrac{1}{2}$ and since $\left(0, \dfrac{1}{2}\right)$ is above

$(0, 0)$, the parabola opens up. The equation of the
parabola is:

$$x^2 = 4ay$$
$$x^2 = 4 \cdot \dfrac{1}{2} \cdot y \Rightarrow x^2 = 2y$$

Letting $y = \dfrac{1}{2}$, we find $x^2 = 1$ or $x = \pm 1$.

The points $\left(1, \dfrac{1}{2}\right)$ and $\left(-1, \dfrac{1}{2}\right)$ define the latus

rectum.

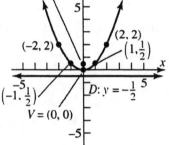

27. Vertex: $(0,0)$. Since the axis of symmetry is
vertical, the parabola opens up or down. Since
$(2, 3)$ is above $(0, 0)$, the parabola opens up. The
equation has the form $x^2 = 4ay$. Substitute the
coordinates of $(2, 3)$ into the equation to find a:

$$2^2 = 4a \cdot 3 \Rightarrow 4 = 12a \Rightarrow a = \dfrac{1}{3}$$

The equation of the parabola is: $x^2 = \dfrac{4}{3}y$. The

focus is $\left(0, \dfrac{1}{3}\right)$. Letting $y = \dfrac{1}{3}$,

we find $x^2 = \dfrac{4}{9}$ or $x = \pm \dfrac{2}{3}$. The points $\left(\dfrac{2}{3}, \dfrac{1}{3}\right)$ and

$\left(-\dfrac{2}{3}, \dfrac{1}{3}\right)$ define the latus rectum.

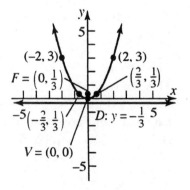

29. The vertex is (2, –3) and the focus is (2, –5). Both lie on the vertical line $x = 2$. $a = \left|-5 - (-3)\right| = 2$ and since (2, –5) is below (2, –3), the parabola opens down. The equation of the parabola is:

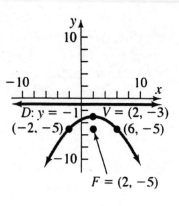

$$(x - h)^2 = -4a(y - k)$$

$$(x - 2)^2 = -4(2)(y - (-3))$$

$$(x - 2)^2 = -8(y + 3)$$

Letting $y = -5$, we find

$$(x - 2)^2 = 16$$

$$x - 2 = \pm 4 \Rightarrow x = -2 \text{ or } x = 6$$

The points (–2, –5) and (6, –5) define the latus rectum.

31. The vertex is (–1, –2) and the focus is (0, –2). Both lie on the horizontal line $y = -2$.
$a = \left|-1 - 0\right| = 1$ and since (0, –2) is to the right of (–1, –2), the parabola opens to the right. The equation of the parabola is:

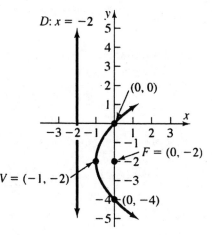

$$(y - k)^2 = 4a(x - h)$$

$$(y - (-2))^2 = 4(1)(x - (-1))$$

$$(y + 2)^2 = 4(x + 1)$$

Letting $x = 0$, we find

$$(y + 2)^2 = 4$$

$$y + 2 = \pm 2 \Rightarrow y = -4 \text{ or } y = 0$$

The points (0, –4) and (0, 0) define the latus rectum.

33. The directrix is $y = 2$ and the focus is (–3, 4). This is a vertical case, so the vertex is (–3, 3). $a = 1$ and since (–3, 4) is above $y = 2$, the parabola opens up. The equation of the parabola is:

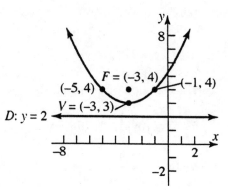

$$(x - h)^2 = 4a(y - k)$$

$$(x - (-3))^2 = 4 \cdot 1 \cdot (y - 3)$$

$$(x + 3)^2 = 4(y - 3)$$

Letting $y = 4$, we find $(x + 3)^2 = 4$ or $x + 3 = \pm 2$. So, $x = -1$ or $x = -5$. The points (–1, 4) and (–5, 4) define the latus rectum.

35. The directrix is $x = 1$ and the focus is $(-3, -2)$. This is a horizontal case, so the vertex is $(-1, -2)$. $a = 2$ and since $(-3, -2)$ is to the left of $x = 1$, the parabola opens to the left. The equation of the parabola is: $(y - k)^2 = -4a(x - h)$

$$(y - (-2))^2 = -4 \cdot 2 \cdot (x - (-1))$$

$$(y + 2)^2 = -8(x + 1)$$

Letting $x = -3$, we find $(y + 2)^2 = 16$ or $y + 2 = \pm 4$. So, $y = 2$ or $y = -6$. The points $(-3, 2)$ and $(-3, -6)$ define the latus rectum.

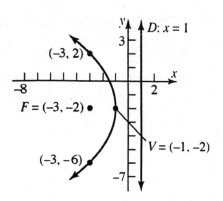

37. The equation $x^2 = 4y$ is in the form $x^2 = 4ay$ where $4a = 4$ or $a = 1$. Thus, we have:
Vertex: $(0, 0)$
Focus: $(0, 1)$
Directrix: $y = -1$

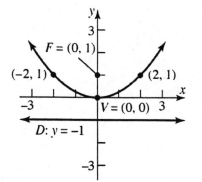

39. The equation $y^2 = -16x$ is in the form $y^2 = -4ax$ where $-4a = -16$ or $a = 4$. Thus, we have:
Vertex: $(0, 0)$
Focus: $(-4, 0)$
Directrix: $x = 4$

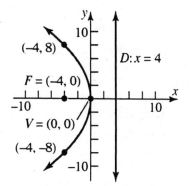

41. The equation $(y - 2)^2 = 8(x + 1)$ is in the form $(y - k)^2 = 4a(x - h)$ where $4a = 8$ or $a = 2$, $h = -1$, and $k = 2$. Thus, we have:
Vertex: $(-1, 2)$
Focus: $(1, 2)$
Directrix: $x = -3$

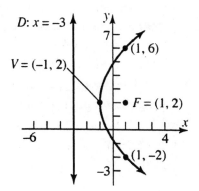

43. The equation $(x-3)^2 = -(y+1)$ is in the form

$(x-h)^2 = -4a(y-k)$ where $-4a = -1$ or $a = \dfrac{1}{4}$,

$h = 3$, and $k = -1$. Thus, we have:

Vertex: $(3, -1)$

Focus: $\left(3, -\dfrac{5}{4}\right)$

Directrix: $y = -\dfrac{3}{4}$

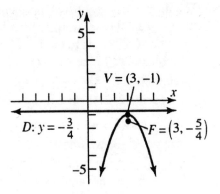

45. The equation $(y+3)^2 = 8(x-2)$ is in the form
$(y-k)^2 = 4a(x-h)$ where $4a = 8$ or $a = 2$,
$h = 2$, and $k = -3$. Thus, we have:
Vertex: $(2, -3)$
Focus: $(4, -3)$
Directrix: $x = 0$

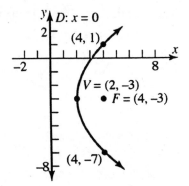

47. Complete the square to put in standard form:
$y^2 - 4y + 4x + 4 = 0$

$y^2 - 4y + 4 = -4x$

$(y-2)^2 = -4x$

The equation is in the form $(y-k)^2 = -4a(x-h)$
where $-4a = -4$ or $a = 1$, $h = 0$, and $k = 2$.
Thus, we have:
Vertex: $(0, 2)$
Focus: $(-1, 2)$
Directrix: $x = 1$

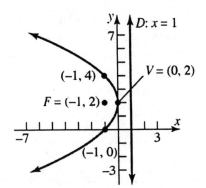

49. Complete the square to put in standard form:
$x^2 + 8x = 4y - 8$

$x^2 + 8x + 16 = 4y - 8 + 16$

$(x+4)^2 = 4(y+2)$

The equation is in the form $(x-h)^2 = 4a(y-k)$
where $4a = 4$ or $a = 1$, $h = -4$, and $k = -2$.
Thus, we have:
Vertex: $(-4, -2)$
Focus: $(-4, -1)$
Directrix: $y = -3$

51. Complete the square to put in standard form:
$y^2 + 2y - x = 0$

$$y^2 + 2y + 1 = x + 1$$
$$(y + 1)^2 = x + 1$$

The equation is in the form

$(y - k)^2 = 4a(x - h)$ where $4a = 1$ or $a = \dfrac{1}{4}$,

$h = -1$, and $k = -1$.
Thus, we have:
Vertex: $(-1, -1)$

Focus: $\left(-\dfrac{3}{4}, -1\right)$

Directrix: $x = -\dfrac{5}{4}$

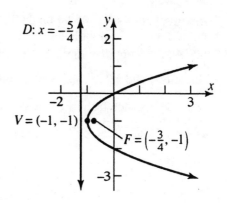

53. Complete the square to put in standard form:
$x^2 - 4x = y + 4$

$$x^2 - 4x + 4 = y + 4 + 4$$
$$(x - 2)^2 = y + 8$$

The equation is in the form

$(x - h)^2 = 4a(y - k)$ where $4a = 1$ or $a = \dfrac{1}{4}$,

$h = 2$, and $k = -8$.
Thus, we have:
Vertex: $(2, -8)$

Focus: $\left(2, -\dfrac{31}{4}\right)$

Directrix: $y = -\dfrac{33}{4}$

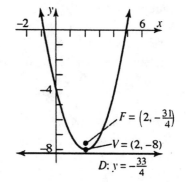

55. $(y - 1)^2 = c(x - 0)$
$(y - 1)^2 = cx$
$(2 - 1)^2 = c(1) \Rightarrow 1 = c$
$(y - 1)^2 = x$

57. $(y - 1)^2 = c(x - 2)$
$(0 - 1)^2 = c(1 - 2)$
$1 = -c \Rightarrow c = -1$
$(y - 1)^2 = -(x - 2)$

59. $(x - 0)^2 = c(y - 1)$
$x^2 = c(y - 1)$
$2^2 = c(2 - 1) \Rightarrow 4 = c$
$x^2 = 4(y - 1)$

61. $(y - 0)^2 = c(x - (-2))$
$y^2 = c(x + 2)$
$1^2 = c(0 + 2) \Rightarrow 1 = 2c \Rightarrow c = \dfrac{1}{2}$
$y^2 = \dfrac{1}{2}(x + 2)$

63. Set up the problem so that the vertex of the parabola is at (0, 0) and it opens up. Then the equation of the parabola has the form: $x^2 = 4ay$. Since the parabola is 10 feet across and 4 feet deep, the points (5, 4) and (–5, 4) are on the parabola.

Substitute and solve for a: $5^2 = 4a(4) \Rightarrow 25 = 16a \Rightarrow a = \dfrac{25}{16}$

a is the distance from the vertex to the focus. Thus, the receiver (located at the focus) is $\dfrac{25}{16} = 1.5625$ feet, or 18.75 inches from the base of the dish, along the axis of the parabola.

65. Set up the problem so that the vertex of the parabola is at (0, 0) and it opens up. Then the equation of the parabola has the form: $x^2 = 4ay$. Since the parabola is 4 inches across and 1 inch deep, the points (2, 1) and (–2, 1) are on the parabola.

Substitute and solve for a: $2^2 = 4a(1) \Rightarrow 4 = 4a \Rightarrow a = 1$, a is the distance from the vertex to the focus. Thus, the bulb (located at the focus) should be 1 inch from the vertex.

67. Set up the problem so that the vertex of the parabola is at (0, 0) and it opens up. Then the equation of the parabola has the form: $x^2 = cy$.
The point (300, 80) is a point on the parabola.
Solve for c and find the equation:
$300^2 = c(80) \Rightarrow c = 1125$

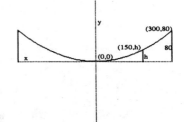

$$x^2 = 1125y$$

Since the height of the cable 150 feet from the center is to be found, the point (150, h) is a point on the parabola. Solve for h:
$150^2 = 1125h \Rightarrow 22,500 = 1125h \Rightarrow h = 20$
The height of the cable 150 feet from the center is 20 feet.

69. Set up the problem so that the vertex of the parabola is at (0, 0) and it opens up. Then the equation of the parabola has the form: $x^2 = 4ay$. a is the distance from the vertex to the focus (where the source is located), so $a = 2$. Since the opening is 5 feet across, there is a point (2.5, y) on the parabola.
Solve for y: $x^2 = 8y \Rightarrow 2.5^2 = 8y \Rightarrow 6.25 = 8y \Rightarrow y = 0.78125$ feet
The depth of the searchlight should be 0.78125 feet.

71. Set up the problem so that the vertex of the parabola is at (0, 0) and it opens up. Then the equation of the parabola has the form: $x^2 = 4ay$. Since the parabola is 20 feet across and 6 feet deep, the points (10, 6) and (–10, 6) are on the parabola.
Substitute and solve for a: $10^2 = 4a(6) \Rightarrow 100 = 24a \Rightarrow a \approx 4.17$ feet
The heat will be concentrated about 4.17 feet from the base, along the axis of symmetry.

73. Set up the problem so that the vertex of the parabola is at $(0, 0)$ and it opens down. Then the equation of the parabola has the form: $x^2 = cy$.

The point $(60, -25)$ is a point on the parabola.

Solve for c and find the equation:

$$60^2 = c(-25) \Rightarrow c = -144$$

$$x^2 = -144y$$

To find the height of the bridge 10 feet from the center the point $(10, y)$ is a point on the parabola. Solve for y:

$$10^2 = -144y \Rightarrow 100 = -144y \Rightarrow y \approx -0.69$$

The height of the bridge 10 feet from the center is about $25 - 0.69 = 24.31$ feet.

To find the height of the bridge 30 feet from the center the point $(30, y)$ is a point on the parabola. Solve for y:

$$30^2 = -144y \Rightarrow 900 = -144y \Rightarrow y \approx -6.25$$

The height of the bridge 30 feet from the center is $25 - 6.25 = 18.75$ feet.

To find the height of the bridge, 50 feet from the center, the point $(50, y)$ is a point on the parabola. Solve for y: $50^2 = -144y \Rightarrow 2500 = -144y \Rightarrow y = -17.36$

The height of the bridge 50 feet from the center is about $25 - 17.36 = 7.64$ feet.

75. $Ax^2 + Ey = 0 \quad A \neq 0, \ E \neq 0$

$$Ax^2 = -Ey \Rightarrow x^2 = -\frac{E}{A}y$$

This is the equation of a parabola with vertex at $(0, 0)$ and axis of symmetry being the y-axis. The focus is $\left(0, -\dfrac{E}{4A}\right)$. The directrix is $y = \dfrac{E}{4A}$.

The parabola opens up if $-\dfrac{E}{A} > 0$ and down if $-\dfrac{E}{A} < 0$.

77. $Ax^2 + Dx + Ey + F = 0 \quad A \neq 0$

(a) If $E \neq 0$, then:

$$Ax^2 + Dx = -Ey - F$$

$$A\left(x^2 + \frac{D}{A}x + \frac{D^2}{4A^2}\right) = -Ey - F + \frac{D^2}{4A}$$

$$\left(x + \frac{D}{2A}\right)^2 = \frac{1}{A}\left(-Ey - F + \frac{D^2}{4A}\right)$$

$$\left(x + \frac{D}{2A}\right)^2 = \frac{-E}{A}\left(y + \frac{F}{E} - \frac{D^2}{4AE}\right)$$

$$\left(x + \frac{D}{2A}\right)^2 = \frac{-E}{A}\left(y - \frac{D^2 - 4AF}{4AE}\right)$$

This is the equation of a parabola whose vertex is $\left(-\dfrac{D}{2A}, \dfrac{D^2 - 4AF}{4AE}\right)$ and whose axis of symmetry is parallel to the y-axis.

(b)   If $E = 0$, then $Ax^2 + Dx + F = 0 \Rightarrow x = \dfrac{-D \pm \sqrt{D^2 - 4AF}}{2A}$

If $D^2 - 4AF = 0$, then $x = -\dfrac{D}{2A}$ is a single vertical line.

(c)   If $E = 0$, then $Ax^2 + Dx + F = 0 \Rightarrow x = \dfrac{-D \pm \sqrt{D^2 - 4AF}}{2A}$

If $D^2 - 4AF > 0$,

then $x = \dfrac{-D + \sqrt{D^2 - 4AF}}{2A}$ and $x = \dfrac{-D - \sqrt{D^2 - 4AF}}{2A}$ are two vertical lines.

(d)   If $E = 0$, then $Ax^2 + Dx + F = 0 \Rightarrow x = \dfrac{-D \pm \sqrt{D^2 - 4AF}}{2A}$

If $D^2 - 4AF < 0$, there is no real solution. The graph contains no points.

Analytic Geometry

6.3　The Ellipse

1. $\sqrt{\left(4-2\right)^2+\left(-2-\left(-5\right)\right)^2}=\sqrt{2^2+3^2}=\sqrt{4+9}=\sqrt{13}$

3. $y^2=16-4x^2$
   x-intercept(s):
   $\quad 0^2=16-4x^2$
   $\quad 4x^2=16$
   $\quad\quad x^2=4\Rightarrow x=-2, x=2$
   $\quad\quad\quad \left(-2,0\right)$ and $\left(2,0\right)$
   y-intercept(s):
   $\quad y^2=16-4\left(0\right)^2$
   $\quad y^2=16\Rightarrow y=-4, y=4$
   $\quad\quad\quad \left(0,-4\right)$ and $\left(0,4\right)$

5. left, 1; down, 4

7. ellipse

9. $\left(0,-5\right),\ \left(0,5\right)$

11. True　　　　13.　*C*　　　　15.　*B*

17. $\dfrac{x^2}{25}+\dfrac{y^2}{4}=1$
    The center of the ellipse is at the origin.
    $a=5,\ b=2$. The vertices are $(5,0)$ and
    $(-5,0)$. Find the value of c:
    $c^2=a^2-b^2=25-4=21\Rightarrow c=\sqrt{21}$
    The foci are $\left(\sqrt{21},0\right)$ and $\left(-\sqrt{21},0\right)$.

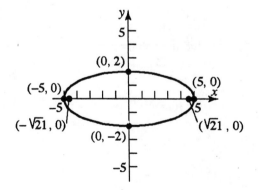

19. $\dfrac{x^2}{9} + \dfrac{y^2}{25} = 1$

The center of the ellipse is at the origin.
$a = 5,\ b = 3$. The vertices are $(0, 5)$ and $(0, -5)$.
Find the value of c:
$c^2 = a^2 - b^2 = 25 - 9 = 16$
$\quad c = 4$
The foci are $(0, 4)$ and $(0, -4)$.

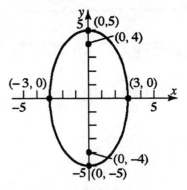

21. $4x^2 + y^2 = 16$

Divide by 16 to put in standard form:
$\dfrac{4x^2}{16} + \dfrac{y^2}{16} = \dfrac{16}{16} \Rightarrow \dfrac{x^2}{4} + \dfrac{y^2}{16} = 1$
The center of the ellipse is at the origin.
$a = 4,\ b = 2$.
The vertices are $(0, 4)$ and $(0, -4)$.
Find the value of c:
$c^2 = a^2 - b^2 = 16 - 4 = 12$
$\quad c = \sqrt{12} = 2\sqrt{3}$
The foci are $\left(0,\ 2\sqrt{3}\right)$ and $\left(0,\ -2\sqrt{3}\right)$.

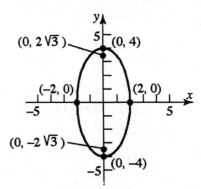

23. $4y^2 + x^2 = 8$

Divide by 8 to put in standard form:
$\dfrac{4y^2}{8} + \dfrac{x^2}{8} = \dfrac{8}{8} \Rightarrow \dfrac{x^2}{8} + \dfrac{y^2}{2} = 1$
The center of the ellipse is at the origin.
$a = \sqrt{8} = 2\sqrt{2},\ b = \sqrt{2}$.
The vertices are $\left(2\sqrt{2}, 0\right)$ and $\left(-2\sqrt{2}, 0\right)$.
Find the value of c:
$c^2 = a^2 - b^2 = 8 - 2 = 6$
$\quad c = \sqrt{6}$
The foci are $\left(\sqrt{6}, 0\right)$ and $\left(-\sqrt{6}, 0\right)$.

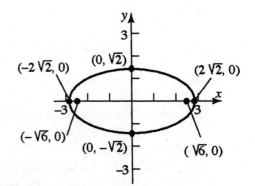

25. $x^2 + y^2 = 16$
     This is the equation of a circle whose center
     is at (0, 0) and radius 4.
     Vertices: (–4,0), (4,0), (0,–4), (0,4)
     Focus: (0,0)

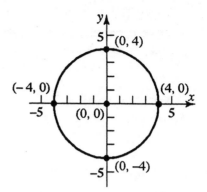

27. Center: (0, 0); Focus: (3, 0); Vertex: (5, 0);
     Major axis is the x-axis; $a = 5$; $c = 3$. Find b:
     $b^2 = a^2 - c^2 = 25 - 9 = 16$
       $b = 4$

     Write the equation: $\dfrac{x^2}{25} + \dfrac{y^2}{16} = 1$

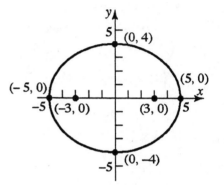

29. Center: (0, 0); Focus: (0, –4); Vertex: (0, 5);
     Major axis is the y-axis; $a = 5$; $c = 4$. Find b:
     $b^2 = a^2 - c^2 = 25 - 16 = 9$
       $b = 3$

     Write the equation: $\dfrac{x^2}{9} + \dfrac{y^2}{25} = 1$

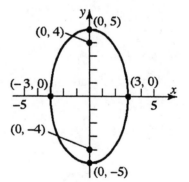

31. Foci: (±2, 0); Length of major axis is 6.
     Center: (0, 0); Major axis is the x-axis;
     $a = 3$; $c = 2$. Find b:
     $b^2 = a^2 - c^2 = 9 - 4 = 5$
       $b = \sqrt{5}$

     Write the equation: $\dfrac{x^2}{9} + \dfrac{y^2}{5} = 1$

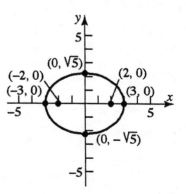

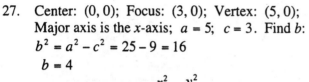

33. Focus: $(-4, 0)$; Vertices: $(\pm 5, 0)$.
    Center: $(0, 0)$; Major axis is the x-axis;
    $a = 5$; $c = 4$. Find b:
    $b^2 = a^2 - c^2 = 25 - 16 = 9$

    $b = 3$

    Write the equation: $\dfrac{x^2}{25} + \dfrac{y^2}{9} = 1$

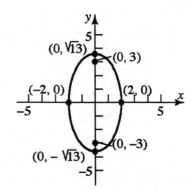

35. Foci: $(0, \pm 3)$; x-intercepts are ± 2. Center: $(0, 0)$;
    Major axis is the y-axis; $c = 3$; $b = 2$. Find a:
    $a^2 = b^2 + c^2 = 4 + 9 = 13$

    $a = \sqrt{13}$

    Write the equation: $\dfrac{x^2}{4} + \dfrac{y^2}{13} = 1$

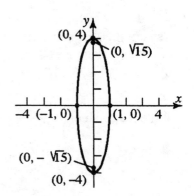

37. Center: $(0, 0)$; Vertex: $(0, 4)$; $b = 1$; Major axis is
    the y-axis; $a = 4$; $b = 1$. Find c:
    $c^2 = a^2 - b^2 = 16 - 1 = 15$

    $c = \sqrt{15}$

    Write the equation: $\dfrac{x^2}{1} + \dfrac{y^2}{16} = 1$

39. $\dfrac{(x+1)^2}{4} + \dfrac{(y-1)^2}{1} = 1$ 41. $\dfrac{(x-1)^2}{1} + \dfrac{y^2}{4} = 1$

43.   The equation $\dfrac{(x-3)^2}{4} + \dfrac{(y+1)^2}{9} = 1$ is in the form

$$\frac{(x-h)^2}{b^2} + \frac{(y-k)^2}{a^2} = 1$$

(major axis parallel to the y-axis) where
$a = 3$, $b = 2$, $h = 3$, and $k = -1$.
Solving for c: $c^2 = a^2 - b^2 = 9 - 4 = 5 \Rightarrow c = \sqrt{5}$
Thus, we have:
Center: $(3, -1)$
Foci: $\left(3, -1 + \sqrt{5}\right), \left(3, -1 - \sqrt{5}\right)$
Vertices: $(3, 2), (3, -4)$

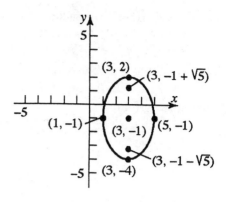

45.   Divide by 16 to put the equation in standard form:
$$(x+5)^2 + 4(y-4)^2 = 16$$

$$\frac{(x+5)^2}{16} + \frac{4(y-4)^2}{16} = \frac{16}{16}$$

$$\frac{(x+5)^2}{16} + \frac{(y-4)^2}{4} = 1$$

The equation is in the form
$\dfrac{(x-h)^2}{a^2} + \dfrac{(y-k)^2}{b^2} = 1$ (major axis parallel to
the x-axis) where $a = 4$, $b = 2$,
$h = -5$, and $k = 4$.
Solving for c:
$c^2 = a^2 - b^2 = 16 - 4 = 12 \Rightarrow c = \sqrt{12} = 2\sqrt{3}$
Thus, we have:
Center: $(-5, 4)$
Foci: $\left(-5 - 2\sqrt{3}, 4\right), \left(-5 + 2\sqrt{3}, 4\right)$
Vertices: $(-9, 4), (-1, 4)$

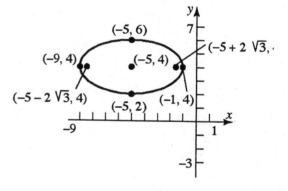

47.   Complete the squares to put the equation in standard form:
$$x^2 + 4x + 4y^2 - 8y + 4 = 0$$

$$(x^2 + 4x + 4) + 4(y^2 - 2y + 1) = -4 + 4 + 4$$

$$(x+2)^2 + 4(y-1)^2 = 4$$

$$\frac{(x+2)^2}{4} + \frac{4(y-1)^2}{4} = \frac{4}{4}$$

$$\frac{(x+2)^2}{4} + \frac{(y-1)^2}{1} = 1$$

The equation is in the form
$$\frac{(x-h)^2}{a^2} + \frac{(y-k)^2}{b^2} = 1$$
(major axis parallel to the x-axis) where
$a = 2$, $b = 1$, $h = -2$, and $k = 1$.
Solving for c:
$$c^2 = a^2 - b^2 = 4 - 1 = 3 \Rightarrow c = \sqrt{3}$$
Thus, we have:
Center: $(-2, 1)$
Foci: $\left(-2 - \sqrt{3}, 1\right), \left(-2 + \sqrt{3}, 1\right)$
Vertices: $(-4, 1)$, $(0, 1)$

49.   Complete the squares to put the equation in standard form:
$$2x^2 + 3y^2 - 8x + 6y + 5 = 0$$
$$2(x^2 - 4x) + 3(y^2 + 2y) = -5$$
$$2(x^2 - 4x + 4) + 3(y^2 + 2y + 1) = -5 + 8 + 3$$
$$2(x-2)^2 + 3(y+1)^2 = 6$$
$$\frac{2(x-2)^2}{6} + \frac{3(y+1)^2}{6} = \frac{6}{6}$$
$$\frac{(x-2)^2}{3} + \frac{(y+1)^2}{2} = 1$$

The equation is in the form $\dfrac{(x-h)^2}{a^2} + \dfrac{(y-k)^2}{b^2} = 1$

(major axis parallel to the x-axis) where
$a = \sqrt{3}$, $b = \sqrt{2}$, $h = 2$, and $k = -1$.
Solving for c: $c^2 = a^2 - b^2 = 3 - 2 = 1 \Rightarrow c = 1$
Thus, we have:
Center: $(2, -1)$
Foci: $(1, -1)$, $(3, -1)$
Vertices: $\left(2 - \sqrt{3}, -1\right), \left(2 + \sqrt{3}, -1\right)$

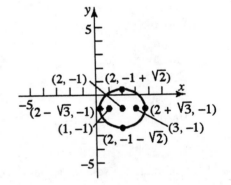

51.   Complete the squares to put the equation in standard form:
$$9x^2 + 4y^2 - 18x + 16y - 11 = 0$$
$$9(x^2 - 2x) + 4(y^2 + 4y) = 11$$
$$9(x^2 - 2x + 1) + 4(y^2 + 4y + 4) = 11 + 9 + 16$$
$$9(x-1)^2 + 4(y+2)^2 = 36$$
$$\frac{9(x-1)^2}{36} + \frac{4(y+2)^2}{36} = \frac{36}{36}$$
$$\frac{(x-1)^2}{4} + \frac{(y+2)^2}{9} = 1$$

The equation is in the form $\dfrac{(x-h)^2}{b^2} + \dfrac{(y-k)^2}{a^2} = 1$
(major axis parallel to the y-axis) where
$a = 3,\ b = 2,\ h = 1,$ and $k = -2$.
Solving for c: $c^2 = a^2 - b^2 = 9 - 4 = 5 \Rightarrow c = \sqrt{5}$
Thus, we have:
Center: $(1,-2)$
Foci: $\left(1, -2 + \sqrt{5}\right),\ \left(1, -2 - \sqrt{5}\right)$
Vertices: $(1, 1),\ (1, -5)$

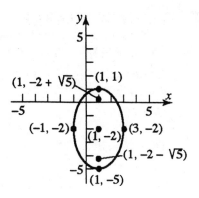

53. Complete the square to put the equation in standard form:
$$4x^2 + y^2 + 4y = 0$$
$$4x^2 + y^2 + 4y + 4 = 4$$
$$4x^2 + (y+2)^2 = 4$$
$$\frac{4x^2}{4} + \frac{(y+2)^2}{4} = \frac{4}{4}$$
$$\frac{x^2}{1} + \frac{(y+2)^2}{4} = 1$$
The equation is in the form
$\dfrac{(x-h)^2}{b^2} + \dfrac{(y-k)^2}{a^2} = 1$ (major axis parallel
to the y-axis) where
$a = 2,\ b = 1,\ h = 0,$ and $k = -2$.
Solving for c:
$c^2 = a^2 - b^2 = 4 - 1 = 3 \ \Rightarrow\ c = \sqrt{3}$
Thus, we have:
Center: $(0,-2)$
Foci: $\left(0, -2 + \sqrt{3}\right),\ \left(0, -2 - \sqrt{3}\right)$
Vertices: $(0, 0),\ (0, -4)$

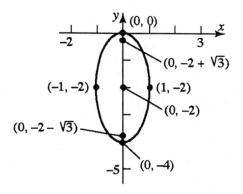

55. Center: $(2, -2)$; Vertex: $(7, -2)$;
Focus: $(4, -2)$; Major axis parallel to the
x-axis; $a = 5;\ c = 2$. Find b:
$$b^2 = a^2 - c^2 = 25 - 4 = 21$$
$$b = \sqrt{21}$$
Write the equation:
$$\frac{(x-2)^2}{25} + \frac{(y+2)^2}{21} = 1$$

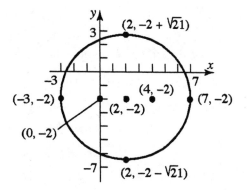

57. Vertices: $(4, 3), (4, 9)$; Focus: $(4, 8)$;
Center: $(4, 6)$; Major axis parallel to the
y-axis; $a = 3$; $c = 2$.
Find b:
$b^2 = a^2 - c^2 = 9 - 4 = 5$

$b = \sqrt{5}$

Write the equation: $\dfrac{(x-4)^2}{5} + \dfrac{(y-6)^2}{9} = 1$

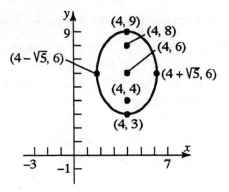

59. Foci: $(5, 1), (-1, 1)$; length of the major axis $= 8$;
Center: $(2, 1)$; Major axis parallel to the x-axis;
$a = 4$; $c = 3$.   Find b:
$b^2 = a^2 - c^2 = 16 - 9 = 7$

$b = \sqrt{7}$

Write the equation: $\dfrac{(x-2)^2}{16} + \dfrac{(y-1)^2}{7} = 1$

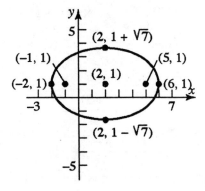

61. Center: $(1, 2)$; Focus: $(4, 2)$; contains the point $(1, 3)$;
Major axis parallel to the x-axis; $c = 3$.

The equation has the form: $\dfrac{(x-1)^2}{a^2} + \dfrac{(y-2)^2}{b^2} = 1.$

Since the point $(1, 3)$ is on the curve:

$\dfrac{0}{a^2} + \dfrac{1}{b^2} = 1$

$\dfrac{1}{b^2} = 1$

$b^2 = 1 \Rightarrow b = 1$

Find a:
$a^2 = b^2 + c^2 = 1 + 9 = 10 \Rightarrow a = \sqrt{10}$

Write the equation: $\dfrac{(x-1)^2}{10} + \dfrac{(y-2)^2}{1} = 1$

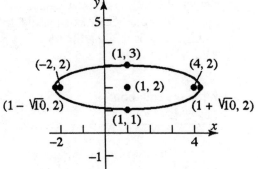

63. Center: $(1, 2)$; Vertex: $(4, 2)$; contains the point $(1, 3)$; Major axis parallel to the x-axis; $a = 3$.

The equation has the form:

$$\frac{(x-1)^2}{a^2} + \frac{(y-2)^2}{b^2} = 1$$

Since the point $(1, 3)$ is on the curve:

$$\frac{0}{a^2} + \frac{1}{b^2} = 1$$

$$\frac{1}{b^2} = 1$$

$$b^2 = 1 \Rightarrow b = 1$$

Find c:

$$c^2 = a^2 - b^2 = 9 - 1 = 8 \Rightarrow c = \sqrt{8} = 2\sqrt{2}$$

Write the equation: $\dfrac{(x-1)^2}{9} + \dfrac{(y-2)^2}{1} = 1$

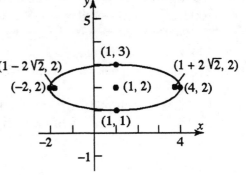

65. Rewrite the equation:

$$y = \sqrt{16 - 4x^2}$$

$$y^2 = 16 - 4x^2, \quad y \geq 0$$

$$4x^2 + y^2 = 16, \quad y \geq 0$$

$$\frac{x^2}{4} + \frac{y^2}{16} = 1, \quad y \geq 0$$

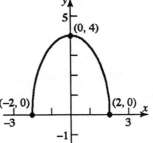

67. Rewrite the equation:

$$y = -\sqrt{64 - 16x^2}$$

$$y^2 = 64 - 16x^2, \quad y \leq 0$$

$$16x^2 + y^2 = 64, \quad y \leq 0$$

$$\frac{x^2}{4} + \frac{y^2}{64} = 1, \quad y \leq 0$$

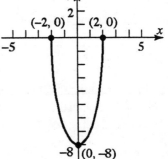

69. The center of the ellipse is $(0, 0)$. The length of the major axis is 20, so $a = 10$. The length of half the minor axis is 6, so $b = 6$. The ellipse is situated with its major axis on the x-axis. The equation is: $\dfrac{x^2}{100} + \dfrac{y^2}{36} = 1$.

71. Assume that the half ellipse formed by the gallery is centered at $(0, 0)$. Since the hall is 100 feet long, $2a = 100$ or $a = 50$. The distance from the center to the foci is 25 feet, so $c = 25$. Find the height of the gallery, which is b:
$$b^2 = a^2 - c^2 = 2500 - 625 = 1875 \implies b = \sqrt{1875} \approx 43.3$$
The ceiling is about 43.3 feet high in the center.

73. Place the semielliptical arch so that the x-axis coincides with the major axis and the y-axis passes through the center of the arch. Since the bridge has a span of 120 feet, the length of the major axis is 120, or $2a = 120$ or $a = 60$. The maximum height of the bridge is 25 feet, so $b = 25$. The equation is: $\dfrac{x^2}{3600} + \dfrac{y^2}{625} = 1$.
The height 10 feet from the center:
$$\frac{10^2}{3600} + \frac{y^2}{625} = 1 \implies \frac{y^2}{625} = 1 - \frac{100}{3600} \implies y^2 = 625 \cdot \frac{3500}{3600} \implies y \approx 24.65 \text{ feet}$$
The height 30 feet from the center:
$$\frac{30^2}{3600} + \frac{y^2}{625} = 1 \implies \frac{y^2}{625} = 1 - \frac{900}{3600} \implies y^2 = 625 \cdot \frac{2700}{3600} \implies y \approx 21.65 \text{ feet}$$
The height 50 feet from the center:
$$\frac{50^2}{3600} + \frac{y^2}{625} = 1 \implies \frac{y^2}{625} = 1 - \frac{2500}{3600} \implies y^2 = 625 \cdot \frac{1100}{3600} \implies y \approx 13.82 \text{ feet}$$

75. Place the semielliptical arch so that the x-axis coincides with the major axis and the y-axis passes through the center of the arch. Since the ellipse is 40 feet wide, the length of the major axis is 40, or $2a = 40$ or $a = 20$. The height is 15 feet at the center, so $b = 15$. The equation is: $\dfrac{x^2}{400} + \dfrac{y^2}{225} = 1$.
The height 10 feet either side of the center:
$$\frac{10^2}{400} + \frac{y^2}{225} = 1 \implies \frac{y^2}{225} = 1 - \frac{100}{400} \implies y^2 = 225 \cdot \frac{3}{4} \implies y \approx 12.99 \text{ feet}$$
The height 20 feet either side of the center:
$$\frac{20^2}{400} + \frac{y^2}{225} = 1 \implies \frac{y^2}{225} = 1 - \frac{400}{400} \implies y^2 = 225 \cdot 0 \implies y \approx 0 \text{ feet}$$

77. Since the mean distance is 93 million miles, $a = 93$ million. The length of the major axis is 186 million. The perihelion is 186 million $-$ 94.5 million $=$ 91.5 million miles. The distance from the center of the ellipse to the sun (focus) is 93 million $-$ 91.5 million $=$ 1.5 million miles; therefore, $c = 1.5$ million. Find b:
$$b^2 = a^2 - c^2 = (93 \times 10^6)^2 - (1.5 \times 10^6)^2 = 8.64675 \times 10^{15} \implies b \approx 92.99 \times 10^6$$
The equation of the orbit is: $\dfrac{x^2}{(93 \times 10^6)^2} + \dfrac{y^2}{(92.99 \times 10^6)^2} = 1$.

79. The mean distance is 507 million – 23.2 million = 483.8 million miles.
    The perihelion is 483.8 million – 23.2 million = 460.6 million miles.
    Since $a = 483.8 \times 10^6$ and $c = 23.2 \times 10^6$, we can find b:
    $$b^2 = a^2 - c^2 = \left(483.8 \times 10^6\right)^2 - \left(23.2 \times 10^6\right)^2 = 2.335242 \times 10^{17} \Rightarrow b \approx 483.2 \times 10^6$$
    The equation of the orbit of Jupiter is: $\dfrac{x^2}{\left(483.8 \times 10^6\right)^2} + \dfrac{y^2}{\left(483.2 \times 10^6\right)^2} = 1$.

81. If the x-axis is placed along the 100 foot length and the y-axis is placed along the 50-foot
    width, the equation for the ellipse is: $\dfrac{x^2}{50^2} + \dfrac{y^2}{25^2} = 1$.
    Find y when $x = 40$:
    $$\frac{40^2}{50^2} + \frac{y^2}{25^2} = 1 \Rightarrow \frac{y^2}{625} = 1 - \frac{1600}{2500} \Rightarrow y^2 = 625 \cdot \frac{9}{25} \Rightarrow y = 15 \text{ feet}$$
    The width 10 feet from a vertex is about 30 feet.

83. (a) Put the equation in standard ellipse form:
    $$Ax^2 + Cy^2 + F = 0 \quad A \neq 0, C \neq 0, F \neq 0$$
    $$Ax^2 + Cy^2 = -F$$
    $$\frac{Ax^2}{-F} + \frac{Cy^2}{-F} = 1$$
    $$\frac{x^2}{(-F/A)} + \frac{y^2}{(-F/C)} = 1$$
    Since the sign of F is opposite that of A and C, $-F/A$ and $-F/C$ are positive.
    This is the equation of an ellipse with center at $(0, 0)$.
    (b) If $A = C$, the equation becomes:
    $$Ax^2 + Ay^2 = -F \Rightarrow x^2 + y^2 = -\frac{F}{A}$$
    This is the equation of a circle with center at $(0, 0)$ and radius of $\sqrt{-\dfrac{F}{A}}$.

85. Answers will vary.

Chapter 6

Analytic Geometry

6.4 The Hyperbola

1. $\sqrt{(-2-3)^2 + (1-(-4))^2} = \sqrt{(-5)^2 + 5^2} = \sqrt{25+25} = \sqrt{50} = 5\sqrt{2}$

3. $y^2 = 9 + 4x^2$
   x-intercept(s):
   $0^2 = 9 + 4x^2$
   $-4x^2 = 9$
   $x^2 = -\dfrac{9}{4} \Rightarrow$ no real solution
   No x-intercepts.
   y-intercept(s):
   $y^2 = 9 + 4(0)^2$
   $y^2 = 9 \Rightarrow y = -3, y = 3$
   $(0,-3)$ and $(0,3)$

5. right, 5; down, 4

7. hyperbola

9. $y = \dfrac{3}{2}x,\ y = -\dfrac{3}{2}x$

11. True

13. *B*

15. *A*

17. Center: $(0,0)$; Focus: $(3,0)$; Vertex: $(1,0)$;
    Transverse axis is the x-axis; $a = 1$; $c = 3$.
    Find the value of b:
    $b^2 = c^2 - a^2 = 9 - 1 = 8$
    $b = \sqrt{8} = 2\sqrt{2}$
    Write the equation: $\dfrac{x^2}{1} - \dfrac{y^2}{8} = 1$.

19. Center: $(0, 0)$; Focus: $(0, -6)$; Vertex: $(0, 4)$
Transverse axis is the y-axis; $a = 4$; $c = 6$.
Find the value of b:
$b^2 = c^2 - a^2 = 36 - 16 = 20$
$b = \sqrt{20} = 2\sqrt{5}$
Write the equation: $\dfrac{y^2}{16} - \dfrac{x^2}{20} = 1$.

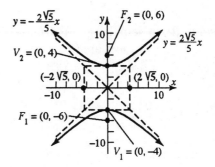

21. Foci: $(-5, 0)$, $(5, 0)$; Vertex: $(3, 0)$
Center: $(0, 0)$; Transverse axis is the
x-axis; $a = 3$; $c = 5$.
Find the value of b:
$b^2 = c^2 - a^2 = 25 - 9 = 16 \Rightarrow b = 4$
Write the equation: $\dfrac{x^2}{9} - \dfrac{y^2}{16} = 1$.

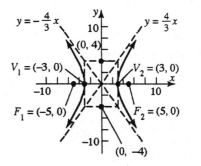

23. Vertices: $(0, -6)$, $(0, 6)$; Asymptote: $y = 2x$;
Center: $(0, 0)$; Transverse axis is the y-axis;
$a = 6$. Find the value of b using the slope of
the asymptote: $\dfrac{a}{b} = \dfrac{6}{b} = 2 \Rightarrow 2b = 6 \Rightarrow b = 3$
Find the value of c:
$c^2 = a^2 + b^2 = 36 + 9 = 45 \Rightarrow c = 3\sqrt{5}$
Write the equation: $\dfrac{y^2}{36} - \dfrac{x^2}{9} = 1$.

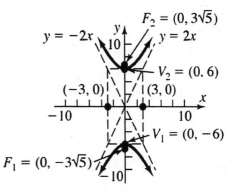

25. Foci: $(-4, 0)$, $(4, 0)$; Asymptote: $y = -x$;
Center: $(0, 0)$; Transverse axis is the
x-axis; $c = 4$. Using the slope of the
asymptote: $-\dfrac{b}{a} = -1 \Rightarrow -b = -a \Rightarrow b = a$.
Find the value of b:
$b^2 = c^2 - a^2 \Rightarrow a^2 + b^2 = c^2$ $(c = 4)$
$b^2 + b^2 = 16 \Rightarrow 2b^2 = 16 \Rightarrow b^2 = 8$
$b = \sqrt{8} = 2\sqrt{2}$
$a = \sqrt{8} = 2\sqrt{2}$ $(a = b)$
Write the equation: $\dfrac{x^2}{8} - \dfrac{y^2}{8} = 1$.

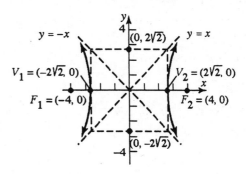

27. $\dfrac{x^2}{25} - \dfrac{y^2}{9} = 1$

The center of the hyperbola is at $(0, 0)$.
$a = 5$, $b = 3$. The vertices are $(5, 0)$ and
$(-5, 0)$. Find the value of c:
$c^2 = a^2 + b^2 = 25 + 9 = 34 \Rightarrow c = \sqrt{34}$
The foci are $\left(\sqrt{34}, 0\right)$ and $\left(-\sqrt{34}, 0\right)$.
The transverse axis is the x-axis.

The asymptotes are $y = \dfrac{3}{5}x$; $y = -\dfrac{3}{5}x$.

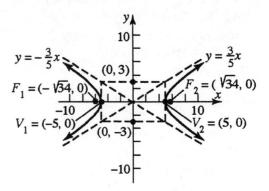

29. $4x^2 - y^2 = 16$

Divide both sides by 16 to put in standard form: $\dfrac{4x^2}{16} - \dfrac{y^2}{16} = \dfrac{16}{16} \Rightarrow \dfrac{x^2}{4} - \dfrac{y^2}{16} = 1$.

The center of the hyperbola is at $(0, 0)$.
$a = 2$, $b = 4$.
The vertices are $(2, 0)$ and $(-2, 0)$.
Find the value of c:
$c^2 = a^2 + b^2 = 4 + 16 = 20$
$c = \sqrt{20} = 2\sqrt{5}$
The foci are $\left(2\sqrt{5}, 0\right)$ and $\left(-2\sqrt{5}, 0\right)$.
The transverse axis is the x-axis.
The asymptotes are $y = 2x$; $y = -2x$.

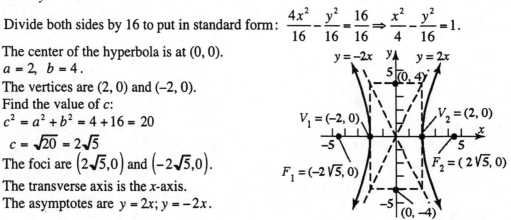

31. $y^2 - 9x^2 = 9$

Divide both sides by 9 to put in standard form: $\dfrac{y^2}{9} - \dfrac{9x^2}{9} = \dfrac{9}{9} \Rightarrow \dfrac{y^2}{9} - \dfrac{x^2}{1} = 1$.

The center of the hyperbola is at $(0, 0)$.
$a = 3$, $b = 1$.
The vertices are $(0, 3)$ and $(0, -3)$.
Find the value of c:
$c^2 = a^2 + b^2 = 9 + 1 = 10$
$c = \sqrt{10}$
The foci are $\left(0, \sqrt{10}\right)$ and $\left(0, -\sqrt{10}\right)$.
The transverse axis is the y-axis.
The asymptotes are $y = 3x$; $y = -3x$.

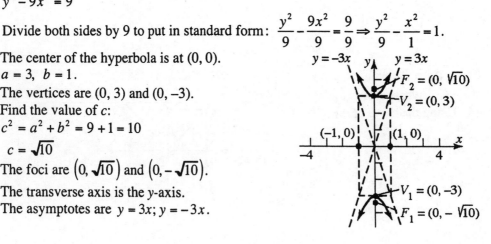

33. $y^2 - x^2 = 25$

Divide both sides by 25 to put in standard form: $\frac{y^2}{25} - \frac{x^2}{25} = 1$.

The center of the hyperbola is at $(0, 0)$.
$a = 5$, $b = 5$. The vertices are $(0, 5)$ and $(0, -5)$.
Find the value of c:
$c^2 = a^2 + b^2 = 25 + 25 = 50$

$c = \sqrt{50} = 5\sqrt{2}$

The foci are $\left(0, 5\sqrt{2}\right)$ and $\left(0, -5\sqrt{2}\right)$.

The transverse axis is the y-axis.
The asymptotes are $y = x$; $y = -x$.

35.   The center of the hyperbola is at $(0, 0)$.
$a = 1$, $b = 1$. The vertices are $(1, 0)$ and $(-1, 0)$.
Find the value of c:
$c^2 = a^2 + b^2 = 1 + 1 = 2$

$c = \sqrt{2}$

The foci are $\left(\sqrt{2}, 0\right)$ and $\left(-\sqrt{2}, 0\right)$.

The transverse axis is the x-axis.
The asymptotes are $y = x$; $y = -x$.
The equation is: $x^2 - y^2 = 1$.

37.   The center of the hyperbola is at $(0, 0)$.
$a = 6$, $b = 3$. The vertices are $(0, -6)$ and $(0, 6)$.
Find the value of c:
$c^2 = a^2 + b^2 = 36 + 9 = 45$

$c = \sqrt{45} = 3\sqrt{5}$

The foci are $\left(0, -3\sqrt{5}\right)$ and $\left(0, 3\sqrt{5}\right)$.

The transverse axis is the y-axis.
The asymptotes are $y = 2x$; $y = -2x$.

The equation is: $\frac{y^2}{36} - \frac{x^2}{9} = 1$.

39.   Center: $(4, -1)$; Focus: $(7, -1)$;
Vertex: $(6, -1)$; Transverse axis is parallel
to the x-axis; $a = 2$; $c = 3$.
Find the value of b:
$$b^2 = c^2 - a^2 = 9 - 4 = 5 \Rightarrow b = \sqrt{5}$$
Write the equation: $\dfrac{(x-4)^2}{4} - \dfrac{(y+1)^2}{5} = 1$.

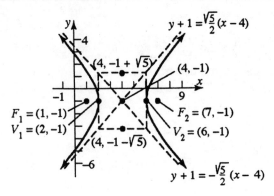

41.   Center: $(-3, -4)$;
Focus: $(-3, -8)$;
Vertex: $(-3, -2)$;
Transverse axis is parallel to the
y-axis; $a = 2$; $c = 4$.
Find the value of b:
$$b^2 = c^2 - a^2 = 16 - 4 = 12$$
$$b = \sqrt{12} = 2\sqrt{3}$$
Write the equation:
$$\frac{(y+4)^2}{4} - \frac{(x+3)^2}{12} = 1.$$

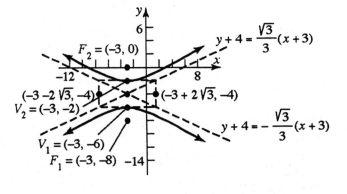

43.   Foci: $(3, 7), (7, 7)$; Vertex: $(6, 7)$;
Center: $(5, 7)$; Transverse axis is parallel to
the x-axis; $a = 1$; $c = 2$.
Find the value of b:
$$b^2 = c^2 - a^2 = 4 - 1 = 3$$
$$b = \sqrt{3}$$
Write the equation: $\dfrac{(x-5)^2}{1} - \dfrac{(y-7)^2}{3} = 1$.

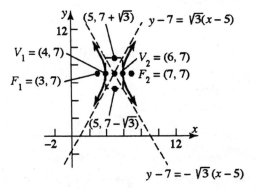

45.   Vertices: $(-1, -1), (3, -1)$;
Center: $(1, -1)$; Transverse axis is
parallel to the x-axis; $a = 2$.

Asymptote: $y + 1 = \dfrac{3}{2}(x - 1)$

Using the slope of the asymptote, find
the value of b:

$\dfrac{b}{a} = \dfrac{b}{2} = \dfrac{3}{2} \Rightarrow b = 3$

Find the value of c:

$c^2 = a^2 + b^2 = 4 + 9 = 13$

$c = \sqrt{13}$

Write the equation: $\dfrac{(x-1)^2}{4} - \dfrac{(y+1)^2}{9} = 1$.

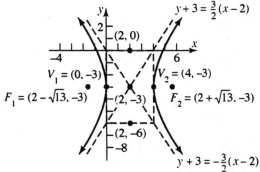

47. $\dfrac{(x-2)^2}{4} - \dfrac{(y+3)^2}{9} = 1$

The center of the hyperbola is at $(2, -3)$.
$a = 2, \ b = 3$.
The vertices are $(0, -3)$ and $(4, -3)$.
Find the value of c:
$c^2 = a^2 + b^2 = 4 + 9 = 13 \Rightarrow c = \sqrt{13}$
Foci: $\left(2 - \sqrt{13}, -3\right)$ and $\left(2 + \sqrt{13}, -3\right)$.
Transverse axis: $y = -3$,
parallel to the x-axis.

Asymptotes: $y + 3 = \dfrac{3}{2}(x - 2)$;

$y + 3 = -\dfrac{3}{2}(x - 2)$.

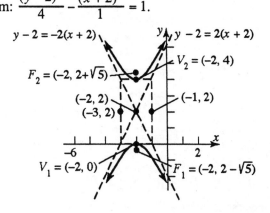

49. $(y - 2)^2 - 4(x + 2)^2 = 4$

Divide both sides by 4 to put in standard form: $\dfrac{(y-2)^2}{4} - \dfrac{(x+2)^2}{1} = 1$.

The center of the hyperbola is at $(-2, 2)$.
$a = 2, \ b = 1$.
The vertices are $(-2, 4)$ and $(-2, 0)$.
Find the value of c:
$c^2 = a^2 + b^2 = 4 + 1 = 5 \Rightarrow c = \sqrt{5}$
Foci: $\left(-2, 2 - \sqrt{5}\right)$ and $\left(-2, 2 + \sqrt{5}\right)$.
Transverse axis: $x = -2$, parallel to the
y-axis.
Asymptotes:
$y - 2 = 2(x + 2); \ y - 2 = -2(x + 2)$.

51. $(x+1)^2 - (y+2)^2 = 4$

Divide both sides by 4 to put in standard form: $\dfrac{(x+1)^2}{4} - \dfrac{(y+2)^2}{4} = 1$.

The center of the hyperbola is $(-1, -2)$.
$a = 2, \ b = 2$.
The vertices are $(-3, -2)$ and $(1, -2)$.
Find the value of c:
$c^2 = a^2 + b^2 = 4 + 4 = 8$

$c = \sqrt{8} = 2\sqrt{2}$
Foci: $\left(-1 - 2\sqrt{2}, -2\right)$ and $\left(-1 + 2\sqrt{2}, -2\right)$.
Transverse axis: $y = -2$, parallel to the x-axis.
Asymptotes: $y + 2 = x + 1$;
$\qquad\qquad\quad\ y + 2 = -(x + 1)$.

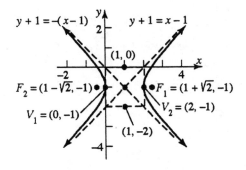

53. Complete the squares to put in standard form:
$$x^2 - y^2 - 2x - 2y - 1 = 0$$
$$(x^2 - 2x + 1) - (y^2 + 2y + 1) = 1 + 1 - 1$$
$$(x-1)^2 - (y+1)^2 = 1$$
The center of the hyperbola is $(1, -1)$.
$a = 1, \ b = 1$.
The vertices are $(0, -1)$ and $(2, -1)$.
Find the value of c:
$c^2 = a^2 + b^2 = 1 + 1 = 2 \Rightarrow c = \sqrt{2}$
Foci: $\left(1 - \sqrt{2}, -1\right)$ and $\left(1 + \sqrt{2}, -1\right)$.
Transverse axis: $y = -1$, parallel to the x-axis.
Asymptotes: $y + 1 = x - 1$; $y + 1 = -(x - 1)$.

55. Complete the squares to put in standard form:
$$y^2 - 4x^2 - 4y - 8x - 4 = 0$$
$$(y^2 - 4y + 4) - 4(x^2 + 2x + 1) = 4 + 4 - 4$$
$$(y - 2)^2 - 4(x + 1)^2 = 4$$
$$\frac{(y-2)^2}{4} - \frac{(x+1)^2}{1} = 1$$
The center of the hyperbola is $(-1, 2)$.
$a = 2, \ b = 1$.
The vertices are $(-1, 4)$ and $(-1, 0)$.
Find the value of c:
$c^2 = a^2 + b^2 = 4 + 1 = 5 \Rightarrow c = \sqrt{5}$
Foci: $\left(-1, 2 - \sqrt{5}\right)$ and $\left(-1, 2 + \sqrt{5}\right)$.
Transverse axis: $x = -1$, parallel to the y-axis.
Asymptotes: $y - 2 = 2(x + 1)$; $y - 2 = -2(x + 1)$.

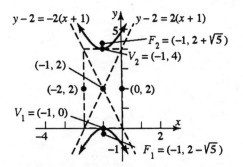

57. Complete the squares to put in standard form:
$$4x^2 - y^2 - 24x - 4y + 16 = 0$$
$$4(x^2 - 6x + 9) - (y^2 + 4y + 4) = -16 + 36 - 4$$
$$4(x - 3)^2 - (y + 2)^2 = 16$$
$$\frac{(x - 3)^2}{4} - \frac{(y + 2)^2}{16} = 1$$

The center of the hyperbola is $(3, -2)$. $a = 2$, $b = 4$.
The vertices are $(1, -2)$ and $(5, -2)$. Find the value of c:
$$c^2 = a^2 + b^2 = 4 + 16 = 20$$
$$c = \sqrt{20} = 2\sqrt{5}$$
Foci:
$$\left(3 - 2\sqrt{5}, -2\right) \text{ and } \left(3 + 2\sqrt{5}, -2\right).$$
Transverse axis: $y = -2$, parallel to the x-axis.
Asymptotes: $y + 2 = 2(x - 3)$;
$$y + 2 = -2(x - 3)$$

59. Complete the squares to put in standard form:
$$y^2 - 4x^2 - 16x - 2y - 19 = 0$$
$$(y^2 - 2y + 1) - 4(x^2 + 4x + 4) = 19 + 1 - 16$$
$$(y - 1)^2 - 4(x + 2)^2 = 4$$
$$\frac{(y - 1)^2}{4} - \frac{(x + 2)^2}{1} = 1$$

The center of the hyperbola is $(-2, 1)$.
$a = 2$, $b = 1$.
The vertices are $(-2, 3)$ and $(-2, -1)$. Find the value of c:
$$c^2 = a^2 + b^2 = 4 + 1 = 5$$
$$c = \sqrt{5}$$
Foci: $\left(-2, 1 - \sqrt{5}\right)$ and $\left(-2, 1 + \sqrt{5}\right)$.
Transverse axis: $x = -2$, parallel to the y-axis.
Asymptotes: $y - 1 = 2(x + 2)$; $y - 1 = -2(x + 2)$.

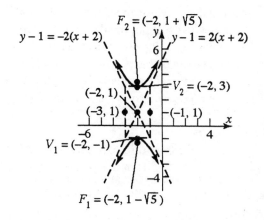

61. Rewrite the equation:
$$y = \sqrt{16 + 4x^2}$$
$$y^2 = 16 + 4x^2, \quad y \geq 0$$
$$y^2 - 4x^2 = 16, \quad y \geq 0$$
$$\frac{y^2}{16} - \frac{x^2}{4} = 1, \quad y \geq 0$$

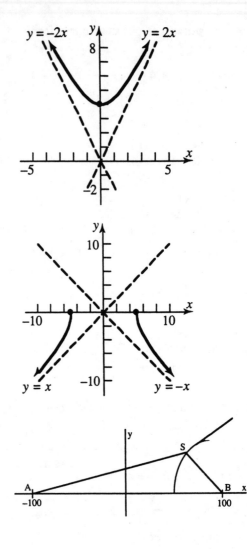

63. Rewrite the equation:
$$y = -\sqrt{-25 + x^2}$$
$$y^2 = -25 + x^2, \quad y \leq 0$$
$$x^2 - y^2 = 25, \quad y \leq 0$$
$$\frac{x^2}{25} - \frac{y^2}{25} = 1, \quad y \leq 0$$

65. (a) Set up a coordinate system so that the two stations lie on the x-axis and the origin is midway between them. The ship lies on a hyperbola whose foci are the locations of the two stations. Since the time difference is 0.00038 second and the speed of the signal is 186,000 miles per second, the difference in the distances of the ships from each station is: $(186,000)(0.00038) = 70.68$ miles
The difference of the distances from the ship to each station, 70.68, equals $2a$, so $a = 35.34$ and the vertex of the corresponding hyperbola is at $(35.34, 0)$. Since the focus is at $(100, 0)$, following this hyperbola, the ship would reach shore 64.66 miles from the master station.

(b) The ship should follow a hyperbola with a vertex at $(80, 0)$. For this hyperbola, $a = 80$, so the constant difference of the distances from the ship to each station is 160. The time difference the ship should look for is: time $= \dfrac{160}{186,000} \approx 0.00086$ second.

(c) Find the equation of the hyperbola with vertex at $(80, 0)$ and a focus at $(100, 0)$. The form of the equation of the hyperbola is $\dfrac{x^2}{a^2} - \dfrac{y^2}{b^2} = 1$ where $a = 80$.
Since $c = 100$ and $b^2 = c^2 - a^2 \Rightarrow b^2 = 100^2 - 80^2 = 3600$.
The equation of the hyperbola is: $\dfrac{x^2}{6400} - \dfrac{y^2}{3600} = 1$.
Since the ship is 50 miles off shore, we have $y = 50$. Solve the equation for x:

$$\frac{x^2}{6400} - \frac{50^2}{3600} = 1 \implies \frac{x^2}{6400} = 1 + \frac{2500}{3600} = \frac{61}{36}$$

$$x^2 = 6400 \cdot \frac{61}{36} \implies x \approx 104 \text{ miles}$$

The ship's location is approximately (104, 50).

67. (a) Set up a rectangular coordinate system so that the two devices lie on the x-axis and the origin is midway between them. The devices serve as foci to the hyperbola so $c = \dfrac{2000}{2} = 1000$. Since the explosion occurs 200 feet from point B, the vertex of the hyperbola is (800, 0); therefore, $a = 800$. Finding b:

$$b^2 = c^2 - a^2 \implies b^2 = 1000^2 - 800^2 = 360,000 \implies b = 600$$

The equation of the hyperbola is: $\dfrac{x^2}{800^2} - \dfrac{y^2}{600^2} = 1$

If $x = 1000$, find y:

$$\frac{1000^2}{800^2} - \frac{y^2}{600^2} = 1 \implies \frac{y^2}{600^2} = \frac{1000^2}{800^2} - 1 = \frac{600^2}{800^2}$$

$$y^2 = 600^2 \cdot \frac{600^2}{800^2} \implies y = 450 \text{ feet}$$

The second detonation should take place 450 feet north of point B.

(b) Answers will vary.

69. If the eccentricity is close to 1, then $c \approx a$ and $b \approx 0$. When b is close to 0, the hyperbola is very narrow, because the slopes of the asymptotes are close to 0.
If the eccentricity is very large, then c is much larger than a and b is very large. The result is a hyperbola that is very wide.

71. $\dfrac{x^2}{4} - y^2 = 1$ $(a = 2, \ b = 1)$

This is a hyperbola with horizontal transverse axis, centered at (0, 0) and has asymptotes: $y = \pm\dfrac{1}{2}x$

$y^2 - \dfrac{x^2}{4} = 1$ $(a = 1, \ b = 2)$

This is a hyperbola with vertical transverse axis, centered at (0, 0) and has asymptotes: $y = \pm\dfrac{1}{2}x$.

Since the two hyperbolas have the same asymptotes, they are conjugate.

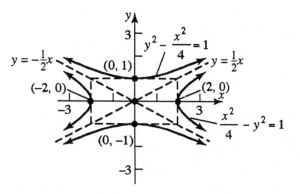

73. Put the equation in standard hyperbola form:

$$Ax^2 + Cy^2 + F = 0 \qquad A \neq 0, \ C \neq 0, \ F \neq 0$$

$$Ax^2 + Cy^2 = -F$$

$$\frac{Ax^2}{-F} + \frac{Cy^2}{-F} = 1$$

$$\frac{x^2}{\left(-\dfrac{F}{A}\right)} + \frac{y^2}{\left(-\dfrac{F}{C}\right)} = 1$$

Since $-F/A$ and $-F/C$ have opposite signs, this is a hyperbola with center $(0, 0)$.

The transverse axis is the x-axis if $-F/A > 0$.

The transverse axis is the y-axis if $-F/A < 0$.

Chapter 6

Analytic Geometry

6.5   Rotation of Axes; General Form of a Conic

1. $\sin\alpha\cos\beta + \cos\alpha\sin\beta$

3. $\sqrt{\dfrac{1-\cos\theta}{2}}$

5. $\cot(2\theta) = \dfrac{A-C}{B}$

7. $x^2 + 2xy + 3y^2 - 2x + 4y + 10 = 0$
    $A = 1$, $B = 2$, and $C = 3$; $B^2 - 4AC = 2^2 - 4(1)(3) = -8$. Since $B^2 - 4AC < 0$, the equation defines an ellipse.

9. True

11. $x^2 + 4x + y + 3 = 0$
    $A = 1$ and $C = 0$; $AC = (1)(0) = 0$. Since $AC = 0$, the equation defines a parabola.

13. $6x^2 + 3y^2 - 12x + 6y = 0$
    $A = 6$ and $C = 3$; $AC = (6)(3) = 18$. Since $AC > 0$ and $A \neq C$, the equation defines an ellipse.

15. $3x^2 - 2y^2 + 6x + 4 = 0$
    $A = 3$ and $C = -2$; $AC = (3)(-2) = -6$. Since $AC < 0$, the equation defines a hyperbola.

17. $2y^2 - x^2 - y + x = 0$
    $A = -1$ and $C = 2$; $AC = (-1)(2) = -2$. Since $AC < 0$, the equation defines a hyperbola.

19. $x^2 + y^2 - 8x + 4y = 0$
    $A = 1$ and $C = 1$; $AC = (1)(1) = 1$. Since $AC > 0$ and $A = C$, the equation defines a circle.

21. $x^2 + 4xy + y^2 - 3 = 0$

$A = 1, B = 4,$ and $C = 1;$

$$\cot(2\theta) = \frac{A-C}{B} = \frac{1-1}{4} = \frac{0}{4} = 0 \Rightarrow 2\theta = \frac{\pi}{2} \Rightarrow \theta = \frac{\pi}{4}$$

$$x = x'\cos\frac{\pi}{4} - y'\sin\frac{\pi}{4} = \frac{\sqrt{2}}{2}x' - \frac{\sqrt{2}}{2}y' = \frac{\sqrt{2}}{2}(x' - y')$$

$$y = x'\sin\frac{\pi}{4} + y'\cos\frac{\pi}{4} = \frac{\sqrt{2}}{2}x' + \frac{\sqrt{2}}{2}y' = \frac{\sqrt{2}}{2}(x' + y')$$

23. $5x^2 + 6xy + 5y^2 - 8 = 0$

$A = 5, B = 6,$ and $C = 5;$

$$\cot(2\theta) = \frac{A-C}{B} = \frac{5-5}{6} = \frac{0}{6} = 0 \Rightarrow 2\theta = \frac{\pi}{2} \Rightarrow \theta = \frac{\pi}{4}$$

$$x = x'\cos\frac{\pi}{4} - y'\sin\frac{\pi}{4} = \frac{\sqrt{2}}{2}x' - \frac{\sqrt{2}}{2}y' = \frac{\sqrt{2}}{2}(x' - y')$$

$$y = x'\sin\frac{\pi}{4} + y'\cos\frac{\pi}{4} = \frac{\sqrt{2}}{2}x' + \frac{\sqrt{2}}{2}y' = \frac{\sqrt{2}}{2}(x' + y')$$

25. $13x^2 - 6\sqrt{3}xy + 7y^2 - 16 = 0$

$A = 13, B = -6\sqrt{3},$ and $C = 7;$

$$\cot(2\theta) = \frac{A-C}{B} = \frac{13-7}{-6\sqrt{3}} = \frac{6}{-6\sqrt{3}} = -\frac{\sqrt{3}}{3} \Rightarrow 2\theta = \frac{2\pi}{3} \Rightarrow \theta = \frac{\pi}{3}$$

$$x = x'\cos\frac{\pi}{3} - y'\sin\frac{\pi}{3} = \frac{1}{2}x' - \frac{\sqrt{3}}{2}y' = \frac{1}{2}\left(x' - \sqrt{3}y'\right)$$

$$y = x'\sin\frac{\pi}{3} + y'\cos\frac{\pi}{3} = \frac{\sqrt{3}}{2}x' + \frac{1}{2}y' = \frac{1}{2}\left(\sqrt{3}x' + y'\right)$$

27. $4x^2 - 4xy + y^2 - 8\sqrt{5}x - 16\sqrt{5}y = 0$

$A = 4, B = -4,$ and $C = 1;$ $\cot(2\theta) = \dfrac{A-C}{B} = \dfrac{4-1}{-4} = -\dfrac{3}{4};$ $\cos 2\theta = -\dfrac{3}{5}$

$$\sin\theta = \sqrt{\frac{1-\left(-\frac{3}{5}\right)}{2}} = \sqrt{\frac{4}{5}} = \frac{2}{\sqrt{5}} = \frac{2\sqrt{5}}{5}; \quad \cos\theta = \sqrt{\frac{1+\left(-\frac{3}{5}\right)}{2}} = \sqrt{\frac{1}{5}} = \frac{1}{\sqrt{5}} = \frac{\sqrt{5}}{5}$$

$$x = x'\cos\theta - y'\sin\theta = \frac{\sqrt{5}}{5}x' - \frac{2\sqrt{5}}{5}y' = \frac{\sqrt{5}}{5}(x' - 2y')$$

$$y = x'\sin\theta + y'\cos\theta = \frac{2\sqrt{5}}{5}x' + \frac{\sqrt{5}}{5}y' = \frac{\sqrt{5}}{5}(2x' + y')$$

29. $25x^2 - 36xy + 40y^2 - 12\sqrt{13}\, x - 8\sqrt{13}\, y = 0$

$A = 25, B = -36,$ and $C = 40$; $\cot(2\theta) = \dfrac{A-C}{B} = \dfrac{25-40}{-36} = \dfrac{5}{12}$; $\cos 2\theta = \dfrac{5}{13}$

$\sin\theta = \sqrt{\dfrac{1 - \dfrac{5}{13}}{2}} = \sqrt{\dfrac{4}{13}} = \dfrac{2}{\sqrt{13}} = \dfrac{2\sqrt{13}}{13}$; $\cos\theta = \sqrt{\dfrac{1 + \dfrac{5}{13}}{2}} = \sqrt{\dfrac{9}{13}} = \dfrac{3}{\sqrt{13}} = \dfrac{3\sqrt{13}}{13}$

$x = x'\cos\theta - y'\sin\theta = \dfrac{3\sqrt{13}}{13}x' - \dfrac{2\sqrt{13}}{13}y' = \dfrac{\sqrt{13}}{13}(3x' - 2y')$

$y = x'\sin\theta + y'\cos\theta = \dfrac{2\sqrt{13}}{13}x' + \dfrac{3\sqrt{13}}{13}y' = \dfrac{\sqrt{13}}{13}(2x' + 3y')$

31. $x^2 + 4xy + y^2 - 3 = 0$; $\theta = 45°$ (see Problem 21)

$\left(\dfrac{\sqrt{2}}{2}(x' - y')\right)^2 + 4\left(\dfrac{\sqrt{2}}{2}(x' - y')\right)\left(\dfrac{\sqrt{2}}{2}(x' + y')\right) + \left(\dfrac{\sqrt{2}}{2}(x' + y')\right)^2 - 3 = 0$

$\dfrac{1}{2}\left(x'^2 - 2x'y' + y'^2\right) + 2\left(x'^2 - y'^2\right) + \dfrac{1}{2}\left(x'^2 + 2x'y' + y'^2\right) - 3 = 0$

$\dfrac{1}{2}x'^2 - x'y' + \dfrac{1}{2}y'^2 + 2x'^2 - 2y'^2 + \dfrac{1}{2}x'^2 + x'y' + \dfrac{1}{2}y'^2 = 3$

$3x'^2 - y'^2 = 3$

$\dfrac{x'^2}{1} - \dfrac{y'^2}{3} = 1$

Hyperbola; center at the origin, transverse axis is the x'-axis, vertices $(\pm 1, 0)$.

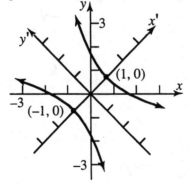

33. $5x^2 + 6xy + 5y^2 - 8 = 0$; $\theta = 45°$ (see Problem 23)

$$5\left(\frac{\sqrt{2}}{2}(x'-y')\right)^2 + 6\left(\frac{\sqrt{2}}{2}(x'-y')\right)\left(\frac{\sqrt{2}}{2}(x'+y')\right) + 5\left(\frac{\sqrt{2}}{2}(x'+y')\right)^2 - 8 = 0$$

$$\frac{5}{2}\left(x'^2 - 2x'y' + y'^2\right) + 3\left(x'^2 - y'^2\right) + \frac{5}{2}\left(x'^2 + 2x'y' + y'^2\right) - 8 = 0$$

$$\frac{5}{2}x'^2 - 5x'y' + \frac{5}{2}y'^2 + 3x'^2 - 3y'^2 + \frac{5}{2}x'^2 + 5x'y' + \frac{5}{2}y'^2 = 8$$

$$8x'^2 + 2y'^2 = 8$$

$$\frac{x'^2}{1} + \frac{y'^2}{4} = 1$$

Ellipse; center at the origin, major axis is the y'-axis, vertices $(0, \pm 2)$.

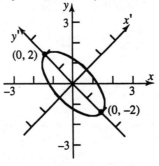

35. $13x^2 - 6\sqrt{3}\,xy + 7y^2 - 16 = 0$; $\theta = 60°$ (see Problem 25)

$$13\left(\frac{1}{2}(x' - \sqrt{3}y')\right)^2 - 6\sqrt{3}\left(\frac{1}{2}(x' - \sqrt{3}y')\right)\left(\frac{1}{2}(\sqrt{3}x' + y')\right) + 7\left(\frac{1}{2}(\sqrt{3}x' + y')\right)^2 - 16 = 0$$

$$\frac{13}{4}\left(x'^2 - 2\sqrt{3}x'y' + 3y'^2\right) - \frac{3\sqrt{3}}{2}\left(\sqrt{3}x'^2 - 2x'y' - \sqrt{3}y'^2\right) + \frac{7}{4}\left(3x'^2 + 2\sqrt{3}x'y' + y'^2\right) = 16$$

$$\frac{13}{4}x'^2 - \frac{13\sqrt{3}}{2}x'y' + \frac{39}{4}y'^2 - \frac{9}{2}x'^2 + 3\sqrt{3}x'y' + \frac{9}{2}y'^2 + \frac{21}{4}x'^2 + \frac{7\sqrt{3}}{2}x'y' + \frac{7}{4}y'^2 = 16$$

$$4x'^2 + 16y'^2 = 16$$

$$\frac{x'^2}{4} + \frac{y'^2}{1} = 1$$

Ellipse; center at the origin, major axis is the x'-axis, vertices $(\pm 2, 0)$.

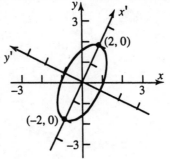

37. $4x^2 - 4xy + y^2 - 8\sqrt{5}\,x - 16\sqrt{5}\,y = 0$; $\theta \approx 63.4°$ (see Problem 27)

$$4\left(\frac{\sqrt{5}}{5}(x'-2y')\right)^2 - 4\left(\frac{\sqrt{5}}{5}(x'-2y')\right)\left(\frac{\sqrt{5}}{5}(2x'+y')\right) + \left(\frac{\sqrt{5}}{5}(2x'+y')\right)^2$$

$$-8\sqrt{5}\left(\frac{\sqrt{5}}{5}(x'-2y')\right) - 16\sqrt{5}\left(\frac{\sqrt{5}}{5}(2x'+y')\right) = 0$$

$$\frac{4}{5}\left(x'^2 - 4x'y' + 4y'^2\right) - \frac{4}{5}\left(2x'^2 - 3x'y' - 2y'^2\right) + \frac{1}{5}\left(4x'^2 + 4x'y' + y'^2\right)$$

$$-8x' + 16y' - 32x' - 16y' = 0$$

$$\frac{4}{5}x'^2 - \frac{16}{5}x'y' + \frac{16}{5}y'^2 - \frac{8}{5}x'^2 + \frac{12}{5}x'y' + \frac{8}{5}y'^2 + \frac{4}{5}x'^2 + \frac{4}{5}x'y' + \frac{1}{5}y'^2 - 40x' = 0$$

$$5y'^2 - 40x' = 0$$

$$y'^2 = 8x'$$

Parabola; vertex at the origin, focus at $(2, 0)$.

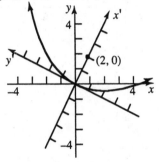

39. $25x^2 - 36xy + 40y^2 - 12\sqrt{13}x - 8\sqrt{13}y = 0$; $\theta \approx 33.7°$ (see Problem 29)

$$25\left(\frac{\sqrt{13}}{13}(3x'-2y')\right)^2 - 36\left(\frac{\sqrt{13}}{13}(3x'-2y')\right)\left(\frac{\sqrt{13}}{13}(2x'+3y')\right) + 40\left(\frac{\sqrt{13}}{13}(2x'+3y')\right)^2$$

$$-12\sqrt{13}\left(\frac{\sqrt{13}}{13}(3x'-2y')\right) - 8\sqrt{13}\left(\frac{\sqrt{13}}{13}(2x'+3y')\right) = 0$$

$$\frac{25}{13}\left(9x'^2 - 12x'y' + 4y'^2\right) - \frac{36}{13}\left(6x'^2 + 5x'y' - 6y'^2\right) + \frac{40}{13}\left(4x'^2 + 12x'y' + 9y'^2\right)$$

$$-36x' + 24y' - 16x' - 24y' = 0$$

$$\frac{225}{13}x'^2 - \frac{300}{13}x'y' + \frac{100}{13}y'^2 - \frac{216}{13}x'^2 - \frac{180}{13}x'y' + \frac{216}{13}y'^2$$

$$+ \frac{160}{13}x'^2 + \frac{480}{13}x'y' + \frac{360}{13}y'^2 - 52x' = 0$$

$$13x'^2 + 52y'^2 - 52x' = 0$$

$$x'^2 - 4x' + 4y'^2 = 0$$

$$\left(x' - 2\right)^2 + 4y'^2 = 4$$

$$\frac{(x'-2)^2}{4} + \frac{y'^2}{1} = 1$$

Ellipse; center at $(2, 0)$, major axis is the x'-axis, vertices $(4, 0)$ and $(0, 0)$.

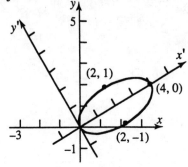

41. $16x^2 + 24xy + 9y^2 - 130x + 90y = 0$

$$A = 16, B = 24, \text{ and } C = 9; \quad \cot(2\theta) = \frac{A-C}{B} = \frac{16-9}{24} = \frac{7}{24} \Rightarrow \cos(2\theta) = \frac{7}{25}$$

$$\sin\theta = \sqrt{\frac{1-\frac{7}{25}}{2}} = \sqrt{\frac{9}{25}} = \frac{3}{5}; \quad \cos\theta = \sqrt{\frac{1+\frac{7}{25}}{2}} = \sqrt{\frac{16}{25}} = \frac{4}{5} \Rightarrow \theta \approx 36.9°$$

$$x = x'\cos\theta - y'\sin\theta = \frac{4}{5}x' - \frac{3}{5}y' = \frac{1}{5}(4x' - 3y')$$

$$y = x'\sin\theta + y'\cos\theta = \frac{3}{5}x' + \frac{4}{5}y' = \frac{1}{5}(3x' + 4y')$$

$$16\left(\frac{1}{5}(4x' - 3y')\right)^2 + 24\left(\frac{1}{5}(4x' - 3y')\right)\left(\frac{1}{5}(3x' + 4y')\right) + 9\left(\frac{1}{5}(3x' + 4y')\right)^2$$

$$-130\left(\frac{1}{5}(4x' - 3y')\right) + 90\left(\frac{1}{5}(3x' + 4y')\right) = 0$$

$$\frac{16}{25}\left(16x'^2 - 24x'y' + 9y'^2\right) + \frac{24}{25}\left(12x'^2 + 7x'y' - 12y'^2\right)$$

$$+ \frac{9}{25}\left(9x'^2 + 24x'y' + 16y'^2\right) - 104x' + 78y' + 54x' + 72y' = 0$$

$$\frac{256}{25}x'^2 - \frac{384}{25}x'y' + \frac{144}{25}y'^2 + \frac{288}{25}x'^2 + \frac{168}{25}x'y' - \frac{288}{25}y'^2$$

$$+ \frac{81}{25}x'^2 + \frac{216}{25}x'y' + \frac{144}{25}y'^2 - 50x' + 150y' = 0$$

$$25x'^2 - 50x' + 150y' = 0$$

$$x'^2 - 2x' = -6y'$$

$$(x' - 1)^2 = -6y' + 1$$

$$(x' - 1)^2 = -6\left(y' - \frac{1}{6}\right)$$

Parabola; vertex $\left(1, \dfrac{1}{6}\right)$, focus $\left(1, -\dfrac{4}{3}\right)$.

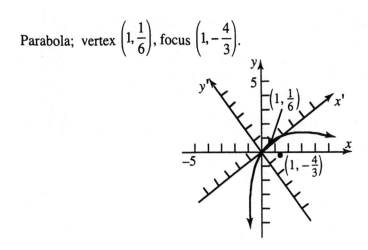

43. $A = 1,\ B = 3,\ C = -2$ $B^2 - 4AC = 3^2 - 4(1)(-2) = 17 > 0;$ hyperbola

45. $A = 1,\ B = -7,\ C = 3$ $B^2 - 4AC = (-7)^2 - 4(1)(3) = 37 > 0;$ hyperbola

47. $A = 9,\ B = 12,\ C = 4$ $B^2 - 4AC = 12^2 - 4(9)(4) = 0;$ parabola

49. $A = 10,\ B = -12,\ C = 4$ $B^2 - 4AC = (-12)^2 - 4(10)(4) = -16 < 0;$ ellipse

51. $A = 3,\ B = -2,\ C = 1$ $B^2 - 4AC = (-2)^2 - 4(3)(1) = -8 < 0;$ ellipse

53.   See equation 6 on page 416.

$A' = A\cos^2\theta + B\sin\theta\cos\theta + C\sin^2\theta$

$B' = B(\cos^2\theta - \sin^2\theta) + 2(C - A)(\sin\theta\cos\theta)$

$C' = A\sin^2\theta - B\sin\theta\cos\theta + C\cos^2\theta$

$D' = D\cos\theta + E\sin\theta$

$E' = -D\sin\theta + E\cos\theta$

$F' = F$

55. $B'^2 - 4A'C'$

$= \left[B(\cos^2\theta - \sin^2\theta) + 2(C - A)\sin\theta\cos\theta \right]^2$

$\qquad - 4\left(A\cos^2\theta + B\sin\theta\cos\theta + C\sin^2\theta \right)\left(A\sin^2\theta - B\sin\theta\cos\theta + C\cos^2\theta \right)$

$= B^2\left(\cos^4\theta - 2\cos^2\theta\sin^2\theta + \sin^4\theta \right) + 4B(C - A)\sin\theta\cos\theta(\cos^2\theta - \sin^2\theta)$

$\qquad + 4(C - A)^2\sin^2\theta\cos^2\theta - 4\big[A^2\sin^2\theta\cos^2\theta - AB\sin\theta\cos^3\theta + AC\cos^4\theta$

$\qquad\quad + AB\sin^3\theta\cos\theta - B^2\sin^2\theta\cos^2\theta + BC\sin\theta\cos^3\theta + AC\sin^4\theta$

$\qquad\quad - BC\sin^3\theta\cos\theta + C^2\sin^2\theta\cos^2\theta \big]$

$$= B^2\left(\cos^4\theta - 2\cos^2\theta\sin^2\theta + \sin^4\theta + 4\sin^2\theta\cos^2\theta\right)$$

$$+ BC\left(4\sin\theta\cos\theta(\cos^2\theta - \sin^2\theta) - 4\sin\theta\cos^3\theta + 4\sin^3\theta\cos\theta\right)$$

$$- AB\left(4\sin\theta\cos\theta(\cos^2\theta - \sin^2\theta) - 4\sin\theta\cos^3\theta + 4\sin^3\theta\cos\theta\right)$$

$$+ 4C^2\left(\sin^2\theta\cos^2\theta - \sin^2\theta\cos^2\theta\right) - 4AC\left(2\sin^2\theta\cos^2\theta + \cos^4\theta + \sin^4\theta\right)$$

$$+ 4A^2\left(\sin^2\theta\cos^2\theta - \sin^2\theta\cos^2\theta\right)$$

$$= B^2\left(\cos^4\theta + 2\sin^2\theta\cos^2\theta + \sin^4\theta\right) - 4AC\left(\cos^4\theta + 2\sin^2\theta\cos^2\theta + \sin^4\theta\right)$$

$$= B^2\left(\cos^2\theta + \sin^2\theta\right)^2 - 4AC\left(\cos^2\theta + \sin^2\theta\right)^2 = B^2 - 4AC$$

57. $d^2 = (y_2 - y_1)^2 + (x_2 - x_1)^2$

$$= \left(x_2'\sin\theta + y_2'\cos\theta - x_1'\sin\theta - y_1'\cos\theta\right)^2$$

$$+ \left(x_2'\cos\theta - y_2'\sin\theta - x_1'\cos\theta + y_1'\sin\theta\right)^2$$

$$= \left((x_2' - x_1')\sin\theta + (y_2' - y_1')\cos\theta\right)^2 + \left((x_2' - x_1')\cos\theta - (y_2' - y_1')\sin\theta\right)^2$$

$$= (x_2' - x_1')^2\sin^2\theta + 2(x_2' - x_1')(y_2' - y_1')\sin\theta\cos\theta + (y_2' - y_1')^2\cos^2\theta$$

$$+ (x_2' - x_1')^2\cos^2\theta - 2(x_2' - x_1')(y_2' - y_1')\sin\theta\cos\theta + (y_2' - y_1')^2\sin^2\theta$$

$$= (x_2' - x_1')^2\sin^2\theta + (x_2' - x_1')^2\cos^2\theta + (y_2' - y_1')^2\cos^2\theta + (y_2' - y_1')^2\sin^2\theta$$

$$= (x_2' - x_1')^2 + (y_2' - y_1')^2$$

59. Answers will vary.

Analytic Geometry

6.6 Polar Equations of Conics

1. $r\cos\theta,\ r\sin\theta$

3. $\dfrac{1}{2}$, ellipse, parallel, 4, below

5. True

7. $e = 1;\quad p = 1;$ parabola; directrix is perpendicular to the polar axis and 1 unit to the right of the pole.

9. $r = \dfrac{4}{2 - 3\sin\theta} = \dfrac{4}{2\left(1 - \dfrac{3}{2}\sin\theta\right)} = \dfrac{2}{1 - \dfrac{3}{2}\sin\theta};\quad ep = 2,\ e = \dfrac{3}{2};\ p = \dfrac{4}{3}$

   Hyperbola; directrix is parallel to the polar axis and $\dfrac{4}{3}$ units below the pole.

11. $r = \dfrac{3}{4 - 2\cos\theta} = \dfrac{3}{4\left(1 - \dfrac{1}{2}\cos\theta\right)} = \dfrac{\dfrac{3}{4}}{1 - \dfrac{1}{2}\cos\theta};\quad ep = \dfrac{3}{4},\ e = \dfrac{1}{2};\ p = \dfrac{3}{2}$

   Ellipse; directrix is perpendicular to the polar axis and $\dfrac{3}{2}$ units to the left of the pole.

13. $r = \dfrac{1}{1 + \cos\theta}$
   $ep = 1,\ e = 1,\ p = 1$
   Parabola; directrix is perpendicular to the
   polar axis 1 unit to the right of the pole;
   vertex is $\left(\dfrac{1}{2}, 0\right)$.

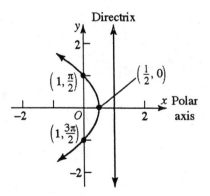

15. $r = \dfrac{8}{4 + 3\sin\theta}$

$r = \dfrac{8}{4\left(1 + \dfrac{3}{4}\sin\theta\right)} = \dfrac{2}{1 + \dfrac{3}{4}\sin\theta}$

$ep = 2,\ e = \dfrac{3}{4},\ p = \dfrac{8}{3}$

Ellipse; directrix is parallel to the polar axis $\dfrac{8}{3}$ units above the pole; vertices are $\left(\dfrac{8}{7}, \dfrac{\pi}{2}\right)$ and $\left(8, \dfrac{3\pi}{2}\right)$.

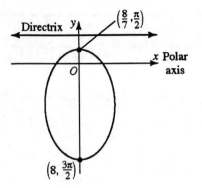

17. $r = \dfrac{9}{3 - 6\cos\theta}$

$r = \dfrac{9}{3(1 - 2\cos\theta)} = \dfrac{3}{1 - 2\cos\theta}$

$ep = 3,\ e = 2,\ p = \dfrac{3}{2}$

Hyperbola; directrix is perpendicular to the polar axis $\dfrac{3}{2}$ units to the left of the pole; vertices are $(-3, 0)$ and $(1, \pi)$.

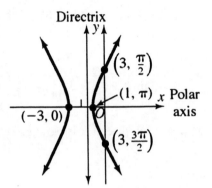

19. $r = \dfrac{8}{2 - \sin\theta}$

$r = \dfrac{8}{2\left(1 - \dfrac{1}{2}\sin\theta\right)} = \dfrac{4}{1 - \dfrac{1}{2}\sin\theta}$

$ep = 4,\ e = \dfrac{1}{2},\ p = 8$

Ellipse; directrix is parallel to the polar axis 8 units below the pole; vertices are $\left(8, \dfrac{\pi}{2}\right)$ and $\left(\dfrac{8}{3}, \dfrac{3\pi}{2}\right)$.

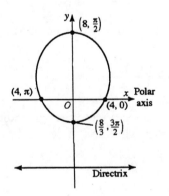

21. $r(3 - 2\sin\theta) = 6 \Rightarrow r = \dfrac{6}{3 - 2\sin\theta}$

$r = \dfrac{6}{3\left(1 - \frac{2}{3}\sin\theta\right)} = \dfrac{2}{1 - \frac{2}{3}\sin\theta}$

$ep = 2, \ e = \dfrac{2}{3}, \ p = 3$

Ellipse; directrix is parallel to the polar axis 3 units below the pole; vertices are $\left(6, \dfrac{\pi}{2}\right)$ and $\left(\dfrac{6}{5}, \dfrac{3\pi}{2}\right)$.

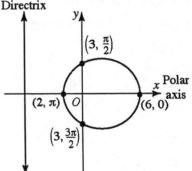

23. $r = \dfrac{6\sec\theta}{2\sec\theta - 1} = \dfrac{6\left(\frac{1}{\cos\theta}\right)}{2\left(\frac{1}{\cos\theta}\right) - 1} = \dfrac{\frac{6}{\cos\theta}}{\frac{2 - \cos\theta}{\cos\theta}} = \left(\dfrac{6}{\cos\theta}\right)\left(\dfrac{\cos\theta}{2 - \cos\theta}\right) = \dfrac{6}{2 - \cos\theta}$

$r = \dfrac{6}{2\left(1 - \frac{1}{2}\cos\theta\right)} = \dfrac{3}{1 - \frac{1}{2}\cos\theta}$

$ep = 3, \ e = \dfrac{1}{2}, \ p = 6$

Ellipse; directrix is perpendicular to the polar axis 6 units to the left of the pole; vertices are $(6, 0)$ and $(2, \pi)$.

25. $r = \dfrac{1}{1 + \cos\theta}$

$r + r\cos\theta = 1$

$r = 1 - r\cos\theta$

$r^2 = (1 - r\cos\theta)^2$

$x^2 + y^2 = (1 - x)^2$

$x^2 + y^2 = 1 - 2x + x^2$

$y^2 + 2x - 1 = 0$

27. $r = \dfrac{8}{4 + 3\sin\theta}$

$4r + 3r\sin\theta = 8$

$4r = 8 - 3r\sin\theta$

$16r^2 = (8 - 3r\sin\theta)^2$

$16(x^2 + y^2) = (8 - 3y)^2$

$16x^2 + 16y^2 = 64 - 48y + 9y^2$

$16x^2 + 7y^2 + 48y - 64 = 0$

29.
$$r = \frac{9}{3 - 6\cos\theta}$$
$$3r - 6r\cos\theta = 9$$
$$3r = 9 + 6r\cos\theta$$
$$r = 3 + 2r\cos\theta$$
$$r^2 = (3 + 2r\cos\theta)^2$$
$$x^2 + y^2 = (3 + 2x)^2$$
$$x^2 + y^2 = 9 + 12x + 4x^2$$
$$3x^2 - y^2 + 12x + 9 = 0$$

31.
$$r = \frac{8}{2 - \sin\theta}$$
$$2r - r\sin\theta = 8$$
$$2r = 8 + r\sin\theta$$
$$4r^2 = (8 + r\sin\theta)^2$$
$$4(x^2 + y^2) = (8 + y)^2$$
$$4x^2 + 4y^2 = 64 + 16y + y^2$$
$$4x^2 + 3y^2 - 16y - 64 = 0$$

33.
$$r(3 - 2\sin\theta) = 6$$
$$3r - 2r\sin\theta = 6$$
$$3r = 6 + 2r\sin\theta$$
$$9r^2 = (6 + 2r\sin\theta)^2$$
$$9(x^2 + y^2) = (6 + 2y)^2$$
$$9x^2 + 9y^2 = 36 + 24y + 4y^2$$
$$9x^2 + 5y^2 - 24y - 36 = 0$$

35.
$$r = \frac{6\sec\theta}{2\sec\theta - 1}$$
$$r = \frac{6}{2 - \cos\theta}$$
$$2r - r\cos\theta = 6$$
$$2r = 6 + r\cos\theta$$
$$4r^2 = (6 + r\cos\theta)^2$$
$$4(x^2 + y^2) = (6 + x)^2$$
$$4x^2 + 4y^2 = 36 + 12x + x^2$$
$$3x^2 + 4y^2 - 12x - 36 = 0$$

37. $r = \dfrac{ep}{1 + e\sin\theta}$
$e = 1; \quad p = 1$
$$r = \frac{1}{1 + \sin\theta}$$

39. $r = \dfrac{ep}{1 - e\cos\theta}$
$e = \dfrac{4}{5}; \quad p = 3$
$$r = \frac{\dfrac{12}{5}}{1 - \dfrac{4}{5}\cos\theta} = \frac{12}{5 - 4\cos\theta}$$

41. $r = \dfrac{ep}{1 - e\sin\theta}$
$e = 6; \quad p = 2$
$$r = \frac{12}{1 - 6\sin\theta}$$

43.
$$d(F, P) = e \cdot d(D, P) \qquad d(D, P) = p - r\cos\theta$$
$$r = e(p - r\cos\theta)$$
$$r = ep - er\cos\theta$$
$$r + er\cos\theta = ep$$
$$r(1 + e\cos\theta) = ep$$
$$r = \frac{ep}{1 + e\cos\theta}$$

45. $\qquad d(F, P) = e \cdot d(D, P) \qquad\qquad d(D, P) = p + r\sin\theta$

$$r = e(p + r\sin\theta)$$

$$r = ep + er\sin\theta$$

$$r - er\sin\theta = ep$$

$$r(1 - e\sin\theta) = ep$$

$$r = \frac{ep}{1 - e\sin\theta}$$

Analytic Geometry

6.7   Plane Curves and Parametric Equations

1. $|3| = 3$, $\dfrac{2\pi}{4} = \dfrac{\pi}{2}$

3.   ellipse

5.   False

7. $x = 3t + 2$, $y = t + 1$, $0 \le t \le 4$

   $x = 3(y - 1) + 2$
   $x = 3y - 3 + 2$
   $x = 3y - 1$
   $x - 3y + 1 = 0$

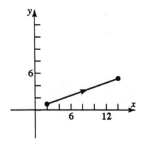

9. $x = t + 2$, $y = \sqrt{t}$, $t \ge 0$

   $y = \sqrt{x - 2}$

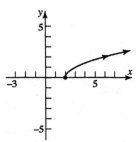

11. $x = t^2 + 4$, $y = t^2 - 4$, $-\infty < t < \infty$

   $y = (x - 4) - 4$
   $y = x - 8$
   For $-\infty < t < 0$ the movement is to the left. For $0 < t < \infty$ the movement is to the right.

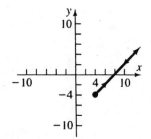

13. $x = 3t^2$, $y = t + 1$, $-\infty < t < \infty$

$x = 3(y-1)^2$

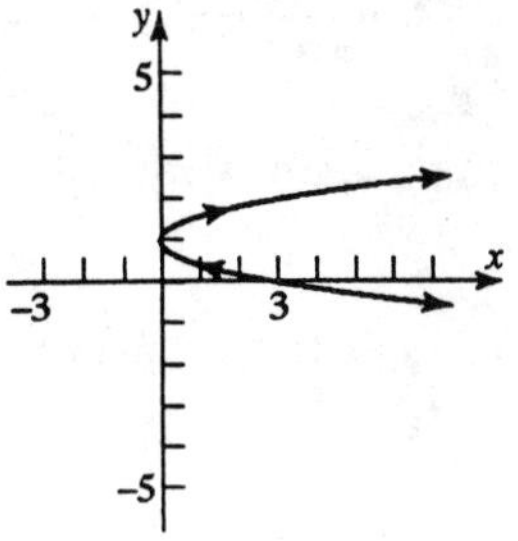

15. $x = 2e^t$, $y = 1 + e^t$, $t \geq 0$

$y = 1 + \dfrac{x}{2}$

$2y = 2 + x$

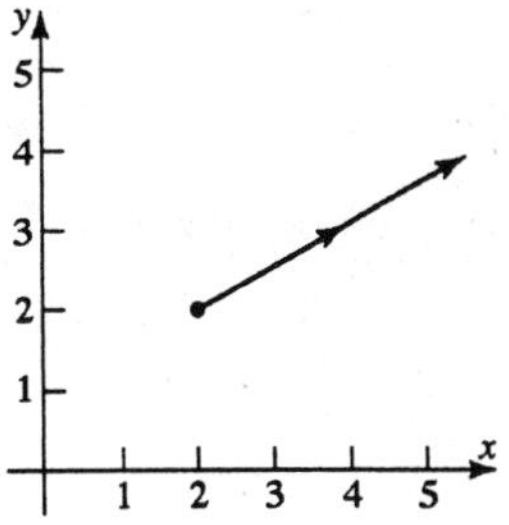

17. $x = \sqrt{t}$, $y = t^{3/2}$, $t \geq 0$

$y = \left(x^2\right)^{3/2}$

$y = x^3$

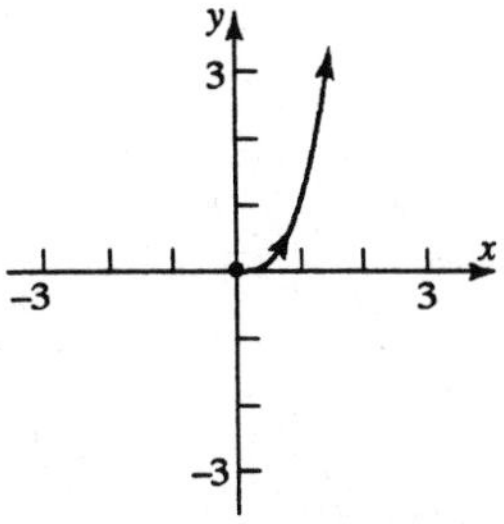

19. $x = 2\cos t$, $y = 3\sin t$, $0 \leq t \leq 2\pi$

$\dfrac{x}{2} = \cos t \qquad \dfrac{y}{3} = \sin t$

$\left(\dfrac{x}{2}\right)^2 + \left(\dfrac{y}{3}\right)^2 = \cos^2 t + \sin^2 t = 1$

$\dfrac{x^2}{4} + \dfrac{y^2}{9} = 1$

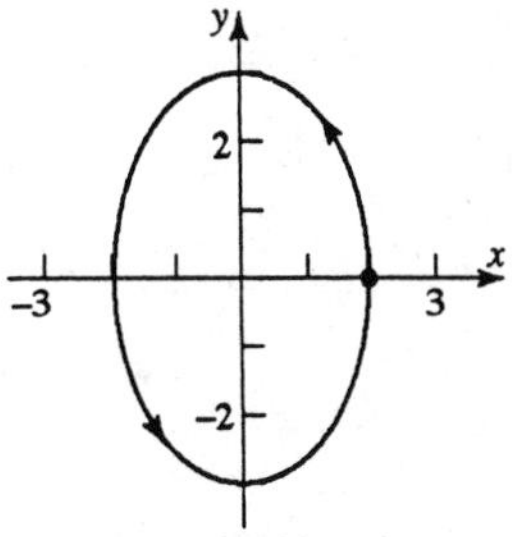

21. $x = 2\cos t,\ \ y = 3\sin t,\ \ -\pi \le t \le 0$

$$\frac{x}{2} = \cos t \qquad \frac{y}{3} = \sin t$$

$$\left(\frac{x}{2}\right)^2 + \left(\frac{y}{3}\right)^2 = \cos^2 t + \sin^2 t = 1$$

$$\frac{x^2}{4} + \frac{y^2}{9} = 1 \qquad y \le 0$$

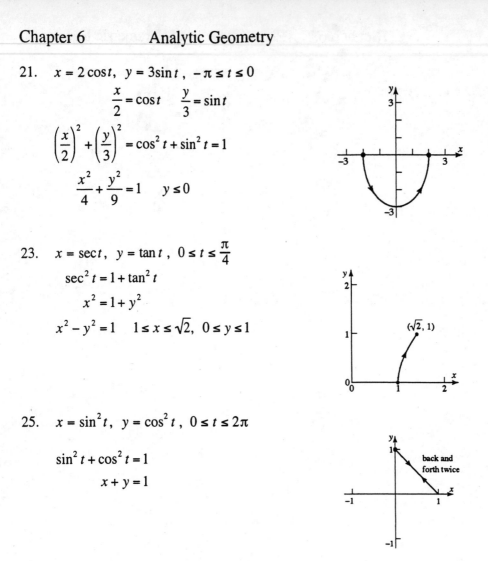

23. $x = \sec t,\ \ y = \tan t,\ \ 0 \le t \le \dfrac{\pi}{4}$

$$\sec^2 t = 1 + \tan^2 t$$

$$x^2 = 1 + y^2$$

$$x^2 - y^2 = 1 \qquad 1 \le x \le \sqrt{2},\ \ 0 \le y \le 1$$

25. $x = \sin^2 t,\ \ y = \cos^2 t,\ \ 0 \le t \le 2\pi$

$$\sin^2 t + \cos^2 t = 1$$

$$x + y = 1$$

27.   (a)   Use equations (2):
$$x = \left(50\cos 90°\right)t = 0$$

$$y = -\frac{1}{2}(32)t^2 + \left(50\sin 90°\right)t + 6 = -16t^2 + 50t + 6$$

(b)   The ball is in the air until $y = 0$. Solve:
$$-16t^2 + 50t + 6 = 0$$

$$t = \frac{-50 \pm \sqrt{50^2 - 4(-16)(6)}}{2(-16)} = \frac{-50 \pm \sqrt{2884}}{-32} \approx -0.12 \text{ or } 3.24$$

The ball is in the air for about 3.24 seconds. (The negative solution is extraneous.)

(c)   The maximum height occurs at the vertex of the quadratic function.
$$t = -\frac{b}{2a} = -\frac{50}{2(-16)} = 1.5625 \text{ seconds}$$

Evaluate the function to find the maximum height:
$$-16(1.5625)^2 + 50(1.5625) + 6 = 45.0625$$

The maximum height is 45.0625 feet.

(d)   We use $x = 3$ so that the line is not on top of the y-axis.

29.   Let $y_1 = 1$ be the train's path and $y_2 = 3$ be Bill's path.

(a)   Train: Using the hint,

$$x_1 = \frac{1}{2}(2)t^2 = t^2$$

$$y_1 = 1$$

Bill:

$$x_2 = 5(t - 5)$$

$$y_2 = 3$$

(b)   Bill will catch the train if $x_1 = x_2$.

$$t^2 = 5(t - 5)$$

$$t^2 = 5t - 25$$

$$t^2 - 5t + 25 = 0$$

Since $b^2 - 4ac = (-5)^2 - 4(1)(25) = 25 - 100 = -75 < 0$, the equation has no real solution. Thus, Bill will not catch the train.

(c)

31.   (a)   Use equations (2):

$$x = (145\cos 20°)t$$

$$y = -\frac{1}{2}(32)t^2 + (145\sin 20°)t + 5$$

(b)   The ball is in the air until $y = 0$. Solve:

$$-16t^2 + (145\sin 20°)t + 5 = 0$$

$$t = \frac{-145\sin 20° \pm \sqrt{(145\sin 20°)^2 - 4(-16)(5)}}{2(-16)}$$

$$\approx -0.10 \text{ or } 3.20$$

The ball is in the air for about 3.20 seconds. (The negative solution is extraneous.)

(c)   The maximum height occurs at the vertex of the quadratic function.

$$t = -\frac{b}{2a} = -\frac{145\sin 20°}{2(-16)} \approx 1.55 \text{ seconds}$$

Evaluate the function to find the maximum height:

$$-16(1.55)^2 + (145\sin 20°)(1.55) + 5 \approx 43.43$$

The maximum height is about 43.43 feet.

(d)   Find the horizontal displacement:

$$x = (145\cos 20°)(3.20) \approx 436 \text{ feet}$$

(e)

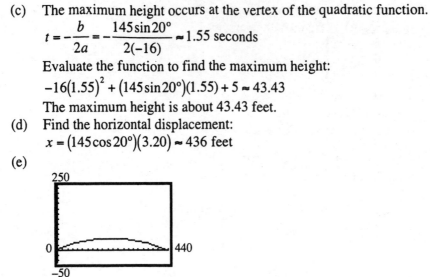

33.   (a)   Use equations (2):

$$x = (40\cos 45°)t = 20\sqrt{2}\,t$$

$$y = -\frac{1}{2}(9.8)t^2 + (40\sin 45°)t + 300 = -4.9t^2 + 20\sqrt{2}\,t + 300$$

(b)   The ball is in the air until $y = 0$. Solve:

$$-4.9t^2 + 20\sqrt{2}\,t + 300 = 0$$

$$t = \frac{-20\sqrt{2} \pm \sqrt{\left(20\sqrt{2}\right)^2 - 4(-4.9)(300)}}{2(-4.9)} \approx -5.45 \text{ or } 11.23$$

The ball is in the air for about 11.23 seconds. (The negative solution is extraneous.)

(c)   The maximum height occurs at the vertex of the quadratic function.

$$t = -\frac{b}{2a} = -\frac{20\sqrt{2}}{2(-4.9)} \approx 2.89 \text{ seconds}$$

Evaluate the function to find the maximum height:

$$-4.9(2.89)^2 + 20\sqrt{2}(2.89) + 300 = 340.8 \text{ meters}$$

(d)   Find the horizontal displacement:

$$x = \left(20\sqrt{2}\,t\right)(11.23) \approx 317.6 \text{ meters}$$

(e)

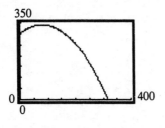

35. (a) At $t = 0$, the Paseo is 5 miles from the intersection (at $(0, 0)$) traveling east (along the x-axis) at 40 mph. Thus, $x = 40t - 5$ describes the position of the Paseo as a function of time. The Bonneville, at $t = 0$, is 4 miles from the intersection traveling north (along the y-axis) at 30 mph. Thus, $y = 30t - 4$ describes the position of the Bonneville as a function of time.

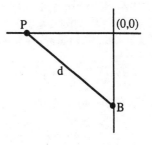

(b) Let d represent the distance between the cars. Use the Pythagorean Theorem to find the distance: $d = \sqrt{(40t - 5)^2 + (30t - 4)^2}$.

(c) Note this is a function graph not a parametric graph.

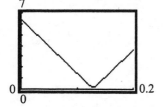

(d) The minimum distance between the cars is 0.2 miles and occurs at 0.128 seconds.

(e) The axes were turned off to get this graph.

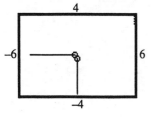

37. $x = t, \ y = 4t - 1$ $x = t + 1, \ y = 4t + 3$

39. $x = t, \ y = t^2 + 1$ $x = t - 1, \ y = t^2 - 2t + 2$

41. $x = t, \ y = t^3$ $x = \sqrt[3]{t}, \ y = t$

43. $x = t^{3/2}, \ y = t$ $x = t, \ y = t^{2/3}$

45. $x = t + 2, \ y = t; \ \ 0 \le t \le 5$

47. $x = 3\cos t, \ y = 2\sin t; \ \ 0 \le t \le 2\pi$

49. Since the motion begins at $(2, 0)$, we want $x = 2$ and $y = 0$ when $t = 0$. For the motion to be clockwise, both x and y must be decreasing.

$x = 2\cos(\omega t), \ y = -3\sin(\omega t)$

$\dfrac{2\pi}{\omega} = 2 \Rightarrow \omega = \pi$

$x = 2\cos(\pi t), \ y = -3\sin(\pi t), \ 0 \le t \le 2$

51. Since the motion begins at $(0, 3)$, we want $x = 0$ and $y = 3$ when $t = 0$. For the motion to be clockwise, x must be increasing and y must be decreasing.

$x = -2\sin(\omega t), \ y = 3\cos(\omega t)$

$\dfrac{2\pi}{\omega} = 1 \Rightarrow \omega = 2\pi$

$x = -2\sin(2\pi t), \ y = 3\cos(2\pi t), \ 0 \le t \le 1$

53. C_1

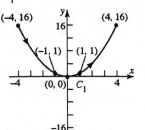

C_2

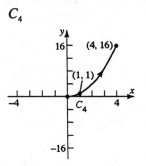

C_3

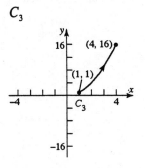

C_4

55. $x = (x_2 - x_1)t + x_1, \ y = (y_2 - y_1)t + y_1, \ -\infty < t < \infty$

$\dfrac{x - x_1}{x_2 - x_1} = t$

$y = (y_2 - y_1)\left(\dfrac{x - x_1}{x_2 - x_1}\right) + y_1$

$y - y_1 = \left(\dfrac{y_2 - y_1}{x_2 - x_1}\right)(x - x_1)$

This is the two-point form for the equation of a line.

Its orientation is from (x_1, y_1) to (x_2, y_2).

57. $x = t\sin t, \quad y = t\cos t$

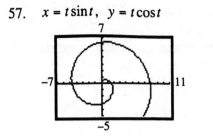

59. $x = 4\sin t - 2\sin(2t)$

$y = 4\cos t - 2\cos(2t)$

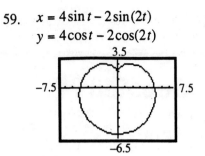

61. (a) $x(t) = \cos^3 t, \quad y(t) = \sin^3 t, \quad 0 \le t \le 2\pi$

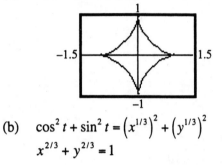

(b) $\cos^2 t + \sin^2 t = \left(x^{1/3}\right)^2 + \left(y^{1/3}\right)^2$

$x^{2/3} + y^{2/3} = 1$

63. Answers will ary.

Analytic Geometry

6.R   Chapter Review

1. $y^2 = -16x$
This is a parabola.
$a = 4$
Vertex: $(0, 0)$
Focus: $(-4, 0)$
Directrix: $x = 4$

3. $\dfrac{x^2}{25} - y^2 = 1$
This is a hyperbola.
$a = 5, \quad b = 1$.

Find the value of c:
$c^2 = a^2 + b^2 = 25 + 1 = 26 \Rightarrow c = \sqrt{26}$
Center: $(0, 0)$
Vertices: $(-5, 0), (5, 0)$
Foci: $\left(-\sqrt{26}, 0\right), \left(\sqrt{26}, 0\right)$
Asymptotes: $y = \dfrac{1}{5}x; \quad y = -\dfrac{1}{5}x$

5. $\dfrac{y^2}{25} + \dfrac{x^2}{16} = 1$
This is an ellipse.
$a = 5, \quad b = 4$.

Find the value of c:
$c^2 = a^2 - b^2 = 25 - 16 = 9 \Rightarrow c = 3$
Center: $(0, 0)$
Vertices: $(0, -5), (0, 5)$
Foci: $(0, -3), (0, 3)$

7. $x^2 + 4y = 4$
This is a parabola.
Write in standard form:
$x^2 = -4y + 4$
$x^2 = -4(y - 1)$

$a = 1$
Vertex: $(0, 1)$
Focus: $(0, 0)$
Directrix: $y = 2$

9. $4x^2 - y^2 = 8$
This is a hyperbola.
Write in standard form:
$\dfrac{x^2}{2} - \dfrac{y^2}{8} = 1$
$a = \sqrt{2}, \ b = \sqrt{8} = 2\sqrt{2}$

Find the value of c:
$c^2 = a^2 + b^2 = 2 + 8 = 10 \Rightarrow c = \sqrt{10}$
Center: $(0, 0)$
Vertices: $\left(-\sqrt{2}, 0\right), \left(\sqrt{2}, 0\right)$
Foci: $\left(-\sqrt{10}, 0\right), \left(\sqrt{10}, 0\right)$
Asymptotes: $y = 2x; \quad y = -2x$

11. $x^2 - 4x = 2y$
This is a parabola.
Write in standard form:
$x^2 - 4x + 4 = 2y + 4$
$(x-2)^2 = 2(y+2)$

$a = \dfrac{1}{2}$

Vertex: $(2, -2)$

Focus: $\left(2, -\dfrac{3}{2}\right)$

Directrix: $y = -\dfrac{5}{2}$

13. $y^2 - 4y - 4x^2 + 8x = 4$
This is a hyperbola.
Write in standard form:
$(y^2 - 4y + 4) - 4(x^2 - 2x + 1) = 4 + 4 - 4$
$(y-2)^2 - 4(x-1)^2 = 4$
$\dfrac{(y-2)^2}{4} - \dfrac{(x-1)^2}{1} = 1$
$a = 2, \ b = 1.$

Find the value of c:
$c^2 = a^2 + b^2 = 4 + 1 = 5 \Rightarrow c = \sqrt{5}$
Center: $(1, 2)$
Vertices: $(1, 0), (1, 4)$
Foci: $\left(1, 2 - \sqrt{5}\right), \left(1, 2 + \sqrt{5}\right)$
Asymptotes:
$y - 2 = 2(x-1); \ \ y - 2 = -2(x-1)$

15. $4x^2 + 9y^2 - 16x - 18y = 11$
This is an ellipse.
Write in standard form:
$4(x^2 - 4x + 4) + 9(y^2 - 2y + 1) = 11 + 16 + 9$
$4(x-2)^2 + 9(y-1)^2 = 36$
$\dfrac{(x-2)^2}{9} + \dfrac{(y-1)^2}{4} = 1$
$a = 3, \ b = 2.$

Find the value of c:
$c^2 = a^2 - b^2 = 9 - 4 = 5 \Rightarrow c = \sqrt{5}$
Center: $(2, 1)$
Vertices: $(-1, 1), (5, 1)$
Foci: $\left(2 - \sqrt{5}, 1\right), \left(2 + \sqrt{5}, 1\right)$

17. $4x^2 - 16x + 16y + 32 = 0$
This is a parabola.
Write in standard form:
$4(x^2 - 4x + 4) = -16y - 32 + 16$
$4(x-2)^2 = -16(y+1)$
$(x-2)^2 = -4(y+1)$

$a = 1$
Vertex: $(2, -1)$
Focus: $(2, -2)$
Directrix: $y = 0$

19. $9x^2 + 4y^2 - 18x + 8y = 23$
This is an ellipse.
Write in standard form:
$9(x^2 - 2x + 1) + 4(y^2 + 2y + 1) = 23 + 9 + 4$
$9(x-1)^2 + 4(y+1)^2 = 36$
$\dfrac{(x-1)^2}{4} + \dfrac{(y+1)^2}{9} = 1$
$a = 3, \ b = 2.$

Find the value of c:
$c^2 = a^2 - b^2 = 9 - 4 = 5 \Rightarrow c = \sqrt{5}$
Center: $(1, -1)$
Vertices: $(1, -4), (1, 2)$
Foci: $\left(1, -1 - \sqrt{5}\right), \left(1, -1 + \sqrt{5}\right)$

21. Parabola: The focus is $(-2, 0)$ and the directrix is $x = 2$. The vertex is $(0, 0)$. $a = 2$ and since $(-2, 0)$ is to the left of $(0, 0)$, the parabola opens to the left. Write the equation:

$$y^2 = -4ax$$
$$y^2 = -4 \cdot 2 \cdot x$$
$$y^2 = -8x$$

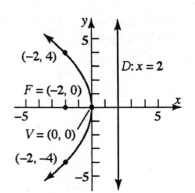

23. Hyperbola: Center: $(0, 0)$; Focus: $(0, 4)$; Vertex: $(0, -2)$; Transverse axis is the y-axis; $a = 2$; $c = 4$.
Find the value of b:
$$b^2 = c^2 - a^2 = 16 - 4 = 12$$
$$b = \sqrt{12} = 2\sqrt{3}$$
Write the equation: $\dfrac{y^2}{4} - \dfrac{x^2}{12} = 1$

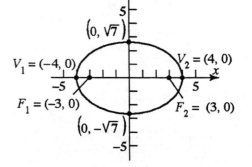

25. Ellipse: Foci: $(-3, 0)$, $(3, 0)$; Vertex: $(4, 0)$; Center: $(0, 0)$; Major axis is the x-axis; $a = 4$; $c = 3$.
Find the value of b:
$$b^2 = a^2 - c^2 = 16 - 9 = 7$$
$$b = \sqrt{7}$$
Write the equation: $\dfrac{x^2}{16} + \dfrac{y^2}{7} = 1$

27. Parabola: The focus is $(2, -4)$ and the vertex is $(2, -3)$. Both lie on the vertical line $x = 2$. $a = 1$ and since $(2, -4)$ is below $(2, -3)$, the parabola opens down. Directrix is $y = -2$. Write the equation:

$$(x - 2)^2 = -4 \cdot 1 \cdot (y - (-3))$$
$$(x - 2)^2 = -4(y + 3)$$

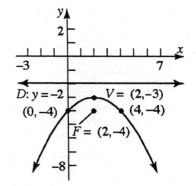

29. Hyperbola: Center: $(-2, -3)$;
    Focus: $(-4, -3)$; Vertex: $(-3, -3)$;
    Transverse axis is parallel to the x-axis;
    $a = 1$; $c = 2$.
    Find the value of b:
    $b^2 = c^2 - a^2 = 4 - 1 = 3$
    $b = \sqrt{3}$
    Write the equation:
    $\dfrac{(x+2)^2}{1} - \dfrac{(y+3)^2}{3} = 1$

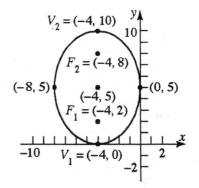

31. Ellipse: Foci: $(-4, 2)$, $(-4, 8)$; Vertex: $(-4, 10)$;
    Center: $(-4, 5)$; Major axis is parallel to the y-axis;
    $a = 5$; $c = 3$.
    Find the value of b:
    $b^2 = a^2 - c^2 = 25 - 9 = 16$
    $b = 4$
    Write the equation: $\dfrac{(x+4)^2}{16} + \dfrac{(y-5)^2}{25} = 1$

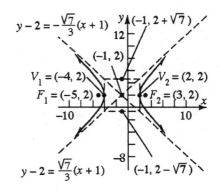

33. Hyperbola: Center: $(-1, 2)$;
    $a = 3$; $c = 4$; Transverse axis parallel to
    the x-axis;
    Find the value of b:
    $b^2 = c^2 - a^2 = 16 - 9 = 7$
    $b = \sqrt{7}$
    Write the equation:
    $\dfrac{(x+1)^2}{9} - \dfrac{(y-2)^2}{7} = 1$

35.   Hyperbola: Vertices: $(0, 1), (6, 1)$; Asymptote: $3y + 2x = 9$; Center: $(3, 1)$;

Transverse axis is parallel to the x-axis; $a = 3$; The slope of the asymptote is $-\dfrac{2}{3}$;

Find the value of b: $\dfrac{-b}{a} = \dfrac{-b}{3} = \dfrac{-2}{3} \Rightarrow -3b = -6 \Rightarrow b = 2$

Write the equation: $\dfrac{(x-3)^2}{9} - \dfrac{(y-1)^2}{4} = 1$

37. $y^2 + 4x + 3y - 8 = 0$
$A = 0$ and $C = 1$; $AC = (0)(1) = 0$. Since $AC = 0$, the equation defines a parabola.

39. $x^2 + 2y^2 + 4x - 8y + 2 = 0$
$A = 1$ and $C = 2$; $AC = (1)(2) = 2$. Since $AC > 0$ and $A \neq C$, the equation defines an ellipse.

41. $9x^2 - 12xy + 4y^2 + 8x + 12y = 0$
$A = 9$, $B = -12$, $C = 4$ $B^2 - 4AC = (-12)^2 - 4(9)(4) = 0$; The equation defines a parabola.

43. $4x^2 + 10xy + 4y^2 - 9 = 0$
$A = 4$, $B = 10$, $C = 4$ $B^2 - 4AC = 10^2 - 4(4)(4) = 36 > 0$; The equation defines a hyperbola.

45. $x^2 - 2xy + 3y^2 + 2x + 4y - 1 = 0$
$A = 1$, $B = -2$, $C = 3$ $B^2 - 4AC = (-2)^2 - 4(1)(3) = -8 < 0$; The equation defines an ellipse.

47. $2x^2 + 5xy + 2y^2 - \dfrac{9}{2} = 0$

$A = 2, B = 5,$ and $C = 2;$ $\cot(2\theta) = \dfrac{A-C}{B} = \dfrac{2-2}{5} = 0 \Rightarrow 2\theta = \dfrac{\pi}{2} \Rightarrow \theta = \dfrac{\pi}{4}$

$x = x'\cos\theta - y'\sin\theta = x'\cos\dfrac{\pi}{4} - y'\sin\dfrac{\pi}{4} = \dfrac{\sqrt{2}}{2}x' - \dfrac{\sqrt{2}}{2}y' = \dfrac{\sqrt{2}}{2}(x' - y')$

$y = x'\sin\theta + y'\cos\theta = x'\sin\dfrac{\pi}{4} + y'\cos\dfrac{\pi}{4} = \dfrac{\sqrt{2}}{2}x' + \dfrac{\sqrt{2}}{2}y' = \dfrac{\sqrt{2}}{2}(x' + y')$

$2\left(\dfrac{\sqrt{2}}{2}(x' - y')\right)^2 + 5\left(\dfrac{\sqrt{2}}{2}(x' - y')\right)\left(\dfrac{\sqrt{2}}{2}(x' + y')\right) + 2\left(\dfrac{\sqrt{2}}{2}(x' + y')\right)^2 - \dfrac{9}{2} = 0$

$\left(x'^2 - 2x'y' + y'^2\right) + \dfrac{5}{2}\left(x'^2 - y'^2\right) + \left(x'^2 + 2x'y' + y'^2\right) - \dfrac{9}{2} = 0$

$\dfrac{9}{2}x'^2 - \dfrac{1}{2}y'^2 = \dfrac{9}{2}$

$9x'^2 - y'^2 = 9$

$\dfrac{x'^2}{1} - \dfrac{y'^2}{9} = 1$

Hyperbola; center $(0, 0)$, transverse axis is the x'-axis, vertices $(\pm 1, 0)$.

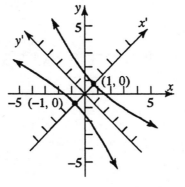

49. $6x^2 + 4xy + 9y^2 - 20 = 0$

$A = 6, B = 4,$ and $C = 9;$ $\cot(2\theta) = \dfrac{A-C}{B} = \dfrac{6-9}{4} = -\dfrac{3}{4} \Rightarrow \cos(2\theta) = -\dfrac{3}{5}$

$\sin\theta = \sqrt{\dfrac{1 - \left(-\dfrac{3}{5}\right)}{2}} = \sqrt{\dfrac{4}{5}} = \dfrac{2\sqrt{5}}{5};$ $\cos\theta = \sqrt{\dfrac{1 + \left(-\dfrac{3}{5}\right)}{2}} = \sqrt{\dfrac{1}{5}} = \dfrac{\sqrt{5}}{5} \Rightarrow \theta \approx 63.4°$

$x = x'\cos\theta - y'\sin\theta = \dfrac{\sqrt{5}}{5}x' - \dfrac{2\sqrt{5}}{5}y' = \dfrac{\sqrt{5}}{5}(x' - 2y')$

$y = x'\sin\theta + y'\cos\theta = \dfrac{2\sqrt{5}}{5}x' + \dfrac{\sqrt{5}}{5}y' = \dfrac{\sqrt{5}}{5}(2x' + y')$

$$6\left(\frac{\sqrt{5}}{5}(x'-2y')\right)^2 + 4\left(\frac{\sqrt{5}}{5}(x'-2y')\right)\left(\frac{\sqrt{5}}{5}(2x'+y')\right) + 9\left(\frac{\sqrt{5}}{5}(2x'+y')\right)^2 - 20 = 0$$

$$\frac{6}{5}\left(x'^2 - 4x'y' + 4y'^2\right) + \frac{4}{5}\left(2x'^2 - 3x'y' - 2y'^2\right) + \frac{9}{5}\left(4x'^2 + 4x'y' + y'^2\right) - 20 = 0$$

$$\frac{6}{5}x'^2 - \frac{24}{5}x'y' + \frac{24}{5}y'^2 + \frac{8}{5}x'^2 - \frac{12}{5}x'y' - \frac{8}{5}y'^2 + \frac{36}{5}x'^2 + \frac{36}{5}x'y' + \frac{9}{5}y'^2 = 20$$

$$10x'^2 + 5y'^2 = 20$$

$$\frac{x'^2}{2} + \frac{y'^2}{4} = 1$$

Ellipse; center at the origin, major axis is the y'-axis, vertices $(0, \pm 2)$.

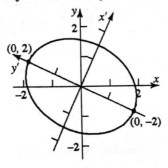

51. $4x^2 - 12xy + 9y^2 + 12x + 8y = 0$

$A = 4, B = -12,$ and $C = 9$; $\cot(2\theta) = \dfrac{A-C}{B} = \dfrac{4-9}{-12} = \dfrac{5}{12} \Rightarrow \cos(2\theta) = \dfrac{5}{13}$

$\sin\theta = \sqrt{\dfrac{1-\dfrac{5}{13}}{2}} = \sqrt{\dfrac{4}{13}} = \dfrac{2\sqrt{13}}{13}$; $\cos\theta = \sqrt{\dfrac{1+\dfrac{5}{13}}{2}} = \sqrt{\dfrac{9}{13}} = \dfrac{3\sqrt{13}}{13} \Rightarrow \theta \approx 33.7°$

$x = x'\cos\theta - y'\sin\theta = \dfrac{3\sqrt{13}}{13}x' - \dfrac{2\sqrt{13}}{13}y' = \dfrac{\sqrt{13}}{13}(3x' - 2y')$

$y = x'\sin\theta + y'\cos\theta = \dfrac{2\sqrt{13}}{13}x' + \dfrac{3\sqrt{13}}{13}y' = \dfrac{\sqrt{13}}{13}(2x' + 3y')$

$$4\left(\frac{\sqrt{13}}{13}(3x'-2y')\right)^2 - 12\left(\frac{\sqrt{13}}{13}(3x'-2y')\right)\left(\frac{\sqrt{13}}{13}(2x'+3y')\right)$$

$$+9\left(\frac{\sqrt{13}}{13}(2x'+3y')\right)^2 + 12\left(\frac{\sqrt{13}}{13}(3x'-2y')\right) + 8\left(\frac{\sqrt{13}}{13}(2x'+3y')\right) = 0$$

$$\frac{4}{13}\left(9x'^2 - 12x'y' + 4y'^2\right) - \frac{12}{13}\left(6x'^2 + 5x'y' - 6y'^2\right)$$

$$+\frac{9}{13}\left(4x'^2 + 12x'y' + 9y'^2\right) + \frac{36\sqrt{13}}{13}x' - \frac{24\sqrt{13}}{13}y' + \frac{16\sqrt{13}}{13}x' + \frac{24\sqrt{13}}{13}y' = 0$$

$$\frac{36}{13}x'^2 - \frac{48}{13}x'y' + \frac{16}{13}y'^2 - \frac{72}{13}x'^2 - \frac{60}{13}x'y' + \frac{72}{13}y'^2$$

$$+\frac{36}{13}x'^2 + \frac{108}{13}x'y' + \frac{81}{13}y'^2 + 4\sqrt{13}x' = 0$$

$$13y'^2 + 4\sqrt{13}x' = 0$$

$$y'^2 = -\frac{4\sqrt{13}}{13}x'$$

Parabola; vertex at the origin, focus $\left(-\dfrac{\sqrt{13}}{13}, 0\right)$.

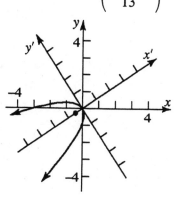

53. $r = \dfrac{4}{1 - \cos\theta}$

$ep = 4, \quad e = 1, \quad p = 4$

Parabola; directrix is perpendicular to the
polar axis 4 units to the left of the pole;
vertex is $(2, \pi)$.

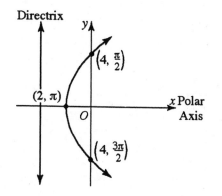

55. $r = \dfrac{6}{2-\sin\theta} = \dfrac{3}{1-\frac{1}{2}\sin\theta}$

$ep = 3, \ e = \dfrac{1}{2}, \ p = 6$

Ellipse; directrix is parallel to the polar
axis, 6 units below the pole; vertices are

$\left(6, \dfrac{\pi}{2}\right)$ and $\left(2, \dfrac{3\pi}{2}\right)$.

57. $r = \dfrac{8}{4+8\cos\theta} = \dfrac{2}{1+2\cos\theta}$

$ep = 2, \ e = 2, \ p = 1$

Hyperbola; directrix is perpendicular to the
polar axis, 1 unit to the right of the pole;

vertices are $\left(\dfrac{2}{3}, 0\right)$ and $(-2, \pi)$.

59.

$$r = \dfrac{4}{1-\cos\theta}$$
$$r - r\cos\theta = 4$$
$$r = 4 + r\cos\theta$$
$$r^2 = (4 + r\cos\theta)^2$$
$$x^2 + y^2 = (4 + x)^2$$
$$x^2 + y^2 = 16 + 8x + x^2$$
$$y^2 - 8x - 16 = 0$$

61.

$$r = \dfrac{8}{4+8\cos\theta}$$
$$4r + 8r\cos\theta = 8$$
$$4r = 8 - 8r\cos\theta$$
$$r = 2 - 2r\cos\theta$$
$$r^2 = (2 - 2r\cos\theta)^2$$
$$x^2 + y^2 = (2 - 2x)^2$$
$$x^2 + y^2 = 4 - 8x + 4x^2$$
$$3x^2 - y^2 - 8x + 4 = 0$$

63. $x = 4t - 2, \ y = 1 - t, \ -\infty < t < \infty$

$$x = 4(1-y) - 2$$
$$x = 4 - 4y - 2$$
$$x + 4y = 2$$

65. $x = 3\sin t,\ y = 4\cos t + 2,\ 0 \le t \le 2\pi$

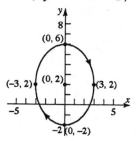

$\dfrac{x}{3} = \sin t,\quad \dfrac{y-2}{4} = \cos t$

$\sin^2 t + \cos^2 t = 1$

$\left(\dfrac{x}{3}\right)^2 + \left(\dfrac{y-2}{4}\right)^2 = 1$

$\dfrac{x^2}{9} + \dfrac{(y-2)^2}{16} = 1$

67. $x = \sec^2 t,\ y = \tan^2 t,\ 0 \le t \le \dfrac{\pi}{4}$

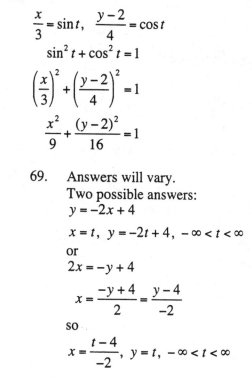

$\tan^2 t + 1 = \sec^2 t$

$y + 1 = x$

69.   Answers will vary.
Two possible answers:
$y = -2x + 4$

$x = t,\ y = -2t + 4,\ -\infty < t < \infty$

or
$2x = -y + 4$

$x = \dfrac{-y+4}{2} = \dfrac{y-4}{-2}$

so

$x = \dfrac{t-4}{-2},\ y = t,\ -\infty < t < \infty$

71.   Since the motion begins at $(4, 0)$, we want $x = 4$ and $y = 0$ when $t = 0$. Furthermore, since the given equation is an ellipse, we begin by letting $\dfrac{x}{4} = \cos(\omega t)$ and $\dfrac{y}{3} = \sin(\omega t)$ for some constant ω. With this choice, when $t = 0$, we have $x = 4$ and $y = 0$. For the motion to be counterclockwise, the motion will have to begin with x decreasing and y increasing as t increases. This requires that $\omega > 0$. Since 1 revolution requires 4 seconds, the period is $\dfrac{2\pi}{\omega} = 4 \Rightarrow 4\omega = 2\pi \Rightarrow \omega = \dfrac{\pi}{2}$. Thus, the desired parametric equations are:

$x = 4\cos\left(\dfrac{\pi}{2}t\right),\ y = 3\sin\left(\dfrac{\pi}{2}t\right),\quad 0 \le t \le 4$.

73.   Write the equation of the ellipse in standard form:

$4x^2 + 9y^2 = 36 \Rightarrow \dfrac{x^2}{9} + \dfrac{y^2}{4} = 1$

The center of the ellipse is $(0, 0)$.
The major axis is the x-axis.
  $a = 3;\ b = 2;$
$c^2 = a^2 - b^2 = 9 - 4 = 5$
  $c = \sqrt{5}$
For the ellipse:
Vertices: $(-3, 0),\ (3, 0)$

Foci: $\left(-\sqrt{5}, 0\right), \left(\sqrt{5}, 0\right)$

For the hyperbola:

Foci: $(-3, 0), (3, 0)$

Vertices: $\left(-\sqrt{5}, 0\right), \left(\sqrt{5}, 0\right)$

Center: $(0, 0)$

$a = \sqrt{5}$; $c = 3$;

$b^2 = c^2 - a^2 = 9 - 5 = 4$

The equation of the hyperbola is: $\dfrac{x^2}{5} - \dfrac{y^2}{4} = 1$.

75.　Let (x, y) be any point in the collection of points.

The distance from (x, y) to $(3, 0) = \sqrt{(x - 3)^2 + y^2}$.

The distance from (x, y) to the line $x = \dfrac{16}{3}$ is $\left| x - \dfrac{16}{3} \right|$.

Relating the distances, we have:

$$\sqrt{(x - 3)^2 + y^2} = \frac{3}{4}\left| x - \frac{16}{3} \right|$$

$$(x - 3)^2 + y^2 = \frac{9}{16}\left(x - \frac{16}{3} \right)^2$$

$$x^2 - 6x + 9 + y^2 = \frac{9}{16}\left(x^2 - \frac{32}{3}x + \frac{256}{9} \right)$$

$$16x^2 - 96x + 144 + 16y^2 = 9x^2 - 96x + 256$$

$$7x^2 + 16y^2 = 112$$

$$\frac{7x^2}{112} + \frac{16y^2}{112} = 1$$

$$\frac{x^2}{16} + \frac{y^2}{7} = 1$$

The set of points is an ellipse.

77.　Locate the parabola so that the vertex is at $(0, 0)$ and opens up. It then has the equation:
$x^2 = 4ay$. Since the light source is located at the focus and is 1 foot from the base, $a = 1$.
The diameter is 2, so the point $(1, y)$ is located on the parabola.
Solve for y: $1^2 = 4(1)y \Rightarrow 1 = 4y \Rightarrow y = 0.25$ foot
The mirror should be 0.25 foot deep, that is, 3 inches deep.

79.　Place the semielliptical arch so that the x-axis coincides with the major axis and the y-axis
passes through the center of the arch. Since the bridge has a span of 60 feet, the length of
the major axis is 60, or $2a = 60$, or $a = 30$. The maximum height of the bridge is 20 feet,
so $b = 20$. The equation is: $\dfrac{x^2}{900} + \dfrac{y^2}{400} = 1$.

The height 5 feet from the center:

$$\frac{5^2}{900} + \frac{y^2}{400} = 1 \Rightarrow \frac{y^2}{400} = 1 - \frac{25}{900} \Rightarrow y^2 = 400 \cdot \frac{875}{900} \Rightarrow y \approx 19.72 \text{ feet}$$

The height 10 feet from the center:
$$\frac{10^2}{900} + \frac{y^2}{400} = 1 \Rightarrow \frac{y^2}{400} = 1 - \frac{100}{900} \Rightarrow y^2 = 400 \cdot \frac{800}{900} \Rightarrow y \approx 18.86 \text{ feet}$$

The height 20 feet from the center:
$$\frac{20^2}{900} + \frac{y^2}{400} = 1 \Rightarrow \frac{y^2}{400} = 1 - \frac{400}{900} \Rightarrow y^2 = 400 \cdot \frac{500}{900} \Rightarrow y \approx 14.91 \text{ feet}$$

81. (a) Set up a coordinate system so that the two stations lie on the x-axis and the origin is midway between them. The ship lies on a hyperbola whose foci are the locations of the two stations. Since the time difference is 0.00032 second and the speed of the signal is 186,000 miles per second, the difference in the distances of the ships from each station is:

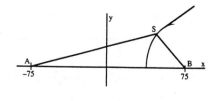

distance = (186,000)(0.00032) = 59.52 miles
The difference of the distances from the ship to each station, 59.52, equals $2a$, so $a = 29.76$ and the vertex of the corresponding hyperbola is at (29.76, 0). Since the focus is at (75, 0), following this hyperbola, the ship would reach shore 45.24 miles from the master station.

(b) The ship should follow a hyperbola with a vertex at (60, 0). For this hyperbola, $a = 60$, so the constant difference of the distances from the ship to each station is 120. The time difference the ship should look for is: time $= \dfrac{120}{186,000} = 0.000645$ second.

(c) Find the equation of the hyperbola with vertex at (60, 0) and a focus at (75, 0). The form of the equation of the hyperbola is: $\dfrac{x^2}{a^2} - \dfrac{y^2}{b^2} = 1$ where $a = 60$.

Since $c = 75$ and $b^2 = c^2 - a^2 \Rightarrow b^2 = 75^2 - 60^2 = 2025$.

The equation of the hyperbola is: $\dfrac{x^2}{3600} - \dfrac{y^2}{2025} = 1$.

Since the ship is 20 miles off shore, we have $y = 20$.
Solve the equation for x:
$$\frac{x^2}{3600} - \frac{20^2}{2025} = 1 \Rightarrow \frac{x^2}{3600} = 1 + \frac{400}{2025} = \frac{97}{81} \Rightarrow x^2 = 3600 \cdot \frac{97}{81}$$
$$x \approx 66 \text{ miles}$$
The ship's location is approximately (66, 20).

83. (a) Use equations (2):
$$x = \left(100\cos 35°\right)t; \qquad y = -\frac{1}{2}\left(32\right)t^2 + \left(100\sin 35°\right)t + 6$$

(b) The ball is in the air until $y = 0$. Solve:
$$-16t^2 + \left(100\sin 35°\right)t + 6 = 0$$

$$t = \frac{-100\sin 35° \pm \sqrt{\left(100\sin 35°\right)^2 - 4(-16)(6)}}{2(-16)} \approx -0.10 \text{ or } 3.69$$

The ball is in the air for about 3.69 seconds. (The negative solution is extraneous.)

(c)   The maximum height occurs at the vertex of the quadratic function.
$$t = -\frac{b}{2a} = -\frac{100\sin 35°}{2(-16)} \approx 1.79 \text{ seconds}$$
Evaluate the function to find the maximum height:
$$-16(1.79)^2 + 100(\sin 35°)(1.79) + 6 \approx 57.4 \text{ feet}$$

(d)   Find the horizontal displacement:
$$x = 100(\cos 35°)(3.69) \approx 302 \text{ feet}$$

(e)

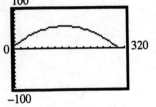

Chapter 6

Analytic Geometry

6.CR Cumulative Review

1. $\sin(2\theta) = 0.5$

$$2\theta = \frac{\pi}{6} + 2k\pi \quad \Rightarrow \quad \theta = \frac{\pi}{12} + k\pi$$

or $\quad 2\theta = \frac{5\pi}{6} + 2k\pi \quad \Rightarrow \quad \theta = \frac{5\pi}{12} + k\pi$,

where k is any integer.

3. Using rectangular coordinates, the circle with center point $(0,4)$ and radius 4 has the equation:

$$(x - h)^2 + (y - k)^2 = r^2$$

$$(x - 0)^2 + (y - 4)^2 = 4^2$$

$$x^2 + y^2 - 8y + 16 = 16$$

$$x^2 + y^2 - 8y = 0$$

Converting to polar coordinates:

$$r^2 - 8r\sin\theta = 0$$

$$r^2 = 8r\sin\theta$$

$$r = 8\sin\theta$$

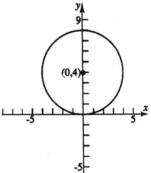

5. $$\frac{f(x+h) - f(x)}{h} = \frac{-3(x+h)^2 + 5(x+h) - 2 - (-3x^2 + 5x - 2)}{h}$$

$$= \frac{-3(x^2 + 2xh + h^2) + 5x + 5h - 2 + 3x^2 - 5x + 2}{h}$$

$$= \frac{-3x^2 - 6xh - 3h^2 + 5x + 5h - 2 + 3x^2 - 5x + 2}{h}$$

$$= \frac{-6xh - 3h^2 + 5h}{h} = \frac{h(-6x - 3h + 5)}{h} = -6x - 3h + 5$$

7. $\sin\alpha = \dfrac{1}{3}$, $\dfrac{\pi}{2} < \alpha < \pi \Rightarrow \alpha$ in quadrant II, and $\tan\beta = \dfrac{1}{2}$, $\pi < \beta < \dfrac{3\pi}{2} \Rightarrow \beta$ in quadrant III.

Since $\sin\alpha = \dfrac{1}{3}$, $\dfrac{\pi}{2} < \alpha < \pi$, let $r = 3$ and $y = 1$.

Solve for x:

$x^2 + 1 = 9 \Rightarrow x^2 = 8 \Rightarrow x = \pm\sqrt{8} = \pm 2\sqrt{2}$.

Since α is in quadrant II, $x = -2\sqrt{2}$.

$$\cos\alpha = \frac{x}{r} = \frac{-2\sqrt{2}}{3} = -\frac{2\sqrt{2}}{3};\qquad \tan\alpha = \frac{y}{x} = \frac{1}{-\dfrac{2\sqrt{2}}{3}} = -\frac{3}{2\sqrt{2}}\cdot\frac{\sqrt{2}}{\sqrt{2}} = -\frac{3\sqrt{2}}{4}$$

Since $\tan\beta = \dfrac{1}{2}$, $\pi < \beta < \dfrac{3\pi}{2}$, let $x = -2$ and $y = -1$.

Solve for r:

$4 + 1 = r^2 \Rightarrow r^2 = 5 \Rightarrow r = \sqrt{5}$.

$$\sin\beta = \frac{y}{r} = \frac{-1}{\sqrt{5}}\cdot\frac{\sqrt{5}}{\sqrt{5}} = -\frac{\sqrt{5}}{5};\qquad \cos\beta = \frac{x}{r} = \frac{-2}{\sqrt{5}}\cdot\frac{\sqrt{5}}{\sqrt{5}} = -\frac{2\sqrt{5}}{5}$$

(a) $\sin(\alpha + \beta) = \sin\alpha\cos\beta + \cos\alpha\sin\beta = \left(\dfrac{1}{3}\right)\cdot\left(-\dfrac{2\sqrt{5}}{5}\right) + \left(-\dfrac{2\sqrt{2}}{3}\right)\cdot\left(-\dfrac{\sqrt{5}}{5}\right) = \dfrac{-2\sqrt{5} + 2\sqrt{10}}{15}$

$$= \frac{2\left(\sqrt{10} - \sqrt{5}\right)}{15}$$

(b) $\sin(2\beta) = 2\sin\beta\cos\beta = 2\cdot\left(-\dfrac{\sqrt{5}}{5}\right)\cdot\left(-\dfrac{2\sqrt{5}}{5}\right) = \dfrac{4}{5}$

(c) $\dfrac{\pi}{2} < \alpha < \pi \Rightarrow \dfrac{\pi}{4} < \dfrac{\alpha}{2} < \dfrac{\pi}{2} \Rightarrow \dfrac{\alpha}{2}$ in quadrant I $\Rightarrow \cos\dfrac{\alpha}{2} > 0$

$$\cos\frac{\alpha}{2} = \sqrt{\frac{1 + \cos\alpha}{2}} = \sqrt{\frac{1 - \dfrac{2\sqrt{2}}{3}}{2}} = \sqrt{\frac{\dfrac{3 - 2\sqrt{2}}{3}}{2}} = \sqrt{\frac{3 - 2\sqrt{2}}{6}} = \frac{\sqrt{3 - 2\sqrt{2}}}{\sqrt{6}}\cdot\frac{\sqrt{6}}{\sqrt{6}}$$

$$= \frac{\sqrt{18 - 12\sqrt{2}}}{6}$$

9.   (a)   This graph is a line containing points $(0, -2)$ and $(1, 0)$.

   $$\text{slope} = \frac{\Delta y}{\Delta x} = \frac{0 - (-2)}{1 - 0} = \frac{2}{1} = 2$$

   using $y - y_1 = m(x - x_1)$:

   $$y - 0 = 2(x - 1)$$

   $$y = 2x - 2 \quad\text{or}\quad 2x - y - 2 = 0$$

(b)   This graph is a circle with center point $(2, 0)$ and radius 2.

   $$(x - h)^2 + (y - k)^2 = r^2$$

   $$(x - 2)^2 + (y - 0)^2 = 2^2$$

   $$(x - 2)^2 + y^2 = 4$$

   $$x^2 - 4x + 4 + y^2 = 4$$

   $$x^2 + y^2 - 4x = 0$$

(c) This graph is an ellipse with center point $(0, 0)$; vertices $(\pm 3, 0)$ and y-intercepts $(0, \pm 2)$.

$$\frac{(x-h)^2}{a^2} + \frac{(y-k)^2}{b^2} = 1$$

$$\frac{(x-0)^2}{3^2} + \frac{(y-0)^2}{2^2} = 1$$

$$\frac{x^2}{9} + \frac{y^2}{4} = 1$$

(d) This graph is a parabola with vertex $(1, 0)$ and y-intercept $(0, 2)$.

$$y - k = 4a(x-h)^2$$

$$y - 0 = 4a(x-1)^2$$

$$2 - 0 = 4a(0-1)^2$$

$$2 = 4a(-1)^2$$

$$2 = 4a \Rightarrow a = \frac{1}{2}$$

$$y - 0 = 4\left(\frac{1}{2}\right)(x-1)^2$$

$$y = 2(x-1)^2$$

(e) This graph is a hyperbola with center $(0,0)$ and vertices $(0, \pm 1)$, containing the point $(3, 2)$.

$$\frac{(y-k)^2}{a^2} - \frac{(x-h)^2}{b^2} = 1$$

$$\frac{y^2}{1} - \frac{x^2}{b^2} = 1$$

$$\frac{(2)^2}{1} - \frac{(3)^2}{b^2} = 1$$

$$\frac{4}{1} - \frac{9}{b^2} = 1$$

$$4 - \frac{9}{b^2} = 1$$

$$3 = \frac{9}{b^2}$$

$$3b^2 = 9$$

$$b^2 = 3 \Rightarrow b = \sqrt{3}$$

The equation of the hyperbola is:

$$\frac{y^2}{1} - \frac{x^2}{(\sqrt{3})^2} = 1$$

$$\frac{y^2}{1} - \frac{x^2}{3} = 1$$

Chapter 7

Exponential and Logarithmic Functions

7.1   Exponential Functions

1. $64; \left(\sqrt[3]{8}\right)^2 = 2^2 = 4; \dfrac{1}{3^2} = \dfrac{1}{9}$

3.   The line $y = 3x - 5$ has slope $= 3$.   5.   False

7.   1   9.   False

11.   (a) $3^{2.2} \approx 11.212$ (b) $3^{2.23} \approx 11.587$ (c) $3^{2.236} \approx 11.664$ (d) $3^{\sqrt{5}} \approx 11.665$

13.   (a) $2^{3.14} \approx 8.815$ (b) $2^{3.141} \approx 8.821$ (c) $2^{3.1415} \approx 8.824$ (d) $2^{\pi} \approx 8.825$

15.   (a) $3.1^{2.7} \approx 21.217$ (b) $3.14^{2.71} \approx 22.217$
      (c) $3.141^{2.718} \approx 22.440$ (d) $\pi^{e} \approx 22.459$

17. $e^{1.2} \approx 3.320$ 19. $e^{-0.85} \approx 0.427$

21.

x	$y = f(x)$	$\dfrac{f(x+1)}{f(x)}$
−1	3	$\dfrac{6}{3} = 2$
0	6	$\dfrac{12}{6} = 2$
1	12	$\dfrac{18}{12} = \dfrac{3}{2}$
2	18	
3	30	

Not an exponential function since the ratio of consecutive terms is not constant.

23.

x	$y = H(x)$	$\dfrac{H(x+1)}{H(x)}$
−1	$\dfrac{1}{4}$	$\dfrac{1}{(1/4)} = 4$
0	1	$\dfrac{4}{1} = 4$
1	4	$\dfrac{16}{4} = 4$
2	16	$\dfrac{64}{16} = 4$
3	64	

Yes, an exponential function since the ratio of consecutive terms is constant with $a = 4$. So the base is 4.

25.

x	$y = f(x)$	$\dfrac{f(x+1)}{f(x)}$
−1	$\dfrac{3}{2}$	$\dfrac{3}{(3/2)} = 2$
0	3	$\dfrac{6}{3} = 2$
1	6	$\dfrac{12}{6} = 2$
2	12	$\dfrac{24}{12} = 2$
3	24	

Yes, an exponential function since the ratio of consecutive terms is constant with $a = 2$. So the base is 2.

27.

x	$y = H(x)$	$\dfrac{H(x+1)}{H(x)}$
−1	2	$\dfrac{4}{2} = 2$
0	4	$\dfrac{6}{4} = \dfrac{3}{2}$
1	6	
2	8	
3	10	

Not an exponential function since the ratio of consecutive terms is not constant.

29. *B*   31. *D*   33. *A*   35. *E*

37. $f(x) = 2^x + 1$

Using the graph of $y = 2^x$, shift the graph up 1 unit.

Domain: $(-\infty, \infty)$

Range: $(1, \infty)$

Horizontal Asymptote: $y = 1$

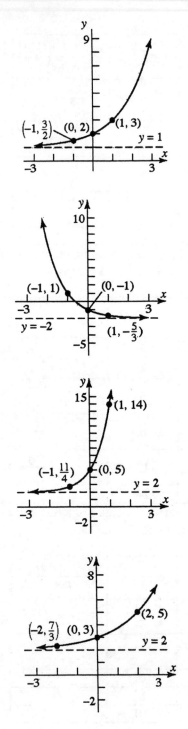

39. $f(x) = 3^{-x} - 2$

Using the graph of $y = 3^x$, reflect the graph about the y-axis, and shift down 2 units.

Domain: $(-\infty, \infty)$

Range: $(-2, \infty)$

Horizontal Asymptote: $y = -2$

41. $f(x) = 2 + 3\left(4^x\right)$

Using the graph of $y = 4^x$, stretch the graph vertically by a factor of 3, and shift up 2 units.

Domain: $(-\infty, \infty)$

Range: $(2, \infty)$

Horizontal Asymptote: $y = 2$

43. $f(x) = 2 + 3^{x/2}$

Using the graph of $y = 3^x$, stretch the graph horizontally by a factor of 2, and shift up 2 units.

Domain: $(-\infty, \infty)$

Range: $(2, \infty)$

Horizontal Asymptote: $y = 2$

45. $f(x) = e^{-x}$
Using the graph of $y = e^x$, reflect the
graph about the y-axis.
Domain: $(-\infty, \infty)$
Range: $(0, \infty)$
Horizontal Asymptote: $y = 0$

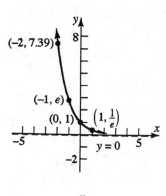

47. $f(x) = e^{x+2}$
Using the graph of $y = e^x$, shift the graph
2 units to the left.
Domain: $(-\infty, \infty)$
Range: $(0, \infty)$
Horizontal Asymptote: $y = 0$

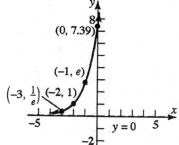

49. $f(x) = 5 - e^{-x}$
Using the graph of $y = e^x$, reflect the
graph about the y-axis, reflect about the
x-axis, and shift up 5 units.
Domain: $(-\infty, \infty)$
Range: $(-\infty, 5)$
Horizontal Asymptote: $y = 5$

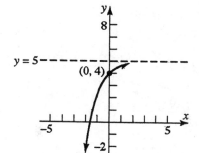

51. $f(x) = 2 - e^{-x/2}$
Using the graph of $y = e^x$, reflect the
graph about the y-axis, stretch
horizontally by a factor of 2, reflect about
the x-axis, and shift up 2 units.
Domain: $(-\infty, \infty)$
Range: $(-\infty, 2)$
Horizontal Asymptote: $y = 2$

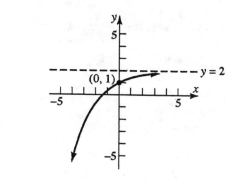

53.
$$2^{2x+1} = 4$$
$$2^{2x+1} = 2^2$$
$$2x + 1 = 2$$
$$2x = 1$$
$$x = \frac{1}{2}$$
The solution set is $\left\{\dfrac{1}{2}\right\}$.

55.
$$3^{x^3} = 9^x$$
$$3^{x^3} = \left(3^2\right)^x$$
$$3^{x^3} = 3^{2x}$$
$$x^3 = 2x$$
$$x^3 - 2x = 0$$
$$x\left(x^2 - 2\right) = 0$$
$$x = 0$$
or
$$x^2 - 2 = 0 \Rightarrow x^2 = 2 \Rightarrow x = \pm\sqrt{2}$$
The solution set is $\left\{-\sqrt{2},\ 0,\ \sqrt{2}\right\}$.

57.
$$8^{x^2-2x} = \frac{1}{2}$$
$$\left(2^3\right)^{x^2-2x} = 2^{-1}$$
$$2^{3x^2-6x} = 2^{-1}$$
$$3x^2 - 6x = -1$$
$$3x^2 - 6x + 1 = 0$$
$$x = \frac{-(-6) \pm \sqrt{(-6)^2 - 4(3)(1)}}{2(3)}$$
$$= \frac{6 \pm \sqrt{24}}{6}$$
$$= \frac{6 \pm 2\sqrt{6}}{6} = \frac{3 \pm \sqrt{6}}{3}$$
The solution set is $\left\{1 - \dfrac{\sqrt{6}}{3},\ 1 + \dfrac{\sqrt{6}}{3}\right\}$.

59.
$$2^x \cdot 8^{-x} = 4^x$$
$$2^x \cdot \left(2^3\right)^{-x} = \left(2^2\right)^x$$
$$2^x \cdot 2^{-3x} = 2^{2x}$$
$$2^{-2x} = 2^{2x}$$
$$-2x = 2x$$
$$-4x = 0 \Rightarrow x = 0$$
The solution set is $\left\{0\right\}$.

61.
$$\left(\frac{1}{5}\right)^{2-x} = 25$$
$$\left(5^{-1}\right)^{2-x} = 5^2$$
$$5^{x-2} = 5^2$$
$$x - 2 = 2 \Rightarrow x = 4$$
The solution set is $\left\{4\right\}$.

63.
$$4^x = 8$$
$$\left(2^2\right)^x = 2^3$$
$$2^{2x} = 2^3$$
$$2x = 3 \Rightarrow x = \frac{3}{2}$$
The solution set is $\left\{\dfrac{3}{2}\right\}$.

65.
$$e^{x^2} = e^{3x} \cdot \frac{1}{e^2}$$
$$e^{x^2} = e^{3x-2}$$
$$x^2 = 3x - 2$$
$$x^2 - 3x + 2 = 0$$
$$(x-1)(x-2) = 0 \Rightarrow x = 1 \text{ or } x = 2$$
The solution set is $\{1,2\}$.

67. Given $4^x = 7$,
$$4^{-2x} = \left(4^x\right)^{-2}$$
$$= 7^{-2}$$
$$= \frac{1}{7^2}$$
$$= \frac{1}{49}$$

69. Given $3^{-x} = 2$,
$$3^{2x} = \left(3^{-x}\right)^{-2}$$
$$= 2^{-2}$$
$$= \frac{1}{2^2}$$
$$= \frac{1}{4}$$

71. We need a function of the form $f(x) = k \cdot a^{p \cdot x}$, with $a > 0$, $a \neq 1$.

The graph contains the points $\left(-1, \frac{1}{3}\right)$, $(0,1)$, $(1,3)$ and $(2,9)$.

In other words, $f(-1) = \frac{1}{3}, f(0) = 1, f(1) = 3$ and $f(2) = 9$.

Therefore, $f(0) = k \cdot a^{p \cdot (0)} = k \cdot a^0 = k \cdot 1 = k \Rightarrow k = 1$.

and $f(1) = a^{p \cdot (1)} = a^p \Rightarrow a^p = 3$.

Let's use $a = 3$, $p = 1$. Then $f(x) = 3^x$.

Now we need to verify that this function yields the other known points on the graph.
$$f(-1) = 3^{-1} = \frac{1}{3}; \qquad f(2) = 3^2 = 9$$

So we have the function $f(x) = 3^x$.

73. We need a function of the form $f(x) = k \cdot a^{p \cdot x}$, with $a > 0$, $a \neq 1$.

The graph contains the points $\left(-1, -\frac{1}{6}\right)$, $(0,-1)$, $(1,-6)$ and $(2,-36)$.

In other words, $f(-1) = -\frac{1}{6}, f(0) = -1, f(1) = -6$ and $f(2) = -36$.

Therefore, $f(0) = k \cdot a^{p \cdot (0)} = k \cdot a^0 = k \cdot 1 = k \Rightarrow k = -1$.

and $f(1) = -a^{p \cdot (1)} = -a^p \Rightarrow -a^p = -6 \Rightarrow a^p = 6$.

Let's use $a = 6$, $p = 1$. Then $f(x) = -6^x$.

Now we need to verify that this function yields the other known points on the graph.
$$f(-1) = -6^{-1} = -\frac{1}{6}; \quad f(2) = -6^2 = -36$$

So we have the function $f(x) = -6^x$.

75. $p = 100e^{-0.03n}$

    (a) $p = 100e^{-0.03(10)} = 100e^{-0.3} \approx 100(0.741) = 74.1\%$ of light

    (b) $p = 100e^{-0.03(25)} = 100e^{-0.75} \approx 100(0.472) = 47.2\%$ of light

77. $w(d) = 50e^{-0.004d}$

    (a) $w(30) = 50e^{-0.004(30)} = 50e^{-0.12} \approx 50(0.887) = 44.35$ watts

    (b) $w(365) = 50e^{-0.004(365)} = 50e^{-1.46} \approx 50(0.232) = 11.61$ watts

79. $D(h) = 5e^{-0.4h}$

    $D(1) = 5e^{-0.4(1)} = 5e^{-0.4} \approx 5(0.670) = 3.35$ milligrams

    $D(6) = 5e^{-0.4(6)} = 5e^{-2.4} \approx 5(0.091) = 0.45$ milligrams

81. $F(t) = 1 - e^{-0.1t}$

    (a) $F(10) = 1 - e^{-0.1(10)} = 1 - e^{-1} \approx 1 - 0.368 = 0.632 = 63.2\%$

         The probability that a car will arrive within 10 minutes of 12:00 PM is 63.2%.

    (b) $F(40) = 1 - e^{-0.1(40)} = 1 - e^{-4} \approx 1 - 0.018 = 0.982 = 98.2\%$

         The probability that a car will arrive within 40 minutes of 12:00 PM is 98.2%

    (c)   As $t \to \infty$, $F(t) = 1 - e^{-0.1t} \to 1 - 0 = 1$

    (d)   Graphing the function:

    (e) $F(7) \approx 50$, so 7 minutes are needed for the probability to reach 50%.

83. $P(x) = \dfrac{20^x e^{-20}}{x!}$

    (a) $P(15) = \dfrac{20^{15} e^{-20}}{15!} \approx 0.0516 = 5.16\%$

         The probability that 15 cars will arrive between 5:00 PM and 6:00 PM is 5.16%.

    (b) $P(20) = \dfrac{20^{20} e^{-20}}{20!} \approx 0.0888 = 8.88\%$

         The probability that 20 cars will arrive between 5:00 PM and 6:00 PM is 8.88%.

85. $p(x) = 16,630(0.90)^x$

    (a) $p(3) = 16,630(0.90)^3 \approx 16,630(0.729) \approx \$12,123$

         A 3-year-old Civic DX Sedan costs \$12,123.

    (b) $p(9) = 16,630(0.90)^9 \approx 16,630(0.387) = \$6442.80$

         A 9-year-old Civic DX Sedan costs \$6443.

87. $I = \dfrac{E}{R}\left[1 - e^{-\left(\frac{R}{L}\right)t}\right]$

(a) $I_1 = \dfrac{120}{10}\left[1 - e^{-\left(\frac{10}{5}\right)0.3}\right] = 12\left[1 - e^{-0.6}\right] \approx 5.414$ amperes after 0.3 second

   $I_1 = \dfrac{120}{10}\left[1 - e^{-\left(\frac{10}{5}\right)0.5}\right] = 12\left[1 - e^{-1}\right] \approx 7.585$ amperes after 0.5 second

   $I_1 = \dfrac{120}{10}\left[1 - e^{-\left(\frac{10}{5}\right)1}\right] = 12\left[1 - e^{-2}\right] \approx 10.376$ amperes after 1 second

(b)   As $t \to \infty, e^{-\left(\frac{10}{5}\right)t} \to 0$. Therefore, the maximum current is 12 amperes.

(c), (f) Graphing the function:

(d) $I_2 = \dfrac{120}{5}\left[1 - e^{-\left(\frac{5}{10}\right)0.3}\right] = 24\left[1 - e^{-0.15}\right] \approx 3.343$ amperes after 0.3 second

   $I_2 = \dfrac{120}{5}\left[1 - e^{-\left(\frac{5}{10}\right)0.5}\right] = 24\left[1 - e^{-0.25}\right] \approx 5.309$ amperes after 0.5 second

   $I_2 = \dfrac{120}{5}\left[1 - e^{-\left(\frac{5}{10}\right)1}\right] = 24\left[1 - e^{-0.5}\right] \approx 9.443$ amperes after 1 second

(e)   As $t \to \infty, e^{-\left(\frac{5}{10}\right)t} \to 0$. Therefore, the maximum current is 24 amperes.

89. $2 + \dfrac{1}{2!} + \dfrac{1}{3!} + \dfrac{1}{4!} + \ldots + \dfrac{1}{n!}$

   $n = 4;\quad 2 + \dfrac{1}{2!} + \dfrac{1}{3!} + \dfrac{1}{4!} \approx 2.7083$

   $n = 6;\quad 2 + \dfrac{1}{2!} + \dfrac{1}{3!} + \dfrac{1}{4!} + \dfrac{1}{5!} + \dfrac{1}{6!} \approx 2.7181$

   $n = 8;\quad 2 + \dfrac{1}{2!} + \dfrac{1}{3!} + \dfrac{1}{4!} + \dfrac{1}{5!} + \dfrac{1}{6!} + \dfrac{1}{7!} + \dfrac{1}{8!} \approx 2.7182788$

   $n = 10;\quad 2 + \dfrac{1}{2!} + \dfrac{1}{3!} + \dfrac{1}{4!} + \dfrac{1}{5!} + \dfrac{1}{6!} + \dfrac{1}{7!} + \dfrac{1}{8!} + \dfrac{1}{9!} + \dfrac{1}{10!} \approx 2.7182818$

   $e \approx 2.718281828$

91. $f(x) = a^x$

$$\frac{f(x+h)-f(x)}{h} = \frac{a^{x+h}-a^x}{h} = \frac{a^x a^h - a^x}{h} = \frac{a^x\left(a^h-1\right)}{h} = a^x\left(\frac{a^h-1}{h}\right)$$

93. $f(x) = a^x$

$$f(-x) = a^{-x} = \frac{1}{a^x} = \frac{1}{f(x)}$$

95. $R = 10^{\left(\frac{4221}{T+459.4} - \frac{4221}{D+459.4} + 2\right)}$

(a) $R = 10^{\left(\frac{4221}{50+459.4} - \frac{4221}{41+459.4} + 2\right)} \approx 70.95\%$

(b) $R = 10^{\left(\frac{4221}{68+459.4} - \frac{4221}{59+459.4} + 2\right)} \approx 72.62\%$

(c) $R = 10^{\left(\frac{4221}{T+459.4} - \frac{4221}{T+459.4} + 2\right)} = 10^2 = 100\%$

97. $\sinh x = \frac{1}{2}\left(e^x - e^{-x}\right)$

(a) $f(-x) = \sinh(-x) = \frac{1}{2}\left(e^{-x} - e^x\right) = -\frac{1}{2}\left(e^x - e^{-x}\right) = -\sinh x = -f(x)$

Therefore, $f(x) = \sinh x$ is an odd function.

(b) Graphing:

99. Since the number of bacteria doubles every minute, half of the container is full one minute before it is full. Thus, it takes 59 minutes to fill the container.

101. Answers will vary.

103. Using the laws of exponents, we have: $a^{-x} = \frac{1}{a^x} = \left(\frac{1}{a}\right)^x$. So $y = a^{-x}$ and $y = \left(\frac{1}{a}\right)^x$ will have the same graph.

Chapter 7

Exponential and Logarithmic Functions

7.2 Logarithmic Functions

1. $3x - 7 \leq 8 - 2x$
    $5x \leq 15$
    $x \leq 3$
    The solution set is $\{x \mid x \leq 3\}$.

3. $\dfrac{1}{4}$

5. $(1,0), (a,1), \left(\dfrac{1}{a}, -1\right)$

7. False

9. $9 = 3^2$ is equivalent to $2 = \log_3 9$

11. $a^2 = 1.6$ is equivalent to $2 = \log_a 1.6$

13. $1.1^2 = M$ is equivalent to $2 = \log_{1.1} M$

15. $2^x = 7.2$ is equivalent to $x = \log_2 7.2$

17. $x^{\sqrt{2}} = \pi$ is equivalent to $\sqrt{2} = \log_x \pi$

19. $e^x = 8$ is equivalent to $x = \ln 8$

21. $\log_2 8 = 3$ is equivalent to $2^3 = 8$

23. $\log_a 3 = 6$ is equivalent to $a^6 = 3$

25. $\log_3 2 = x$ is equivalent to $3^x = 2$

27. $\log_2 M = 1.3$ is equivalent to $2^{1.3} = M$

29. $\log_{\sqrt{2}} \pi = x$ is equivalent to $\left(\sqrt{2}\right)^x = \pi$

31. $\ln 4 = x$ is equivalent to $e^x = 4$

33. $\log_2 1 = 0$ since $2^0 = 1$

35. $\log_5 25 = 2$ since $5^2 = 25$

37. $\log_{1/2} 16 = -4$ since $\left(\dfrac{1}{2}\right)^{-4} = 2^4 = 16$

39. $\log_{10} \sqrt{10} = \dfrac{1}{2}$ since $10^{1/2} = \sqrt{10}$

41. $\log_{\sqrt{2}} 4 = 4$ since $\left(\sqrt{2}\right)^4 = 4$

43. $\ln \sqrt{e} = \dfrac{1}{2}$ since $e^{1/2} = \sqrt{e}$

45. $f(x) = \ln(x - 3)$ requires
    $x - 3 > 0$
    $x > 3$
    The domain of f is $\{x \mid x > 3\}$.

47. $F(x) = \log_2 x^2$ requires $x^2 > 0$.
    $x^2 > 0$ for all $x \neq 0$.
    The domain of F is $\{x \mid x \neq 0\}$.

49. $f(x) = 3 - 2\log_4 \dfrac{x}{2}$ requires $\dfrac{x}{2} > 0$.

$\dfrac{x}{2} > 0$

$x > 0$

The domain of f is $\{x \mid x > 0\}$.

51. $f(x) = \ln\left(\dfrac{1}{x+1}\right)$ requires $p(x) = \dfrac{1}{x+1}$

$\dfrac{1}{x+1} > 0$ p is undefined when $x = -1$.

Interval	$(-\infty, -1)$	$(-1, \infty)$
Number Chosen	-2	0
Value of p	-1	1
Conclusion	Negative	Positive

The domain of f is $\{x \mid x > -1\}$.

53. $g(x) = \log_5\left(\dfrac{x+1}{x}\right)$ requires $p(x) = \dfrac{x+1}{x}$

$\dfrac{x+1}{x} > 0$ $p(x)$ is zero or undefined when $x = -1$ or $x = 0$.

Interval	$(-\infty, -1)$	$(-1, 0)$	$(0, \infty)$
Number Chosen	-2	-0.5	1
Value of p	0.5	-1	2
Conclusion	Positive	Negative	Positive

The domain of g is $\{x \mid x < -1 \text{ or } x > 0\}$

55. $f(x) = \sqrt{\ln x}$ requires $\ln x \geq 0$ and $x > 0$ 57. $\ln\dfrac{5}{3} \approx 0.511$

$\ln x \geq 0$

$\Rightarrow x \geq e^0$

$x \geq 1$

The domain of h is $\{x \mid x \geq 1\}$.

59. $\dfrac{\ln(10/3)}{0.04} \approx 30.099$

61.   For $f(x) = \log_a x$, find a so that $f(2) = \log_a 2 = 2$ or $a^2 = 2$ or $a = \sqrt{2}$.

(The base a must be positive by definition.)

63. $y = \log_3 x$

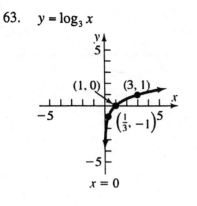

65. $y = \log_{1/4} x$

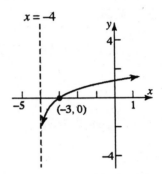

67.   B   69.   D   71.   A   73.   E

75. $f(x) = \ln(x + 4)$
Using the graph of $y = \ln x$, shift the
graph 4 units to the left.
Domain: $(-4, \infty)$
Range: $(-\infty, \infty)$
Vertical Asymptote: $x = -4$

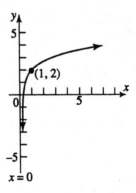

77. $f(x) = 2 + \ln x = \ln x + 2$
Using the graph of $y = \ln x$, shift up 2
units.
Domain: $(0, \infty)$
Range: $(-\infty, \infty)$
Vertical Asymptote: $x = 0$

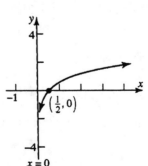

79. $g(x) = \ln(2x)$
Using the graph of $y = \ln x$, compress the
graph horizontally by a factor of $\dfrac{1}{2}$.
Domain: $(0, \infty)$
Range: $(-\infty, \infty)$
Vertical Asymptote: $x = 0$

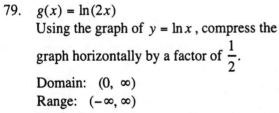

361

81. $f(x) = 3\ln x$
Using the graph of $y = \ln x$, stretch the
graph vertically by a factor of 3.
Domain: $(0, \infty)$
Range: $(-\infty, \infty)$
Vertical Asymptote: $x = 0$

83. $f(x) = \log(x - 4)$
Using the graph of $y = \log x$, shift 4 units
to the right.
Domain: $(4, \infty)$
Range: $(-\infty, \infty)$
Vertical Asymptote: $x = 4$

85. $h(x) = 4\log x$
Using the graph of $y = \log x$, stretch the
graph vertically by a factor of 4.
Domain: $(0, \infty)$
Range: $(-\infty, \infty)$
Vertical Asymptote: $x = 0$

87. $F(x) = \log(2x)$
Using the graph of $y = \log x$, compress
the graph horizontally by a factor of $\dfrac{1}{2}$.
Domain: $(0, \infty)$
Range: $(-\infty, \infty)$
Vertical Asymptote: $x = 0$

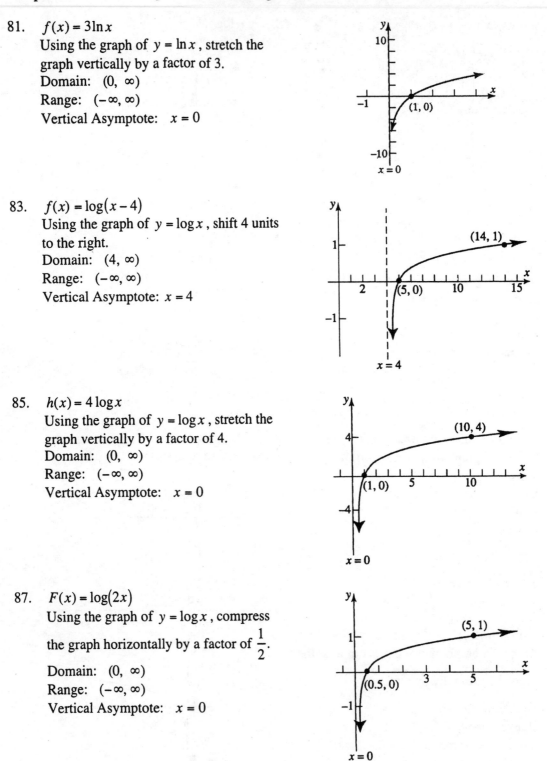

89. $f(x) = 3 + \log(x + 2) = \log(x + 2) + 3$
Using the graph of $y = \log x$, shift 2 units
to the left, and shift up 3 units.
Domain: $(-2, \infty)$
Range: $(-\infty, \infty)$
Vertical Asymptote: $x = -2$

91. $\log_3 x = 2$
$\quad x = 3^2$
$\quad x = 9$
The solution set is $\{9\}$.

93. $\log_2(2x + 1) = 3$
$\quad 2x + 1 = 2^3$
$\quad 2x + 1 = 8$
$\quad\quad 2x = 7$
$\quad\quad\quad x = \dfrac{7}{2}$
The solution set is $\left\{\dfrac{7}{2}\right\}$.

95. $\log_x 4 = 2$
$\quad x^2 = 4$
$\quad x = 2 \quad (x \neq -2, \text{ base is positive})$
The solution set is $\{2\}$.

97. $\ln e^x = 5$
$\quad e^x = e^5$
$\quad x = 5$
The solution set is $\{5\}$.

99. $\log_4 64 = x$
$\quad 4^x = 64$
$\quad 4^x = 4^3$
$\quad x = 3$
The solution set is $\{3\}$.

101. $\log_3 243 = 2x + 1$
$\quad 3^{2x+1} = 243$
$\quad 3^{2x+1} = 3^5$
$\quad 2x + 1 = 5$
$\quad\quad 2x = 4$
$\quad\quad\quad x = 2$
The solution set is $\{2\}$.

103. $e^{3x} = 10$
$\quad 3x = \ln(10)$
$\quad x = \dfrac{\ln(10)}{3}$
The solution set is $\left\{\dfrac{\ln(10)}{3}\right\}$.

105. $e^{2x+5} = 8$
$\quad 2x + 5 = \ln(8)$
$\quad 2x = \ln(8) - 5$
$\quad x = \dfrac{\ln(8) - 5}{2}$
The solution set is $\left\{\dfrac{\ln(8) - 5}{2}\right\}$.

107. $\log_3(x^2+1)=2$

$x^2+1=3^2$

$x^2+1=9$

$x^2=8$

$x=-\sqrt{8}$ or $x=\sqrt{8}$

$x=-2\sqrt{2}$ or $x=2\sqrt{2}$

The solution set is $\left\{-2\sqrt{2},\ 2\sqrt{2}\right\}$.

109. $\log_2 8^x=-3$

$8^x=2^{-3}$

$\left(2^3\right)^x=2^{-3}$

$2^{3x}=2^{-3}$

$3x=-3\Rightarrow x=-1$

The solution set is $\{-1\}$.

111. $pH=-\log_{10}\left[H^+\right]$

(a) $pH=-\log_{10}\left[0.1\right]=-(-1)=1$

(b) $pH=-\log_{10}\left[0.01\right]=-(-2)=2$

(c) $pH=-\log_{10}\left[0.001\right]=-(-3)=3$

(d) As the H^+ decreases, the pH increases.

(e) $3.5=-\log_{10}\left[H^+\right]\Rightarrow-3.5=\log_{10}\left[H^+\right]\Rightarrow\left[H^+\right]=10^{-3.5}\approx3.16\times10^{-4}=0.000316$

(f) $7.4=-\log_{10}\left[H^+\right]\Rightarrow-7.4=\log_{10}\left[H^+\right]\Rightarrow\left[H^+\right]=10^{-7.4}\approx3.981\times10^{-8}=0.00000003981$

113. $p=760e^{-0.145h}$

(a) $320=760e^{-0.145h}$

$\dfrac{320}{760}=e^{-0.145h}$

$\ln\left(\dfrac{320}{760}\right)=-0.145h$

$h=\dfrac{\ln\left(\dfrac{320}{760}\right)}{-0.145}\approx5.97$ km

(b) $667=760e^{-0.145h}$

$\dfrac{667}{760}=e^{-0.145h}$

$\ln\left(\dfrac{667}{760}\right)=-0.145h$

$h=\dfrac{\ln\left(\dfrac{667}{760}\right)}{-0.145}\approx0.90$ km

115. $F(t)=1-e^{-0.1t}$

(a) $0.5=1-e^{-0.1t}$

$-0.5=-e^{-0.1t}$

$0.5=e^{-0.1t}\Rightarrow\ln(0.5)=-0.1t$

$t=\dfrac{\ln(0.5)}{-0.1}\approx6.93$

Approximately 7 minutes.

(b) $0.8=1-e^{-0.1t}$

$-0.2=-e^{-0.1t}$

$0.2=e^{-0.1t}\Rightarrow\ln(0.2)=-0.1t$

$t=\dfrac{\ln(0.2)}{-0.1}\approx16.09$

Approximately 16 minutes.

(c) It is impossible for the probability to reach 100% because $e^{-0.1t}$ will never equal zero; thus, $F(t)=1-e^{-0.1t}$ will never equal 1.

117. $D = 5e^{-0.4h}$
         $2 = 5e^{-0.4h}$
         $0.4 = e^{-0.4h}$
         $\ln(0.4) = -0.4h$
         $h = \dfrac{\ln(0.4)}{-0.4} \approx 2.29$

Approximately 2.3 hours.

119. $I = \dfrac{E}{R}\left[1 - e^{-(R/L)t}\right]$

0.5 ampere:

$0.5 = \dfrac{12}{10}\left[1 - e^{-(10/5)t}\right]$

$\dfrac{5}{12} = 1 - e^{-2t}$

$e^{-2t} = \dfrac{7}{12}$

$-2t = \ln(7/12)$

$t = \dfrac{\ln(7/12)}{-2} \approx 0.2695$ seconds

1.0 ampere:

$1.0 = \dfrac{12}{10}\left[1 - e^{-(10/5)t}\right]$

$\dfrac{10}{12} = 1 - e^{-2t}$

$e^{-2t} = \dfrac{1}{6}$

$-2t = \ln(1/6)$

$t = \dfrac{\ln(1/6)}{-2} \approx 0.8959$ seconds

Graphing:

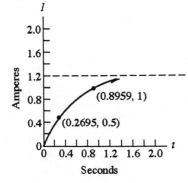

121. $L(10^{-7}) = 10 \log\left(\dfrac{10^{-7}}{10^{-12}}\right) = 10 \log\left(10^{5}\right) = 10 \cdot 5 = 50$ decibels

123. $L(10^{-1}) = 10 \log\left(\dfrac{10^{-1}}{10^{-12}}\right) = 10 \log\left(10^{11}\right) = 10 \cdot 11 = 110$ decibels

125. $M(125,892) = \log\left(\dfrac{125,892}{10^{-3}}\right) \approx 8.1$

127. $R = 3e^{kx}$

(a) $10 = 3e^{k(0.06)}$

$3.3333 = e^{0.06k}$

$\ln(3.3333) = 0.06\,k$

$k = \dfrac{\ln(3.3333)}{0.06}$

$k \approx 20.07$

(b) $R = 3e^{20.066(0.17)}$

$R = 3e^{3.41122}$

$R \approx 91\%$

(c) $100 = 3e^{20.066x}$

$33.3333 = e^{20.066x}$

$\ln(33.3333) = 20.066x$

$x = \dfrac{\ln(33.3333)}{20.07}$

$x \approx 0.175$

(d) $15 = 3e^{20.066x}$

$5 = e^{20.066x}$

$\ln(5) = 20.066x$

$x = \dfrac{\ln(5)}{20.066}$

$x \approx 0.08$

129.   If the base of a logarithmic function equals 1, we would have the following:

$$f(x) = \log_1(x) \Rightarrow f^{-1}(x) = 1^x = 1 \text{ for every real number } x.$$

In other words, f^{-1} would be a constant function and, therefore, f^{-1} would not be one-to-one.

Exponential and Logarithmic Functions

7.3   Properties of Logarithms

1.   sum

3. $r \log_a M$

5.   False

7. $\log_3 3^{71} = 71$

9. $\ln e^{-4} = -4$

11. $2^{\log_2 7} = 7$

13. $\log_8 2 + \log_8 4 = \log_8 (4 \cdot 2) = \log_8 8 = 1$

15. $\log_6 18 - \log_6 3 = \log_6 \dfrac{18}{3} = \log_6 6 = 1$

17. $\begin{aligned} \log_2 6 \cdot \log_6 4 &= \log_6 4^{\log_2 6} \\ &= \log_6 \left(2^2\right)^{\log_2 6} \\ &= \log_6 (2)^{2 \log_2 6} \\ &= \log_6 (2)^{\log_2 6^2} \\ &= \log_6 6^2 \\ &= 2 \end{aligned}$

19. $3^{\log_3 5 - \log_3 4} = 3^{\log_3 \frac{5}{4}} = \dfrac{5}{4}$

21. $e^{\log_{e^2} 16}$
      Simplify the exponent.
      Let $a = \log_{e^2} 16$, then $\left(e^2\right)^a = 16$.
      $$e^{2a} = 16$$
      $$e^{2a} = 4^2$$
      $$\left(e^{2a}\right)^{1/2} = \left(4^2\right)^{1/2}$$
      $$e^a = 4$$
      $$a = \ln 4$$

      Thus, $e^{\log_{e^2} 16} = e^{\ln 4} = 4$.

23. $\ln 6 = \ln(3 \cdot 2) = \ln 3 + \ln 2 = b + a$

25. $\ln 1.5 = \ln\dfrac{3}{2} = \ln 3 - \ln 2 = b - a$ 27. $\ln 8 = \ln 2^3 = 3 \cdot \ln 2 = 3a$

29. $\ln\sqrt[5]{6} = \ln 6^{1/5} = \dfrac{1}{5} \cdot \ln 6 = \dfrac{1}{5} \cdot \ln(2 \cdot 3) = \dfrac{1}{5} \cdot (\ln 2 + \ln 3) = \dfrac{1}{5} \cdot (a + b)$

31. $\log_5(25x) = \log_5 25 + \log_5 x = 2 + \log_5 x$

33. $\log_2 z^3 = 3\log_2 z$ 35. $\ln(ex) = \ln e + \ln x = 1 + \ln x$

37. $\ln\left(xe^x\right) = \ln x + \ln e^x = \ln x + x$

39. $\log_a\left(u^2 v^3\right) = \log_a u^2 + \log_a v^3 = 2\log_a u + 3\log_a v$

41. $\ln\left(x^2\sqrt{1-x}\right) = \ln x^2 + \ln\sqrt{1-x} = \ln x^2 + \ln(1-x)^{1/2} = 2\ln x + \dfrac{1}{2}\ln(1-x)$

43. $\log_2\left(\dfrac{x^3}{x-3}\right) = \log_2 x^3 - \log_2(x-3) = 3\log_2 x - \log_2(x-3)$

45. $\log\left[\dfrac{x(x+2)}{(x+3)^2}\right] = \log(x(x+2)) - \log(x+3)^2 = \log x + \log(x+2) - 2\log(x+3)$

47. $\ln\left[\dfrac{x^2-x-2}{(x+4)^2}\right]^{1/3} = \dfrac{1}{3}\ln\left[\dfrac{(x-2)(x+1)}{(x+4)^2}\right]$

$= \dfrac{1}{3}\left[\ln(x-2)(x+1) - \ln(x+4)^2\right]$

$= \dfrac{1}{3}\left[\ln(x-2) + \ln(x+1) - 2\ln(x+4)\right]$

$= \dfrac{1}{3}\ln(x-2) + \dfrac{1}{3}\ln(x+1) - \dfrac{2}{3}\ln(x+4)$

49. $\ln\dfrac{5x\sqrt{1+3x}}{(x-4)^3} = \ln\left(5x\sqrt{1+3x}\right) - \ln(x-4)^3$

$= \ln 5 + \ln x + \ln\sqrt{1+3x} - 3\ln(x-4)$

$= \ln 5 + \ln x + \ln(1+3x)^{1/2} - 3\ln(x-4)$

$= \ln 5 + \ln x + \dfrac{1}{2}\ln(1+3x) - 3\ln(x-4)$

51. $3\log_5 u + 4\log_5 v = \log_5 u^3 + \log_5 v^4 = \log_5(u^3 v^4)$

53. $\log_3 \sqrt{x} - \log_3 x^3 = \log_3 \left(\dfrac{\sqrt{x}}{x^3} \right) = \log_3 \left(\dfrac{x^{1/2}}{x^3} \right) = \log_3 x^{-5/2} = -\dfrac{5}{2} \log_3 x$

55. $\log_4 \left(x^2 - 1 \right) - 5 \log_4 (x + 1) = \log_4 \left(x^2 - 1 \right) - \log_4 (x + 1)^5$

$$= \log_4 \left(\frac{x^2 - 1}{(x + 1)^5} \right)$$

$$= \log_4 \left(\frac{(x + 1)(x - 1)}{(x + 1)^5} \right)$$

$$= \log_4 \left(\frac{x - 1}{(x + 1)^4} \right)$$

57. $\ln \left(\dfrac{x}{x-1} \right) + \ln \left(\dfrac{x+1}{x} \right) - \ln \left(x^2 - 1 \right) = \ln \left[\dfrac{x}{x-1} \cdot \dfrac{x+1}{x} \right] - \ln \left(x^2 - 1 \right)$

$$= \ln \left[\frac{x+1}{x-1} \div \left(x^2 - 1 \right) \right]$$

$$= \ln \left[\frac{x+1}{(x-1)(x-1)(x+1)} \right]$$

$$= \ln \left(\frac{1}{(x-1)^2} \right)$$

$$= \ln(x-1)^{-2}$$

$$= -2 \ln(x-1)$$

59. $8 \log_2 \sqrt{3x - 2} - \log_2 \left(\dfrac{4}{x} \right) + \log_2 4 = \log_2 \left(\sqrt{3x - 2} \right)^8 - \left(\log_2 4 - \log_2 x \right) + \log_2 4$

$$= \log_2 (3x - 2)^4 - \log_2 4 + \log_2 x + \log_2 4$$

$$= \log_2 \left[x(3x - 2)^4 \right]$$

61. $2 \log_a \left(5x^3 \right) - \dfrac{1}{2} \log_a (2x + 3) = \log_a \left(5x^3 \right)^2 - \log_a (2x - 3)^{1/2} = \log_a \left[\dfrac{25x^6}{(2x - 3)^{1/2}} \right]$

63. $2\log_2(x+1)-\log_2(x+3)-\log_2(x-1)=\log_2(x+1)^2-\log_2(x+3)-\log_2(x-1)$

$$=\log_2\frac{(x+1)^2}{(x+3)}-\log_2(x-1)$$

$$=\log_2\frac{\dfrac{(x+1)^2}{(x+3)}}{(x-1)}$$

$$=\log_2\frac{(x+1)^2}{(x+3)(x-1)}$$

65. $\log_3 21=\dfrac{\log 21}{\log 3}\approx\dfrac{1.32222}{0.47712}\approx 2.771$

67. $\log_{1/3}71=\dfrac{\log 71}{\log(1/3)}=\dfrac{\log 71}{-\log 3}\approx\dfrac{1.85126}{-0.47712}\approx -3.880$

69. $\log_{\sqrt{2}}7=\dfrac{\log 7}{\log\sqrt{2}}\approx\dfrac{0.84510}{0.15051}\approx 5.615$

71. $\log_{\pi}e=\dfrac{\ln e}{\ln\pi}\approx\dfrac{1}{1.14473}\approx 0.874$

73. $y=\log_4 x=\dfrac{\ln x}{\ln 4}$ or $y=\dfrac{\log x}{\log 4}$

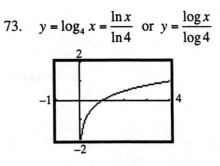

75. $y=\log_2(x+2)=\dfrac{\ln(x+2)}{\ln 2}$

       or $y=\dfrac{\log(x+2)}{\log 2}$

77. $y=\log_{x-1}(x+1)=\dfrac{\ln(x+1)}{\ln(x-1)}$

       or $y=\dfrac{\log(x+1)}{\log(x-1)}$

79. $\ln y=\ln x+\ln C$
       $\ln y=\ln(xC)$
           $y=Cx$

81. $\ln y=\ln x+\ln(x+1)+\ln C$
       $\ln y=\ln\big(x(x+1)C\big)$
           $y=Cx(x+1)$

83.
$$\ln y = 3x + \ln C$$
$$\ln y = \ln e^{3x} + \ln C$$
$$\ln y = \ln\left(Ce^{3x}\right)$$
$$y = Ce^{3x}$$

85.
$$\ln(y-3) = -4x + \ln C$$
$$\ln(y-3) = \ln e^{-4x} + \ln C$$
$$\ln(y-3) = \ln\left(Ce^{-4x}\right)$$
$$y - 3 = Ce^{-4x}$$
$$y = Ce^{-4x} + 3$$

87.
$$3\ln y = \frac{1}{2}\ln(2x+1) - \frac{1}{3}\ln(x+4) + \ln C$$
$$\ln y^3 = \ln(2x+1)^{1/2} - \ln(x+4)^{1/3} + \ln C$$
$$\ln y^3 = \ln\left[\frac{C(2x+1)^{1/2}}{(x+4)^{1/3}}\right]$$
$$y^3 = \frac{C(2x+1)^{1/2}}{(x+4)^{1/3}}$$
$$y = \left[\frac{C(2x+1)^{1/2}}{(x+4)^{1/3}}\right]^{1/3}$$
$$y = \frac{\sqrt[3]{C}(2x+1)^{1/6}}{(x+4)^{1/9}}$$

89. $\log_2 3 \cdot \log_3 4 \cdot \log_4 5 \cdot \log_5 6 \cdot \log_6 7 \cdot \log_7 8$
$$= \frac{\log 3}{\log 2}\cdot\frac{\log 4}{\log 3}\cdot\frac{\log 5}{\log 4}\cdot\frac{\log 6}{\log 5}\cdot\frac{\log 7}{\log 6}\cdot\frac{\log 8}{\log 7} = \frac{\log 8}{\log 2} = \frac{\log 2^3}{\log 2} = \frac{3\log 2}{\log 2} = 3$$

91. $\log_2 3 \cdot \log_3 4 \cdots \log_n(n+1) \cdot \log_{n+1} 2$
$$= \frac{\log 3}{\log 2}\cdot\frac{\log 4}{\log 3}\cdots\frac{\log(n+1)}{\log n}\cdot\frac{\log 2}{\log(n+1)} = \frac{\log 2}{\log 2} = 1$$

93. $\log_a\left(x+\sqrt{x^2-1}\right) + \log_a\left(x-\sqrt{x^2-1}\right) = \log_a\left[\left(x+\sqrt{x^2-1}\right)\left(x-\sqrt{x^2-1}\right)\right]:$
$$= \log_a\left[x^2 - \left(x^2-1\right)\right]$$
$$= \log_a\left[x^2 - x^2 + 1\right]$$
$$= \log_a 1$$
$$= 0$$

95. $2x + \ln(1 + e^{-2x}) = \ln e^{2x} + \ln(1 + e^{-2x})$
$$= \ln(e^{2x}(1 + e^{-2x}))$$
$$= \ln(e^{2x} + e^0)$$
$$= \ln(e^{2x} + 1)$$

97. $f(x) = \log_a x$
$x = a^{f(x)}$

$x^{-1} = a^{-f(x)} = (a^{-1})^{f(x)} = \left(\dfrac{1}{a}\right)^{f(x)}$

Therefore, $\log_{1/a} x^{-1} = f(x) \Rightarrow -\log_{1/a} x = f(x) \Rightarrow -f(x) = \log_{1/a} x$.

99. $f(x) = \log_a x$
$a^{f(x)} = x$

$\dfrac{1}{a^{f(x)}} = \dfrac{1}{x}$

$a^{-f(x)} = \dfrac{1}{x}$

Therefore, $-f(x) = \log_a \dfrac{1}{x} = f\left(\dfrac{1}{x}\right)$.

101. If $A = \log_a M$ and $B = \log_a N$, then $a^A = M$ and $a^B = N$.
$$\log_a\left(\frac{M}{N}\right) = \log_a\left(\frac{a^A}{a^B}\right)$$
$$= \log_a a^{A-B}$$
$$= A - B$$
$$= \log_a M - \log_a N$$

103. The domain of $f(x) = \log_a x^2$ is $\{x \mid x \neq 0\}$. The domain of $g(x) = 2\log_a x$ is $\{x \mid x > 0\}$.
These two domains are different because the logarithm property $\log_a x^n = n \cdot \log_a x$ holds only when $\log_a x$ exists.

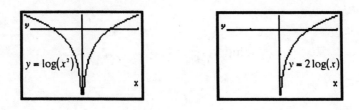

Exponential and Logarithmic Functions

7.4   Logarithmic and Exponential Equations

1. $\log_4(x+2) = \log_4 8$
$$x+2 = 8$$
$$x = 6$$

The solution set is $\{6\}$.

3. $\dfrac{1}{2}\log_3 x = 2\log_3 2$
$$\log_3 x^{1/2} = \log_3 2^2$$
$$x^{1/2} = 4$$
$$x = 16$$

The solution set is $\{16\}$.

5. $2\log_5 x = 3\log_5 4$
$$\log_5 x^2 = \log_5 4^3$$
$$x^2 = 64$$
$$x = \pm 8$$
Since $\log_5(-8)$ is undefined, the solution set is $\{8\}$.

7. $3\log_2(x-1) + \log_2 4 = 5$
$$\log_2(x-1)^3 + \log_2 4 = 5$$
$$\log_2\left(4(x-1)^3\right) = 5$$
$$4(x-1)^3 = 2^5$$
$$(x-1)^3 = \frac{32}{4}$$
$$(x-1)^3 = 8$$
$$x-1 = 2$$
$$x = 3$$
The solution set is $\{3\}$.

9. $\log x + \log(x+15) = 2$
$$\log\left(x(x+15)\right) = 2$$
$$x(x+15) = 10^2$$
$$x^2 + 15x - 100 = 0$$
$$(x+20)(x-5) = 0$$
$$x = -20 \text{ or } x = 5$$
Since $\log(-20)$ is undefined, the solution set is $\{5\}$.

11. $\ln x + \ln(x+2) = 4$

$\ln(x(x+2)) = 4$

$x(x+2) = e^4$

$x^2 + 2x - e^4 = 0$

$x = \dfrac{-2 \pm \sqrt{2^2 - 4(1)(-e^4)}}{2(1)}$

$\quad = \dfrac{-2 \pm \sqrt{4 + 4e^4}}{2}$

$\quad = \dfrac{-2 \pm 2\sqrt{1 + e^4}}{2}$

$\quad = -1 \pm \sqrt{1 + e^4}$

$x = -1 - \sqrt{1 + e^4}$ or $x = -1 + \sqrt{1 + e^4}$

$\quad \approx -8.456 \qquad\qquad \approx 6.456$

Since $\ln(-8.456)$ is undefined, the solution set is $\left\{-1 + \sqrt{1 + e^4} \approx 6.456\right\}$.

13. $2^{2x} + 2^x - 12 = 0$

$\left(2^x\right)^2 + 2^x - 12 = 0$

$\left(2^x - 3\right)\left(2^x + 4\right) = 0$

$2^x - 3 = 0 \qquad$ or $2^x + 4 = 0$

$2^x = 3 \qquad$ or $\qquad 2^x = -4$

$x = \log_2 3 \qquad\qquad$ No solution

$\quad = \dfrac{\log 3}{\log 2} \approx 1.585$

The solution set is $\left\{\log_2 3 \approx 1.585\right\}$.

15. $3^{2x} + 3^{x+1} - 4 = 0$

$\left(3^x\right)^2 + 3 \cdot 3^x - 4 = 0$

$\left(3^x - 1\right)\left(3^x + 4\right) = 0$

$3^x - 1 = 0 \quad$ or $\qquad 3^x + 4 = 0$

$3^x = 1 \quad$ or $\qquad 3^x = -4$

$x = 0 \qquad\qquad$ No solution

The solution set is $\{0\}$.

17.
$$2^x = 10$$
$$\log(2^x) = \log 10$$
$$x\log 2 = 1$$
$$x = \frac{1}{\log 2} \approx 3.322$$
The solution set is $\left\{\dfrac{1}{\log 2} \approx 3.322\right\}$

19.
$$8^{-x} = 1.2$$
$$\log(8^{-x}) = \log(1.2)$$
$$-x\log 8 = \log(1.2)$$
$$x = \frac{\log(1.2)}{-\log 8} \approx -0.088$$
The solution set is $\left\{\dfrac{\log(1.2)}{-\log 8} \approx -0.088\right\}$.

21.
$$3^{1-2x} = 4^x$$
$$\log(3^{1-2x}) = \log(4^x)$$
$$(1-2x)\log 3 = x\log 4$$
$$\log 3 - 2x\log 3 = x\log 4$$
$$\log 3 = x\log 4 + 2x\log 3$$
$$\log 3 = x(\log 4 + 2\log 3)$$
$$x = \frac{\log 3}{\log 4 + 2\log 3} \approx 0.307$$
The solution set is
$$\left\{\frac{\log 3}{\log 4 + 2\log 3} \approx 0.307\right\}.$$

23.
$$\left(\frac{3}{5}\right)^x = 7^{1-x}$$
$$\log\left(\left(\frac{3}{5}\right)^x\right) = \log(7^{1-x})$$
$$x\log\left(\frac{3}{5}\right) = (1-x)\log 7$$
$$x(\log 3 - \log 5) = \log 7 - x\log 7$$
$$x\log 3 - x\log 5 + x\log 7 = \log 7$$
$$x(\log 3 - \log 5 + \log 7) = \log 7$$
$$x = \frac{\log 7}{\log 3 - \log 5 + \log 7} \approx 1.356$$
The solution set is $\left\{\dfrac{\log 7}{\log 3 - \log 5 + \log 7} \approx 1.356\right\}.$

25.
$$1.2^x = (0.5)^{-x}$$
$$\log 1.2^x = \log(0.5)^{-x}$$
$$x \log(1.2) = -x \log(0.5)$$
$$x \log(1.2) + x \log(0.5) = 0$$
$$x(\log(1.2) + \log(0.5)) = 0$$
$$x = 0$$
The solution set is $\{0\}$.

27.
$$\pi^{1-x} = e^x$$
$$\ln \pi^{1-x} = \ln e^x$$
$$(1-x)\ln \pi = x$$
$$\ln \pi - x \ln \pi = x$$
$$\ln \pi = x + x \ln \pi$$
$$\ln \pi = x(1 + \ln \pi)$$
$$x = \frac{\ln \pi}{1 + \ln \pi} \approx 0.534$$
The solution set is $\left\{ \dfrac{\ln \pi}{1 + \ln \pi} \approx 0.534 \right\}$.

29.
$$5(2^{3x}) = 8$$
$$2^{3x} = \frac{8}{5}$$
$$\log 2^{3x} = \log\left(\frac{8}{5}\right)$$
$$3x \log 2 = \log 8 - \log 5$$
$$x = \frac{\log 8 - \log 5}{3 \log 2} \approx 0.226$$
The solution set is $\left\{ \dfrac{\log 8 - \log 5}{3 \log 2} \approx 0.226 \right\}$.

31. $\log_a(x-1) - \log_a(x+6) = \log_a(x-2) - \log_a(x+3)$
$$\log_a\left(\frac{x-1}{x+6}\right) = \log_a\left(\frac{x-2}{x+3}\right)$$
$$\frac{x-1}{x+6} = \frac{x-2}{x+3}$$
$$(x-1)(x+3) = (x-2)(x+6)$$
$$x^2 + 2x - 3 = x^2 + 4x - 12$$
$$2x - 3 = 4x - 12$$
$$9 = 2x$$
$$x = \frac{9}{2}$$

Since each of the original logarithms is defined for $x = \dfrac{9}{2}$, the solution set is $\left\{\dfrac{9}{2}\right\}$.

33. $\log_{1/3}(x^2 + x) - \log_{1/3}(x^2 - x) = -1$

$$\log_{1/3}\left(\frac{x^2 + x}{x^2 - x}\right) = -1$$

$$\frac{x^2 + x}{x^2 - x} = \left(\frac{1}{3}\right)^{-1}$$

$$\frac{x(x+1)}{x(x-1)} = 3$$

$$x + 1 = 3(x - 1)$$

$$x + 1 = 3x - 3$$

$$-2x = -4$$

$$x = 2$$

Since each of the original logarithms is defined for $x = 2$, the solution set is $\{2\}$.

35. $\log_2(x + 1) - \log_4 x = 1$

$$\log_2(x + 1) - \frac{\log_2 x}{\log_2 4} = 1$$

$$\log_2(x + 1) - \frac{\log_2 x}{2} = 1$$

$$2\log_2(x + 1) - \log_2 x = 2$$

$$\log_2(x + 1)^2 - \log_2 x = 2$$

$$\log_2\left(\frac{(x+1)^2}{x}\right) = 2$$

$$\frac{(x + 1)^2}{x} = 2^2$$

$$x^2 + 2x + 1 = 4x$$

$$x^2 - 2x + 1 = 0$$

$$(x - 1)^2 = 0$$

$$x - 1 = 0$$

$$x = 1$$

Since each of the original logarithms is defined for $x = 1$, the solution set is $\{1\}$.

37. $\log_{16} x + \log_4 x + \log_2 x = 7$

$$\frac{\log_2 x}{\log_2 16} + \frac{\log_2 x}{\log_2 4} + \log_2 x = 7$$

$$\frac{\log_2 x}{4} + \frac{\log_2 x}{2} + \log_2 x = 7$$

$$\log_2 x + 2\log_2 x + 4\log_2 x = 28$$

$$7\log_2 x = 28$$

$$\log_2 x = 4$$

$$x = 2^4 = 16$$

Since each of the original logarithms is defined for $x = 16$, the solution set is $\{16\}$.

39.

$$\left(\sqrt[3]{2}\right)^{2-x} = 2^{x^2}$$

$$\left(2^{1/3}\right)^{2-x} = 2^{x^2}$$

$$2^{\frac{1}{3}(2-x)} = 2^{x^2}$$

$$\frac{1}{3}(2-x) = x^2$$

$$2 - x = 3x^2$$

$$3x^2 + x - 2 = 0$$

$$(3x - 2)(x + 1) = 0$$

$$x = \frac{2}{3} \text{ or } x = -1$$

The solution set is $\left\{-1, \dfrac{2}{3}\right\}$.

41.

$$\frac{e^x + e^{-x}}{2} = 1$$

$$e^x + e^{-x} = 2$$

$$e^x\left(e^x + e^{-x}\right) = 2e^x$$

$$e^{2x} + 1 = 2e^x$$

$$(e^x)^2 - 2e^x + 1 = 0$$

$$\left(e^x - 1\right)^2 = 0$$

$$e^x - 1 = 0$$

$$e^x = 1$$

$$x = 0$$

The solution set is $\{0\}$.

43.

$$\frac{e^x - e^{-x}}{2} = 2$$

$$e^x - e^{-x} = 4$$

$$e^x\left(e^x - e^{-x}\right) = 4e^x$$

$$e^{2x} - 1 = 4e^x$$

$$(e^x)^2 - 4e^x - 1 = 0$$

$$e^x = \frac{-(-4) \pm \sqrt{(-4)^2 - 4(1)(-1)}}{2(1)}$$

$$= \frac{4 \pm \sqrt{20}}{2}$$

$$= \frac{4 \pm 2\sqrt{5}}{2} = 2 \pm \sqrt{5}$$

$$x = \ln\left(2 - \sqrt{5}\right) \text{ or } x = \ln\left(2 + \sqrt{5}\right)$$

$$x \approx \ln(-0.236) \text{ or } x \approx 1.444$$

Since $\ln(-0.236)$ is undefined, the solution set is $\left\{\ln\left(2 + \sqrt{5}\right) \approx 1.444\right\}$.

45. Using INTERSECT to solve:
$y_1 = \ln(x) / \ln(5) + \ln(x) / \ln(3)$
$y_2 = 1$

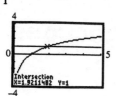

The solution is $x \approx 1.92$.

47. Using INTERSECT to solve:
$y_1 = \ln(x+1) / \ln(5) - \ln(x-2) / \ln(4)$
$y_2 = 1$

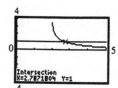

The solution is $x \approx 2.79$.

49. Using INTERSECT to solve:
$y_1 = e^x$; $y_2 = -x$

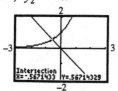

The solution is $x \approx -0.57$.

51. Using INTERSECT to solve:
$y_1 = e^x$; $y_2 = x^2$

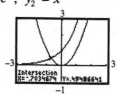

The solution is $x \approx -0.70$.

53. Using INTERSECT to solve:
$y_1 = \ln x$; $y_2 = -x$

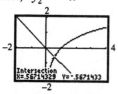

The solution is $x \approx 0.57$.

55. Using INTERSECT to solve:
$y_1 = \ln x$; $y_2 = x^3 - 1$

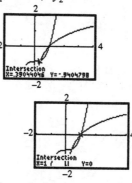

The solutions are $x \approx 0.39$ and $x = 1$.

57. Using INTERSECT to solve:
$y_1 = e^x + \ln x$; $y_2 = 4$

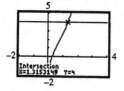

The solution is $x \approx 1.32$.

59. Using INTERSECT to solve:
$y_1 = e^{-x}$; $y_2 = \ln x$

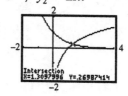

The solution is $x \approx 1.31$.

61. Answers will vary.

Exponential and Logarithmic Functions

7.5 Compound Interest

1. True

3. $P = \$100$, $r = 0.04$, $n = 4$, $t = 2$

$$A = P\left(1 + \frac{r}{n}\right)^{nt} = 100\left(1 + \frac{0.04}{4}\right)^{(4)(2)} = \$108.29$$

5. $P = \$500$, $r = 0.08$, $n = 4$, $t = 2.5$

$$A = P\left(1 + \frac{r}{n}\right)^{nt} = 500\left(1 + \frac{0.08}{4}\right)^{(4)(2.5)} = \$609.50$$

7. $P = \$600$, $r = 0.05$, $n = 365$, $t = 3$

$$A = P\left(1 + \frac{r}{n}\right)^{nt} = 600\left(1 + \frac{0.05}{365}\right)^{(365)(3)} = \$697.09$$

9. $P = \$10$, $r = 0.11$, $t = 2$

$A = Pe^{rt} = 40e^{(0.07)(3)} = \$49.35$

11. $P = \$100$, $r = 0.10$, $t = 2.25$

$A = Pe^{rt} = 100e^{(0.10)(2.25)} = \$125.23$

13. $A = \$100$, $r = 0.06$, $n = 12$, $t = 2$

$$P = A\left(1 + \frac{r}{n}\right)^{-nt} = 100\left(1 + \frac{0.06}{12}\right)^{(-12)(2)} = \$88.72$$

15. $A = \$1000$, $r = 0.06$, $n = 365$, $t = 2.5$

$$P = A\left(1 + \frac{r}{n}\right)^{-nt} = 1000\left(1 + \frac{0.06}{365}\right)^{(-365)(2.5)} = \$860.72$$

17. $A = \$600$, $r = 0.04$, $n = 4$, $t = 2$

$$P = A\left(1 + \frac{r}{n}\right)^{-nt} = 600\left(1 + \frac{0.04}{4}\right)^{(-4)(2)} = \$554.09$$

19. $A = \$80$, $r = 0.09$, $t = 3.25$

$P = Ae^{-rt} = 80e^{(-0.09)(3.25)} = \$59.71$

21. $A = \$400, \; r = 0.10, \; t = 1$
$P = Ae^{-rt} = 400e^{(-0.10)(1)} = \$361.93$

23. \$1000 invested for 1 year at $5\frac{1}{4}\%$
compounded quarterly yields
$$100\left(1 + \frac{0.0525}{4}\right)^{(4)(1)} = \$1053.54.$$
Since \$53.54 is 5.354% of \$1000, the
effective interest rate is 5.354%.

25. $2P = P(1 + r)^3$
$2 = (1 + r)^3$
$\sqrt[3]{2} = 1 + r$
$r = \sqrt[3]{2} - 1$
$\approx 1.26 - 1$
$= 0.26$
$r \approx 26\%$

27. 6% compounded quarterly:
$$A = 10,000\left(1 + \frac{0.06}{4}\right)^{(4)(1)} = \$10,613.64$$
$6\frac{1}{4}\%$ compounded annually:
$A = 10,000(1 + 0.0625)^1 = \$10,625$
$6\frac{1}{4}\%$ compounded annually yields the larger amount.

29. 9% compounded monthly:
$$A = 10,000\left(1 + \frac{0.09}{12}\right)^{(12)(1)} = \$10,938.07$$
8.8% compounded daily:
$$A = 10,000\left(1 + \frac{0.088}{365}\right)^{365} = \$10,919.77$$
9% compounded monthly yields the larger amount.

31. Compounded monthly:
$$2P = P\left(1 + \frac{0.08}{12}\right)^{12t}$$
$2 \approx (1.006667)^{12t}$
$\ln 2 \approx 12t \ln(1.006667)$
$t \approx \dfrac{\ln 2}{12 \ln(1.006667)} \approx 8.69$ years

Compounded continuously:
$2P = Pe^{0.08t}$
$2 = e^{0.08t}$
$\ln 2 = 0.08t$
$t = \dfrac{\ln 2}{0.08} \approx 8.66$ years

33. Compounded monthly:

$$150 = 100\left(1 + \frac{0.08}{12}\right)^{12t}$$

$$1.5 \approx (1.006667)^{12t}$$

$$\ln 1.5 \approx 12t \ln(1.006667)$$

$$t \approx \frac{\ln 1.5}{12 \ln(1.006667)} \approx 5.085 \text{ years}$$

Compounded continuously:

$$150 = 100e^{0.08t}$$

$$1.5 = e^{0.08\,t}$$

$$\ln 1.5 = 0.08t$$

$$t = \frac{\ln 1.5}{0.08} \approx 5.068 \text{ years}$$

35. $$25{,}000 = 10{,}000e^{0.06t}$$

$$2.5 = e^{0.06t}$$

$$\ln 2.5 = 0.06t$$

$$t = \frac{\ln 2.5}{0.06} \approx 15.27 \text{ years}$$

37. $A = 90{,}000(1 + 0.03)^5 = \$104{,}335$

39. $P = 15{,}000e^{(-0.05)(3)} \approx \$12{,}910.62$

41. $A = 1500(1 + 0.15)^5 = 1500(1.15)^5 \approx \$3017$

43. $$850{,}000 = 650{,}000(1 + r)^3$$

$$\frac{85}{65} = (1 + r)^3$$

$$\sqrt[3]{\frac{85}{65}} = 1 + r$$

$$r \approx \sqrt[3]{1.3077} - 1 \approx 0.0935$$

$$r \approx 9.35\%$$

45. 5.6% compounded continuously:
$$A = 1000e^{(0.056)(1)} = \$1057.60$$
Jim will not have enough money to buy the computer.
5.9% compounded monthly:

$$A = 1000\left(1 + \frac{0.059}{12}\right)^{12} = \$1060.62$$

The second bank offers the better deal.

47. Will: 9% compounded semiannually:

$$A = 2000\left(1 + \frac{0.09}{2}\right)^{(2)(20)} = \$11{,}632.73$$

Henry: 8.5% compounded continuously:
$$A = 2000e^{(0.085)(20)} = \$10{,}947.89$$
Will has more money after 20 years.

49. $P = 50,000;\ t = 5$

(a) Simple interest at 12% per annum:
$A = 50,000 + 50,000(0.12)(5) = \$80,000$

(b) 11.5% compounded monthly:
$$A = 50,000\left(1 + \frac{0.115}{12}\right)^{(12)(5)} = \$88,613.59$$

(c) 11.25% compounded continuously:
$A = 50,000e^{(0.1125)(5)} = \$87,752.73$
Subtract $50,000 from each to get the amount of interest:
(a) $30,000   (b) $38,613.59   (c) $37.752.73
Option (a) results in the least interest.

51. (a) $A = \$10,000,\ r = 0.10,\ n = 12,\ t = 20$
$$P = 10,000\left(1 + \frac{0.10}{12}\right)^{(-12)(20)} = \$1364.62$$

(b) $A = \$10,000,\ r = 0.10,\ t = 20$
$P = 10,000e^{(-0.10)(20)} = \$1353.35$

53. $A = \$10,000,\ r = 0.08,\ n = 1,\ t = 10$
$$P = 10,000\left(1 + \frac{0.08}{1}\right)^{(-1)(10)} = \$4631.93$$

55. (a) $t = \dfrac{\ln 2}{1 \cdot \ln\left(1 + \dfrac{0.12}{1}\right)} = \dfrac{\ln 2}{\ln(1.12)} \approx 6.12$ years

(b) $t = \dfrac{\ln 3}{4 \cdot \ln\left(1 + \dfrac{0.06}{4}\right)} = \dfrac{\ln 3}{4\ln(1.015)} \approx 18.45$ years

(c) $mP = P\left(1 + \dfrac{r}{n}\right)^{nt}$

$m = \left(1 + \dfrac{r}{n}\right)^{nt}$

$\ln m = nt \cdot \ln\left(1 + \dfrac{r}{n}\right)$

$t = \dfrac{\ln m}{n \cdot \ln\left(1 + \dfrac{r}{n}\right)}$

57–59. Answers will vary.

Exponential and Logarithmic Functions

7.6 Exponential Growth and Decay; Newton's Law; Logistic Models

1. $P(t) = 500e^{0.02t}$
    (a) $P(0) = 500e^{(0.02)\cdot(0)} = 500$ flies
    (b) growth rate = 2 %
    (c) $P(10) = 500e^{(0.02)\cdot(10)} = 611$ flies
    (d) Find t when $P = 800$:
    $$800 = 500e^{0.02t}$$
    $$1.6 = e^{0.02t}$$
    $$\ln 1.6 = 0.02t$$
    $$t = \frac{\ln 1.6}{0.02} \approx 23.5 \text{ days}$$

    (e) Find t when $P = 1000$:
    $$1000 = 500e^{0.02t}$$
    $$2 = e^{0.02t}$$
    $$\ln 2 = 0.02t$$
    $$t = \frac{\ln 2}{0.02} \approx 34.7 \text{ days}$$

3. $A(t) = A_0 e^{-0.0244t} = 500e^{-0.0244t}$
    (a) decay rate = 2.44 %
    (b) $A(10) = 500e^{(-0.0244)(10)} \approx 391.74$ grams
    (c) Find t when $A = 400$:
    $$400 = 500e^{-0.0244t}$$
    $$0.8 = e^{-0.0244t}$$
    $$\ln 0.8 = -0.0244t$$
    $$t = \frac{\ln 0.8}{-0.0244} \approx 9.15 \text{ years}$$

    (d) Find t when $A = 250$:
    $$250 = 500e^{-0.0244t}$$
    $$0.5 = e^{-0.0244t}$$
    $$\ln 0.5 = -0.0244t$$
    $$t = \frac{\ln 0.5}{-0.0244} \approx 28.4 \text{ years}$$

5. Use $N(t) = N_0 e^{kt}$ and solve for k:
    $$1800 = 1000e^{k(1)}$$
    $$1.8 = e^{k}$$
    $$k = \ln 1.8$$
    When $t = 3$:
    $$N(3) = 1000e^{(\ln 1.8)(3)} = 5832 \text{ mosquitos}$$

    Find t when $N(t) = 10{,}000$:
    $$10{,}000 = 1000e^{(\ln 1.8)t}$$
    $$10 = e^{(\ln 1.8)t}$$
    $$\ln 10 = (\ln 1.8)t$$
    $$t = \frac{\ln 10}{\ln 1.8} \approx 3.9 \text{ days}$$

7. Use $P(t) = P_0 e^{kt}$ and solve for k:

$2P_0 = P_0 e^{k(1.5)}$

$2 = e^{1.5k}$

$\ln 2 = 1.5k$

$k = \dfrac{\ln 2}{1.5}$

When $t = 2$:

$P(2) = 10{,}000 e^{\left(\frac{\ln 2}{1.5}\right)(2)} = 25{,}198$ is the population 2 years from now.

9. Use $A = A_0 e^{kt}$ and solve for k:

$0.5 A_0 = A_0 e^{k(1590)}$

$0.5 = e^{1590k}$

$\ln 0.5 = 1590k$

$k = \dfrac{\ln 0.5}{1590}$

When $A_0 = 10$ and $t = 50$: $A = 5 e^{\left(\frac{\ln 0.5}{1590}\right)(50)} \approx 10.220$ grams

11. Use $A = A_0 e^{kt}$ and solve for k:

half-life $= 5600$ years

$0.5 A_0 = A_0 e^{k(5600)}$

$0.5 = e^{5600k}$

$\ln 0.5 = 5600k$

$k = \dfrac{\ln 0.5}{5600}$

Solve for t when $A = 0.3 A_0$:

$0.3 A_0 = A_0 e^{\left(\frac{\ln 0.5}{5600}\right)t}$

$0.3 = e^{\left(\frac{\ln 0.5}{5600}\right)t}$

$\ln 0.3 = \left(\dfrac{\ln 0.5}{5600}\right)t$

$t = \dfrac{\ln 0.3}{\dfrac{\ln 0.5}{5600}}$

$t \approx 9710$

The tree died approximately 9710 years ago.

13. (a) Using $u = T + (u_0 - T)e^{kt}$ where $t = 5$,

$T = 70$, $u_0 = 450$, $u = 300$:

$$300 = 70 + (450 - 70)e^{k(5)}$$

$$230 = 380e^{5k}$$

$$\frac{230}{380} = e^{5k}$$

$$\ln\left(\frac{230}{380}\right) = 5k$$

$$k = \frac{\ln\left(\frac{230}{380}\right)}{5} \approx -0.1004$$

$T = 70$, $u_0 = 450$, $u = 135$:

$$135 = 70 + (450 - 70)e^{-0.1004\,t}$$

$$65 = 380e^{-0.1004\,t}$$

$$\frac{65}{380} = e^{-0.1004\,t}$$

$$\ln\left(\frac{65}{380}\right) = -0.1004\,t$$

$$t = \frac{\ln\left(\frac{65}{380}\right)}{-0.1004} \approx 17.6 \text{ minutes}$$

The pizza will be cool enough to eat at 5:18 PM.

(b) $T = 70$, $u_0 = 450$, $u = 160$:

$$160 = 70 + (450 - 70)e^{-0.1004\,t}$$

$$90 = 380e^{-0.1004\,t}$$

$$\frac{90}{380} = e^{-0.1004\,t}$$

$$\ln\left(\frac{90}{380}\right) = -0.1004\,t$$

$$t = \frac{\ln(90/380)}{-0.1004} \approx 14.3$$

The pizza will be 160°F after about 14.3 minutes.

(c) As time passes, the temperature gets closer to 70°F.

15. Using $u = T + (u_0 - T)e^{kt}$ where $t = 3$,

$T = 35$, $u_0 = 8$, $u = 15$:

$$15 = 35 + (8 - 35)e^{k(3)}$$

$$-20 = -27e^{3k}$$

$$\frac{20}{27} = e^{3k}$$

$$\ln\left(\frac{20}{27}\right) = 3k$$

$$k = \frac{\ln(20/27)}{3}$$

At $t = 5$: $u = 35 + (8 - 35)e^{\left(\frac{\ln(20/27)}{3}\right)(5)} \approx 18.63°C$

At $t = 10$: $u = 35 + (8 - 35)e^{\left(\frac{\ln(20/27)}{3}\right)(10)} \approx 25.1°C$

17. Use $A = A_0e^{kt}$ and solve for k:

$$15 = 25e^{k(10)}$$

$$0.6 = e^{10k}$$

$$\ln 0.6 = 10k$$

$$k = \frac{\ln 0.6}{10}$$

When $A_0 = 25$ and $t = 24$:

$$A = 25e^{\left(\frac{\ln 0.6}{10}\right)(24)} \approx 7.33 \text{ kilograms}$$

Find t when $A = 0.5A_0$:

$$0.5 = 25e^{\left(\frac{\ln 0.6}{10}\right)t}$$

$$0.02 = e^{\left(\frac{\ln 0.6}{10}\right)t}$$

$$\ln 0.02 = \left(\frac{\ln 0.6}{10}\right)t$$

$$t = \frac{\ln 0.02}{\left(\frac{\ln 0.6}{10}\right)} \approx 76.6 \text{ hours}$$

19. Use $A = A_0e^{kt}$ and solve for k:

$$0.5A_0 = A_0e^{k(8)}$$

$$0.5 = e^{8k}$$

$$\ln 0.5 = 8k$$

$$k = \frac{\ln 0.5}{8}$$

Find t when $A = 0.1A_0$:

$$0.1A_0 = A_0e^{\left(\frac{\ln 0.5}{8}\right)t}$$

$$0.1 = e^{\left(\frac{\ln 0.5}{8}\right)t}$$

$$\ln 0.1 = \left(\frac{\ln 0.5}{8}\right)t$$

$$t = \frac{\ln 0.1}{\frac{\ln 0.5}{8}} \approx 26.6 \text{ days}$$

The farmers need to wait about 27 days before using the hay.

21. (a) $P(0) = \dfrac{0.9}{1 + 6e^{-0.32(0)}} = \dfrac{0.9}{1 + 6 \cdot 1} = \dfrac{0.9}{7} = 0.1286$

In 2004, 12.86% of U.S. households owned a DVD.

(b) The maximum proportion is the carrying capacity, $c = 0.9 = 90\%$.

(c) Find t such that $P = 0.8$:

$$0.8 = \dfrac{0.9}{1 + 6e^{-0.32t}}$$

$$0.8\left(1 + 6e^{-0.32t}\right) = 0.9$$

$$1 + 6e^{-0.32t} = 1.125$$

$$6e^{-0.32t} = 0.125$$

$$e^{-0.32t} = \dfrac{0.125}{6}$$

$$-0.32t = \ln\left(\dfrac{0.125}{6}\right)$$

$$t = \dfrac{\ln\left(\dfrac{0.125}{6}\right)}{-0.32} \approx 12.1$$

80% of households will own a DVD in 2016 ($t = 12$).

23. (a) As $t \to \infty$, $e^{-0.439t} \to 0$. Thus, $P(t) \to 1000$. The carrying capacity is 1000 bacteria. Growth rate = 43.9%.

(b) $P(0) = \dfrac{1000}{1 + 32.33e^{-0.439(0)}} = \dfrac{1000}{33.33} = 30$ bacteria

(c) Find t such that $P = 800$:

$$800 = \dfrac{1000}{1 + 32.33e^{-0.439t}}$$

$$800\left(1 + 32.33e^{-0.439t}\right) = 1000$$

$$1 + 32.33e^{-0.439t} = 1.25$$

$$32.33e^{-0.439t} = 0.25$$

$$e^{-0.439t} = \dfrac{0.25}{32.33}$$

$$-0.439t = \ln\left(\dfrac{0.25}{32.33}\right)$$

$$t = \dfrac{\ln\left(\dfrac{0.25}{32.33}\right)}{-0.439} \approx 11.08$$

The amount of bacteria will be 800 after approximately 11.08 hours.

Exponential and Logarithmic Functions

7.7 Fitting Data to Exponential, Logarithmic, and Logistic Functions

1. (a) Scatter diagram

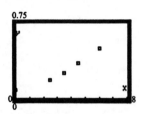

    (b) Using EXPonential REGression on the data yields: $y = 0.0903(1.3384)^x$

    (c) $y = 0.0903(1.3384)^x = 0.0903\left(e^{\ln(1.3384)}\right)^x = 0.0903e^{\ln(1.3384)x}$
         $N(t) = 0.0903e^{\ln(1.3384)t} = 0.0903e^{0.2915t}$

    (d) Graphing: $y_1 = 0.0903e^{0.2915x}$

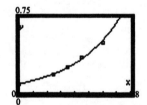

    (e) $N(7) = 0.0903e^{(0.2915)\cdot 7} \approx 0.695$ bacteria

    (f) Find t when $N(t) = 0.75$

         $0.0903e^{(0.2915)\cdot t} = 0.75$

         $$e^{(0.2915)\cdot t} = \frac{0.75}{0.0903}$$

         $$0.2915t = \ln\left(\frac{0.75}{0.0903}\right)$$

         $$t \approx \frac{\ln\left(\dfrac{0.75}{0.0903}\right)}{0.2915} \approx 7.26 \text{ hours}$$

3.   (a)   Scatter diagram

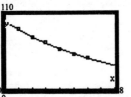

(b)   Using EXPonential REGression on the data yields: $y = 100.3263(0.8769)^x$

(c) $y = 100.3263(0.8769)^x = 100.3263\left(e^{\ln(0.8769)}\right)^x = 100.3263e^{\ln(0.8769)x}$
$A(t) = 100.3263e^{(-0.1314)t}$

(d)   Graphing: $y_1 = 100.3263e^{(-0.1314)x}$

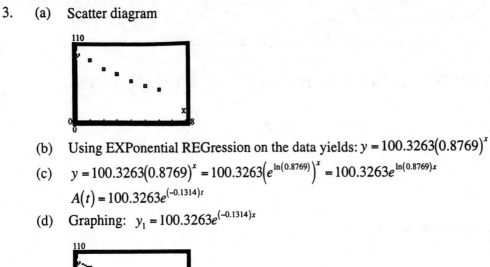

(e)   Find t when $A(t) = 0.5 \cdot A_0$

$$100.3263e^{(-0.1314)t} = (0.5)(100.3263)$$

$$e^{(-0.1314)t} = 0.5$$

$$-0.1314t = \ln 0.5$$

$$t = \frac{\ln 0.5}{-0.1314} \approx 5.28 \text{ weeks}$$

(f) $A(50) = 100.3263e^{(-0.1314) \cdot 50} \approx 0.141$ grams

(g)   Find t when $A(t) = 20$

$$100.3263e^{(-0.1314)t} = 20$$

$$e^{(-0.1314)t} = \frac{20}{100.3263}$$

$$-0.1314t = \ln\left(\frac{20}{100.3263}\right)$$

$$t = \frac{\ln\left(\dfrac{20}{100.3263}\right)}{-0.1314} \approx 12.27 \text{ weeks}$$

5.   (a)   Let $x = 1$ correspond to 1994, $x = 2$ correspond to 1995, etc.

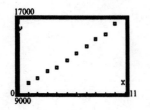

(b) Using EXPonential REGression on the data yields: $y = 9478.4453(1.0566)^x$

(c) The average annual rate of return over the 10 years is $0.0566 = 5.66\%$.

(d) In the year 2021, $x = 28$, so $y = 9478.4453(1.0566)^{28} = \$44,282.70$.

(e) Find x when $y = 50,000$

$$9478.4453(1.0566)^x = 50,000$$

$$(1.0566)^x = \frac{50,000}{9478.4453}$$

$$x \ln 1.0566 = \ln\left(\frac{50,000}{9478.4453}\right)$$

$$x = \frac{\ln\left(\dfrac{50,000}{9478.4453}\right)}{\ln 1.0566} \approx 30.21 \text{ years, that is, in the year 2023.}$$

7. (a) Scatter diagram

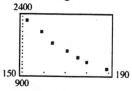

(b) Using LnREGression on the data yields: $y = 32,741.02369 - 6070.956754 \ln x$

(c) Graphing $y_1 = 32,741.02369 - 6070.956754 \ln x$

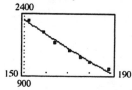

(d) Find x when $y = 1650$:

$$1650 = 32,741.02369 - 6070.956754 \ln x$$

$$-31,091.02369 = -6070.956754 \ln x$$

$$\frac{-31,091.02369}{-6070.956754} = \ln x$$

$$5.1213 \approx \ln x$$

$$e^{5.1213} \approx x$$

$$x \approx 168 \text{ computers}$$

9. (a) Let $x = 0$ correspond to 1900, $x = 1$ correspond to 1910, etc.

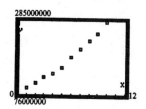

(b)   Using LOGISTIC REGression on the data yields:

$$y = \frac{799,475,916.5}{1 + 9.1968e^{-0.1603x}}$$

(c)   Graphing $y_1 = \dfrac{799,475,916.5}{1 + 9.1968e^{-0.1603x}}$:

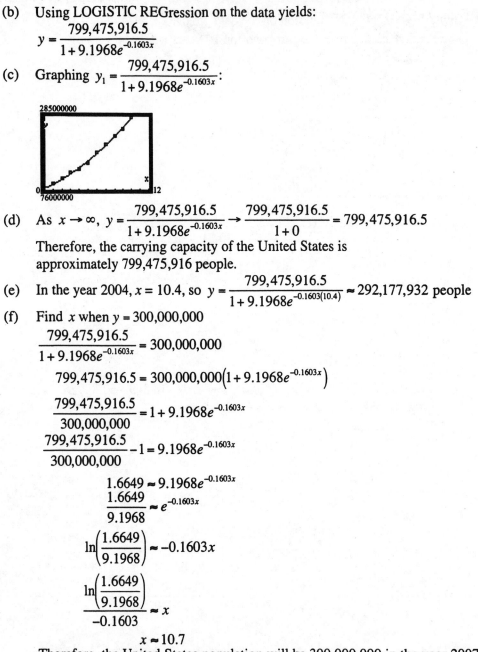

(d)   As $x \to \infty$, $y = \dfrac{799,475,916.5}{1 + 9.1968e^{-0.1603x}} \to \dfrac{799,475,916.5}{1 + 0} = 799,475,916.5$

Therefore, the carrying capacity of the United States is approximately 799,475,916 people.

(e)   In the year 2004, $x = 10.4$, so $y = \dfrac{799,475,916.5}{1 + 9.1968e^{-0.1603(10.4)}} \approx 292,177,932$ people

(f)   Find x when $y = 300,000,000$

$$\frac{799,475,916.5}{1 + 9.1968e^{-0.1603x}} = 300,000,000$$

$$799,475,916.5 = 300,000,000\left(1 + 9.1968e^{-0.1603x}\right)$$

$$\frac{799,475,916.5}{300,000,000} = 1 + 9.1968e^{-0.1603x}$$

$$\frac{799,475,916.5}{300,000,000} - 1 = 9.1968e^{-0.1603x}$$

$$1.6649 \approx 9.1968e^{-0.1603x}$$

$$\frac{1.6649}{9.1968} \approx e^{-0.1603x}$$

$$\ln\left(\frac{1.6649}{9.1968}\right) \approx -0.1603x$$

$$\frac{\ln\left(\dfrac{1.6649}{9.1968}\right)}{-0.1603} \approx x$$

$$x \approx 10.7$$

Therefore, the United States population will be 300,000,000 in the year 2007.

11. (a)   Let $x = 0$ correspond to 1900, $x = 1$ correspond to 1910, etc.

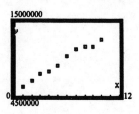

(b) Using LOGISTIC REGression on the data yields:

$$y = \frac{14{,}471{,}245.24}{1 + 2.01527e^{-0.2458x}}$$

(c) Graphing $y_1 = \dfrac{14{,}471{,}245.24}{1 + 2.01527e^{-0.2458x}}$:

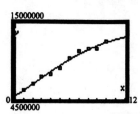

(d) As $x \to \infty$, $y = \dfrac{14{,}471{,}245.24}{1 + 2.01527e^{-0.2458x}} \to \dfrac{14{,}471{,}245.24}{1 + 0} = 14{,}471{,}245.24$

Therefore, the carrying capacity of Illinois is approximately 14,471,245 people.

(e) In the year 2010, $x = 11$, so $y = \dfrac{14{,}471{,}245.24}{1 + 2.01527e^{-0.2458(11)}} \approx 12{,}750{,}854$ people.

Exponential and Logarithmic Functions

7.R   Chapter Review

1.   (a) $f(4) = 3^4 = 81$ (b) $g(9) = \log_3(9) = \log_3(3^2) = 2$

   (c) $f(-2) = 3^{-2} = \dfrac{1}{9}$ (d) $g\left(\dfrac{1}{27}\right) = \log_3\left(\dfrac{1}{27}\right) = \log_3(3^{-3}) = -3$

3. $5^2 = z$ is equivalent to $2 = \log_5 z$ 5. $\log_5 u = 13$ is equivalent to $5^{13} = u$

7. $f(x) = \log(3x - 2)$ requires:
        $3x - 2 > 0$

        $x > \dfrac{2}{3}$

   Domain: $\left\{ x \middle| x > \dfrac{2}{3} \right\}$

9. $H(x) = \log_2(x^2 - 3x + 2)$ requires $p(x) = (x - 2)(x - 1)$
        $x^2 - 3x + 2 > 0$ $x = 2$ and $x = 1$ are the zeros of p.

   $(x - 2)(x - 1) > 0$

Interval	$(-\infty, 1)$	$(1, 2)$	$(2, \infty)$
Number Chosen	0	1.5	3
Value of p	2	−0.25	2
Conclusion	Positive	Negative	Positive

   The domain of is $\{ x \mid x < 1 \text{ or } x > 2 \}$.

11. $\log_2\left(\dfrac{1}{8}\right) = \log_2 2^{-3} = -3\log_2 2 = -3$ 13. $\ln e^{\sqrt{2}} = \sqrt{2}$

15. $2^{\log_2 0.4} = 0.4$

17. $\log_3\left(\dfrac{uv^2}{w}\right) = \log_3 uv^2 - \log_3 w = \log_3 u + \log_3 v^2 - \log_3 w = \log_3 u + 2\log_3 v - \log_3 w$

19. $\log\left(x^2\sqrt{x^3 + 1}\right) = \log x^2 + \log(x^3 + 1)^{1/2} = 2\log x + \dfrac{1}{2}\log(x^3 + 1)$

21. $\ln\left(\dfrac{x\sqrt[3]{x^2+1}}{x-3}\right) = \ln\left(x\sqrt[3]{x^2+1}\right) - \ln(x-3)$

$= \ln x + \ln\left(x^2+1\right)^{1/3} - \ln(x-3)$

$= \ln x + \dfrac{1}{3}\ln\left(x^2+1\right) - \ln(x-3)$

23. $3\log_4 x^2 + \dfrac{1}{2}\log_4 \sqrt{x} = \log_4\left(x^2\right)^3 + \log_4\left(x^{1/2}\right)^{1/2}$

$= \log_4 x^6 + \log_4 x^{1/4}$

$= \log_4\left(x^6 \cdot x^{1/4}\right)$

$= \log_4 x^{25/4}$

$= \dfrac{25}{4}\log_4 x$

25. $\ln\left(\dfrac{x-1}{x}\right) + \ln\left(\dfrac{x}{x+1}\right) - \ln\left(x^2-1\right) = \ln\left(\dfrac{x-1}{x} \cdot \dfrac{x}{x+1}\right) - \ln\left(x^2-1\right)$

$= \ln\left[\dfrac{\dfrac{x-1}{x+1}}{x^2-1}\right]$

$= \ln\left(\dfrac{x-1}{x+1} \cdot \dfrac{1}{(x-1)(x+1)}\right)$

$= \ln\dfrac{1}{(x+1)^2}$

$= \ln(x+1)^{-2}$

$= -2\ln(x+1)$

27. $2\log 2 + 3\log x - \dfrac{1}{2}\left[\log(x+3) + \log(x-2)\right] = \log 2^2 + \log x^3 - \dfrac{1}{2}\log\left[(x+3)(x-2)\right]$

$= \log\left(4x^3\right) - \log\left((x+3)(x-2)\right)^{1/2}$

$= \log\left[\dfrac{4x^3}{\left((x+3)(x-2)\right)^{1/2}}\right]$

29. $\log_4 19 = \dfrac{\log 19}{\log 4} \approx 2.124$

31. $y = \log_3 x = \dfrac{\ln x}{\ln 3}$

33. $f(x) = 2^{x-3}$

Using the graph of $y = 2^x$, shift the graph 3 units to the right.
Domain: $(-\infty, \infty)$
Range: $(0, \infty)$
Horizontal Asymptote: $y = 0$

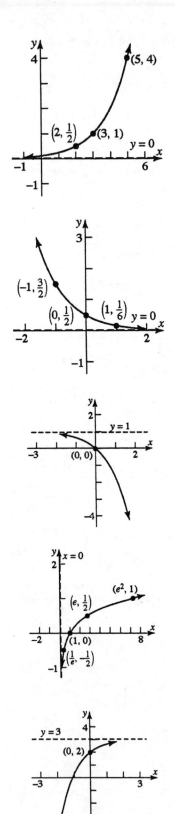

35. $f(x) = \dfrac{1}{2}\left(3^{-x}\right)$

Using the graph of $y = 3^x$, reflect the graph about the y-axis, and shrink vertically by a factor of $\dfrac{1}{2}$.

Domain: $(-\infty, \infty)$
Range: $(0, \infty)$
Horizontal Asymptote: $y = 0$

37. $f(x) = 1 - e^x$

Using the graph of $y = e^x$, reflect about the x-axis, and shift up 1 unit.
Domain: $(-\infty, \infty)$
Range: $(-\infty, 1)$
Horizontal Asymptote: $y = 1$

39. $f(x) = \dfrac{1}{2}\ln x$

Using the graph of $y = \ln x$, shrink vertically by a factor of $\dfrac{1}{2}$.

Domain: $(0, \infty)$
Range: $(-\infty, \infty)$
Vertical Asymptote: $x = 0$

41. $f(x) = 3 - e^{-x}$

Using the graph of $y = e^x$, reflect the graph about the y-axis, reflect about the x-axis, and shift up 3 units.
Domain: $(-\infty, \infty)$
Range: $(-\infty, 3)$
Horizontal Asymptote: $y = 3$

43.
$$4^{1-2x} = 2$$
$$\left(2^2\right)^{1-2x} = 2$$
$$2^{2-4x} = 2^1$$
$$2 - 4x = 1$$
$$-4x = -1$$
$$x = \frac{1}{4}$$
The solution set is $\left\{\dfrac{1}{4}\right\}$.

45.
$$3^{x^2+x} = \sqrt{3}$$
$$3^{x^2+x} = 3^{1/2}$$
$$x^2 + x = \frac{1}{2}$$
$$2x^2 + 2x - 1 = 0$$
$$x = \frac{-2 \pm \sqrt{2^2 - 4(2)(-1)}}{2(2)}$$
$$= \frac{-2 \pm \sqrt{12}}{4}$$
$$= \frac{-2 \pm 2\sqrt{3}}{4} = \frac{-1 \pm \sqrt{3}}{2}$$
$$x = \frac{-1 - \sqrt{3}}{2} \quad \text{or} \quad x = \frac{-1 + \sqrt{3}}{2}$$
The solution set is $\left\{\dfrac{-1-\sqrt{3}}{2}, \dfrac{-1+\sqrt{3}}{2}\right\}$.

47.
$$\log_x 64 = -3$$
$$x^{-3} = 64$$
$$\left(x^{-3}\right)^{-1/3} = 64^{-1/3}$$
$$x = \frac{1}{\sqrt[3]{64}} = \frac{1}{4}$$
The solution set is $\left\{\dfrac{1}{4}\right\}$.

49.
$$5^x = 3^{x+2}$$
$$\log\left(5^x\right) = \log\left(3^{x+2}\right)$$
$$x\log 5 = (x+2)\log 3$$
$$x\log 5 = x\log 3 + 2\log 3$$
$$x\log 5 - x\log 3 = 2\log 3$$
$$x(\log 5 - \log 3) = 2\log 3$$
$$x = \frac{2\log 3}{\log 5 - \log 3}$$
The solution set is $\left\{\dfrac{2\log 3}{\log 5 - \log 3}\right\}$.

51. $9^{2x} = 27^{3x-4}$

$\left(3^2\right)^{2x} = \left(3^3\right)^{3x-4}$

$3^{4x} = 3^{9x-12}$

$4x = 9x - 12$

$-5x = -12$

$x = \dfrac{12}{5}$

The solution set is $\left\{\dfrac{12}{5}\right\}$.

53. $\log_3 \sqrt{x-2} = 2$

$\sqrt{x-2} = 3^2$

$\sqrt{x-2} = 9$

$x - 2 = 9^2$

$x - 2 = 81$

$x = 83$

Check: $x = 83$:

$\log_3 \sqrt{83-2} = \log_3 \sqrt{81}$

$= \log_3 \sqrt{3^4}$

$= \log_3 3^2$

$= 2$

The solution set is $\{83\}$.

55. $8 = 4^{x^2} \cdot 2^{5x}$

$2^3 = \left(2^2\right)^{x^2} \cdot 2^{5x}$

$2^3 = 2^{2x^2+5x}$

$3 = 2x^2 + 5x$

$0 = 2x^2 + 5x - 3$

$0 = (2x-1)(x+3)$

$x = \dfrac{1}{2}$ or $x = -3$

The solution set is $\left\{-3, \dfrac{1}{2}\right\}$.

57. $\log_6(x+3) + \log_6(x+4) = 1$

$\log_6\left((x+3)(x+4)\right) = 1$

$(x+3)(x+4) = 6^1$

$x^2 + 7x + 12 = 6$

$x^2 + 7x + 6 = 0$

$(x+6)(x+1) = 0$

$x = -6$ or $x = -1$

Since $\log_6(-6+3) = \log_6(-3)$ is undefined, the solution set is $\{-1\}$.

59. $e^{1-x} = 5$

$1 - x = \ln 5$

$-x = -1 + \ln 5$

$x = 1 - \ln 5$

The solution set is $\{1 - \ln 5\}$.

61. $2^{3x} = 3^{2x+1}$

$\ln 2^{3x} = \ln 3^{2x+1}$

$3x \ln 2 = (2x+1)\ln 3$

$3x \ln 2 = 2x \ln 3 + \ln 3$

$3x \ln 2 - 2x \ln 3 = \ln 3$

$x(3\ln 2 - 2\ln 3) = \ln 3$

$x = \dfrac{\ln 3}{3\ln 2 - 2\ln 3}$

The solution set is $\left\{\dfrac{\ln 3}{3\ln 2 - 2\ln 3}\right\}$.

63. $h(300) = (30(0) + 8000)\log\left(\dfrac{760}{300}\right) \approx 8000\log(2.53333) \approx 3229.5$ meters

65. $P = 25e^{0.1d}$
     (a) $P = 25e^{0.1(4)}$
          $= 25e^{0.4}$
          ≈ 37.3 watts

     (b) $50 = 25e^{0.1d}$
          $2 = e^{0.1d}$
          $\ln 2 = 0.1d$
          $d = \dfrac{\ln 2}{0.1} \approx 6.9$ decibels

67. (a) $n = \dfrac{\log 10,000 - \log 90,000}{\log(1 - 0.20)} \approx 9.85$ years

     (b) $n = \dfrac{\log(0.5i) - \log(i)}{\log(1 - 0.15)} = \dfrac{\log\left(\dfrac{0.5i}{i}\right)}{\log 0.85} = \dfrac{\log 0.5}{\log 0.85} \approx 4.27$ years

69. $P = A\left(1 + \dfrac{r}{n}\right)^{-nt} = 85,000\left(1 + \dfrac{0.04}{2}\right)^{-2(18)} = \$41,668.97$

71. $A = A_0 e^{kt}$
     $0.5A_0 = A_0 e^{k(5600)}$
     $0.5 = e^{5600k}$
     $\ln 0.5 = 5600k$
     $k = \dfrac{\ln 0.5}{5600}$

     $0.05A_0 = A_0 e^{\left(\frac{\ln 0.5}{5600}\right)t}$
     $0.05 = e^{\left(\frac{\ln 0.5}{5600}\right)t}$
     $\ln 0.05 = \left(\dfrac{\ln 0.5}{5600}\right)t \Rightarrow t = \dfrac{\ln 0.05}{\dfrac{\ln 0.5}{5600}} \approx 24,200$

     Therefore, the man died approximately 24,200 years ago.

73. $P = P_0 e^{kt} = 6,302,486,693e^{0.0167(7)} \approx 6,835,600,129$ people

75. (a) $P(0) = \dfrac{0.8}{1 + 1.67e^{-0.16(0)}} = \dfrac{0.8}{1 + 1.67} = 0.2996$
          In 2003, 30% of cars had a GPS.
     (b) The maximum proportion is the carrying capacity, $c = 0.80 = 80\%$
     (c) Graphing:

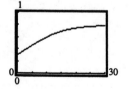

(d)   Find t such that $P(t) = 0.75$.

$$\frac{0.8}{1+1.67e^{-0.16t}} = 0.75$$

$$0.8 = 0.75\left(1+1.67e^{-0.16t}\right)$$

$$\frac{0.8}{0.75} = 1+1.67e^{-0.16t}$$

$$\frac{0.8}{0.75} - 1 = 1.67e^{-0.16t}$$

$$\frac{\dfrac{0.8}{0.75}-1}{1.67} = e^{-0.16t}$$

$$\ln\left(\frac{\dfrac{0.8}{0.75}-1}{1.67}\right) = -0.16t$$

$$t = \frac{\ln\left(\dfrac{\dfrac{0.8}{0.75}-1}{1.67}\right)}{-0.16} \approx 20.13$$

So 75% of new cars will have GPS in 2023.

77.   (a)   Scatter diagram

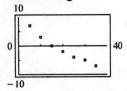

(b)   Using LnREGression on the data yields: $y = 18.9028 - 7.0963\ln x$

(c)   Graphing $y_1 = 18.9028 - 7.0963\ln x$

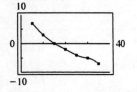

(d)   If $x = 23$, $y = 18.9028 - 7.0963\ln 23 \approx -3.33°F$.

Exponential and Logarithmic Functions

7.CR Cumulative Review

1. The graph represents a function since it passes the Vertical Line Test. The function is not a one-to-one function since the graph fails the Horizontal Line Test.

3. $x^2 + y^2 = 1$

   (a) $\left(\frac{1}{2}\right)^2 + \left(\frac{1}{2}\right)^2 = \frac{1}{4} + \frac{1}{4} = \frac{1}{2} \ne 1$; $\left(\frac{1}{2}, \frac{1}{2}\right)$ is not on the graph.

   (b) $\left(\frac{1}{2}\right)^2 + \left(\frac{\sqrt{3}}{2}\right)^2 = \frac{1}{4} + \frac{3}{4} = 1$; $\left(\frac{1}{2}, \frac{\sqrt{3}}{2}\right)$ is on the graph.

5. $2x - 4y = 16$
   x-intercept:
   $$2x - 4(0) = 16 \Rightarrow 2x = 16 \Rightarrow x = 8$$
   y-intercept:
   $$2(0) - 4y = 16 \Rightarrow -4y = 16 \Rightarrow y = -4$$

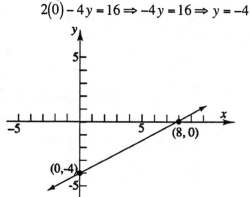

7. This is the graph of an exponential function with y-intercept $(0,1)$, containing the point $(1,4)$.

   $y = A \cdot b^x$

   y-intercept $(0,1)$

   $\Rightarrow 1 = A \cdot b^0 = A \cdot 1 \Rightarrow A = 1$

   point: $(1,4) \Rightarrow 4 = b^1 = b$

   Therefore, $y = 4^x$.

9. (a) $g(x) = 3^x + 2$
        Using the graph of $y = 3^x$, shift up 2 units.
        Domain: $(-\infty, \infty)$
        Range: $(2, \infty)$
        Horizontal Asymptote: $y = 2$

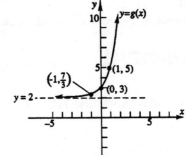

    (b) $g(x) = 3^x + 2$

$$y = 3^x + 2$$

$$x = 3^y + 2 \qquad \text{Inverse}$$

$$x - 2 = 3^y$$

$$\ln(x - 2) = \ln(3^y)$$

$$\ln(x - 2) = y \cdot \ln(3)$$

$$\frac{\ln(x - 2)}{\ln(3)} = y$$

$$g^{-1}(x) = \frac{\ln(x - 2)}{\ln(3)} = \log_3(x - 2)$$

    Domain: $(2, \infty)$
    Range: $(-\infty, \infty)$
    Vertical Asymptote: $x = 2$

    (c)

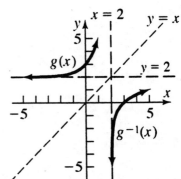

11. $\log_3(x + 1) + \log_3(2x - 3) = \log_9 9$
     $\log_3((x + 1)(2x - 3)) = 1$

$$(x + 1)(2x - 3) = 3^1$$

$$2x^2 - x - 3 = 3$$

$$2x^2 - x - 6 = 0$$

$$(2x + 3)(x - 2) = 0$$

$$x = -\frac{3}{2} \quad \text{or} \quad x = 2$$

Since $\log_3\left(-\frac{3}{2} + 1\right) = \log_3\left(-\frac{1}{2}\right)$ is undefined the

solution set is $\{2\}$.

13. (a) Scatter diagram:

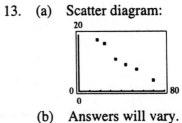

     (b) Answers will vary.
     (c) Answers will vary.

Review

A.1 Algebra Review

1. variable

3. strict

5. $|-5| = 5$

7. False

9. $x = -2, y = 3 \Rightarrow x + 2y = -2 + 2 \cdot 3 = -2 + 6 = 4$

11. $x = -2, y = 3 \Rightarrow 5xy + 2 = 5(-2)(3) + 2 = -30 + 2 = -28$

13. $x = -2, y = 3 \Rightarrow \dfrac{2x}{x - y} = \dfrac{2(-2)}{-2 - 3} = \dfrac{-4}{-5} = \dfrac{4}{5}$

15. $x = -2, y = 3 \Rightarrow \dfrac{3x + 2y}{2 + y} = \dfrac{3(-2) + 2(3)}{2 + 3} = \dfrac{-6 + 6}{5} = \dfrac{0}{5} = 0$

17. $\dfrac{x^2 - 1}{x}$ Value (c) must be excluded.

    The value $x = 0$ must be excluded from the domain because it causes division by 0.

19. $\dfrac{x}{x^2 - 9} = \dfrac{x}{(x - 3)(x + 3)}$ Value (a) must be excluded.

    The values $x = -3$ and $x = 3$ must be excluded from the domain because they cause division by 0.

21. $\dfrac{x^2}{x^2 + 1}$ None of the given values are excluded. The domain is all real numbers.

23. $\dfrac{x^2 + 5x - 10}{x^3 - x} = \dfrac{x^2 + 5x - 10}{x(x - 1)(x + 1)}$ Values (b), (c), and (d) must be excluded.

    The values $x = 0$, $x = 1$, and $x = -1$ must be excluded from the domain because they cause division by 0.

25. $\dfrac{4}{x - 5}$ Domain $= \{x | x \neq 5\}$

27. $\dfrac{x}{x + 4}$ Domain $= \{x | x \neq -4\}$

29.

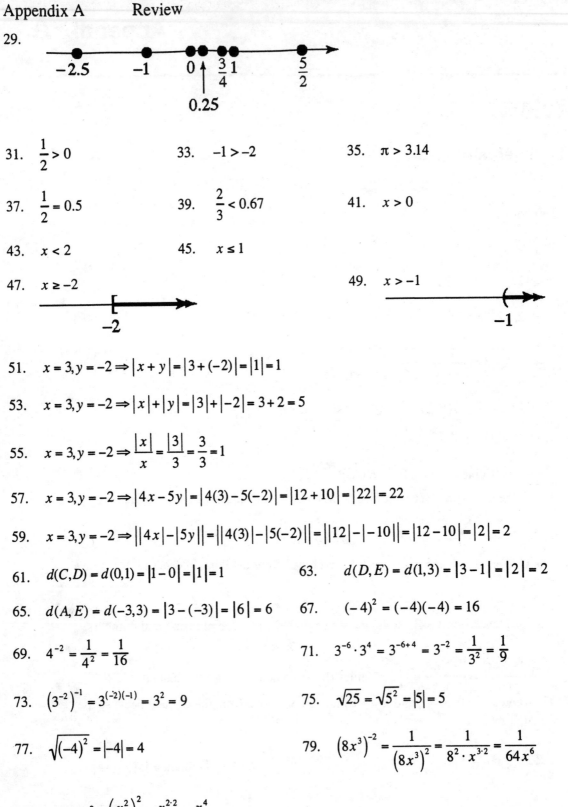

31. $\dfrac{1}{2} > 0$

33. $-1 > -2$

35. $\pi > 3.14$

37. $\dfrac{1}{2} = 0.5$

39. $\dfrac{2}{3} < 0.67$

41. $x > 0$

43. $x < 2$

45. $x \le 1$

47. $x \ge -2$

49. $x > -1$

51. $x = 3, y = -2 \Rightarrow |x + y| = |3 + (-2)| = |1| = 1$

53. $x = 3, y = -2 \Rightarrow |x| + |y| = |3| + |-2| = 3 + 2 = 5$

55. $x = 3, y = -2 \Rightarrow \dfrac{|x|}{x} = \dfrac{|3|}{3} = \dfrac{3}{3} = 1$

57. $x = 3, y = -2 \Rightarrow |4x - 5y| = |4(3) - 5(-2)| = |12 + 10| = |22| = 22$

59. $x = 3, y = -2 \Rightarrow ||4x| - |5y|| = ||4(3)| - |5(-2)|| = ||12| - |-10|| = |12 - 10| = |2| = 2$

61. $d(C,D) = d(0,1) = |1 - 0| = |1| = 1$

63. $d(D,E) = d(1,3) = |3 - 1| = |2| = 2$

65. $d(A,E) = d(-3,3) = |3 - (-3)| = |6| = 6$

67. $(-4)^2 = (-4)(-4) = 16$

69. $4^{-2} = \dfrac{1}{4^2} = \dfrac{1}{16}$

71. $3^{-6} \cdot 3^4 = 3^{-6+4} = 3^{-2} = \dfrac{1}{3^2} = \dfrac{1}{9}$

73. $\left(3^{-2}\right)^{-1} = 3^{(-2)(-1)} = 3^2 = 9$

75. $\sqrt{25} = \sqrt{5^2} = |5| = 5$

77. $\sqrt{(-4)^2} = |-4| = 4$

79. $\left(8x^3\right)^{-2} = \dfrac{1}{\left(8x^3\right)^2} = \dfrac{1}{8^2 \cdot x^{3 \cdot 2}} = \dfrac{1}{64x^6}$

81. $\left(x^2 y^{-1}\right)^2 = \left(\dfrac{x^2}{y}\right)^2 = \dfrac{x^{2 \cdot 2}}{y^{1 \cdot 2}} = \dfrac{x^4}{y^2}$

83. $\dfrac{x^{-2}y^3}{xy^4} = \dfrac{x^{-2}}{x} \cdot \dfrac{y^3}{y^4} = x^{-2-1}y^{3-4} = x^{-3}y^{-1} = \dfrac{1}{x^3} \cdot \dfrac{1}{y} = \dfrac{1}{x^3 y}$

85. $\dfrac{(-2)^3 x^4 (y\,z)^2}{3^2 x y^3 z} = \dfrac{-8 x^4 y^2 z^2}{9 x y^3 z} = \dfrac{-8}{9} x^{4-1} y^{2-3} z^{2-1} = \dfrac{-8}{9} x^3 y^{-1} z^1 = \dfrac{-8}{9} x^3 \cdot \dfrac{1}{y} \cdot z = -\dfrac{8 x^3 z}{9y}$

87. $\left(\dfrac{3x^{-1}}{4y^{-1}}\right)^{-2} = \left(\dfrac{3y^1}{4x^1}\right)^{-2} = \dfrac{1}{\left(\dfrac{3y^1}{4x^1}\right)^2} = \dfrac{1}{\dfrac{3^2 y^{1\cdot 2}}{4^2 x^{1\cdot 2}}} = \dfrac{1}{\dfrac{9y^2}{16x^2}} = \dfrac{16x^2}{9y^2}$

89. $A = l \cdot w$

91. $C = \pi \cdot d$

93. $A = \dfrac{\sqrt{3}}{4} \cdot x^2$

95. $V = \dfrac{4}{3} \cdot \pi \cdot r^3$

97. $V = x^3$

99. $|x - 115| \le 5$
    (a) $|x - 115| = |113 - 115| = |-2| = 2 \le 5$ 113 volts is acceptable.
    (b) $|x - 115| = |109 - 115| = |-6| = 6 > 5$ 109 volts is not acceptable.

101. $|x - 3| \le 0.01$
    (a) $|x - 3| = |2.999 - 3| = |-0.001| = 0.001 \le 0.01$
        A radius of 2.999 centimeters is acceptable.
    (b) $|x - 3| = |2.89 - 3| = |-0.11| = 0.11 > 0.01$
        A radius of 2.89 centimeters is _not_ acceptable.

103. $\dfrac{1}{3} = 0.333333\ldots > 0.333 \;\Rightarrow\; \dfrac{1}{3}$ is larger by approximately $0.0003333\ldots$

105. No. Suppose that $c =$ the number closest to 0, with $c > 0$. Then $c/2 < c$, and $c/2$ is half-way between 0 and c. Therefore, the number c can't be the number closest to 0.

107. Answers will vary.

Review

A.2 Geometry Review

1. right, hypotenuse
3. $C = 2\pi r$
5. True

7. $a = 5,\ b = 12,\ c^2 = a^2 + b^2 = 5^2 + 12^2 = 25 + 144 = 169 \Rightarrow c = 13$

9. $a = 10,\ b = 24,\ c^2 = a^2 + b^2 = 10^2 + 24^2 = 100 + 576 = 676 \Rightarrow c = 26$

11. $a = 7,\ b = 24,\ c^2 = a^2 + b^2 = 7^2 + 24^2 = 49 + 576 = 625 \Rightarrow c = 25$

13. $5^2 = 3^2 + 4^2 \Rightarrow 25 = 9 + 16 \Rightarrow 25 = 25$
    The given triangle is a right triangle. The length of the hypotenuse is 5.

15. $6^2 = 4^2 + 5^2 \Rightarrow 36 = 16 + 25 \Rightarrow 36 \neq 41$
    The given triangle is not a right triangle.

17. $25^2 = 7^2 + 24^2 \Rightarrow 625 = 49 + 576 \Rightarrow 625 = 625$
    The given triangle is a right triangle. The length of the hypotenuse is 25.

19. $6^2 = 3^2 + 4^2 \Rightarrow 36 = 9 + 16 \Rightarrow 36 \neq 25$
    The given triangle is not a right triangle.

21. $A = lw = 4 \cdot 2 = 8 \text{ in}^2$
23. $A = \dfrac{1}{2}bh = \dfrac{1}{2}(2)(4) = 4 \text{ in}^2$

25. $A = \pi r^2 = \pi(5)^2 = 25\pi \text{ m}^2 \qquad C = 2\pi r = 2\pi(5) = 10\pi \text{ m}$

27. $V = lwh = 8 \cdot 4 \cdot 7 = 224 \text{ ft}^3 \qquad S = 2(lw + lh + wh) = 2 \cdot (8 \cdot 4 + 8 \cdot 7 + 4 \cdot 7) = 232 \text{ ft}^2$

29. $V = \dfrac{4}{3}\pi r^3 = \dfrac{4}{3}\pi \cdot 4^3 = \dfrac{256}{3}\pi \text{ cm}^3 \qquad S = 4\pi r^2 = 4\pi \cdot 4^2 = 64\pi \text{ cm}^2$

31. $V = \pi r^2 h = \pi(9)^2(8) = 648\pi \text{ in}^3$
    $S = 2\pi r^2 + 2\pi rh = 2\pi \cdot 9^2 + 2\pi \cdot 9 \cdot 8 = 306\pi \text{ in}^2$

33. The diameter of the circle is 2, so its radius is 1. $A = \pi r^2 = \pi(1)^2 = \pi$ square units

35. The diameter of the circle is the length of the diagonal of the square.

$d^2 = 2^2 + 2^2 = 4 + 4 = 8 \implies d = \sqrt{8} = 2\sqrt{2} \implies r = \sqrt{2}$

The area of the circle is: $A = \pi r^2 = \pi \left(\sqrt{2}\right)^2 = 2\pi$ square units

37. The total distance traveled is 4 times the circumference of the wheel.

Total distance $= 4C = 4(\pi d) = 4\pi \cdot 16 = 64\pi \approx 201.1$ inches ≈ 16.8 feet

39. Area of the border $=$ area of $EFGH$ $-$ area of $ABCD$ $= 10^2 - 6^2 = 100 - 36 = 64$ ft^2

41. Area of the window $=$ area of the rectangle $+$ area of the semicircle.

$$A = (6)(4) + \frac{1}{2}\pi \cdot 2^2 = 24 + 2\pi \approx 30.28 \text{ ft}^2$$

Perimeter of the window $=$ 2 heights $+$ width $+$ one-half the circumference.

$$P = 2(6) + 4 + \frac{1}{2}\pi(4) = 12 + 4 + 2\pi = 16 + 2\pi \approx 22.28 \text{ feet}$$

43. Convert 20 feet to miles, and use the Pythagorean theorem to find the distance:

$20 \text{ feet} = 20 \text{ feet} \cdot \dfrac{1 \text{ mile}}{5280 \text{ feet}} \approx 0.003788 \text{ miles}$

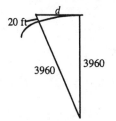

$d^2 \approx (3960 + 0.003788)^2 - 3960^2 \approx 30$

$d \approx 5.477$ miles

45. Convert 100 feet to miles, and use the Pythagorean theorem to find the distance:

$$100 \text{ feet} = 100 \text{ feet} \cdot \dfrac{1 \text{ mile}}{5280 \text{ feet}} \approx 0.018939 \text{ miles}$$

$$d^2 \approx (3960 + 0.018939)^2 - 3960^2 \approx 150 \implies d \approx 12.247 \text{ miles}$$

Convert 150 feet to miles, and solve the Pythagorean theorem to find the distance:

$$150 \text{ feet} = 150 \text{ feet} \cdot \dfrac{1 \text{ mile}}{5280 \text{ feet}} \approx 0.028409 \text{ miles}$$

$$d^2 \approx (3960 + 0.028409)^2 - 3960^2 \approx 225 \implies d \approx 15 \text{ miles}$$

47. Given a rectangle with perimeter $= 1000$ feet, the largest area will be enclosed by a square with dimensions 250 by 250 feet. Then, the area $= 250^2 = 62,500$ square feet.

A circular pool with circumference $= 1000$ feet yields the equation : $2\pi r = 1000 \implies r = \dfrac{500}{\pi}$

The area enclosed by the circular pool is:

$$A = \pi r^2 = \pi \left(\frac{500}{\pi}\right)^2 = \frac{500^2}{\pi} \approx 79,577.47 \text{ square feet}$$

Therefore, a circular pool will enclose the most area.

Appendix A

Review

A.3 Solving Equations

1. 3

3. $\left\{-\dfrac{5}{3}, 3\right\}$

5. equivalent

7. False

9. add, $\left(\dfrac{5}{2}\right)^2 = \dfrac{25}{4}$

11. False

13. $3x = 21$
$\dfrac{3x}{3} = \dfrac{21}{3}$
$x = 7$

15. $5x + 15 = 0$
$5x + 15 - 15 = 0 - 15$
$5x = -15$
$\dfrac{5x}{5} = \dfrac{-15}{5}$
$x = -3$

17. $2x - 3 = 5$
$2x - 3 + 3 = 5 + 3$
$2x = 8$
$\dfrac{2x}{2} = \dfrac{8}{2}$
$x = 4$

19. $\dfrac{1}{3}x = \dfrac{5}{12}$
$(3)\left(\dfrac{1}{3}x\right) = \left(\dfrac{5}{12}\right)(3)$
$x = \dfrac{5}{4}$

21. $6 - x = 2x + 9$
$6 - x - 6 = 2x + 9 - 6$
$-x = 2x + 3$
$-x - 2x = 2x + 3 - 2x$
$-3x = 3$
$\dfrac{-3x}{-3} = \dfrac{3}{-3}$
$x = -1$

23. $2(3 + 2x) = 3(x - 4)$
$6 + 4x = 3x - 12$
$6 + 4x - 6 = 3x - 12 - 6$
$4x = 3x - 18$
$4x - 3x = 3x - 18 - 3x$
$x = -18$

25.
$$8x - (2x + 1) = 3x - 10$$
$$8x - 2x - 1 = 3x - 10$$
$$6x - 1 = 3x - 10$$
$$6x - 1 + 1 = 3x - 10 + 1$$
$$6x = 3x - 9$$
$$6x - 3x = 3x - 9 - 3x$$
$$3x = -9$$
$$\frac{3x}{3} = \frac{-9}{3}$$
$$x = -3$$

27.
$$\frac{1}{2}x - 4 = \frac{3}{4}x$$
$$\frac{1}{2}x - 4 + 4 = \frac{3}{4}x + 4$$
$$\frac{1}{2}x = \frac{3}{4}x + 4$$
$$\frac{1}{2}x - \frac{3}{4}x = \frac{3}{4}x + 4 - \frac{3}{4}x$$
$$\frac{2}{4}x - \frac{3}{4}x = 4$$
$$-\frac{1}{4}x = 4$$
$$(-4)\left(-\frac{1}{4}x\right) = (4)(-4)$$
$$x = -16$$

29.
$$0.9t = 0.4 + 0.1t$$
$$0.9t - 0.1t = 0.4 + 0.1t - 0.1t$$
$$0.8t = 0.4$$
$$\frac{0.8t}{0.8} = \frac{0.4}{0.8}$$
$$t = 0.5$$

31.
$$\frac{2}{y} + \frac{4}{y} = 3$$
$$y\left(\frac{2}{y} + \frac{4}{y}\right) = y(3)$$
$$2 + 4 = 3y$$
$$6 = 3y$$
$$\frac{6}{3} = \frac{3y}{3}$$
$$y = 2$$

Since $y = 2$ does not cause a denominator to equal zero, the solution set is $\{2\}$.

33.
$$(x + 7)(x - 1) = (x + 1)^2$$
$$x^2 + 6x - 7 = x^2 + 2x + 1$$
$$x^2 + 6x - 7 - x^2 = x^2 + 2x + 1 - x^2$$
$$6x - 7 = 2x + 1$$
$$6x - 7 + 7 = 2x + 1 + 7$$
$$6x = 2x + 8$$
$$6x - 2x = 2x + 8 - 2x$$
$$4x = 8$$
$$\frac{4x}{4} = \frac{8}{4}$$
$$x = 2$$

35.
$$z(z^2 + 1) = 3 + z^3$$
$$z^3 + z = 3 + z^3$$
$$z^3 + z - z^3 = 3 + z^3 - z^3$$
$$z = 3$$

37.
$$x^2 = 9x$$
$$x^2 - 9x = 0$$
$$x(x - 9) = 0$$
$$x = 0$$
or $x - 9 = 0 \Rightarrow x = 9$
The solution set is $\{0, 9\}$.

39.
$$t^3 - 9t^2 = 0$$
$$t^2(t - 9) = 0$$
$$t^2 = 0 \Rightarrow t = 0$$
or $t - 9 = 0 \Rightarrow t = 9$
The solution set is $\{0, 9\}$.

41.
$$\frac{3}{2x - 3} = \frac{2}{x + 5}$$

$$(2x - 3)(x + 5)\left(\frac{3}{2x - 3}\right) = \left(\frac{2}{x + 5}\right)(2x - 3)(x + 5)$$

$$(x + 5)(3) = (2)(2x - 3)$$
$$3x + 15 = 4x - 6$$
$$3x + 15 - 4x = 4x - 6 - 4x$$
$$15 - x = -6$$
$$15 - x - 15 = -6 - 15$$
$$-x = -21$$
$$x = 21$$

Since $x = 21$ does not cause any denominator to equal zero, the solution set is $\{21\}$.

43.
$$(x + 2)(3x) = (x + 2)(6)$$
$$3x^2 + 6x = 6x + 12$$
$$3x^2 + 6x - 6x = 6x + 12 - 6x$$
$$3x^2 = 12$$
$$3x^2 - 12 = 12 - 12$$
$$3x^2 - 12 = 0$$
$$3(x^2 - 4) = 0$$
$$3(x - 2)(x + 2) = 0$$
$$x - 2 = 0 \Rightarrow x = 2$$
or $x + 2 = 0 \Rightarrow x = -2$
The solution set is $\{-2, 2\}$.

45.
$$\frac{2}{x-2} = \frac{3}{x+5} + \frac{10}{(x+5)(x-2)}$$

$$(x-2)(x+5)\left(\frac{2}{x-2}\right) = \left(\frac{3}{x+5} + \frac{10}{(x+5)(x-2)}\right)(x-2)(x+5)$$

$$(x+5)(2) = (3)(x-2) + 10$$

$$2x + 10 = 3x - 6 + 10$$

$$2x + 10 = 3x + 4$$

$$2x + 10 - 10 = 3x + 4 - 10$$

$$2x = 3x - 6$$

$$2x - 3x = 3x - 6 - 3x$$

$$-x = -6$$

$$x = 6$$

Since $x = 6$ does not cause any denominator to equal zero, the solution set is $\{6\}$.

47. $|2x| = 6$

$2x = 6$ or $2x = -6$

$x = 3$ or $x = -3$

The solution set is $\{-3, 3\}$.

49. $|2x + 3| = 5$

$2x + 3 = 5$ or $2x + 3 = -5$

$2x = 2$ or $2x = -8$

$x = 1$ or $x = -4$

The solution set is $\{-4, 1\}$.

51. $|1 - 4t| = 5$

$1 - 4t = 5$ or $1 - 4t = -5$

$-4t = 4$ or $-4t = -6$

$t = -1$ or $t = \dfrac{3}{2}$

The solution set is $\left\{-1, \dfrac{3}{2}\right\}$.

53. $|-2x| = 8$

$-2x = 8$ or $-2x = -8$

$x = -4$ or $x = 4$

The solution set is $\{-4, 4\}$.

55. $|-2|x = 4$

$2x = 4$

$x = 2$

The solution set is $\{2\}$.

57. $|x - 2| = -\dfrac{1}{2}$

The equation has no solution, since absolute value always yields a non-negative number.

59. $\left|x^2 - 4\right| = 0$

$\qquad x^2 - 4 = 0$

$\qquad x^2 = 4$

$\qquad x = \pm 2$

The solution set is $\{-2, 2\}$.

61. $\left|x^2 - 2x\right| = 3$

$\qquad x^2 - 2x = 3 \quad$ or $\quad x^2 - 2x = -3$

$\qquad x^2 - 2x - 3 = 0 \quad$ or $\quad x^2 - 2x + 3 = 0$

$\qquad (x - 3)(x + 1) = 0 \Rightarrow x = 3, x = -1$

or $\quad x = \dfrac{2 \pm \sqrt{4 - 12}}{2}$

$\qquad = \dfrac{2 \pm \sqrt{-8}}{2} \Rightarrow$ no real solution

The solution set is $\{-1, 3\}$.

63. $\left|x^2 + x - 1\right| = 1$

$\qquad x^2 + x - 1 = 1 \quad$ or $\quad x^2 + x - 1 = -1$

$\qquad x^2 + x - 2 = 0 \quad$ or $\qquad x^2 + x = 0$

$\qquad (x - 1)(x + 2) = 0 \quad$ or $\qquad x(x + 1) = 0$

$\qquad x = 1, x = -2 \qquad$ or $\qquad x = 0, x = -1$

The solution set is $\{-2, -1, 0, 1\}$.

65. $\qquad x^2 = 4x$

$\quad x^2 - 4x = 0$

$\quad x(x - 4) = 0$

$\qquad x = 0$

or $x - 4 = 0 \Rightarrow x = 4$

The solution set is $\{0, 4\}$.

67. $z^2 + 4z - 12 = 0$

$(z + 6)(z - 2) = 0$

$\qquad z + 6 = 0 \Rightarrow z = -6$

or $z - 2 = 0 \Rightarrow z = 2$

The solution set is $\{-6, 2\}$.

69. $\qquad 2x^2 - 5x - 3 = 0$

$\qquad (2x + 1)(x - 3) = 0$

$\qquad\qquad 2x + 1 = 0$

$\qquad\qquad 2x = -1 \Rightarrow x = -\dfrac{1}{2}$

or $x - 3 = 0 \Rightarrow x = 3$

The solution set is $\left\{-\dfrac{1}{2}, 3\right\}$.

71. $x(x - 7) + 12 = 0$

$\quad x^2 - 7x + 12 = 0$

$\quad (x - 4)(x - 3) = 0$

$\qquad x - 4 = 0 \Rightarrow x = 4$

or $x - 3 = 0 \Rightarrow x = 3$

The solution set is $\{3, 4\}$.

73. $\qquad 4x^2 + 9 = 12x$

$\quad 4x^2 - 12x + 9 = 0$

$\qquad (2x - 3)^2 = 0 \Rightarrow x = \dfrac{3}{2}$

The solution set is $\left\{\dfrac{3}{2}\right\}$.

75.

$$6x - 5 = \frac{6}{x}$$

$$6x^2 - 5x = 6$$

$$6x^2 - 5x - 6 = 0$$

$$(3x + 2)(2x - 3) = 0$$

$$3x + 2 = 0 \Rightarrow x = -\frac{2}{3}$$

$$\text{or } 2x - 3 = 0 \Rightarrow x = \frac{3}{2}$$

Since neither of these values causes a denominator to equal zero, the solution set is $\left\{-\frac{2}{3}, \frac{3}{2}\right\}$.

77.

$$\frac{4(x-2)}{x-3} + \frac{3}{x} = \frac{-3}{x(x-3)}$$

$$x(x-3)\left(\frac{4(x-2)}{x-3} + \frac{3}{x}\right) = \left(\frac{-3}{x(x-3)}\right)x(x-3)$$

$$x(4(x-2)) + (x-3)(3) = -3$$

$$4x^2 - 8x + 3x - 9 = -3$$

$$4x^2 - 5x - 6 = 0$$

$$(4x + 3)(x - 2) = 0$$

$$4x + 3 = 0 \Rightarrow x = -\frac{3}{4}$$

$$\text{or } x - 2 = 0 \Rightarrow x = 2$$

Since neither of these values causes a denominator to equal zero, the solution set is $\left\{-\frac{3}{4}, 2\right\}$.

79. $x^2 = 25$

$$x = \pm\sqrt{25}$$

$$x = \pm 5$$

The solution set is $\{-5, 5\}$.

81. $(x - 1)^2 = 4$

$$x - 1 = \pm\sqrt{4}$$

$$x - 1 = \pm 2$$

$$x - 1 = 2 \Rightarrow x = 3$$

$$\text{or } x - 1 = -2 \Rightarrow x = -1$$

The solution set is $\{-1, 3\}$.

83. $(2x+3)^2 = 9$

   $2x+3 = \pm\sqrt{9}$

   $2x+3 = \pm 3$

   $2x+3 = 3$

   $2x = 0 \Rightarrow x = 0$

   or $2x+3 = -3$

   $2x = -6 \Rightarrow x = -3$

   The solution set is $\{-3, 0\}$.

85. $\left(\dfrac{8}{2}\right)^2 = 4^2 = 16$

87. $\left(\dfrac{\left(\dfrac{1}{2}\right)}{2}\right)^2 = \left(\dfrac{1}{4}\right)^2 = \dfrac{1}{16}$

89. $\left(\dfrac{\left(-\dfrac{2}{3}\right)}{2}\right)^2 = \left(-\dfrac{1}{3}\right)^2 = \dfrac{1}{9}$

91. $x^2 + 4x = 21$

   $x^2 + 4x + 4 = 21 + 4$

   $(x+2)^2 = 25$

   $x+2 = \pm\sqrt{25}$

   $x+2 = \pm 5$

   $x+2 = 5 \Rightarrow x = 3$

   or $x+2 = -5 \Rightarrow x = -7$
   The solution set is $\{-7, 3\}$.

93. $x^2 - \dfrac{1}{2}x - \dfrac{3}{16} = 0$

   $x^2 - \dfrac{1}{2}x = \dfrac{3}{16}$

   $x^2 - \dfrac{1}{2}x + \dfrac{1}{16} = \dfrac{3}{16} + \dfrac{1}{16}$

   $\left(x - \dfrac{1}{4}\right)^2 = \dfrac{1}{4}$

   $x - \dfrac{1}{4} = \pm\sqrt{\dfrac{1}{4}}$

   $x - \dfrac{1}{4} = \pm\dfrac{1}{2}$

   $x - \dfrac{1}{4} = \dfrac{1}{2} \Rightarrow x = \dfrac{3}{4}$

   or $x - \dfrac{1}{4} = -\dfrac{1}{2} \Rightarrow x = -\dfrac{1}{4}$

   The solution set is $\left\{-\dfrac{1}{4}, \dfrac{3}{4}\right\}$.

95.
$$3x^2 + x - \frac{1}{2} = 0$$

$$x^2 + \frac{1}{3}x - \frac{1}{6} = 0$$

$$x^2 + \frac{1}{3}x = \frac{1}{6}$$

$$x^2 + \frac{1}{3}x + \frac{1}{36} = \frac{1}{6} + \frac{1}{36}$$

$$\left(x + \frac{1}{6}\right)^2 = \frac{7}{36}$$

$$x + \frac{1}{6} = \pm\sqrt{\frac{7}{36}}$$

$$x + \frac{1}{6} = \pm\frac{\sqrt{7}}{6}$$

$$x + \frac{1}{6} = \frac{\sqrt{7}}{6} \Rightarrow x = -\frac{1}{6} + \frac{\sqrt{7}}{6}$$

or $x + \frac{1}{6} = -\frac{\sqrt{7}}{6} \Rightarrow x = -\frac{1}{6} - \frac{\sqrt{7}}{6}$

The solution set is $\left\{-\frac{1}{6} - \frac{\sqrt{7}}{6}, \ -\frac{1}{6} + \frac{\sqrt{7}}{6}\right\}$.

97.
$$x^2 - 4x + 2 = 0$$
$$a = 1, \quad b = -4, \quad c = 2$$

$$x = \frac{-(-4) \pm \sqrt{(-4)^2 - 4(1)(2)}}{2(1)}$$

$$= \frac{4 \pm \sqrt{16 - 8}}{2} = \frac{4 \pm \sqrt{8}}{2}$$

$$= \frac{4 \pm 2\sqrt{2}}{2} = 2 \pm \sqrt{2}$$

The solution set is $\left\{2 - \sqrt{2}, 2 + \sqrt{2}\right\}$.

99.
$$x^2 - 5x - 1 = 0$$
$$a = 1, \quad b = -5, \quad c = -1$$

$$x = \frac{-(-5) \pm \sqrt{(-5)^2 - 4(1)(-1)}}{2(1)}$$

$$= \frac{5 \pm \sqrt{25 + 4}}{2} = \frac{5 \pm \sqrt{29}}{2}$$

The solution set is $\left\{\frac{5 - \sqrt{29}}{2}, \frac{5 + \sqrt{29}}{2}\right\}$.

101.
$$2x^2 - 5x + 3 = 0$$
$$a = 2, \quad b = -5, \quad c = 3$$

$$x = \frac{-(-5) \pm \sqrt{(-5)^2 - 4(2)(3)}}{2(2)}$$

$$= \frac{5 \pm \sqrt{25 - 24}}{4} = \frac{5 \pm 1}{4}$$

The solution set is $\left\{1, \frac{3}{2}\right\}$.

103. $4y^2 - y + 2 = 0$
$a = 4, \quad b = -1, \quad c = 2$

$$y = \frac{-(-1) \pm \sqrt{(-1)^2 - 4(4)(2)}}{2(4)}$$

$$= \frac{1 \pm \sqrt{1 - 32}}{8} = \frac{1 \pm \sqrt{-31}}{8}$$

No real solution.

105. $4x^2 = 1 - 2x \Rightarrow 4x^2 + 2x - 1 = 0$
$a = 4, \quad b = 2, \quad c = -1$

$$x = \frac{-2 \pm \sqrt{2^2 - 4(4)(-1)}}{2(4)}$$

$$= \frac{-2 \pm \sqrt{4 + 16}}{8} = \frac{-2 \pm \sqrt{20}}{8}$$

$$= \frac{-2 \pm 2\sqrt{5}}{8} = \frac{-1 \pm \sqrt{5}}{4}$$

The solution set is $\left\{ \dfrac{-1 - \sqrt{5}}{4}, \dfrac{-1 + \sqrt{5}}{4} \right\}$.

107. $x^2 + \sqrt{3}x - 3 = 0$
$a = 1, \quad b = \sqrt{3}, \quad c = -3$

$$x = \frac{-\left(\sqrt{3}\right) \pm \sqrt{\left(\sqrt{3}\right)^2 - 4(1)(-3)}}{2(1)}$$

$$= \frac{-\sqrt{3} \pm \sqrt{3 + 12}}{2} = \frac{-\sqrt{3} \pm \sqrt{15}}{2}$$

The solution set is $\left\{ \dfrac{-\sqrt{3} - \sqrt{15}}{2}, \dfrac{-\sqrt{3} + \sqrt{15}}{2} \right\}$.

109. $x^2 - 5x + 7 = 0$
$\qquad a = 1, \quad b = -5, \quad c = 7$

$b^2 - 4ac = (-5)^2 - 4(1)(7)$

$\qquad\qquad = 25 - 28 = -3$

Since the discriminant is negative, there are no real solutions.

111. $9x^2 - 30x + 25 = 0$
$\qquad a = 9, \quad b = -30, \quad c = 25$

$b^2 - 4ac = (-30)^2 - 4(9)(25)$

$\qquad\qquad = 900 - 900 = 0$

Since the discriminant is zero, there is one repeated real solution.

113. $3x^2 + 5x - 8 = 0$
$\qquad a = 3, \quad b = 5, \quad c = -8$

$b^2 - 4ac = 5^2 - 4(3)(-8)$

$\qquad\qquad = 25 + 96 = 121$

Since the discriminant is positive, there are two unequal real solutions.

115. $\qquad ax - b = c, \quad a \neq 0$

$\qquad ax - b + b = c + b$

$\qquad\qquad ax = c + b$

$$\frac{ax}{a} = \frac{c + b}{a}$$

$$x = \frac{c + b}{a}$$

117.
$$\frac{x}{a} + \frac{x}{b} = c, \quad a \neq 0, b \neq 0, a \neq -b$$

$$ab\left(\frac{x}{a} + \frac{x}{b}\right) = ab \cdot c$$

$$bx + ax = abc$$

$$x(a+b) = abc$$

$$\frac{x(a+b)}{a+b} = \frac{abc}{a+b}$$

$$x = \frac{abc}{a+b}$$

119.
$$\frac{1}{x-a} + \frac{1}{x+a} = \frac{2}{x-1}$$

$$(x-a)(x+a)(x-1)\left(\frac{1}{x-a} + \frac{1}{x+a}\right) = \left(\frac{2}{x-1}\right)(x-a)(x+a)(x-1)$$

$$(x+a)(x-1)(1) + (x-a)(x-1)(1) = (2)(x-a)(x+a)$$

$$x^2 - x + ax - a + x^2 - x - ax + a = 2x^2 - 2a^2$$

$$2x^2 - 2x = 2x^2 - 2a^2$$

$$-2x = -2a^2$$

$$\frac{-2x}{-2} = \frac{-2a^2}{-2}$$

$$x = a^2$$

such that $x \neq \pm a, x \neq 1$

121. Solving for R:
$$\frac{1}{R} = \frac{1}{R_1} + \frac{1}{R_2}$$

$$RR_1R_2\left(\frac{1}{R}\right) = RR_1R_2\left(\frac{1}{R_1} + \frac{1}{R_2}\right)$$

$$R_1R_2 = RR_2 + RR_1$$

$$R_1R_2 = R(R_2 + R_1)$$

$$\frac{R_1R_2}{R_2 + R_1} = \frac{R(R_2 + R_1)}{R_2 + R_1}$$

$$\frac{R_1R_2}{R_2 + R_1} = R$$

123. Solving for R:
$$F = \frac{mv^2}{R}$$

$$RF = R\left(\frac{mv^2}{R}\right)$$

$$RF = mv^2$$

$$\frac{RF}{F} = \frac{mv^2}{F} \Rightarrow R = \frac{mv^2}{F}$$

125. Solving for r:

$$S = \frac{a}{1-r}$$

$$S(1-r) = \left(\frac{a}{1-r}\right)(1-r)$$

$$S - Sr = a$$

$$S - Sr - S = a - S$$

$$-Sr = a - S$$

$$\frac{-Sr}{-S} = \frac{a-S}{-S}$$

$$r = \frac{S-a}{S}$$

127. Given a quadratic equation $ax^2 + bx + c = 0$, the solutions are given by $x = \dfrac{-b + \sqrt{b^2 - 4ac}}{2a}$ and $x = \dfrac{-b - \sqrt{b^2 - 4ac}}{2a}$.

Adding these two values we get

$$\frac{-b + \sqrt{b^2 - 4ac}}{2a} + \frac{-b - \sqrt{b^2 - 4ac}}{2a} = \frac{-b + \sqrt{b^2 - 4ac} - b - \sqrt{b^2 - 4ac}}{2a} = \frac{-2b}{2a} = -\frac{b}{a}$$

129. The quadratic equation $kx^2 + x + k = 0$ will have a repeated solution provided the discriminant is 0. That is, we need $b^2 - 4ac = 0$ in the given quadratic equation.
$b^2 - 4ac = (1)^2 - 4(k)(k) = 1 - 4k^2$

So we solve

$$1 - 4k^2 = 0$$

$$1 = 4k^2$$

$$\frac{1}{4} = k^2 \Rightarrow \pm\sqrt{\frac{1}{4}} = k \Rightarrow \pm\frac{1}{2} = k$$

131. The quadratic equation $ax^2 + bx + c = 0$ has solutions given by

$$x_1 = \frac{-b + \sqrt{b^2 - 4ac}}{2a} \quad \text{and} \quad x_2 = \frac{-b - \sqrt{b^2 - 4ac}}{2a}.$$

The quadratic equation $ax^2 - bx + c = 0$ has solutions given by

$$x_3 = \frac{-(-b) + \sqrt{(-b)^2 - 4ac}}{2a} = \frac{b + \sqrt{b^2 - 4ac}}{2a} = -x_2$$

and

$$x_4 = \frac{-(-b) - \sqrt{(-b)^2 - 4ac}}{2a} = \frac{b - \sqrt{b^2 - 4ac}}{2a} = -x_1$$

So we have the negatives of the first pair of solutions.

133–139.   Answers will vary.

Appendix A

Review

A.4 Complex Numbers; Quadratic Equations in the Complex Number System

1. True

3. False

5. $\{-2i, 2i\}$

7. True

9. $(2 - 3i) + (6 + 8i) = (2 + 6) + (-3 + 8)i = 8 + 5i$

11. $(-3 + 2i) - (4 - 4i) = (-3 - 4) + (2 - (-4))i = -7 + 6i$

13. $(2 - 5i) - (8 + 6i) = (2 - 8) + (-5 - 6)i = -6 - 11i$

15. $3(2 - 6i) = 6 - 18i$

17. $2i(2 - 3i) = 4i - 6i^2 = 4i - 6(-1) = 6 + 4i$

19. $(3 - 4i)(2 + i) = 6 + 3i - 8i - 4i^2 = 6 - 5i - 4(-1) = 10 - 5i$

21. $(-6 + i)(-6 - i) = 36 + 6i - 6i - i^2 = 36 - (-1) = 37$

23. $\dfrac{10}{3 - 4i} = \dfrac{10}{3 - 4i} \cdot \dfrac{3 + 4i}{3 + 4i} = \dfrac{30 + 40i}{9 + 16} = \dfrac{30 + 40i}{25} = \dfrac{30}{25} + \dfrac{40}{25}i = \dfrac{6}{5} + \dfrac{8}{5}i$

25. $\dfrac{2 + i}{i} = \dfrac{2 + i}{i} \cdot \dfrac{-i}{-i} = \dfrac{-2i - i^2}{-i^2} = \dfrac{-2i - (-1)}{-(-1)} = \dfrac{1 - 2i}{1} = 1 - 2i$

27. $\dfrac{6 - i}{1 + i} = \dfrac{6 - i}{1 + i} \cdot \dfrac{1 - i}{1 - i} = \dfrac{6 - 7i + (-1)}{1 + 1} = \dfrac{5 - 7i}{2} = \dfrac{5}{2} - \dfrac{7}{2}i$

29. $\left(\dfrac{1}{2} + \dfrac{\sqrt{3}}{2}i\right)^2 = \dfrac{1}{4} + 2\left(\dfrac{1}{2}\right)\left(\dfrac{\sqrt{3}}{2}i\right) + \dfrac{3}{4}i^2 = \dfrac{1}{4} + \dfrac{\sqrt{3}}{2}i + \dfrac{3}{4}(-1) = -\dfrac{1}{2} + \dfrac{\sqrt{3}}{2}i$

31. $(1 + i)^2 = 1 + 2i + i^2 = 1 + 2i + (-1) = 2i$

33. $i^{23} = i^{20+3} = i^{20} \cdot i^3 = \left(i^4\right)^5 \cdot i^3 = (1)^5(-i) = -i$

35. $i^{-15} = \dfrac{1}{i^{15}} = \dfrac{1}{i^{12+3}} = \dfrac{1}{i^{12} \cdot i^3} = \dfrac{1}{\left(i^4\right)^3 \cdot i^3} = \dfrac{1}{(1)^3(-i)} = \dfrac{1}{(1)(-i)} = \dfrac{1}{-i} \cdot \dfrac{i}{i} = \dfrac{i}{-i^2} = \dfrac{i}{-(-1)} = i$

37. $i^6 - 5 = i^4 \cdot i^2 - 5 = (1)(-1) - 5 = -1 - 5 = -6$

39. $6i^3 - 4i^5 = i^3\left(6 - 4i^2\right) = i^2 \cdot i\left(6 - 4(-1)\right) = -1 \cdot i(10) = -10i$

41. $(1+i)^3 = (1+i)(1+i)(1+i) = \left(1 + 2i + i^2\right)(1+i) = (1 + 2i - 1)(1+i) = 2i(1+i)$
$\quad = 2i + 2i^2 = 2i + 2(-1) = -2 + 2i$

43. $i^7\left(1 + i^2\right) = i^7\left(1 + (-1)\right) = i^7(0) = 0$

45. $i^6 + i^4 + i^2 + 1 = \left(i^2\right)^3 + \left(i^2\right)^2 + i^2 + 1 = (-1)^3 + (-1)^2 + (-1) + 1 = -1 + 1 - 1 + 1 = 0$

47. $\sqrt{-4} = 2i$ 49. $\sqrt{-25} = 5i$

51. $\sqrt{(3 + 4i)(4i - 3)} = \sqrt{12i - 9 + 16i^2 - 12i} = \sqrt{-9 + 16(-1)} = \sqrt{-25} = 5i$

53. $x^2 + 4 = 0$ 55. $x^2 - 16 = 0$
$\qquad x^2 = -4$ $\qquad x^2 = 16$
$\qquad x = \pm\sqrt{-4} = \pm 2i$ $\qquad x = \pm\sqrt{16} = \pm 4$
The solution set is $\{\pm 2i\}$.   The solution set is $\{\pm 4\}$.

57. $x^2 - 6x + 13 = 0$
$a = 1, b = -6, c = 13, \quad b^2 - 4ac = (-6)^2 - 4(1)(13) = 36 - 52 = -16$

$x = \dfrac{-(-6) \pm \sqrt{-16}}{2(1)} = \dfrac{6 \pm 4i}{2} = 3 \pm 2i$

The solution set is $\{3 - 2i, 3 + 2i\}$.

59. $x^2 - 6x + 10 = 0$
$a = 1, b = -6, c = 10, \quad b^2 - 4ac = (-6)^2 - 4(1)(10) = 36 - 40 = -4$

$x = \dfrac{-(-6) \pm \sqrt{-4}}{2(1)} = \dfrac{6 \pm 2i}{2} = 3 \pm i$

The solution set is $\{3 - i, 3 + i\}$.

61. $8x^2 - 4x + 1 = 0$
$a = 8, b = -4, c = 1,\quad b^2 - 4ac = (-4)^2 - 4(8)(1) = 16 - 32 = -16$

$x = \dfrac{-(-4) \pm \sqrt{-16}}{2(8)} = \dfrac{4 \pm 4i}{16} = \dfrac{1}{4} \pm \dfrac{1}{4}i$

The solution set is $\left\{ \dfrac{1}{4} - \dfrac{1}{4}i,\ \dfrac{1}{4} + \dfrac{1}{4}i \right\}$.

63. $5x^2 + 1 = 2x \Rightarrow 5x^2 - 2x + 1 = 0$
$a = 5, b = -2, c = 1,\quad b^2 - 4ac = (-2)^2 - 4(5)(1) = 4 - 20 = -16$

$x = \dfrac{-(-2) \pm \sqrt{-16}}{2(5)} = \dfrac{2 \pm 4i}{10} = \dfrac{1}{5} \pm \dfrac{2}{5}i$

The solution set is $\left\{ \dfrac{1}{5} - \dfrac{2}{5}i,\ \dfrac{1}{5} + \dfrac{2}{5}i \right\}$.

65. $x^2 + x + 1 = 0$
$a = 1, b = 1, c = 1,\quad b^2 - 4ac = 1^2 - 4(1)(1) = 1 - 4 = -3$

$x = \dfrac{-1 \pm \sqrt{-3}}{2(1)} = \dfrac{-1 \pm \sqrt{3}\,i}{2} = -\dfrac{1}{2} \pm \dfrac{\sqrt{3}}{2}i$

The solution set is $\left\{ -\dfrac{1}{2} - \dfrac{\sqrt{3}}{2}i,\ -\dfrac{1}{2} + \dfrac{\sqrt{3}}{2}i \right\}$.

67. $x^3 - 8 = 0$
$(x - 2)\left(x^2 + 2x + 4\right) = 0$

$x - 2 = 0 \Rightarrow x = 2$

$x^2 + 2x + 4 = 0$
$a = 1, b = 2, c = 4,\quad b^2 - 4ac = 2^2 - 4(1)(4) = 4 - 16 = -12$

$x = \dfrac{-2 \pm \sqrt{-12}}{2(1)} = \dfrac{-2 \pm 2\sqrt{3}\,i}{2} = -1 \pm \sqrt{3}i$

The solution set is $\left\{ 2,\ -1 - \sqrt{3}i,\ -1 + \sqrt{3}i \right\}$.

69. $x^4 = 16 \Rightarrow x^4 - 16 = 0$
$\left(x^2 - 4\right)\left(x^2 + 4\right) = 0$

$(x - 2)(x + 2)\left(x^2 + 4\right) = 0$

$x - 2 = 0 \Rightarrow x = 2$

$x + 2 = 0 \Rightarrow x = -2$

$x^2 + 4 = 0 \Rightarrow x^2 = -4 \Rightarrow x = \pm\sqrt{-4} \Rightarrow x = \pm 2i$

The solution set is $\left\{ -2,\ 2,\ -2i,\ 2i \right\}$.

71. $x^4 + 13x^2 + 36 = 0$
    $\left(x^2 + 9\right)\left(x^2 + 4\right) = 0$

    $x^2 + 9 = 0 \Rightarrow x^2 = -9 \Rightarrow x = \pm\sqrt{-9} \Rightarrow x = \pm 3i$

    $x^2 + 4 = 0 \Rightarrow x^2 = -4 \Rightarrow x = \pm\sqrt{-4} \Rightarrow x = \pm 2i$

    The solution set is $\{-3i,\ 3i,\ -2i,\ 2i\}$.

73. $3x^2 - 3x + 4 = 0$
    $a = 3, b = -3, c = 4,\quad b^2 - 4ac = (-3)^2 - 4(3)(4) = 9 - 48 = -39$
    The equation has two complex conjugate solutions.

75. $2x^2 + 3x = 4 \Rightarrow 2x^2 + 3x - 4 = 0$
    $a = 2, b = 3, c = -4,\quad b^2 - 4ac = 3^2 - 4(2)(-4) = 9 + 32 = 41$
    The equation has two unequal real-number solutions.

77. $9x^2 - 12x + 4 = 0$
    $a = 9, b = -12, c = 4,\quad b^2 - 4ac = (-12)^2 - 4(9)(4) = 144 - 144 = 0$
    The equation has a repeated real-number solution.

79. The other solution is the conjugate of $2 + 3i$, that is, $2 - 3i$.

81. $z + \bar{z} = 3 - 4i + \overline{3 - 4i} = 3 - 4i + 3 + 4i = 6$

83. $z\bar{z} = (3 - 4i)\left(\overline{3 - 4i}\right) = (3 - 4i)(3 + 4i) = 9 + 12i - 12i - 16i^2 = 9 - 16(-1) = 25$

85. $z + \bar{z} = a + bi + \overline{a + bi} = a + bi + a - bi = 2a$
    $z - \bar{z} = a + bi - \left(\overline{a + bi}\right) = a + bi - (a - bi) = a + bi - a + bi = 2bi$

87. $\overline{z + w} = \overline{(a + bi) + (c + di)} = \overline{(a + c) + (b + d)i} = (a + c) - (b + d)i$
    $\qquad\qquad = (a - bi) + (c - di) = \overline{a + bi} + \overline{c + di} = \bar{z} + \bar{w}$

89. Answers will vary.

Review

A.5 Interval Notation; Solving Inequalities

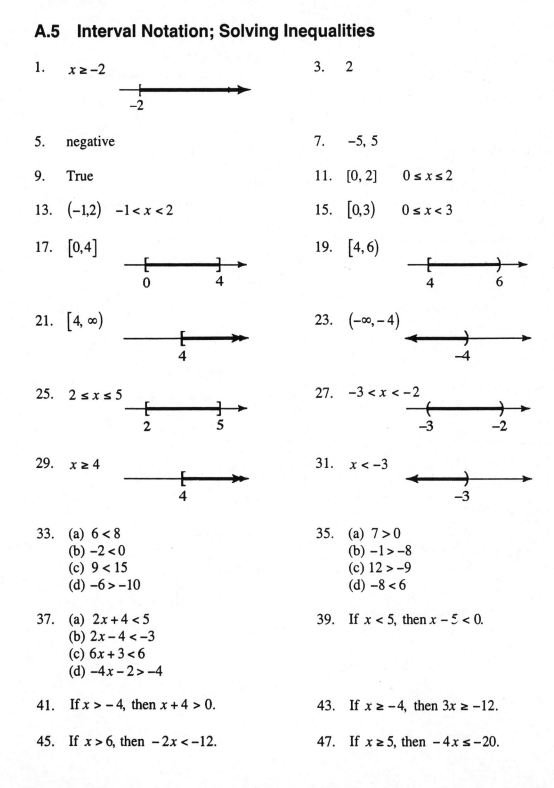

1. $x \geq -2$

3. 2

5. negative

7. $-5, 5$

9. True

11. $[0, 2]$ $0 \leq x \leq 2$

13. $(-1, 2)$ $-1 < x < 2$

15. $[0, 3)$ $0 \leq x < 3$

17. $[0, 4]$

19. $[4, 6)$

21. $[4, \infty)$

23. $(-\infty, -4)$

25. $2 \leq x \leq 5$

27. $-3 < x < -2$

29. $x \geq 4$

31. $x < -3$

33. (a) $6 < 8$
     (b) $-2 < 0$
     (c) $9 < 15$
     (d) $-6 > -10$

35. (a) $7 > 0$
     (b) $-1 > -8$
     (c) $12 > -9$
     (d) $-8 < 6$

37. (a) $2x + 4 < 5$
     (b) $2x - 4 < -3$
     (c) $6x + 3 < 6$
     (d) $-4x - 2 > -4$

39. If $x < 5$, then $x - 5 < 0$.

41. If $x > -4$, then $x + 4 > 0$.

43. If $x \geq -4$, then $3x \geq -12$.

45. If $x > 6$, then $-2x < -12$.

47. If $x \geq 5$, then $-4x \leq -20$.

49. If $2x > 6$, then $x > 3$.

51. If $-\dfrac{1}{2}x \le 3$, then $x \ge -6$.

53. $x + 1 < 5$

$\qquad x < 4$

$\qquad \{x \mid x < 4\}$ or $(-\infty, 4)$

4

55. $1 - 2x \le 3$

$\qquad -2x \le 2 \Rightarrow x \ge -1$

$\qquad \{x \mid x \ge -1\}$ or $[-1, \infty)$

−1

57. $3x - 7 > 2$

$\qquad 3x > 9 \Rightarrow x > 3$

$\qquad \{x \mid x > 3\}$ or $(3, \infty)$

3

59. $3x - 1 \ge 3 + x$

$\qquad 2x \ge 4 \Rightarrow x \ge 2$

$\qquad \{x \mid x \ge 2\}$ or $[2, \infty)$

2

61. $-2(x + 3) < 8$

$\qquad x + 3 > -4$

$\qquad x > -7$

$\qquad \{x \mid x > -7\}$ or $(-7, \infty)$

−7

63. $4 - 3(1 - x) \le 3$

$\qquad 4 - 3 + 3x \le 3$

$\qquad 3x + 1 \le 3$

$\qquad 3x \le 2 \Rightarrow x \le \dfrac{2}{3}$

$\qquad \left\{x \mid x \le \dfrac{2}{3}\right\}$ or $\left(-\infty, \dfrac{2}{3}\right]$

$\dfrac{2}{3}$

65. $\dfrac{1}{2}(x - 4) > x + 8$

$\qquad \dfrac{1}{2}x - 2 > x + 8$

$\qquad -\dfrac{1}{2}x > 10 \Rightarrow x < -20$

$\qquad \{x \mid x < -20\}$ or $(-\infty, -20)$

−20

67. $\dfrac{x}{2} \ge 1 - \dfrac{x}{4}$

$\qquad 2x \ge 4 - x$

$\qquad 3x \ge 4 \Rightarrow x \ge \dfrac{4}{3}$

$\qquad \left\{x \mid x \ge \dfrac{4}{3}\right\}$ or $\left[\dfrac{4}{3}, \infty\right)$

$\dfrac{4}{3}$

69. $0 \leq 2x - 6 \leq 4$

    $6 \leq 2x \leq 10$

    $3 \leq x \leq 5$

    $\{x | 3 \leq x \leq 5\}$ or $[3, 5]$

71. $-5 \leq 4 - 3x \leq 2$

    $-9 \leq -3x \leq -2$

    $3 \geq x \geq \dfrac{2}{3}$

    $\dfrac{2}{3} \leq x \leq 3$

    $\left\{x \Big| \dfrac{2}{3} \leq x \leq 3\right\}$ or $\left[\dfrac{2}{3}, 3\right]$

73. $-3 < \dfrac{2x - 1}{4} < 0$

    $-12 < 2x - 1 < 0$

    $-11 < 2x < 1 \Rightarrow -\dfrac{11}{2} < x < \dfrac{1}{2}$

    $\left\{x \Big| -\dfrac{11}{2} < x < \dfrac{1}{2}\right\}$ or $\left(-\dfrac{11}{2}, \dfrac{1}{2}\right)$

75. $1 < 1 - \dfrac{1}{2}x < 4$

    $0 < -\dfrac{1}{2}x < 3$

    $0 > x > -6 \Rightarrow -6 < x < 0$

    $\{x | -6 < x < 0\}$ or $(-6, 0)$

77. $(4x + 2)^{-1} < 0$

    $\dfrac{1}{4x + 2} < 0$

    $4x + 2 < 0$

    $x < -\dfrac{1}{2}$

    $\left\{x \Big| x < -\dfrac{1}{2}\right\}$ or $\left(-\infty, -\dfrac{1}{2}\right)$

79. $0 < \dfrac{2}{x} < \dfrac{3}{5} \Rightarrow 0 < \dfrac{2}{x}$ and $\dfrac{2}{x} < \dfrac{3}{5}$

$0 < \dfrac{2}{x} \Rightarrow x > 0$ therefore $\dfrac{2}{x} < \dfrac{3}{5} \Rightarrow 10 < 3x \Rightarrow \dfrac{10}{3} < x$

$\left\{ x \middle| x > \dfrac{10}{3} \right\}$ or $\left(\dfrac{10}{3}, \infty \right)$

10/3

81. $|2x| < 8$

$-8 < 2x < 8$

$-4 < x < 4$

$\{x| -4 < x < 4\}$ or $(-4, 4)$

$-4 \qquad 4$

83. $|3x| > 12$

$3x < -12$ or $3x > 12$

$x < -4$ or $x > 4$

$\{x| x < -4 \text{ or } x > 4\}$ or

$(-\infty, -4)$ or $(4, \infty)$

$-4 \qquad 4$

85. $|2x - 1| \le 1$

$-1 \le 2x - 1 \le 1$

$0 \le \ 2x \ \le 2$

$0 \le \ \ x \ \ \le 1$

$\{x| 0 \le x \le 1\}$ or $[0, 1]$

$0 \qquad 1$

87. $|1 - 2x| > 3$

$1 - 2x < -3$ or $1 - 2x > 3$

$-2x < -4$ or $-2x > 2$

$x > 2$ or $x < -1$

$\{x| x < -1 \text{ or } x > 2\}$

or $(-\infty, -1)$ or $(2, \infty)$

$-1 \qquad 2$

89. $|-4x| + |-5| \le 9$

$|4x| + 5 \le 9$

$|4x| \le 4$

$-4 \le 4x \le 4$

$-1 \le x \le 1$

$\{x| -1 \le x \le 1\}$ or $[-1, 1]$

$-1 \qquad 1$

91. $|-2x| > |-4|$

$|2x| > 4$

$2x < -4$ or $2x > 4$

$x < -2$ or $x > 2$

$\{x| x < -2 \text{ or } x > 2\}$

or $(-\infty, -2)$ or $(2, \infty)$

$-2 \qquad 2$

93. x differs from 2 by less than $\dfrac{1}{2}$

$$|x-2|<\frac{1}{2}$$

$$-\frac{1}{2}<x-2<\frac{1}{2}$$

$$\frac{3}{2}<\ x\ <\frac{5}{2}$$

$$\left\{x\,\middle|\,\frac{3}{2}<x<\frac{5}{2}\right\}$$

95. x differs from -3 by more than 2

$$|x-(-3)|>2$$

$$x+3<-2 \ \text{ or } \ x+3>2$$

$$x<-5 \ \text{ or } \quad x>-1$$

$$\{x\,|\,x<-5 \ \text{ or } \ x>-1\}$$

97. $21 <$ young adult's age < 30

99.   A temperature x that differs from 98.6°F by at least 1.5°

$$|x-98.6°|\ge 1.5°$$

$$x-98.6°\le -1.5° \ \text{ or } \ x-98.6°\ge 1.5°$$

$$x\le 97.1° \ \text{ or } \qquad x\ge 100.1°$$

The temperatures that are considered unhealthy are those that are less than 97.1°F or greater than 100.1°F, inclusive.

101.   (a)   An average 25-year-old male can expect to live at least 48.4 more years.
$25 + 48.4 = 73.4$. Therefore, the average life expectancy of a 25-year-old male will be ≥ 73.4.
(b)   An average 25-year-old female can expect to live at least 54.7 more years.
$25 + 54.7 = 79.7$. Therefore, the average life expectancy of a 25-year-old female will be ≥ 79.7.
(c)   A female can expect to live 6.3 years longer.

103.   Let P represent the selling price and C represent the commission.
Calculating the commission:
$$C = 45,000 + 0.25(P - 900,000)$$

$$= 45,000 + 0.25P - 225,000$$

$$= 0.25P - 180,000$$

Calculate the commission range, given the price range:
$$900,000 \le \qquad P \qquad \le 1,100,000$$

$$0.25(900,000) \le \quad 0.25P \quad \le 0.25(1,100,000)$$

$$225,000 \le \quad 0.25P \quad \le 275,000$$

$$225,000 - 180,000 \le 0.25P - 180,000 \le 275,000 - 180,000$$

$$45,000 \le \qquad C \qquad \le 95,000$$

The agent's commission ranges from \$45,000 to \$95,000, inclusive.
$$\frac{45,000}{900,000} = 0.05 = 5\% \ \text{ to } \ \frac{95,000}{1,100,000} \approx 0.086 \approx 8.6\%, \text{ inclusive.}$$

As a percent of selling price, the commission ranges from 5% to about 8.6%.

105. Let W represent the weekly wage and T represent the tax withheld.
     In terms of wages the tax is
     $$T = 74.35 + 0.25(W - 592) = 74.35 + 0.25W - 148 = 0.25W - 73.65$$
     Now calculate the tax range given a wage range of \$600 to \$800, inclusive.
     $$600 \le \qquad W \qquad \le 800$$
     $$(0.25)600 \le \qquad 0.25W \qquad \le (0.25)800$$
     $$150 \le \qquad 0.25W \qquad \le 200$$
     $$150 - 73.65 \le 0.25W - 73.65 \le 200 - 73.65$$
     $$76.35 \le 0.25W - 73.65 \le 126.35$$
     The amount of tax withheld ranges from \$76.35 to \$126.35, inclusive.

107. Let K represent the monthly usage in kilowatt-hours.
     Let C represent the monthly customer bill.
     Calculating the bill:
     $$C = 0.08275K + 7.58$$
     Calculating the range of kilowatt-hours, given the range of bills:
     $$63.47 \le \qquad C \qquad \le 214.53$$
     $$63.47 \le 0.08275K + 7.58 \le 214.53$$
     $$55.89 \le \qquad 0.08275K \qquad \le 206.95$$
     $$675.41 \le \qquad K \qquad \le 2500.91$$
     The range of usage in kilowatt-hours varied from 675.41 to 2500.91.

109. Let C represent the dealer's cost and M represent the markup over dealer's cost.
     If the price is \$8800, then $8800 = C + MC = C(1 + M)$.
     Solving for C: $\quad C = \dfrac{8800}{1 + M}$
     Calculating the range of dealer costs, given the range of markups:
     $$0.12 \le \quad M \quad \le 0.18$$
     $$1.12 \le 1 + M \le 1.18$$
     $$\frac{1}{1.12} \ge \frac{1}{1 + M} \ge \frac{1}{1.18}$$
     $$\frac{8800}{1.12} \ge \frac{8800}{1 + M} \ge \frac{8800}{1.18}$$
     $$7857.14 \ge \quad C \quad \ge 7457.63$$
     The dealer's cost ranged from \$7457.63 to \$7857.14.

111. Let T represent the score on the last test and G represent the course grade.
     Calculating the course grade and solving for the last test:
     $$G = \frac{68 + 82 + 87 + 89 + T}{5} = \frac{326 + T}{5} \Rightarrow T = 5G - 326$$
     Calculating the range of scores on the last test, given the grade range:
     $$80 \le \quad G \quad < 90$$
     $$400 \le \quad 5G \quad < 450$$
     $$74 \le 5G - 326 < 124$$
     $$74 \le \quad T \quad < 124$$
     The fifth test score must be greater than or equal to 74.

113. Since $a < b$

$$\frac{a}{2} < \frac{b}{2} \qquad\qquad\qquad \frac{a}{2} < \frac{b}{2}$$

$$\frac{a}{2} + \frac{a}{2} < \frac{a}{2} + \frac{b}{2} \qquad\qquad \frac{a}{2} + \frac{b}{2} < \frac{b}{2} + \frac{b}{2}$$

$$a < \frac{a+b}{2} \qquad\qquad\qquad \frac{a+b}{2} < b$$

Thus, $a < \dfrac{a+b}{2} < b$.

115. If $0 < a < b$, then $0 < a^2 < ab$ and $0 < ab < b^2$.

$$0 < a^2 < ab \qquad\qquad 0 < ab < b^2$$

$$0 < a^2 < \left(\sqrt{ab}\right)^2 \qquad 0 < \left(\sqrt{ab}\right)^2 < b^2$$

$$0 < a < \sqrt{ab} \qquad\qquad 0 < \sqrt{ab} < b$$

Thus, $a < \sqrt{ab} < b$.

117. For $0 < a < b$, $\dfrac{1}{h} = \dfrac{1}{2}\left(\dfrac{1}{a} + \dfrac{1}{b}\right)$

$$h \cdot \frac{1}{h} = \frac{1}{2}\left(\frac{b+a}{ab}\right) \cdot h \;\Rightarrow\; 1 = \frac{1}{2}\left(\frac{b+a}{ab}\right) \cdot h \;\Rightarrow\; \frac{2ab}{a+b} = h$$

$$h - a = \frac{2ab}{a+b} - a \qquad\qquad b - h = b - \frac{2ab}{a+b}$$

$$= \frac{2ab - a(a+b)}{a+b} \qquad\qquad = \frac{b(a+b) - 2ab}{a+b}$$

$$= \frac{2ab - a^2 - ab}{a+b}\cdot \qquad\qquad = \frac{ab + b^2 - 2ab}{a+b}$$

$$= \frac{ab - a^2}{a+b} \qquad\qquad = \frac{b^2 - ab}{a+b}$$

$$= \frac{a(b-a)}{a+b} > 0 \qquad\qquad = \frac{b(b-a)}{a+b} > 0$$

Therefore, $h > a$.   Therefore, $h < b$.

Thus, $a < h < b$.

119. Answers will vary.

121. Answers will vary.

Review

A.6 *n*th Roots; Rational Exponents; Radical Equations

1. False

3. index

5. True

7. $\sqrt[3]{27} = \sqrt[3]{3^3} = 3$

9. $\sqrt[3]{-8} = \sqrt[3]{(-2)^3} = -2$

11. $\sqrt{8} = \sqrt{4 \cdot 2} = 2\sqrt{2}$

13. $\sqrt[3]{-8x^4} = \sqrt[3]{-8 \cdot x^3 \cdot x} = -2x\sqrt[3]{x}$

15. $\sqrt[4]{x^{12}y^8} = \sqrt[4]{(x^3)^4(y^2)^4} = x^3 y^2$

17. $\sqrt[4]{\dfrac{x^9 y^7}{x y^3}} = \sqrt[4]{x^8 y^4} = x^2 y$

19. $\sqrt{36x} = 6\sqrt{x}$

21. $\sqrt{3x^2}\sqrt{12x} = \sqrt{36x^2 \cdot x} = 6x\sqrt{x}$

23. $\left(\sqrt{5}\,\sqrt[3]{9}\right)^2 = 5\left(\sqrt[3]{81}\right) = 5\left(\sqrt[3]{27 \cdot 3}\right) = 5 \cdot 3\left(\sqrt[3]{3}\right) = 15\sqrt[3]{3}$

25. $\left(3\sqrt{6}\right)\left(2\sqrt{2}\right) = 6\sqrt{12} = 6\sqrt{4 \cdot 3} = 12\sqrt{3}$

27. $\left(\sqrt{3} + 3\right)\left(\sqrt{3} - 1\right) = \left(\sqrt{3}\right)^2 - \sqrt{3} + 3\sqrt{3} - 3 = 3 + 2\sqrt{3} - 3 = 2\sqrt{3}$

29. $\left(\sqrt{x} - 1\right)^2 = \left(\sqrt{x}\right)^2 - 2\sqrt{x} + 1 = x - 2\sqrt{x} + 1$

31. $3\sqrt{2} - 4\sqrt{8} = 3\sqrt{2} - 4\sqrt{4 \cdot 2} = 3\sqrt{2} - 8\sqrt{2} = -5\sqrt{2}$

33. $\sqrt[3]{16x^4} - \sqrt[3]{2x} = \sqrt[3]{8 \cdot 2 \cdot x^3 \cdot x} - \sqrt[3]{2x} = \sqrt[3]{8 \cdot x^3 \cdot 2 \cdot x} - \sqrt[3]{2x}$

$$= \sqrt[3]{(8x^3) \cdot 2x} - \sqrt[3]{2x}$$

$$= \sqrt[3]{(8x^3)} \cdot \sqrt[3]{2x} - \sqrt[3]{2x}$$

$$= 2x\sqrt[3]{2x} - \sqrt[3]{2x}$$

$$= (2x - 1)\sqrt[3]{2x}$$

35. $\dfrac{1}{\sqrt{2}} \cdot \dfrac{\sqrt{2}}{\sqrt{2}} = \dfrac{\sqrt{2}}{2}$

37. $\dfrac{-\sqrt{3}}{\sqrt{5}} \cdot \dfrac{\sqrt{5}}{\sqrt{5}} = \dfrac{-\sqrt{15}}{5} = -\dfrac{\sqrt{15}}{5}$

39. $\dfrac{\sqrt{3}}{5-\sqrt{2}} \cdot \dfrac{5+\sqrt{2}}{5+\sqrt{2}} = \dfrac{\sqrt{3}\left(5+\sqrt{2}\right)}{25-2} = \dfrac{\sqrt{3}\left(5+\sqrt{2}\right)}{23}$

41. $\dfrac{2-\sqrt{5}}{2+3\sqrt{5}} \cdot \dfrac{2-3\sqrt{5}}{2-3\sqrt{5}} = \dfrac{4-6\sqrt{5}-2\sqrt{5}+3\left(\sqrt{5}\right)^2}{4-9\left(\sqrt{5}\right)^2} = \dfrac{4-8\sqrt{5}+3\cdot 5}{4-9\cdot 5}$

$$= \dfrac{4-8\sqrt{5}+15}{4-45} = \dfrac{19-8\sqrt{5}}{-41}$$

$$= \dfrac{-19+8\sqrt{5}}{41}$$

43. $\dfrac{5}{\sqrt[3]{2}} \cdot \dfrac{\left(\sqrt[3]{2}\right)^2}{\left(\sqrt[3]{2}\right)^2} = \dfrac{5\left(\sqrt[3]{2}\right)^2}{\left(\sqrt[3]{2}\right)^3} = \dfrac{5\left(\sqrt[3]{2^2}\right)}{2} = \dfrac{5\sqrt[3]{4}}{2}$

45. $\dfrac{\sqrt{x+h}-\sqrt{x}}{\sqrt{x+h}+\sqrt{x}} \cdot \dfrac{\sqrt{x+h}-\sqrt{x}}{\sqrt{x+h}-\sqrt{x}} = \dfrac{\left(\sqrt{x+h}\right)^2 - 2\sqrt{x}\cdot\sqrt{x+h}+\left(\sqrt{x}\right)^2}{\left(\sqrt{x+h}\right)^2 - \left(\sqrt{x}\right)^2}$

$$= \dfrac{x+h-2\sqrt{x(x+h)}+x}{x+h-x}$$

$$= \dfrac{2x+h-2\sqrt{x(x+h)}}{h}$$

47.
$$\sqrt[3]{2t-1} = 2$$
$$\left(\sqrt[3]{2t-1}\right)^3 = 2^3$$
$$2t-1 = 8$$
$$2t = 9$$
$$t = \dfrac{9}{2}$$

Check $t = \dfrac{9}{2}$:
$$\sqrt[3]{2\left(\dfrac{9}{2}\right)-1} = 2$$
$$\sqrt[3]{9-1} = 2$$
$$\sqrt[3]{8} = 2$$
$$2 = 2$$
The solution is $t = \dfrac{9}{2}$.

49.
$$\sqrt{15-2x} = x$$
$$\left(\sqrt{15-2x}\right)^2 = x^2$$
$$15-2x = x^2$$
$$0 = x^2 + 2x - 15$$
$$0 = (x+5)(x-3)$$
$$x = -5, x = 3$$

Check $x = -5$:
$$\sqrt{15-2(-5)} = -5$$
$$\sqrt{15+10} = -5$$
$$\sqrt{25} = -5$$
$$5 \neq -5$$
Check $x = 3$:
$$\sqrt{15-2(3)} = 3$$
$$\sqrt{15-6} = 3$$
$$\sqrt{9} = 3$$
$$3 = 3$$
The solution is $x = 3$.

51. $8^{2/3} = \left(2^3\right)^{2/3} = 2^2 = 4$

53. $(-27)^{1/3} = \left((-3)^3\right)^{1/3} = -3$

55. $16^{3/2} = \left(4^2\right)^{3/2} = 4^3 = 64$

57. $9^{-3/2} = \left(3^2\right)^{-3/2} = 3^{-3} = \dfrac{1}{3^3} = \dfrac{1}{27}$

59. $\left(\dfrac{9}{8}\right)^{3/2} = \dfrac{9^{3/2}}{8^{3/2}} = \dfrac{\left(3^2\right)^{3/2}}{\left(2^3\right)^{3/2}} = \dfrac{3^{6/2}}{2^{9/2}} = \dfrac{3^3}{2^4 \cdot 2^{1/2}} = \dfrac{27}{16 \cdot \sqrt{2}} \cdot \dfrac{\sqrt{2}}{\sqrt{2}} = \dfrac{27\sqrt{2}}{32}$

61. $\left(\dfrac{8}{9}\right)^{-3/2} = \left(\dfrac{9}{8}\right)^{3/2} = \left(\dfrac{3^2}{2^3}\right)^{3/2} = \dfrac{3^3}{2^{9/2}} = \dfrac{27}{2^4 \cdot 2^{1/2}} = \dfrac{27}{16 \cdot \sqrt{2}} \cdot \dfrac{\sqrt{2}}{\sqrt{2}} = \dfrac{27\sqrt{2}}{16 \cdot 2} = \dfrac{27\sqrt{2}}{32}$

63. $x^{3/4} \cdot x^{1/3} \cdot x^{-1/2} = x^{3/4+1/3-1/2} = x^{(9+4-6)/12} = x^{7/12}$

65. $\left(x^3 y^6\right)^{1/3} = \left(x^3\right)^{1/3}\left(y^6\right)^{1/3} = x y^2$

67. $\left(x^2 y\right)^{1/3}\left(x y^2\right)^{2/3} = x^{2/3} y^{1/3} x^{2/3} y^{4/3} = x^{4/3} y^{5/3}$

69. $\left(16 x^2 y^{-1/3}\right)^{3/4} = \left(2^4 x^2 y^{-1/3}\right)^{3/4} = 2^{4 \cdot 3/4} x^{2 \cdot 3/4} y^{(-1/3)(3/4)} = 2^3 x^{3/2} y^{-1/4} = \dfrac{8 x^{3/2}}{y^{1/4}}$

71. $\dfrac{x}{(1+x)^{1/2}} + 2(1+x)^{1/2} = \dfrac{x + 2(1+x)^{1/2}(1+x)^{1/2}}{(1+x)^{1/2}} = \dfrac{x + 2(1+x)}{(1+x)^{1/2}} = \dfrac{x+2+2x}{(1+x)^{1/2}} = \dfrac{3x+2}{(1+x)^{1/2}}$

73. $2x(x^2+1)^{1/2} + x^2 \cdot \dfrac{1}{2}(x^2+1)^{-1/2} \cdot 2x = 2x(x^2+1)^{1/2} + \dfrac{x^3}{(x^2+1)^{1/2}}$

$$= \frac{2x(x^2+1)^{1/2} \cdot (x^2+1)^{1/2} + x^3}{(x^2+1)^{1/2}} = \frac{2x(x^2+1)+x^3}{(x^2+1)^{1/2}}$$

$$= \frac{2x^3 + 2x + x^3}{(x^2+1)^{1/2}} = \frac{3x^3 + 2x}{(x^2+1)^{1/2}}$$

$$= \frac{x(3x^2+2)}{(x^2+1)^{1/2}}$$

75. $\sqrt{4x+3} \cdot \dfrac{1}{2\sqrt{x-5}} + \sqrt{x-5} \cdot \dfrac{1}{5\sqrt{4x+3}} = \dfrac{\sqrt{4x+3}}{2\sqrt{x-5}} + \dfrac{\sqrt{x-5}}{5\sqrt{4x+3}}$

$$= \frac{\sqrt{4x+3} \cdot 5 \cdot \sqrt{4x+3} + \sqrt{x-5} \cdot 2 \cdot \sqrt{x-5}}{10\sqrt{x-5}\sqrt{4x+3}}$$

$$= \frac{5(4x+3)+2(x-5)}{10\sqrt{(x-5)(4x+3)}} = \frac{20x+15+2x-10}{10\sqrt{(x-5)(4x+3)}}$$

$$= \frac{22x+5}{10\sqrt{(x-5)(4x+3)}}$$

77. $\dfrac{\sqrt{1+x} - x \cdot \dfrac{1}{2\sqrt{1+x}}}{1+x} = \dfrac{\sqrt{1+x} - \dfrac{x}{2\sqrt{1+x}}}{1+x} = \dfrac{\dfrac{2\sqrt{1+x}\sqrt{1+x} - x}{2\sqrt{1+x}}}{1+x}$

$$= \frac{2(1+x)-x}{2(1+x)^{1/2}} \cdot \frac{1}{1+x}$$

$$= \frac{2+x}{2(1+x)^{3/2}}$$

79. $\dfrac{(x+4)^{1/2} - 2x(x+4)^{-1/2}}{x+4} = \dfrac{(x+4)^{1/2} - \dfrac{2x}{(x+4)^{1/2}}}{x+4} = \dfrac{\dfrac{(x+4)^{1/2}(x+4)^{1/2}}{(x+4)^{1/2}} - \dfrac{2x}{(x+4)^{1/2}}}{x+4}$

$$= \frac{\dfrac{x+4-2x}{(x+4)^{1/2}}}{x+4} = \frac{-x+4}{(x+4)^{1/2}} \cdot \frac{1}{x+4} = \frac{-x+4}{(x+4)^{3/2}}$$

$$= \frac{4-x}{(x+4)^{3/2}}$$

81.
$$\frac{\dfrac{x^2}{\left(x^2-1\right)^{1/2}}-\left(x^2-1\right)^{1/2}}{x^2}=\frac{\dfrac{x^2-\left(x^2-1\right)^{1/2}\cdot\left(x^2-1\right)^{1/2}}{\left(x^2-1\right)^{1/2}}}{x^2}$$

$$=\frac{x^2-\left(x^2-1\right)^{1/2}\cdot\left(x^2-1\right)^{1/2}}{\left(x^2-1\right)^{1/2}}\cdot\frac{1}{x^2}$$

$$=\frac{x^2-\left(x^2-1\right)}{\left(x^2-1\right)^{1/2}}\cdot\frac{1}{x^2}=\frac{x^2-x^2+1}{\left(x^2-1\right)^{1/2}}\cdot\frac{1}{x^2}$$

$$=\frac{1}{x^2\left(x^2-1\right)^{1/2}}$$

83.
$$\frac{\dfrac{1+x^2}{2\sqrt{x}}-2x\sqrt{x}}{\left(1+x^2\right)^2}=\frac{\dfrac{1+x^2-\left(2\sqrt{x}\right)\left(2x\sqrt{x}\right)}{2\sqrt{x}}}{\left(1+x^2\right)^2}$$

$$=\frac{1+x^2-\left(2\sqrt{x}\right)\left(2x\sqrt{x}\right)}{2\sqrt{x}}\cdot\frac{1}{\left(1+x^2\right)^2}$$

$$=\frac{1+x^2-4x^2}{2\sqrt{x}}\cdot\frac{1}{\left(1+x^2\right)^2}$$

$$=\frac{1-3x^2}{2\sqrt{x}\left(1+x^2\right)^2}$$

85. $(x+1)^{3/2}+x\cdot\dfrac{3}{2}(x+1)^{1/2}=(x+1)^{1/2}\left(x+1+\dfrac{3}{2}x\right)=(x+1)^{1/2}\left(\dfrac{5}{2}x+1\right)=\dfrac{1}{2}(x+1)^{1/2}(5x+2)$

87. $6x^{1/2}\left(x^2+x\right)-8x^{3/2}-8x^{1/2}=2x^{1/2}\left(3\left(x^2+x\right)-4x-4\right)=2x^{1/2}\left(3x^2-x-4\right)$
$$=2x^{1/2}(3x-4)(x+1)$$

89. $3\left(x^2+4\right)^{4/3}+x\cdot4\left(x^2+4\right)^{1/3}\cdot2x=\left(x^2+4\right)^{1/3}\left[3\left(x^2+4\right)+8x^2\right]$
$$=\left(x^2+4\right)^{1/3}\left[3x^2+12+8x^2\right]$$
$$=\left(x^2+4\right)^{1/3}\left(11x^2+12\right)$$

91. $4(3x+5)^{1/3}(2x+3)^{3/2}+3(3x+5)^{4/3}(2x+3)^{1/2}$
$$=(3x+5)^{1/3}(2x+3)^{1/2}\left[4(2x+3)+3(3x+5)\right]=(3x+5)^{1/3}(2x+3)^{1/2}(8x+12+9x+15)$$
$$=(3x+5)^{1/3}(2x+3)^{1/2}(17x+27)$$

93. $3x^{-1/2} + \dfrac{3}{2}x^{1/2} = \dfrac{3}{x^{1/2}} + \dfrac{3}{2}x^{1/2} = \dfrac{3 \cdot 2 + 3x^{1/2} \cdot x^{1/2}}{2x^{1/2}} = \dfrac{6 + 3x}{2x^{1/2}}$

$$= \dfrac{3(2 + x)}{2x^{1/2}}$$

95. $x\left(\dfrac{1}{2}\right)\left(8 - x^2\right)^{-1/2}(-2x) + \left(8 - x^2\right)^{1/2} = \dfrac{-x^2}{\left(8 - x^2\right)^{1/2}} + \left(8 - x^2\right)^{1/2}$

$$= \dfrac{-x^2 + \left(8 - x^2\right)^{1/2} \cdot \left(8 - x^2\right)^{1/2}}{\left(8 - x^2\right)^{1/2}}$$

$$= \dfrac{-x^2 + 8 - x^2}{\left(8 - x^2\right)^{1/2}} = \dfrac{8 - 2x^2}{\left(8 - x^2\right)^{1/2}} = \dfrac{2\left(4 - x^2\right)}{\left(8 - x^2\right)^{1/2}}$$

$$= \dfrac{2(2 - x)(2 + x)}{\left(8 - x^2\right)^{1/2}}$$

Review

A.7 Lines

1. undefined, 0

3. $y = b$, y-intercept

5. False

7. $m_1 = m_2$, y-intercepts, $m_1 \cdot m_2 = -1$

9. $-\dfrac{1}{2}$

11. (a) Slope $= \dfrac{1-0}{2-0} = \dfrac{1}{2}$

    (b) If x increases by 2 units, y will increase by 1 unit.

13. (a) Slope $= \dfrac{1-2}{1-(-2)} = -\dfrac{1}{3}$

    (b) If x increases by 3 units, y will decrease by 1 unit.

15. $(x_1, y_1) \quad (x_2, y_2)$
    $(2,3) \quad (4,0)$

    Slope $= \dfrac{y_2 - y_1}{x_2 - x_1} = \dfrac{0-3}{4-2} = -\dfrac{3}{2}$

17. $(x_1, y_1) \quad (x_2, y_2)$
    $(-2,3) \quad (2,1)$

    Slope $= \dfrac{y_2 - y_1}{x_2 - x_1} = \dfrac{1-3}{2-(-2)} = \dfrac{-2}{4} = -\dfrac{1}{2}$

19. $(x_1, y_1) \quad (x_2, y_2)$

$(-3, -1) \quad (2, -1)$

Slope $= \dfrac{y_2 - y_1}{x_2 - x_1} = \dfrac{-1 - (-1)}{2 - (-3)} = \dfrac{0}{5} = 0$

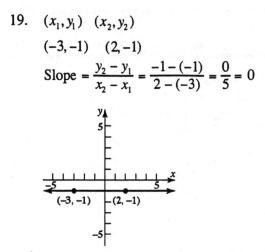

21. $(x_1, y_1) \quad (x_2, y_2)$

$(-1, 2) \quad (-1, -2)$

Slope $= \dfrac{y_2 - y_1}{x_2 - x_1} = \dfrac{-2 - 2}{-1 - (-1)} = \dfrac{-4}{0}$

Slope is undefined.

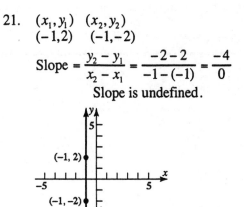

23.

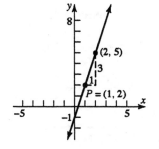

25.

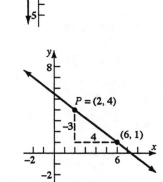

27.

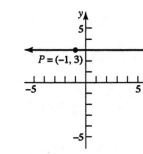

29.

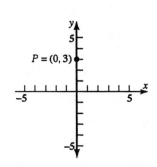

31. $(0,0)$ and $(2,1)$ are points on the line.

Slope $= \dfrac{1 - 0}{2 - 0} = \dfrac{1}{2}$

y-intercept is 0; using $y = mx + b$:

$y = \dfrac{1}{2}x + 0$

$2y = x$

$0 = x - 2y$

$x - 2y = 0 \ $ or $\ y = \dfrac{1}{2}x$

33. $(-2,2)$ and $(1,1)$ are points on the line.

Slope $= \dfrac{1 - 2}{1 - (-2)} = \dfrac{-1}{3} = -\dfrac{1}{3}$

Using $y - y_1 = m(x - x_1)$

$y - 1 = -\dfrac{1}{3}(x - 1)$

$y - 1 = -\dfrac{1}{3}x + \dfrac{1}{3}$

$y = -\dfrac{1}{3}x + \dfrac{4}{3}$

$x + 3y = 4 \ $ or $\ y = -\dfrac{1}{3}x + \dfrac{4}{3}$

35. $y - y_1 = m(x - x_1), \quad m = 2$
$\quad\quad y - 3 = 2(x - 3)$
$\quad\quad y - 3 = 2x - 6$
$\quad\quad\quad\quad y = 2x - 3$
$\quad 2x - y = 3 \ \text{ or } \ y = 2x - 3$

37. $y - y_1 = m(x - x_1), \quad m = -\dfrac{1}{2}$
$\quad\quad y - 2 = -\dfrac{1}{2}(x - 1)$
$\quad\quad y - 2 = -\dfrac{1}{2}x + \dfrac{1}{2}$
$\quad\quad\quad\quad y = -\dfrac{1}{2}x + \dfrac{5}{2}$
$\quad x + 2y = 5 \ \text{ or } \ y = -\dfrac{1}{2}x + \dfrac{5}{2}$

39. Slope = 3; containing $(-2, 3)$
$\quad\quad y - y_1 = m(x - x_1)$
$\quad\quad y - 3 = 3(x - (-2))$
$\quad\quad y - 3 = 3x + 6$
$\quad\quad\quad\quad y = 3x + 9$
$\quad 3x - y = -9 \ \text{ or } \ y = 3x + 9$

41. Slope = $-\dfrac{2}{3}$; containing $(1, -1)$
$\quad\quad y - y_1 = m(x - x_1)$
$\quad\quad y - (-1) = -\dfrac{2}{3}(x - 1)$
$\quad\quad y + 1 = -\dfrac{2}{3}x + \dfrac{2}{3}$
$\quad\quad\quad\quad y = -\dfrac{2}{3}x - \dfrac{1}{3}$
$\quad 2x + 3y = -1 \ \text{ or } \ y = -\dfrac{2}{3}x - \dfrac{1}{3}$

43. Containing $(1, 3)$ and $(-1, 2)$
$\quad m = \dfrac{2 - 3}{-1 - 1} = \dfrac{-1}{-2} = \dfrac{1}{2}$
$\quad\quad y - y_1 = m(x - x_1)$
$\quad\quad y - 3 = \dfrac{1}{2}(x - 1)$
$\quad\quad y - 3 = \dfrac{1}{2}x - \dfrac{1}{2}$
$\quad\quad\quad\quad y = \dfrac{1}{2}x + \dfrac{5}{2}$
$\quad x - 2y = -5 \ \text{ or } \ y = \dfrac{1}{2}x + \dfrac{5}{2}$

45. Slope = -3; y-intercept = 3
$\quad\quad y = mx + b$
$\quad\quad y = -3x + 3$
$\quad 3x + y = 3 \ \text{ or } \ y = -3x + 3$

47. x-intercept = 2; y-intercept = -1
Points are $(2, 0)$ and $(0, -1)$
$\quad m = \dfrac{-1 - 0}{0 - 2} = \dfrac{-1}{-2} = \dfrac{1}{2}$
$\quad\quad y = mx + b$
$\quad\quad y = \dfrac{1}{2}x - 1$
$\quad x - 2y = 2 \ \text{ or } \ y = \dfrac{1}{2}x - 1$

49. Slope undefined; containing the point $(2, 4)$
This is a vertical line.
$\quad x = 2$
No slope-intercept form.

51. Horizontal; containing the point $(-3,2)$
    slope $= 0$
    $$y = 2$$

53. Parallel to $y = 2x$; Slope $= 2$
    Containing $(-1,2)$
    $$y - y_1 = m(x - x_1)$$
    $$y - 2 = 2(x - (-1))$$
    $$y - 2 = 2x + 2$$
    $$y = 2x + 4$$
    $$2x - y = -4 \text{ or } y = 2x + 4$$

55. Parallel to $2x - y = -2$; Slope $= 2$
    Containing $(0,0)$
    $$y - y_1 = m(x - x_1)$$
    $$y - 0 = 2(x - 0)$$
    $$y = 2x$$
    $$2x - y = 0 \text{ or } y = 2x$$

57. Parallel to $x = 5$
    Containing $(4,2)$
    This is a vertical line.
    $$x = 4$$
    No slope - intercept form.

59. Perpendicular to $y = \dfrac{1}{2}x + 4$
    Slope of perpendicular $= -2$
    Containing $(1,-2)$
    $$y - y_1 = m(x - x_1)$$
    $$y - (-2) = -2(x - 1)$$
    $$y + 2 = -2x + 2$$
    $$y = -2x$$
    $$2x + y = 0 \text{ or } y = -2x$$

61. Perpendicular to $2x + y = 2$
    $$2x + y = 2 \Rightarrow y = -2x + 2$$
    Slope of perpendicular $= \dfrac{1}{2}$
    Containing $(-3,0)$
    $$y - y_1 = m(x - x_1)$$
    $$y - 0 = \dfrac{1}{2}(x - (-3)) \Rightarrow y = \dfrac{1}{2}x + \dfrac{3}{2}$$
    $$x - 2y = -3 \text{ or } y = \dfrac{1}{2}x + \dfrac{3}{2}$$

63. Perpendicular to $x = 8$
    Slope of perpendicular $= 0$
    $\Rightarrow$ horizontal line
    Containing the point $(3,4)$
    $$y = 4$$

65. $y = 2x + 3$
    Slope $= 2$
    y-intercept $= 3$

67. $\frac{1}{2}y = x - 1$

$y = 2x - 2$

Slope = 2

y-intercept = -2

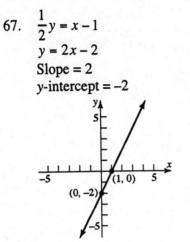

69. $y = \frac{1}{2}x + 2$

Slope = $\frac{1}{2}$

y-intercept = 2

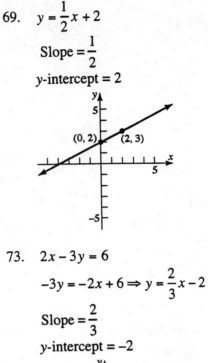

71. $x + 2y = 4$

$2y = -x + 4 \Rightarrow y = -\frac{1}{2}x + 2$

Slope = $-\frac{1}{2}$

y-intercept = 2

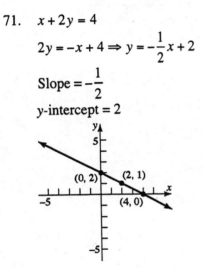

73. $2x - 3y = 6$

$-3y = -2x + 6 \Rightarrow y = \frac{2}{3}x - 2$

Slope = $\frac{2}{3}$

y-intercept = -2

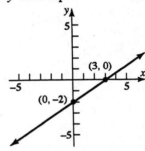

75. $x + y = 1$

$y = -x + 1$

Slope = -1

y-intercept = 1

76 diagram

77. $x = -4$

Slope is undefined

y-intercept: none

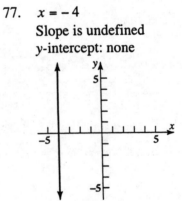

79. $y = 5$
Slope $= 0$
y-intercept $= 5$

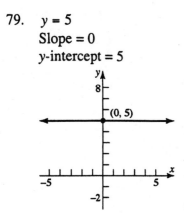

81. $y - x = 0$
$y = x$
Slope $= 1$
y-intercept $= 0$

83. $2y - 3x = 0$

$2y = 3x \Rightarrow y = \dfrac{3}{2}x$

Slope $= \dfrac{3}{2};$ y-intercept $= 0$

85. $y = 2x - 3 \Rightarrow$ slope $= 2$
$y = 2x + 4 \Rightarrow$ slope $= 2$
The lines are parallel.

87. $y = 4x + 5 \Rightarrow$ slope $= 4$
$y = -4x + 2 \Rightarrow$ slope $= -4$
The lines are neither parallel nor
perpendicular.

89. Consider the points $A(-2,5)$, $B(1,3)$ and $C(-1,0)$

slope of $\overline{AB} = \dfrac{3-5}{1-(-2)} = -\dfrac{2}{3};$ slope of $\overline{AC} = \dfrac{0-5}{-1-(-2)} = -5;$ slope of $\overline{BC} = \dfrac{0-3}{-1-1} = \dfrac{3}{2}$

Therefore, $\triangle ABC$ has a right angle at vertex B since

slope $\overline{AB} = -\dfrac{2}{3}$ and slope $\overline{BC} = \dfrac{3}{2} \Rightarrow \overline{AB}$ is perpendicular to $\overline{BC}$.

91. Consider the points $A(-1,0)$, $B(2,3)$, $C(1,-2)$ and $D(4,1)$

slope of $\overline{AB} = \dfrac{3-0}{2-(-1)} = 1;$ slope of $\overline{CD} = \dfrac{1-(-2)}{4-1} = 1$

slope of $\overline{AC} = \dfrac{-2-0}{1-(-1)} = -1;$ slope of $\overline{BD} = \dfrac{1-3}{4-2} = -1$

Therefore, the quadrilateral $ACDB$ is a parallelogram since

slope $\overline{AB} = 1$ and slope $\overline{CD} = 1 \Rightarrow \overline{AB}$ is parallel to $\overline{CD}$

slope $\overline{AC} = -1$ and slope $\overline{BD} = -1 \Rightarrow \overline{AC}$ is parallel to $\overline{BD}$

Furthermore,

slope $\overline{AB} = 1$ and slope $\overline{BD} = -1 \Rightarrow \overline{AB}$ is perpendicular to $\overline{BD}$

slope $\overline{AC} = -1$ and slope $\overline{CD} = 1 \Rightarrow \overline{AC}$ is perpendicular to $\overline{CD}$

So the quadrilateral $ACDB$ is a rectangle.

93. Slope $= 1$; y-intercept $= 2$

$y = x + 2$ or $x - y = -2$

95. Slope $= -\dfrac{1}{3}$; y-intercept $= 1$

$y = -\dfrac{1}{3}x + 1$ or $x + 3y = 3$

97. The equation of the x-axis is $y = 0$. (The slope is 0 and the y-intercept is 0.)

99. Let $x =$ number of miles driven, and let $C =$ cost in dollars.
Total cost $=$ (cost per mile)(number of miles) + fixed cost
$C = 0.07x + 29$
When $x = 110$, $C = (0.07)(110) + 29 = \$36.70$.
When $x = 230$, $C = (0.07)(230) + 29 = \$45.10$.

101. Let $x =$ number newspapers delivered, and let $C =$ cost in dollars.
Total cost $=$ (delivery cost per paper)(number of papers delivered) + fixed cost
$C = 0.53x + 1{,}070{,}000$

103. (a) $C = 0.08275x + 7.58$
(c) For 100 kWh,
$\quad C = 0.08275(100) + 7.58 = \$15.86$
(d) For 300 kWh,
$\quad C = 0.08725(300) + 7.58 = \$32.41$
(e) For each usage increase of 1 kWh,
the monthly charge increases by 8.275
cents

(b)

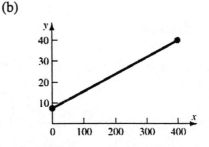

105. $(°C, °F) = (0, 32);\quad (°C, °F) = (100, 212)$

$\text{slope } = \dfrac{212 - 32}{100 - 0} = \dfrac{180}{100} = \dfrac{9}{5}$

$°F - 32 = \dfrac{9}{5}(°C - 0)$

$°F - 32 = \dfrac{9}{5}(°C)$

$°C = \dfrac{5}{9}(°F - 32)$

If $°F = 70$, then

$°C = \dfrac{5}{9}(70 - 32) = \dfrac{5}{9}(38)$

$°C \approx 21°$

107. (a)   Let x = number of boxes sold, A = money, in dollars, spent on advertising.
We have the points $(x_1, A_1) = (100,000, 40,000); (x_2, A_2) = (200,000, 60,000)$

$$\text{slope } = \frac{60,000 - 40,000}{200,000 - 100,000} = \frac{20,000}{100,000} = \frac{1}{5}$$

$$A - 40,000 = \frac{1}{5}(x - 100,000)$$

$$A - 40,000 = \frac{1}{5}x - 20,000$$

$$A = \frac{1}{5}x + 20,000$$

(b)   If $x = 300,000$, then $A = \frac{1}{5}(300,000) + 20,000 = \$80,000$

(c)   To increase the number of boxes sold by 5 units, the amount spent on advertising needs to increase by 1 dollar.

109. (b), (c), (e) and (g)   111. (c)

113. (a)   Since the tangent line intersects the circle in a single point, there is exactly one point on the line $y = mx + b$ such that $x^2 + y^2 = r^2$. That is $x^2 + (mx + b)^2 = r^2$ has exactly one solution.

$$x^2 + (mx + b)^2 = r^2$$
$$x^2 + m^2x^2 + 2bmx + b^2 = r^2$$
$$(1 + m^2)x^2 + 2bmx + b^2 - r^2 = 0$$

There is one solution if and only if the discriminant is zero.

$$(2bm)^2 - 4(1 + m^2)(b^2 - r^2) = 0$$
$$4b^2m^2 - 4b^2 + 4r^2 - 4b^2m^2 + 4m^2r^2 = 0$$
$$-4b^2 + 4r^2 + 4m^2r^2 = 0$$
$$-b^2 + r^2 + m^2r^2 = 0$$
$$r^2(1 + m^2) = b^2$$

(b)   Use the quadratic formula, knowing that the discriminant is zero:

$$x = \frac{-2bm}{2\left(1 + m^2\right)} = \frac{-bm}{\dfrac{b^2}{r^2}} = \frac{-bmr^2}{b^2} = \frac{-mr^2}{b}$$

$$y = m\left(\frac{-mr^2}{b}\right) + b = \frac{-m^2r^2}{b} + b = \frac{-m^2r^2 + b^2}{b} = \frac{r^2}{b}$$

(c)   The slope of the tangent line is m.
The slope of the line joining the point of tangency and the center is:

$$\frac{\dfrac{r^2}{b} - 0}{\dfrac{-mr^2}{b} - 0} = \frac{r^2}{b} \cdot \frac{b}{-mr^2} = -\frac{1}{m}$$

115. $x^2 + y^2 - 4x + 6y + 4 = 0$
$(x^2 - 4x + 4) + (y^2 + 6y + 9) = -4 + 4 + 9$
$(x-2)^2 + (y+3)^2 = 9$

Center: $(2, -3)$

Slope from center to $\left(3, 2\sqrt{2} - 3\right)$ is $\dfrac{2\sqrt{2} - 3 - (-3)}{3 - 2} = \dfrac{2\sqrt{2}}{1} = 2\sqrt{2}$

Slope of the tangent line is: $\dfrac{-1}{2\sqrt{2}} = -\dfrac{\sqrt{2}}{4}$

Equation of the tangent line:

$$y - \left(2\sqrt{2} - 3\right) = -\frac{\sqrt{2}}{4}(x - 3)$$

$$y - 2\sqrt{2} + 3 = -\frac{\sqrt{2}}{4}x + \frac{3\sqrt{2}}{4}$$

$$4y - 8\sqrt{2} + 12 = -\sqrt{2}x + 3\sqrt{2}$$

$$\sqrt{2}x + 4y = 11\sqrt{2} - 12$$

117. Find the centers of the two circles:
$$x^2 + y^2 - 4x + 6y + 4 = 0$$
$$(x^2 - 4x + 4) + (y^2 + 6y + 9) = -4 + 4 + 9$$
$$(x-2)^2 + (y+3)^2 = 9 \qquad \text{Center: } (2, -3)$$
$$x^2 + y^2 + 6x + 4y + 9 = 0$$
$$(x^2 + 6x + 9) + (y^2 + 4y + 4) = -9 + 9 + 4$$
$$(x+3)^2 + (y+2)^2 = 4 \qquad \text{Center: } (-3, -2)$$

Find the slope of the line containing the centers:
$$m = \frac{-2 - (-3)}{-3 - 2} = -\frac{1}{5}$$

Find the equation of the line containing the centers:

$$y + 3 = -\frac{1}{5}(x - 2)$$

$$5y + 15 = -x + 2$$

$$x + 5y = -13$$

119. $2x - y = C$

Graph the lines:
$2x - y = 4 \Rightarrow y = 2x + 4$

$2x - y = 0 \Rightarrow y = 2x$

$2x - y = 2 \Rightarrow y = 2x - 2$

All the lines have the same slope, 2.
The lines are parallel.

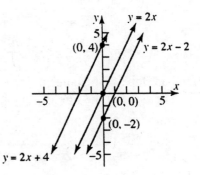

121. Consider the following diagram:

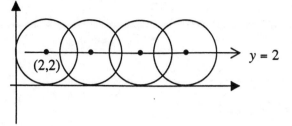

The path of the center of the circle is the line $y = 2$.

123. Answers will vary.

125. Not every line has two distinct intercepts since a horizontal line might not touch the x-axis and a vertical line might not touch the y-axis. Also, a non-vertical, non-horizontal line that passes through the origin will have only one intercept, $(0, 0)$.
A line must have at least one intercept since a vertical line always crosses the x-axis, a horizontal line always crosses the y-axis and a non-vertical, non-horizontal line always crosses both axes.

127. Two lines with the same non-zero x-intercept and the same y-intercept must have the same slope and therefore must be represented by equivalent equations.

129. Two lines that have the same y-intercept but different slopes can only have the same x-intercept if the y-intercept is zero.
Assume Line 1 has equation $y = m_1 x + b$ and Line 2 has equation $y = m_2 x + b$,

Line 1 has x-intercept $-\dfrac{b}{m_1}$ and y-intercept b.

Line 2 has x-intercept $-\dfrac{b}{m_2}$ and y-intercept b.

Assume also that Line 1 and Line 2 have unequal slopes, that is $m_1 \neq m_2$.

If the lines have the same x-intercept, then $-\dfrac{b}{m_1} = -\dfrac{b}{m_2}$.

$$-\frac{b}{m_1} = -\frac{b}{m_2}$$
$$-m_2 b = -m_1 b$$
$$-m_2 b + m_1 b = 0$$
$$\text{But } -m_2 b + m_1 b = 0 \Rightarrow b(m_1 - m_2) = 0$$
$$\Rightarrow b = 0$$
$$\text{or } m_1 - m_2 = 0 \Rightarrow m_1 = m_2$$

Since we are assuming that $m_1 \neq m_2$, the only way that the two lines can have the same x-intercept is if $b = 0$.

131. Answers will vary.

Review

A.8   Scatter Diagrams; Linear Curve Fitting

1. scatter diagram

3. Linear, $m > 0$

5. Linear, $m < 0$

7. Nonlinear

9. (a), (c)

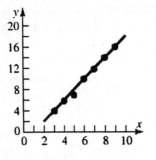

(d) Using the LINear REGresssion program, the line of best fit is:
$$y = 2.0357x - 2.3571$$

(e)

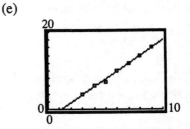

(b) Answers will vary. We select (3,4) and (9,16). The slope of the line containing these points is: $m = \dfrac{16 - 4}{9 - 3} = \dfrac{12}{6} = 2.$

The equation of the line is:
$$y - y_1 = m(x - x_1)$$
$$y - 4 = 2(x - 3)$$
$$y - 4 = 2x - 6$$
$$y = 2x - 2$$

11. (a), (c)

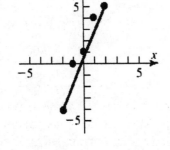

(d) Using the LINear REGresssion program, the line of best fit is:
$$y = 2.2x + 1.2$$

(e)

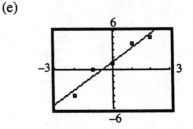

(b)   Answers will vary. We select (–2,–4) and (2,5). The slope of the line containing these points is: $m = \dfrac{5-(-4)}{2-(-2)} = \dfrac{9}{4}$.

The equation of the line is:

$$y - y_1 = m(x - x_1)$$

$$y - (-4) = \frac{9}{4}(x - (-2))$$

$$y + 4 = \frac{9}{4}x + \frac{9}{2} \Rightarrow y = \frac{9}{4}x + \frac{1}{2}$$

13.   (a), (c)

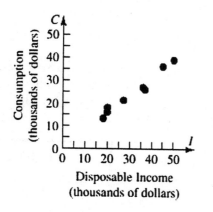

(d)   Using the LINear REGresssion program, the line of best fit is:

$$y = 3.8613x + 180.2920$$

(e)

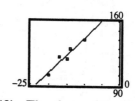

(b)   Answers will vary. We select (–20,100) and (–10,140). The slope of the line containing these points is: $m = \dfrac{140-100}{-10-(-20)} = \dfrac{40}{10} = 4$.

The equation of the line is:

$$y - y_1 = m(x - x_1)$$

$$y - 100 = 4(x - (-20))$$

$$y - 100 = 4x + 80 \Rightarrow y = 4x + 180$$

15.   (a)

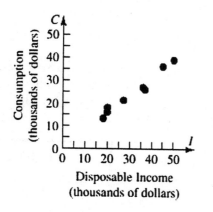

Disposable Income
(thousands of dollars)

(b)   Using points $(20,16)$ and $(50,39)$,

$$\text{slope} = \frac{39-16}{50-20} = \frac{23}{30}.$$

The point-slope formula yields

$$C - 16 = \frac{23}{30}(I - 20)$$

$$C = \frac{23}{30}I - \frac{460}{30} + 16$$

$$C \approx 0.77I + 0.67$$

(c)   As disposable income increases by $1000, personal consumption expenditure increases by about $770.

(d) $C = 0.77(42) + 0.67 = \$33.01$
A family with disposable income of $42,000 has personal consumption expenditure of about $33,010.

(e) $C = 0.7549I + 0.6266$

447

17. (a) (Data used in graphs is in thousands.)

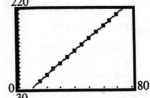

(b) $L = 2.9814I - 0.0761$

(c)

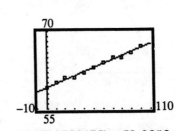

(d) As annual income increases by $1000, the loan amount increases by about $2981.40.

(e) $L = 2.9814(42) - 0.0761 \approx 125.143$
An individual with an annual income of $42,000 would qualify for a loan of about $125,143.

19. (a)

(b) $T = 0.0782h + 59.0909$

(c)

(d) As relative humidity increases by 1%, the apparent temperature increases by $0.0782°$.

(e) $T = 0.0782(75) + 59.0909 \approx 64.96$
A relative humidity of 75% would give an apparent temperature of $65°$.

Graphing Utilities

B.1 The Viewing Rectangle

1. $(-1, 4)$

3. $(3, 1)$

5. $X \min = -6$
$X \max = 6$
$X \text{scl} = 2$
$Y \min = -4$
$Y \max = 4$
$Y \text{scl} = 2$

7. $X \min = -6$
$X \max = 6$
$X \text{scl} = 2$
$Y \min = -1$
$Y \max = 3$
$Y \text{scl} = 1$

9. $X \min = 3$
$X \max = 9$
$X \text{scl} = 1$
$Y \min = 2$
$Y \max = 10$
$Y \text{scl} = 2$

11. $X \min = -11$
$X \max = 5$
$X \text{scl} = 1$
$Y \min = -3$
$Y \max = 6$
$Y \text{scl} = 1$

13. $X \min = -30$
$X \max = 50$
$X \text{scl} = 10$
$Y \min = -90$
$Y \max = 50$
$Y \text{scl} = 10$

15. $X \min = -10$
$X \max = 110$
$X \text{scl} = 10$
$Y \min = -10$
$Y \max = 160$
$Y \text{scl} = 10$

17. $P_1 = (1,3); \ P_2 = (5,15)$
$$\begin{aligned} d(P_1,P_2) &= \sqrt{(5-1)^2 + (15-3)^2} \\ &= \sqrt{(4)^2 + (12)^2} \\ &= \sqrt{16 + 144} \\ &= \sqrt{160} = 2\sqrt{10} \end{aligned}$$

19. $P_1 = (-4,6); \ P_2 = (4,-8)$
$$\begin{aligned} d(P_1,P_2) &= \sqrt{(4-(-4))^2 + (-8-6)^2} \\ &= \sqrt{(8)^2 + (-14)^2} \\ &= \sqrt{64 + 196} \\ &= \sqrt{260} = 2\sqrt{65} \end{aligned}$$

Graphing Utilities

B.2   Using a Graphing Utility to Graph Equations

1.   (a)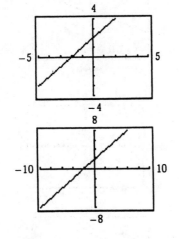

(b)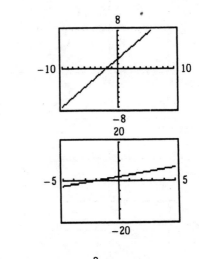

(c)

(d)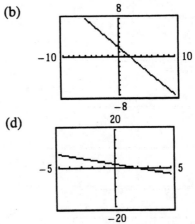

3.   (a)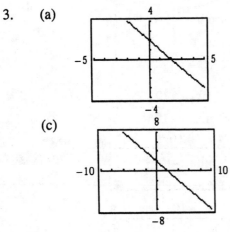

(b)

(c)

(d)

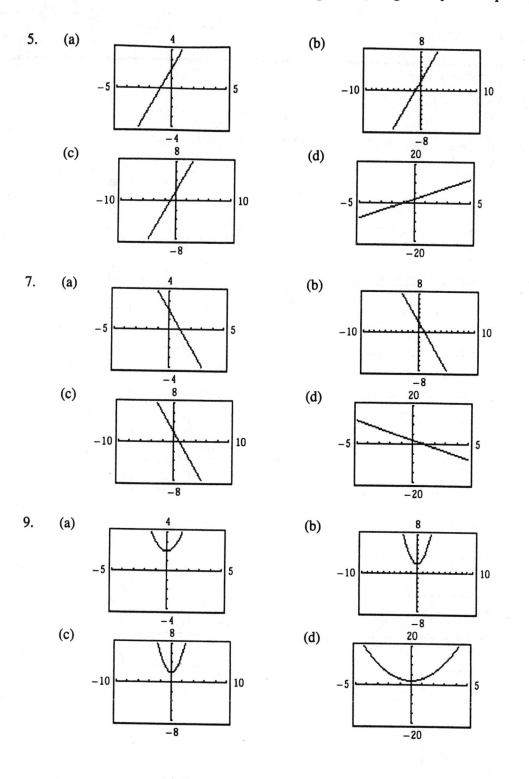

5.   (a)   (b)

      (c)   (d)

7.   (a)   (b)

      (c)   (d)

9.   (a)   (b)

      (c)   (d)

11. (a)   (b)

(c)   (d)

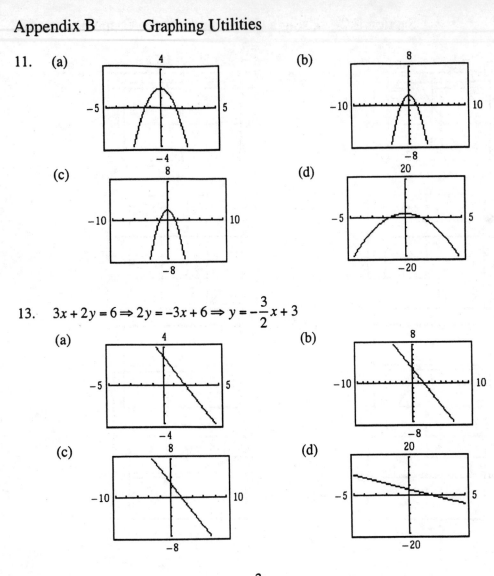

13. $3x + 2y = 6 \Rightarrow 2y = -3x + 6 \Rightarrow y = -\frac{3}{2}x + 3$

(a)   (b)

(c)   (d)

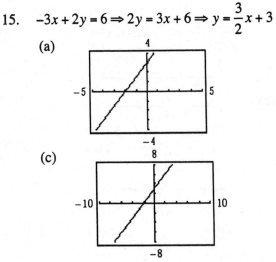

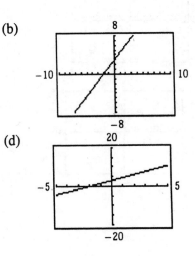

15. $-3x + 2y = 6 \Rightarrow 2y = 3x + 6 \Rightarrow y = \frac{3}{2}x + 3$

(a)   (b)

(c)   (d)

17. $y = x + 2;\quad -3 \le x \le 3$

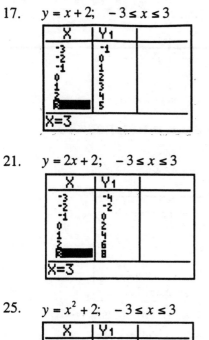

X	Y1	
-3	-1	
-2	0	
-1	1	
0	2	
1	3	
2	4	
3	5	
X=3		

19. $y = -x + 2;\quad -3 \le x \le 3$

X	Y1	
-3	5	
-2	4	
-1	3	
0	2	
1	1	
2	0	
3	-1	
X=3		

21. $y = 2x + 2;\quad -3 \le x \le 3$

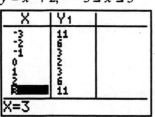

X	Y1	
-3	-4	
-2	-2	
-1	0	
0	2	
1	4	
2	6	
3	8	
X=3		

23. $y = -2x + 2;\quad -3 \le x \le 3$

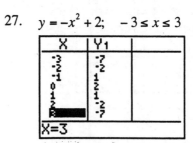

X	Y1	
-3	8	
-2	6	
-1	4	
0	2	
1	0	
2	-2	
3	-4	
X=3		

25. $y = x^2 + 2;\quad -3 \le x \le 3$

X	Y1	
-3	11	
-2	6	
-1	3	
0	2	
1	3	
2	6	
3	11	
X=3		

27. $y = -x^2 + 2;\quad -3 \le x \le 3$

X	Y1	
-3	-7	
-2	-2	
-1	1	
0	2	
1	1	
2	-2	
3	-7	
X=3		

29. $3x + 2y = 6;\quad -3 \le x \le 3$

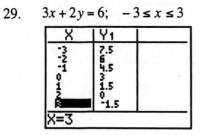

X	Y1	
-3	7.5	
-2	6	
-1	4.5	
0	3	
1	1.5	
2	0	
3	-1.5	
X=3		

31. $-3x + 2y = 6;\quad -3 \le x \le 3$

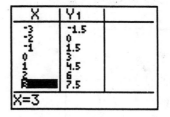

X	Y1	
-3	-1.5	
-2	0	
-1	1.5	
0	3	
1	4.5	
2	6	
3	7.5	
X=3		

Graphing Utilities

B.3 Using a Graphing Utility to Locate Intercepts and Check for Symmetry

1.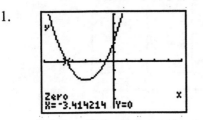

The smaller x-intercept is $x \approx -3.41$.

3.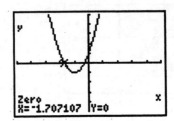

The smaller x-intercept is $x \approx -1.71$.

5.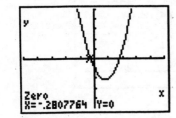

The smaller x-intercept is $x \approx -0.28$.

7.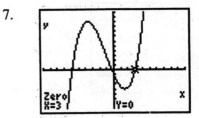

The positive x-intercept is $x = 3.00$.

9.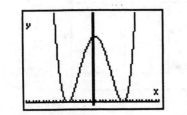

We zoom in on the positive x-intercept:

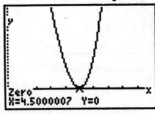

The positive x-intercept is $x \approx 4.50$.

11.

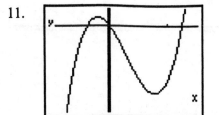

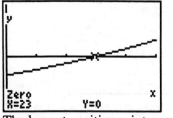

The largest positive x-intercept is
$x \approx 12.30$.

We zoom in on the positive x-intercept:

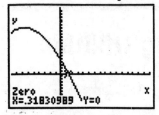

The smallest positive x-intercept is
$x \approx 0.32$.

13.

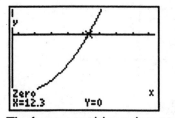

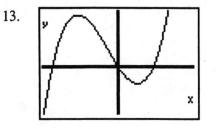

The largest positive x-intercept is
$x = 23.00$.

We zoom in on the positive x-intercept:

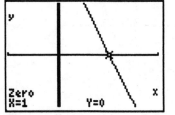

The smallest positive x-intercept is
$x = 1.00$.

Graphing Utilities

B.5   Square Screens

1.   Yes
   X min = -3
   X max = 3
   X scl = 2
   Y min = -2
   Y max = 2
   Y scl = 2

3.   Yes
   X min = 0
   X max = 9
   X scl = 3
   Y min = -2
   Y max = 4
   Y scl = 2

5.   No
   X min = -6
   X max = 6
   X scl = 1
   Y min = -2
   Y max = 2
   Y scl = 0.5

7.   Yes
   X min = 0
   X max = 9
   X scl = 1
   Y min = -2
   Y max = 4
   Y scl = 1

9.   One possible answer:
   X min = -4
   X max = 8
   X scl = 1
   Y min = 4
   Y max = 12
   Y scl = 1